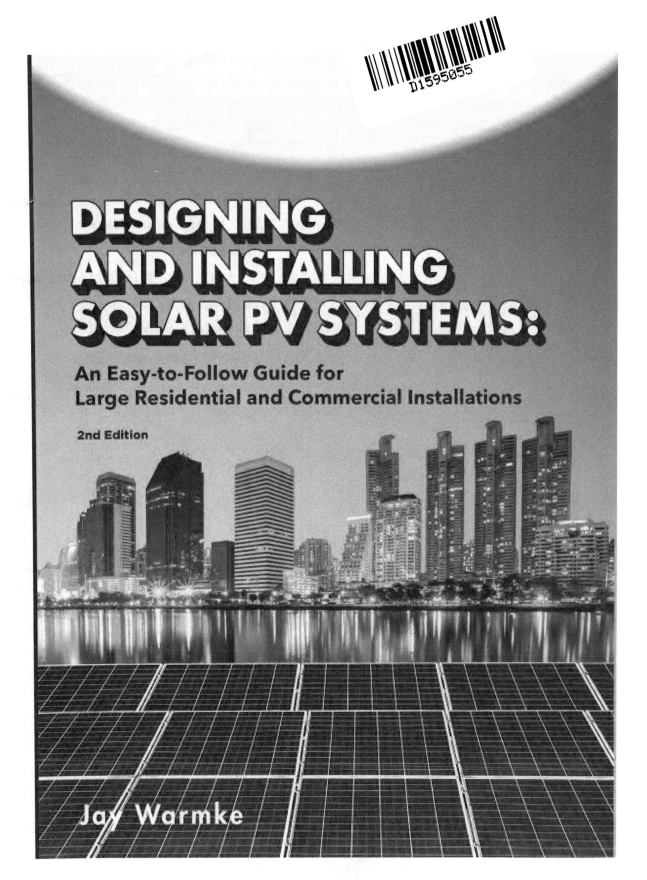

DESIGNING AND INSTALLING SOLAR PV SYSTEMS:

An Easy-to-Follow Guide for Large Residential and Commercial Installations

2nd Edition

Jay Warmke

BRS Press

www.SolarPVTraining.com

Published by BRS Press

ISBN-13: 978-1-957113-02-9

Copyright © 2022 Jay and Annie Warmke

2nd Edition

Tables & Figures (unless otherwise noted) © Jay and Annie Warmke

Layout and design by BRS Press

Edited by Annie Warmke

Cover Design by Ryan Evans

Contact us at:

BRS Press
1190 Virginia Ridge Road
Philo, OH 43771
740-674-4300
annie@bluerockstation.com
www.solarpvtraining.com

Table of Contents

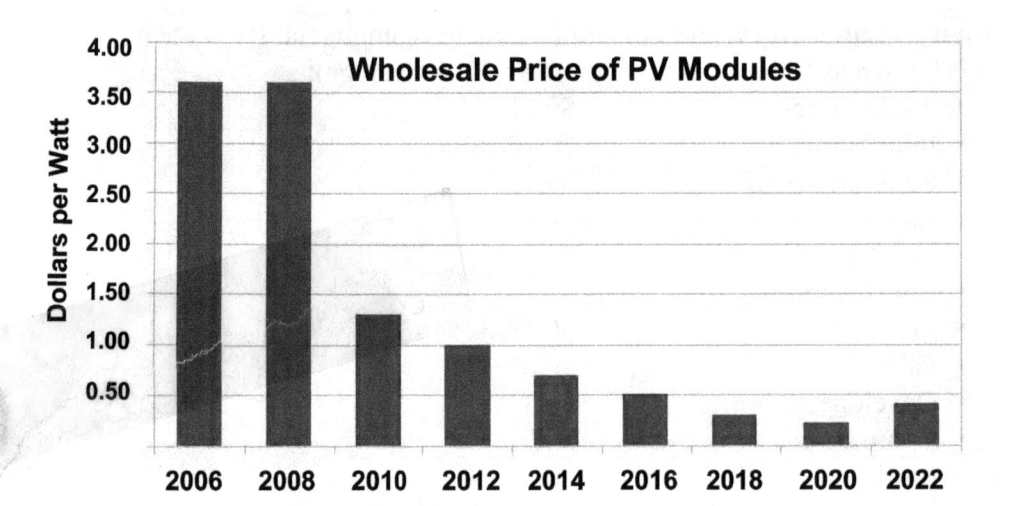

FIGURE 1-2: WHOLESALE PRICE OF PV MODULES (2006- 2022)

Worldwide wholesale prices for solar modules continued to drop, hitting a low of around $0.20/W in 2020. However, due to supply chain disruptions, the price of modules increased to around $044/W in 2022. This has led many industry pundits to speculate that a more stable pricing structure for solar modules will be the norm over the coming years.

In the last decade, the total cost of an installed PV system has also fallen dramatically. In 2020 the average installed cost of a PV system in the United States (seen in Figure 1-3) were:
- Residential = $2.71 per watt
- Rooftop Commercial = $1.72 per watt
- Utility Scale (fixed tilt) = $0.94 per watt

Just ten years earlier (2010), the average US installed costs were:
- Residential = $7.53 per watt
- Rooftop Commercial = $5.57 per watt
- Utility Scale (fixed tilt) = $4.75 per watt

While modules are an important part of a solar PV installation, they are by no means the major cost element. According to **NREL - National Renewable**

NATIONAL RENEWABLE ENERGY LABORATORY (NREL)

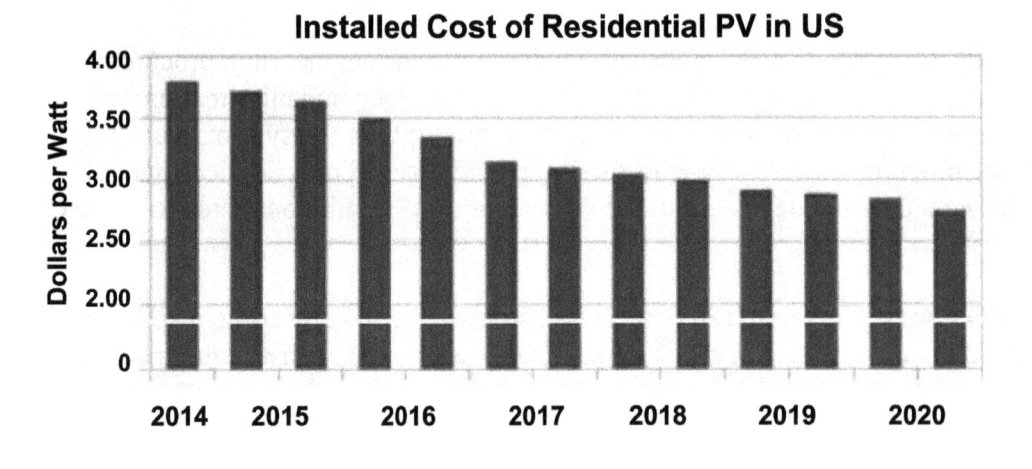

FIGURE 1-3: AVERAGE INSTALLED COST OF A 10 kW RESIDENTIAL PV SYSTEMS IN US (2014- 2020)

Energy Laboratory, costs of a fully installed commercial PV system breakdown as follows (assuming the $1.72/W average):

- PV Modules — $0.41
- Inverter(s) — $0.12
- Structural BOS — $0.11
- Electrical BOS — $0.13
- Installation Labor — $0.15
- EPC Overhead — $0.16
- PII Costs — $0.11
- Sales Tax — $0.05
- Developer Overhead — $0.33
- Contingencies — $0.04
- Profit — $0.11

Inverter prices continue to fall as well. In 2010 (according to NREL), the average cost of a single-phase string inverter was $0.35 per watt/DC. By 2020 it had fallen to about $0.12 per watt/DC.

In 2020, the average per watt/DC for inverter types were:

- Microinverters — $0.30
- Residential w/optimizers — $0.27
- Commercial w/optimizers — $0.12
- Residential string inverter — $0.12
- Commercial string inverter — $0.08
- Utility central inverter — $0.07

Terms used in defining the cost structure of a project include:

Structural BOS: The structural **balance of systems** (all the non-electrical hardware in the system) includes, but is not limited to: racks, rails, footers, trenches, mounting hardware, etc.

Electrical BOS: The electrical balance of systems includes all the electrical components within the system, other than the panels and the inverters. This may include the wires, switches, breakers, etc.

EPC Overhead: EPC in the solar industry means engineering, procurement, and construction. It is a term that is widely used by companies that provide end-to-end solar energy services, including designing the system, managing the procurement process, and installing the project. These services may be provided by the developer of the project, or may be sub-contracted to an EPC installation firm.

PII Costs: This term refers to costs associated with permitting, inspection, and interconnection of the system. These may include construction permit

BALANCE OF
SYSTEMS (BOS)

EPC OVERHEAD

PII COSTS

fees, interconnection study fees for an existing substation, testing, and commissioning.

Those costs associated with a project that are not a part of the actual purchase of equipment are often referred to as **soft costs** (as opposed to hard costs which describes the cost of hardware).

SOFT COSTS

These soft costs may include: taxes, shipping, permits, administrative overhead, engineering and design, profits, and more. While installation labor is also a soft cost, it is normally classified as its own expense category.

The soft costs associated with a project can be significant. According to NREL, in 2020 the soft costs made up 64% of an average residential installation budget, 55% of an average commercial installation, and 35% of the average utility-scale PV project.

Industry experts estimate that as of 2013, most of the nation had reached a point where the cost of photovoltaic electricity is less than or equal to the cost of electricity purchased from the local electric company (a situation known as **grid parity**).

GRID PARITY

Incentive Programs

For the past several decades, it has been U.S. government policy (national, state and local) to attempt to "kick start" the development of photovoltaic systems by offering incentives to offset the relatively high cost of installing a system.

The incentives for residential and business customers, often referred to as **behind-the-meter** PV systems (because they are privately owned systems on the customer's side of the electric meter) have largely been in the form of a combination of:

BEHIND-THE-METER

- cash incentives (provided through federal, state and/or utility PV incentive programs),
- federal and/or state **investment tax credits (ITC)**,
- federal grants in lieu of tax credits,
- revenues from the sale of **renewable energy certificates (REC)**, and
- accelerated depreciation of the capital investments made on the installation of solar energy systems.

INVESTMENT TAX CREDIT (ITC)

RENEWABLE ENERGY CERTIFICATE (REC)

State/Utility Cash Incentives

Most of the state or utility incentive programs have provided cash up-front to help reduce the final cost of an installed PV system. These are based either on system capacity, a percentage of installed cost, or a projection of the annual energy production of the system.

A study by the Lawrence Berkeley National Labs found that these cash incentives peaked in 2002 at around $5/W for installed systems. Since that time the programs have declined significantly as prices for PV systems have dropped.

State policies can include:
- Renewable Portfolio Standards (RPS)
- Renewable Energy Certificates (RECs) and Solar Renewable Energy Certificates (SRECs)
- Net Metering and Virtual Net Metering
- Third-Party Financing, including Power Purchase Agreements (PPAs) and solar leases
- Clean Energy Funds
- Low-Interest Loans
- On-Bill Financing and repayment

Federal Tax Credits

On January 1, 2006, the U.S. federal investment tax credit (ITC) for commercial PV systems rose from 10% to 30% of project costs, and a 30% ITC (capped at $2,000) was established for residential PV systems. In 2008 the $2,000 cap was lifted on residential systems installed after January 1, 2009.

The federal tax credits for solar electric systems has been extended a number of times by Congress. The 30% income tax credit was reduced to 26% in 2020. It is scheduled to decline to 22% in 2023. Then in 2024 it will be reduced to 10% for commercial and utility scale systems, and eliminated altogether for residential systems.

Solar industry proponents anticipate that the ITC will once again be extended before it is further reduced. To date, no such legislation has as of yet been introduced.

Accelerated Depreciation

Depreciation is an accounting method that allows owners of a physical asset to deduct the cost of that asset of its useful life or life expectancy. For example, if a solar array costs $25,000 to install, and it was expected to last 25 years, then the owner could deduct $1,000 per year (the reduction in value of the asset over time) for 25 years. This method is known as **straight-line depreciation.**

Depreciating assets helps companies earn revenue from an asset while expensing a portion of its cost each year the asset is in use. In order to encourage companies to invest in physical assets, the IRS will allow some items to be depreciated much faster than their life expectancy might indicate.

DEPRECIATION

STRAIGHT-LINE
DEPRECIATION

Accelerated depreciation is any method of depreciation used for accounting or income tax purposes that allows greater depreciation expenses in the early years of the life of an asset.

ACCELERATED DEPRECIATION

The Tax Cut and Jobs Act of 2017 contained a provision that allows for 100% depreciation on solar PV systems in their first year of operation. Depending on the tax rate paid by the company that owns the system, this can represent a significant up-front cash incentive.

For equipment on which an investment tax credit (ITC) is claimed, the owner must reduce the project's depreciable basis by one-half the value of the ITC. So, if the tax credit is 26%, as it was in 2022, then the depreciable basis would be 87% of the total cost (100% - [26% X .5]). For example, if the solar PV system cost $100,000, base cost for depreciation purposes would be $87,000.

Renewable Energy Certificates (RECs)

Another form of incentive currently available to some owners of installed PV systems are renewable energy certificates, or **SRECs (solar renewable energy certificates).**

SOLAR RENEWABLE ENERGY CERTIFICATE (SREC)

Many states encourage the development of renewable energy systems by establishing goals that require a certain percentage of all the energy used within the state be generated through renewable sources. These are referred to as **renewable portfolio standards (RPS)**. Often these standards require that a portion of this renewable energy must be generated using photovoltaic systems, a provision known as a **solar set-aside.**

RENEWABLE PORTFOLIO STANDARD (RPS)

SOLAR SET-ASIDE

If utilities do not meet these goals, there are often fines that will be levied against them by the state. Effectively, utilities have a number of options available to reach these targets.

They can:
- build their own solar generation capacity,
- purchase power from a third-party that generates power from a solar array,
- or purchase the right to claim as part of their portfolio (in the form of an SREC) the power generated by the owner of a solar array that is connected to the grid. It is important to note that the utility is not purchasing the actual power, but simply the "carbon credit" for the fact that solar power is being produced and connected to the grid.

As a result, a market has developed where utilities purchase renewable energy credits from PV system owners to demonstrate they have met a portion of the mandated goal.

As might be expected, in states with aggressive goals and larger fines, the price of a REC is higher than in states where there are modest or no goals in place. In 2010 the average price of SRECs in states with an RPS in place with solar set-asides ranged from a high of $600/MWh in New Jersey to a low of about $60/MWh in New Hampshire, with the average ranging between $300-$400/MWh. Amortized over the expected life of a PV system (say 20 years), the net effect is to lower the installed cost by $3-$4/W for the average system.

As more and more PV systems are installed, and utilities begin to reach their solar obligations, the value of SRECs decline. If no fines are imposed, then no SREC market exists in that state.

As of 2022, only a handful of states had an active SREC market. These include: District of Columbia; Delaware; Illinois; Maryland; Massachusetts; New Jersey; Pennsylvania; and Ohio.

Net Metering

Net metering is a policy designed to compensate electric utility customers for the electricity they export to the grid. Most PV systems are designed so that the electricity produced is used directly in the residence or business, with any excess amount sent back to the utility. Net metering provides a financial credit to customers based on the value of the electricity not used on-site.

At the end of each billing cycle, if the exported amount exceeds the imported amount, the customer receives a credit that can be used to offset electricity bill payments in future billing cycles. Depending on the policy, these credits can either roll forward indefinitely or expire at the end of some fixed term, such as the end of the calendar year.

Net metering policies usually address the following issues:
- Eligible Technologies: These policies stipulate which renewable energy sources can be net metered, typically including solar PV.
- System Size: They often specify the maximum allowable system size that can be net metered. These size caps can either be in terms of total capacity (e.g., kW) or percentage-based (e.g., percentage of maximum daily load).
- Program Size Caps: Net metering policies usually set a limit on the total amount of net metering systems installed in a particular region or utility territory.
- Customer Type: Net metering policies specify which electricity customers are eligible (e.g., residential, commercial, etc.).
- Net Excess Generation: Net metering policies establish how the customers will be billed for excess electricity distributed to the grid (e.g, whether customers are credited at retail rate or wholesale rate, as well as when the credits expire).
- Ownership of RECs: Most net metering policies allow customers to maintain ownership of the RECs associated with their electricity output.

Property and Sales Tax Incentives

State and local governments may offer additional solar incentives, including exemptions to property and sales tax. Property tax exemptions allow businesses and homeowners to exclude the added value of a solar system from the valuation of their property for taxation purposes.

Sales tax incentives generally provide an exemption from the state sales tax (or sales and use tax) on the purchase of a renewable energy system. This type of exemption helps to reduce the up front costs of a renewable energy project

A complete database of US renewable energy incentive programs can be found online at the **Database of State Incentives for Renewables & Efficiency (DSIRE)**.

DSIRE

Government Mandates

Renewable Portfolio Standards (RPS) require that a specified percentage of the electricity utilities sell within a state comes from renewable resources. States have created these standards in an effort to encourage the development of renewable energy production within their borders.

In 1983, Iowa was the first state to establish an RPS. Over the years, more than half of the states in the US have established renewable energy targets. Thirty states, Washington, D.C., and two territories have active renewable or clean energy requirements (as of 2022), while an additional three states and one territory have set voluntary renewable energy goals.

As with many policies in recent years, renewable energy mandates have become a politically polarizing issue. Since 2018, 15 states, two territories, and Washington, D.C., have passed legislation to increase or expand their renewable or clean energy targets (11 states have established 100% renewable energy goals). At the same time, 11 states and one territory have allowed their RPS targets to expire.

The federal government is the largest landowner and energy consumer in the United States. On December 8, 2021, US President Joe Biden signed an executive order that directed the federal government to become carbon neutral by 2050. As part of this order, 100% of the electricity used by the federal government will be carbon pollution-free (non-fossil fuel generated) by 2030.

Corporate Mandates

In addition to government mandates, corporations are increasingly requiring that the energy they consume be generated from renewable sources. Corporate solar adoption has expanded rapidly over the past several years, with two thirds of all capacity installed since 2015.

A number of well-known brands have adopted aggressive net-zero carbon emissions goals (according to the EPA). These include: Google (93% of electric generated from solar and/or wind as of 2022), Microsoft (100%), Intel (100%), Proctor & Gamble (100%), Apple (101%), Bank of America (109%), PepsiCo (100%), General Motors (41%), Cisco Systems (100%), Starbucks (100%), General Mills (107%), PayPal (98%), Netflix (100%) and many more.

These goals have proven to be not only beneficial from a marketing perspective, but also make sound financial sense as renewable energy has fast become the least expensive source of electricity.

High tech firms have been quick to adopt renewable energy targets. It is estimated that data centers (often referred to as "the cloud") account for about 2% of all global electricity demand.

Residential vs Commercial vs Utility Scale

In 2020, the U.S. solar market set a new annual record with 19.2 GW installed.

Utility-Scale Solar

By far the lion's share of these installations were utility-scale projects. Of the 19.2 GW of new solar, just under 14 GW were utility-scale (73%).

SOLAR ENERGY INDUSTRY ASSOCIATION

Not every source agrees as to what system should be considered a utility-scale system. Some base this distinction on size. For example, **SEIA (Solar Energy Industry Association)** defines utility scale as any system greater than 1 MW. Other studies, such a one conducted by the University of Michigan, set the threshold for utility-scale projects at 50 MW.

It is generally conceded, however, that utility-scale systems feed power directly into the grid, supplying a utility with energy. Virtually every utility-scale solar facility has a power purchase Agreement (PPA) with a utility.

Community Solar

COMMUNITY SOLAR

A growing sector within the solar marketplace is **community solar**. The U.S. Department of Energy defines community solar as any solar project where multiple customers such as individuals, businesses, non-profits, and other groups own or lease a portion of an array. Community solar projects are generally considered within the larger utility-scale market segment.

Recent studies have shown that as many as 80% of residential properties are unsuitable for solar installations. Either the roof is too small or otherwise unsuitable, there are shading issues, the residence is shared by multiple families or a rental (which may make solar impractical), or the owner is not credit worthy and cannot afford a system.

Community solar seeks to address this problem by building a large solar array and selling or leasing a portion of that array to multiple customers. In that way, those who might not otherwise find solar a practical solution can offset their electric bill with solar and take advantage of lower installation costs based on the economies of scale.

However for community solar to work, the local utility must participate to properly allocate solar production to individual customer's bills. Many utilities are reluctant to do so.

As of 2020, about a third of the states have passed legislation that promote and/or require utilities to participate in community solar projects. Community solar programs that exist outside of those states are generally developed and managed by utilities themselves, rather than outside investors.

In 2020, about 1.5 GW of community solar was installed, representing about 8% of total US solar installations. The majority of installations were concentrated in a few states with favorable community solar legislation: Colorado, Minnesota, California, and New York.

Commercial Installations

Commercial solar is somewhat of a catchall category that covers all solar power outside of the residential market (solar panels on homes) or utility-scale systems (solar power plants). Commercial solar doesn't just apply to businesses, but also to industry, agricultural, governmental organizations and non-profits, as well.

In 2020, the commercial sector accounted for about 2 GW or about 10% of all US solar installations. While commercial systems tend to vary widely in size, NREL reported that the average US commercial rooftop mounted system was around 200 kW, while the average commercial ground mounted system was about 400 kW in size.

Residential Systems

Residential systems grew by 3.2 GW in the US in 2020, making up about 17% of the total installation market share. Residential systems have trended larger in recent years, growing on average from just over 5 kW in 2010 to nearly 6.5 kW in 2020.

Residential systems are increasingly incorporating battery backup as well. In 2019 only 3.9% of all residential and commercial systems incorporated storage. That number grew to 13.9% in 2022 and is expected to exceed 25% by 2025.

Differences between a Commercial Project and a Residential Project

There are a number of differences between between designing and installing a commercial project as compared to a residential project. Aside from the obvious fact that most commercial/industrial projects are larger (300 kW versus 6.5 kW), differences include:

- Time involved. A typical residential solar project may take 4-6 weeks from the time the contract is signed to the moment the system begins generating power. Much of this time is spent waiting on permits (2-4 weeks), waiting on inspections (a week or so) and waiting on the utility to activate the system (1-2 weeks). The actual design and installation of a typical residential PV system is a fairly quick process. Commercial systems normally demand more complex permitting, corporate approval processes, and involved financial negotiations. Given these various factors, a commercial system can be up and running in a few weeks, or it may take half a year.

- Complexity. With commercial systems, there are normally much more technical concepts involved. For example, the electrical equipment may be rated much higher, perhaps 2,000-3,000 A as opposed to 30-60 A in a residential installation. There may be a need for transformer upgrades based on whether the local lines can handle the solar backfeed. There may also be leasehold concerns and business disruption concerns that will need to be addressed.

- Communication. Managing communications between the design/installation team and the customer can vary enormously. With a residential install, there is normally just one owner or point of contact. Commercial systems may involve multiple departments and individuals that may have very different concerns and perspectives. Also, the project may span many months, so periodic and effective communication is necessary with all concerned parties to keep the project on track.

- Financing. Even though the per watt installation cost on a commercial project can be much lower than the cost of residential, the overall cost of the project can be large. Normally there are many levels of financing involved, including development loans, construction loans, and permanent financing. Because the financial risks are so great, very tight and detailed contractual provisions may restrict any flexibility in how the project can proceed. Changes may require not only the approval of the customer, but approval from lawyers, lenders and authorities having jurisdiction. A construction cash-flow waterfall will likely be in place that governs all project cash; requiring that all available cash flows to be applied to pay budgeted project costs and then, typically, required debt service, lender expenses, and any mandatory prepayments.

Reasons Businesses go Solar

While there are a great number of reasons a business or individual may choose to invest in solar, they generally fall in the following general categories.

- Reduce operating costs: For the past decade or so, over the expected life of a system, it has been cheaper to install and operate a solar array than to continue to purchase electricity on a retail basis from the local utility.

- Good return on investment: Given current prices and available incentives, the average commercial solar installation will pay for itself in energy savings in 5-7 years. This represents a guaranteed 15-20% return on investment.

- Environmental leadership: Customers, employees and tenants are increasingly evaluating a company's sustainability goals/policies/targets when deciding whether to work for or buy from that business. Solar power is a cost-effective way to make progress towards a carbon-neutral corporate footprint.

- Incentives and tax advantages: Federal, state and local incentives are currently in place which help reduce the cost of installing solar. The limited life expectancy of some of these incentive programs may prompt some businesses to install solar while the incentives are still available.

- Energy Cost Stability: Accurately predicting future costs is often critical to the success of a business. Electricity costs have risen over 70% over the past decade and continue to do so in a volatile way. With solar, a business can accurately forecast the cost of energy use for more than 25 years.

- Resiliency: Electricity from the grid is becoming increasingly unreliable. According to the Energy Information Administration (EIA), 2020 was a record-breaking year for power outages in the United States. On average, businesses in the US went over eight hours without electricity in 2020, more than twice as long as in 2013, the year that the EIA started keeping track. Solar power, paired with batteries and microgrids, provides a more resilient source of power when disaster strikes.

- Improved property value: Not only is solar electric less expense than power from the grid, it actually adds value to the property. The American Association of Appraisers has found that a building with a solar PV array has a higher market value than the same building without, as well as almost always decreasing marketing time to sale. A study by the Appraisal Institute obtained similar results, finding that buildings with solar sold at a 4% average premium over those without.

- Flexible financing options: There are a number of flexible financing options available for commercial businesses, including options that require little to no up-front costs. Lease or lease/purchase options also allow commercial businesses to invest in solar, lowering their monthly energy costs without investing any of their own capital up front.

- Low maintenance: While a solar array does require some maintenance and cleaning to operate at full efficiency, there is virtually no day-to-day maintenance. This results in extremely low operating and maintenance costs over the life of the installation.

Connecting to the Grid

In the early days of PV systems, most were stand-alone, relying on battery systems charged by the PV panels to provide energy in remote locations where no electrical service was available or practical. In more recent years, the vast majority of PV systems in developed countries are grid-tied, allowing customers to use the solar power from their systems when it is available, and to use power from the grid when there is not enough sunlight necessary to generate the electricity required to meet their immediate needs.

DISTRIBUTED
ENERGY SYSTEM

The reaction to this new **distributed energy system** linking into a utility's grid varies dramatically from utility to utility. Some utility systems that are in need of additional generating capacity might embrace these PV systems, viewing them as additional power plants that the utility has access to without having to make any investment in construction. Other utilities that are having trouble selling all the power they can currently generate might attempt to block these interlopers from their system.

INTERCONNECTION

With this in mind, many states have, in recent years, adopted rules that regulate the **interconnection** (the attaching of distributed energy systems to the grid) of PV systems. These regulations typically address issues such as: who qualifies, size of systems allowed, disconnection systems required, insurance required, dispute resolution, billing agreements, interconnection and engineering charges, etc. As of 2014, 20 states still had either not enacted interconnection rules, or had in place rules so restrictive as to impede rather than help people connect their PV systems to the grid. (according to the **Interstate Renewable Energy Council - IREC**).

INTERSTATE
RENEWABLE ENERGY
COUNCIL (IREC)

NET METERING

In all but six states as of 2014, legislatures have put in place net metering requirements for investor-owned utilities (typically municipal systems and energy co-ops are excluded from these rules). **Net metering** essentially requires that utilities pay for energy sold back to them by the owner of the PV system.

For example, on a sunny day when the owner of a home with a PV system is at work and energy consumption at home is low, the system may be generating much more energy than is being used. This excess energy is "sold" to the utility company. In effect, the PV system becomes a small power plant, feeding energy onto the grid. As it does so, the electric meter runs backward, taking kilowatt hours off the "clock" - so to speak.

In the evening, when the homeowner returns and starts turning on lights and appliances, the rate of energy sold back will slow. As the sun sets, the energy produced by the system will drop to zero, and the homeowner will receive all

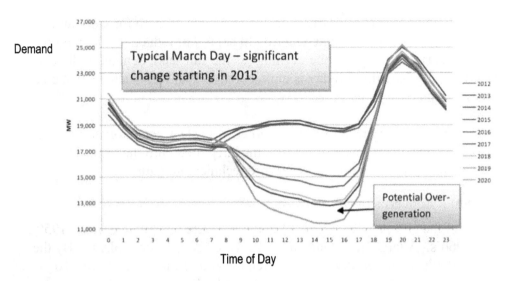

Demand

MW

Time of Day

Typical March Day – significant change starting in 2015

Potential Over-generation

2012
2013
2014
2015
2016
2017
2018
2019
2020

FIGURE 1-4: DUCK SHAPED ELECTRIC UTILITY DEMAND CURVE AS ROOFTOP SOLAR ADDED TO GRID

(GRAPH FROM CAISO)

their power from the grid (the meter will run the opposite way). In effect, the homeowner is using the utility grid as a large battery backup system. At the end of the stated period of time (a month, a year), the homeowner will pay only the net effect of their energy use (how much they used less how much they generated back to the utility).

These net metering agreements can get fairly complicated, addressing issues such as: who qualifies, system capacity limits, overall program capacity limits, restrictions on "rollover" credits from one period to another, who pays for the electric meter and how many are required, who owns the RECs, what insurance is required, what other fees can be assessed (access fees, distribution fees, etc), at what rate is excess energy "sold" back to the utility, and many more.

Grid-Tied Growing Pains

The electrical grid has little or no storage capacity. It operates by matching supply and demand on a second-by-second basis. When more power is needed, the utilities ramp up production.

However, as more rooftop solar units come on line, the production of electricity is increasingly taken away from the utilities and put in the hands of the consumer.

At first it might appear that solar is an excellent match with electrical demand. Peak demand for electricity typically falls in the late afternoon, the time of day when solar generation is at its highest.

However, a comprehensive study by the **California Independent Systems Operator (CAISO)**, California's bulk electric system operator, anticipates a growing mismatch as solar comes to dominate the grid. Figure 1-4, often referred to as the **duck curve**, anticipates two peak daily demand points.

CAISO

DUCK CURVE

The first will occur in the early morning as people prepare for work and the sun is not yet up. Then the availability of solar will reduce the demand from the grid during the day. In the evening (as the sun sets), demand will once again spike. The grid of today is unprepared to deal with such sudden and dramatic spikes.

In recent years grid operators have worked with state regulators to retard the growth of customer-owned solar systems integrated onto the grid. The reasons for this are economic, others are technical in nature.

Economic Concerns of Utilities

Many of the power plants operated in the US were constructed in the 1950's and 1960's. A large percentage of these were coal-powered plants. By the early 2000's, many of these had reached the end of their useful life. To upgrade them to meet modern emission standards was, in most cases, not economically practical.

At the same time, dwindling domestic coal reserves sent the price of the traditional fuel used in power plants skyrocketing. In order to maintain their generation capacity, utilities were faced with the choice of building increasingly expensive coal power plants, opting for natural gas plants (which are more flexible, cheaper and powered by relatively inexpensive and abundant fuel) or installing relatively low-cost wind turbines where a wind resource is available.

Regardless of the power option selected, the early 2000's saw a large-scale rebuilding of the power generation infrastructure in the US. These new power plants need several decades of a steady or growing customer base to pay for their construction.

Then came the dramatic rise of solar. Solar PV systems are typically owned by the power users and have the cumulative effect of lowering the demand for power generated by traditional utilities. In the early years of this growth, the effect on the financial bottom line of utilities was slight. But as the installed base of customer-owned PV systems grew, and continues to grow, utilities have become worried as to how they will pay for their investment in power generating plants.

Technical Concerns of Utilities

The grid was designed to send power from a central generating facility, through a number of transformers, to the customer. When additional generating facilities are added to the existing system, generation sources not controlled by the utility, unanticipated problems may occur.

These problems include:

VOLTAGE VIOLATION
- **voltage violations,**

- increased **demand ramping,**
- system instability,
- simultaneous tripping and re-closing.

DEMAND RAMPING

Voltage Violations

The grid is designed to provide power when needed. This is a very complex task, requiring constant adjustment to ensure there is enough power flowing to meet demand, but not too much power - which will cause an increase in voltage within the system.

The US grid is designed to operate within a narrow voltage range of plus or minus 5% of its optimal voltage. For example, if the delivered voltage was 240 Vac, then the acceptable voltage range would be between 228 Vac (240 V - 5%) and 252 Vac (240 V + 5%).

Utilities can control their own generation, but have little or no control over power pushed onto the grid by owners of distributed energy systems. Power flowing onto the grid from a PV system may cause the voltage on the grid to rise at the point where it connects, or the **point of common coupling (PCC)**.

POINT OF COMMON COUPLING (PCC)

IMPEDANCE

This rise is due to **impedance** on the grid as there is no load demand ready to accept the power generated by the PV system.

This voltage fluctuation can be made even more profound due to the variable nature of solar; output rising and falling unpredictably as the sun shines brighter or is covered by clouds.

If this voltage rise is extreme enough, the inverter within the PV system may shut off, disconnecting power flow to the grid. It then must sit idle for a period of time before it can reconnect to the grid. This unwanted tripping not

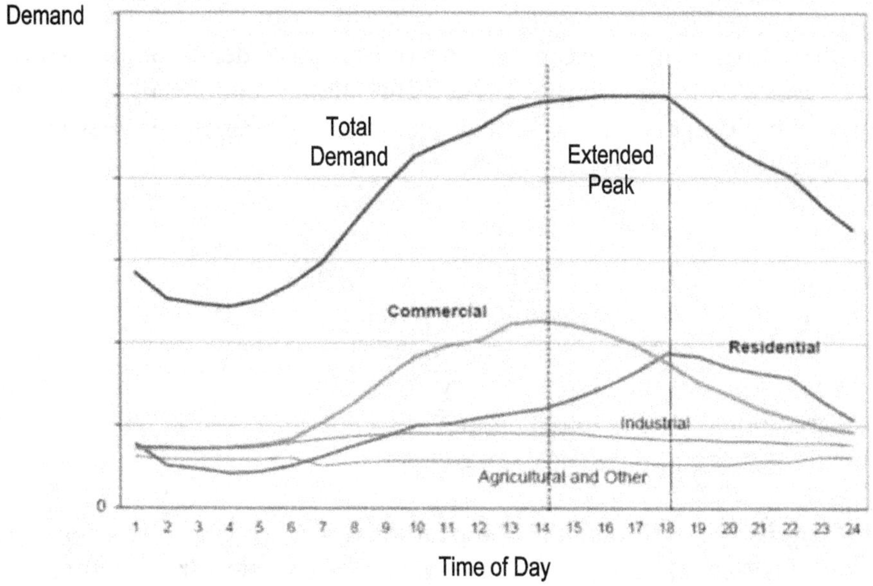

FIGURE 1-5: TRADITIONAL ELECTRIC UTILITY DEMAND CURVE

(GRAPH FROM EXTREME TECH)

only stresses the PV system, but results in the loss of potential power as the PV system sits idle.

Additionally, the integration of large numbers of electric vehicle (EV) charging stations is beginning to change the traditional load profile on the grid. If significant numbers of EVs are connected at the same time, the sudden load demand may cause voltages to drop.

Demand Ramping

The variable nature of PV system power production can cause utilities to deal with changes in their demand ramping response process.

Electricity demand is constantly changing as loads are turned on and off. In order to maintain system stability, control mechanisms have been developed to manage variability and uncertainty and maintain reliable operation.

These control processes generally fall into three categories:

REGULATION

AUTOMATIC GENERATION CONTROLS (AGC)

- **Regulation:** Grid regulations refers to the unplanned and unscheduled response to changes in load that occur on a real-time basis. **Automatic generation controls (AGC)** automatically respond to minute-by-minute load deviations. These variations typically range from several seconds to five minutes.

LOAD FOLLOWING

- **Load Following**: Load following response refers to longer term load events, typically ranging from five minutes to a few hours. Generating units that have been previously committed or can be started quickly are placed in service to provide power to meet this increased demand.

UNIT COMMITMENT

- **Unit Commitment**: Variations in demand that occur over several hours to several days are generally fairly predictable. Often they follow a daily demand profile as illustrated in Figure 1-5. Generating units are scheduled in advance to meet anticipated demand.

RAMP RATE

How quickly a generator can increase (ramp up) or decrease (ramp down) generation is referred to as its **ramp rate**. Different types of generating units have very different generating characteristics, making some types more suited to supplying certain needed functions.

BASELOAD UNITS

TURN-DOWN CAPABILITY

Baseload Units: Large nuclear and coal-fired power plants generally supply the same amount of energy 24/7 when operating. These units have slow ramp rates and relatively high minimum generation levels, referred to as **turn-down capability**. They also can take a long time (days in some cases) to start back up once they have been cycled off. For these reasons, these units have traditionally been relied upon to generate the a steady and constant amount of power, known as the baseload.

PEAKING UNITS

Peaking Units: Intermediate and peaking units, are generally natural gas or oil-fired facilities, have faster ramp rates, relatively lower minimum generation levels, and can be shut down and started up relatively quickly. These units have traditionally been used to manage short periods of high energy demand.

As illustrated by the duck curve, peaks and valleys in demand will result in either the utility maintaining unused generating capacity for long periods of time, or require them to purchase high-cost power from other providers during **peak load demand**.

PEAK LOAD DEMAND

Future Trends

Predicting the future is a hazardous occupation, but in the case of PV, dramatic growth seems all but certain. Over the past ten years, installations of PV systems in the United States have grown at an average annual rate of 42% and the cost of solar has fallen by over 70%.

The industry continues to evolve and mature, and as it becomes a greater share of the energy generation mix, it will continue to have a profound impact on the electrical system.

The power grid is undergoing the greatest transformation since it was first envisioned and built over a century ago. Much of the change is driven by the rise of **distributed energy resources (DERs)**.

DER

DER technologies (primarily solar and wind) have gained a significant market share in recent years, representing approximately 15% of total US generation in 2022. In order to meet carbon emission goals, the US Department of Energy projects that wind and solar generation combined will provide 75% of the nation's electricity by 2035 and 90% by 2050. In order to achieve these goals, the US electrical system will need to be completely transformed.

Changes in supply management (such as energy storage systems and micro grids) and load management (such as demand response) will feature heavily in the evolution of the solar industry.

Supply Management

The widespread integration of DERs has made providing reliable power to the grid a more complex task. The electrical distribution network is changing from a single-source radial network to a multi-source grid. In the past the grid operators controlled all sources of power, reacting to changing demand profiles. Now they must not only react to changing and evolving load demand, but also must adjust power output to support and augment supply that comes from thousands of new supply resources, bi-directional power flows and greater variability.

These challenges mean that utilities must operate the grid in a much more agile manner. Essentially the grid needs to get "smart."

SMART GRID

Smart Grid

The US Department of Energy (DOE) defines the **smart grid** as:

"An automated, widely distributed energy delivery network, the Smart Grid will be characterized by a two-way flow of electricity and information and will be capable of monitoring everything from power plants to customer preferences to individual appliances. It incorporates into the grid the benefits of distributed computing and communications to deliver real-time information and enable the near-instantaneous balance of supply and demand at the device level"

In other words, the grid will not only become a bi-directional power delivery system, but also will become a communications system where devices are communicating with other devices in real time (a significant portion of the **Internet of Things- IoT**).

INTERNET OF THINGS

According to the DOE, some benefits of the smart grid include:
- improved grid reliability,
- increased physical, operational, and cyber security resilience against attack or natural disasters,
- ease of repair, particularly remote repair,
- increased information available to consumers regarding their energy use,
- increased energy efficiency along with the environmental benefits gained by such efficiency,
- the integration of a greater percentage of intermittent renewable energy sources,
- the integration of large numbers of plug-in electric vehicles,
- a reduction in peak load demand.

There are tools that have been developed to monitor and control power grid assets, such as SCADA, DERMS and ADMS, allowing DERs to work at their maximum potential while still allowing utilities to optimize their operations.

SCADA

SCADA is not a specific technology, but a type of application. SCADA stands for **supervisory control and data acquisition**. Any application that gets data about a system in order to control that system is a SCADA application. Electric utilities use SCADA systems to detect current flow and line voltage, to monitor the operation of circuit breakers, and to take sections of the power grid online or offline.

DERMS

A **distributed energy resource management system**, or **DERMS**, is software used to manage distributed energy resources (DERs), such as solar arrays, wind turbines, behind-the-meter batteries, or electric vehicles. The goal is to balance demand with supply as both dynamically change.

At its most basic, DERMS allow utilities to take thousands of distributed energy resources that happen to be clustered in a specific region and operate them as a **virtual power plant (VPP)**.

An **advanced distribution management system (ADMS)** is software employed by utilities designed to automate power outage restoration and optimize the performance of the distribution grid. Additional functions include: fault location, isolation and restoration; volt/voltampere reactive optimization; conservation through voltage reduction; peak demand management; and support for distributed energy resources, microgrids and electric vehicles.

VIRTUAL POWER PLANT (VPP)

ADMS

Load Management

One main component of the smart grid is the possibility of customer participation in the overall grid energy management. Collectively known as **demand response** or demand side management, the utilities seek to better match available power supply with demand by providing incentives for customers to shift their load demand over time. In exchange, customers are given financial incentives or are provided with partial autonomy to participate in selling and buying energy to and from the grid.

DEMAND RESPONSE

Ultimately the goal of these programs is to reduced loads during periods of peak load demand or when power supplies are limited, shifting that load demand to times when ample power is available.

There are three basic categories of demand response programs currently in use. They include: emergency demand response, economic demand response and ancillary services demand response.

Emergency Demand Response

Emergency or interruptible load demand response programs are where the utility pays participating customers to shed a portion of their electric load during peak load events on the grid, or during power system emergencies.

EMERGENCY DEMAND RESPONSE

Utilities always have extra capacity available to cover spikes in demand created by emergency or unforeseen events (such as equipment failure). This is called the **capacity reserve margin**.

CAPACITY RESERVE MARGIN

Emergency demand response programs can allow utilities to more quickly replace that capacity reserve margin in case another event should occur before the first one is over.

Customers participating in demand response programs agree to a pre-specified amount of demand reduction. This allows the utility to call on those load reductions to maintain capacity reserve margins. A classic and early example of such a program was when utilities paid customers a small monthly fee in exchange for allowing the shutoff of electric water heaters during emergency situations.

Economic Demand Response

ECONOMIC DEMAND RESPONSE

Wholesale electrical generation prices can fluctuate dramatically, becoming especially high on a hot summer day when the demand for electricity is high.

Historically, electricity rates are often flat or two-tiered, meaning there is usually a complete disconnect between what customers pay for electricity and what it costs the utility. That is changing. Increasingly utilities are switching to a tiered or real-time pricing model. When wholesale energy costs increase, so to do prices charged to customers.

Many "smart" appliances can now monitor electric prices and adjust operations based on power rates. For example, a hot water heater or EV charger may be programmed to turn off in the middle of the afternoon when rates are high, and then resume operation at night when rates are lower.

Customers can also be notified (via text message) of emergency events or price fluctuations and control their load demand (remotely by phone) at the individual circuit level or appliance level through smart appliances and circuit breakers.

Ancillary Services Demand Response

ANCILLARY SERVICES DEMAND RESPONSE

Ancillary services on the grid enable the reliable transmission of electric power. The need for these services is growing as grid operators face new challenges, including transmission congestion and the increasing role of intermittent renewable power generation.

SYNCHRONIZED RESERVE

FREQUENCY REGULATION

Ancillary services include both **synchronized reserve** and **frequency regulation**. Synchronized reserve supplies electricity if the grid has an unexpected need for more power on short notice. Frequency regulation manages the quality of energy on the grid, balancing generation and load to keep the system frequency reliably at 60 Hz.

The synchronized reserve (also called spinning reserve or 10-minute reserve) is standby capacity maintained by utilities to handle short term fluctuations in supply or demand.

Utilities can lower excess standby capacity if they know they can call on additional reserve resources through an ancillary services demand response program if demand rises higher than expected for a brief period, or if a generator suddenly fails.

Both generators and demand resources can provide this response, by either adding or removing energy quickly. The duration of these events are generally between 5-30 minutes. Energy storage systems, such as behind-the-meter battery banks and EVs, are excellent resources to provide needed power quickly during these short term power fluctuations.

Chapter 1 Review Questions

1) As of 2020, the average installed cost of a rooftop commercial PV system in the US was _____ .
   A) $4.59 per watt
   b) $2.71 per watt
   c) $1.72 per watt
   d) $0.94 per watt

2) When pricing out a commercial PV system installation, generally the largest (per watt) line item cost is/are _____ .
   a) the solar modules
   b) installation
   c) the balance of systems (BOS)
   d) profits

3) EPC overhead refers to:
   a) environmental protection costs
   b) equipment procurement costs
   c) energy production capital
   d) engineering, procurement, and construction

4) Which of the following would **NOT** be considered a soft cost associated with a project?
   a) EPC overhead
   b) PII costs
   c) BOS purchases
   d) developer overhead

5) Behind-the-meter incentives are aimed at:
   a) the energy end user who owns the solar PV system
   b) the utility company who provides the power
   c) non-profit organizations that do not qualify for tax incentives
   d) improving in the energy distribution infrastructure

6) An investor pays $50,000 for the installation of a PV system. She has determined it has a useful life of 25 years. Each year (for the next 25 years) she deducts $2,000 from her taxes as a loss to reflect the loss of value of the system. This is known as:
   a) tax fraud
   b) accelerated depreciation
   c) modified accelerated cost-recovery system (MACRS)
   d) straight-line depreciation

7) Net metering laws typically address all of the following issues **EXCEPT**:
   a) insolation limitations
   b) generation limits
   c) limits on the size of the array
   d) limits on the number of systems that can participate in the program

8) A government mandate that defines the percentage of a state's electricity that must come from renewable sources is known as a:
   a) renewable portfolio standard (RPS)
   b) renewable energy certificate (REC)
   c) investment tax credit (ITC)
   d) regional transmission obligation (RTO)

9) A project where multiple customers purchase or lease a portion of a large array is referred to as:
   a) utility-scale solar
   b) investor-owned solar
   c) community solar
   d) commercial solar

10) As of 2020, utility-scale solar (as opposed to residential and commercial) installations accounted for_____ of all solar capacity installed each year in the United States.
   a) 10%
   b) 17%
   c) 42%
   d) 73%

11) Which of the following is **NOT** generally a key difference between designing and installation a commercial PV system versus a residential system?
   a) the time involved
   b) the complexity of the system
   c) the type of products used
   d) the amount of communication required with those involved

12) Attaching a distributed energy system to the grid is known as:
   a) interconnecting
   b) commissioning
   c) grid parity
   d) common coupling

13) Concerns by utilities that the widespread adoption of distributed system within the grid might lead to overproduction during the middle of the afternoon is graphically expressed by:
   a) the CAISO curve
   b) the IV curve
   c) the duck curve
   d) the phase waveform curve

14) Which of the following is **NOT** a generation problem or concern faced by utilities?
   a) voltage violations
   b) common coupling
   c) demand ramping
   d) harmonic distortion

15) Utilities generally face their highest cost of energy during:
   a) time-of-use shifts
   b) peak load demand
   c) the duck curve
   d) phase shifting

16) Which of the following is **NOT** a standard control process followed by utilities to address demand ramping?
   a) load leading
   b) regulation
   c) load following
   d) unit commitment

17) Which of the following is **NOT** a benefit of the smart grid as identified by the Department of Energy (DOE)?
   a) improved grid reliability
   b) lower energy costs
   c) faster and easier repairs on the grid
   d) allows for a higher percentage of renewables to be added to the grid

18) Which of the following is **NOT** a a tool used by utilities to monitor and control power on the grid?
   a) MACRS
   b) SCADA
   c) ADMS
   d) DERMS

19) The extra generation capacity utilities have available to handle spikes in load demand (over and above normal operating requirements) is referred to as:
   a) emergency demand response
   b) economic demand response
   c) ancillary services demand response
   d) capacity reserve margin

Chapter 2

How the Grid Works

Chapter Objectives:

- Become familiar with how the modern electrical grid operates.
- Define single phase/split phase as well as three-phase electrical services.
- Explore the regulatory structure of the electrical grid.
- Understand how the grid responds to load demand.
- Define real power, apparent power, and reactive power and their relationship with each other.
- Examine the power quality issues that face utilities.
- Learn various energy storage techniques employed by utilities.
- Become acquainted with several energy pricing options.
- Investigate substations and transformers and their impact on PV systems and the grid.
- Imagine the utility of the future and the integration of virtual power plants.

Most photovoltaic systems designed and installed in today's market will be connected in some way to the electrical grid. It is therefore important to understand how the grid works, and how it will impact the decisions made in designing the right PV system for the client.

What is the Grid?

Getting power to a home or business requires a number of integrated systems.

First, the power must be **generated** in some way.

GENERATION

As of January 2021 (according to the US Energy Administration), there were 23,417 electric generators at about 11,070 utility-scale electric power plants in the United States. Utility-scale power plants have a total nameplate electricity generation capacity of at least 1 megawatt (MW).

These generators could be powered by coal, natural gas, nuclear energy, water (hydro), wind, solar or a number of other lesser used options. A power plant may have more than one generator, and some generators may use more than one type of fuel.

Once the power is generated, it must somehow make its way from the power plant to where it will be used. This is done through a network of wires.

This network is normally organized into two parts, **transmission** and **distribution**.

TRANSMISSION

DISTRIBUTION

There are over 450,000 miles of high-voltage power lines and about 160,000 miles of overhead transmission lines in the United States. These lines connect electrical power plants to sub-stations located closer to the home or business where it will be used to power loads.

FIGURE 2-1: A TYPICAL ELECTRIC UTILITY DISTRIBUTION SUB-STATION

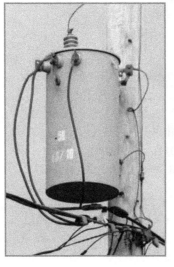

DISTRIBUTION SUB-STATION

TRANSFORMER

The maximum distance for a high voltage transmission line is about 300 miles. The electricity on these lines is normally in the range of between 138,000 to 765,000 volts. The higher the voltage, the less energy is lost as it travels long distances.

The high voltage transmission lines terminate at a **distribution sub-station**, as shown in Figure 2-1. At this point the electricity enters the distribution system. At the sub-station several things happen. The voltage is stepped down with the use of **transformers**. The sub-station also may feed the electricity into multiple distribution systems, as well as provide a method to disconnect that section of the grid in case of problems.

FIGURE 2-2: TRANSFORMER DRUM AT CUSTOMER'S SITE

Power leaving the distribution sub-station is considered part of the primary distribution system. Voltages within this part of the system range from 4 kV to 13 kV . Only large consumers (such as industrial facilities) are fed directly from substations at distribution voltages ranging from 26 kV to 69 kV.

The power from the sub-stations is distributed to more than 145 million homes and businesses through millions of miles of local electrical lines.

At each home, the power is reduced in voltage again within the transformer drum that normally is attached to a power pole, like the one pictured in Figure 2-2.

Single Phase Power

For residential service, this power is typically stepped down to 240 volts. The service from the transformer to the home is normally provided at either 100 or 200 amps of current. The greater the amps, the larger the wire required to safely transmit the power from the final transformer to the home's service panel.

The power coming from a typical transformer drum to a home is referred to as **single-phase** electric. This refers to the waveform of the AC power. As illustrated in Figure 2-3, a two wire single-phase signal (in the US) will have a voltage of 120 volts, and a frequency of 60 hertz (cycles per second).

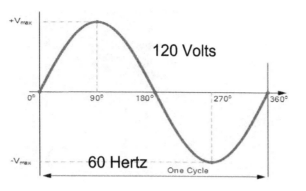

FIGURE 2-3: SINGLE-PHASE WAVEFORM

SINGLE-PHASE

This is similar to the power that supplies a standard (US) electrical outlet. There is a "hot" conductor (black) a neutral (white) and a bare copper wire known as the ground as shown in Figure 2-4.

But the service coming into a typical home has three, rather than two wires. These carry two 120-volt power lines that share a common neutral. The first 120-volt AC power line runs exactly ½ cycle, or 180° out of phase with the second 120 Volt AC power line (as shown in Figure 2-5). This is called **split phase** power, because the 240-volt signal from the transformer is split into two 120-volt circuits, that operate 180 degrees apart.

FIGURE 2-4: STANDARD US SINGLE-PHASE WALL OUTLET

SPLIT-PHASE

In the main electrical panel of the building (where the circuit breakers are located), phase 1 and phase 2 are connected within the panel to separate busbars that essentially "zigzag" and interlock. As a result, each single-pole circuit breaker (on the left side, and the right side) is powered by a different phase. In other words, the top right breaker is powered by phase 1, the one below it by phase 2, the one below that by phase 1, below that by phase 2, and so on.

By doing this, a double-pole breaker that fits into two slots, rather than one, will receive power from both phases - or at 240 volts rather

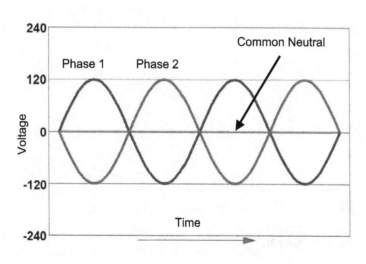

FIGURE 2-5: SPLIT PHASE WAVEFORM

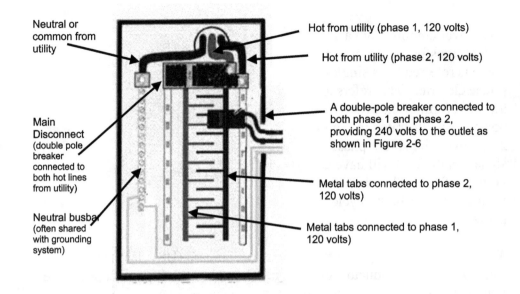

FIGURE 2-6: TYPICAL SINGLE-PHASE SPLIT PHASE SERVICE PANEL WITH DOUBLE-POLE BREAKER FEEDING A LOAD

Neutral or common from utility

Hot from utility (phase 1, 120 volts)

Hot from utility (phase 2, 120 volts)

A double-pole breaker connected to both phase 1 and phase 2, providing 240 volts to the outlet as shown in Figure 2-6

Main Disconnect (double pole breaker connected to both hot lines from utility)

Neutral busbar (often shared with grounding system)

Metal tabs connected to phase 2, 120 volts)

Metal tabs connected to phase 1, 120 volts)

than 120 volts as shown in Figure 2-6.

Appliances that require 120 volts are connected to only one leg (either phase 1 or phase 2) through a single-pole breaker in the service panel. Appliances that receive 240 volts must be wired to both of the hot wires, as well as the common neutral, as illustrated in Figure 2-7. In a residential setting, the color coding will typically be black and red, for the "hot" wires, and white for the common neutral.

Role of the Neutral

In a single phase system, current flows to the load through the hot wire (phase 1 in this example), and back through the neutral (through the service panel) to the service neutral. For example, if only one load was turned on that draws one amp of current, then one amp will flow through the hot to the load, and

FIGURE 2-7: OUTLET WIRING FOR 120-VOLT OUTLET (LEFT) AND 240-VOLT OUTLET (RIGHT)

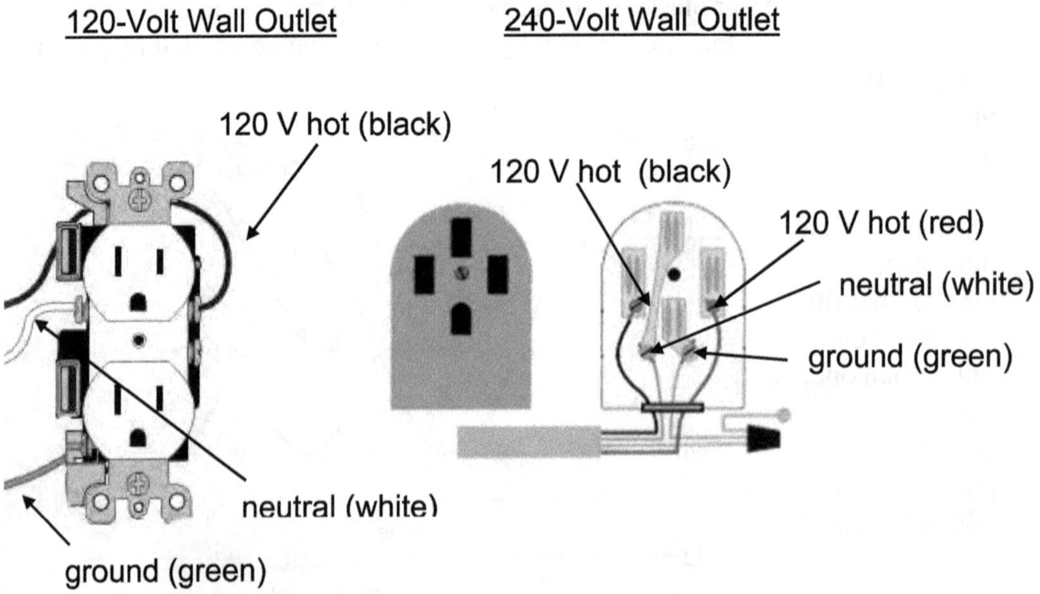

<u>120-Volt Wall Outlet</u>

120 V hot (black)

neutral (white)

ground (green)

<u>240-Volt Wall Outlet</u>

120 V hot (black)

120 V hot (red)

neutral (white)

ground (green)

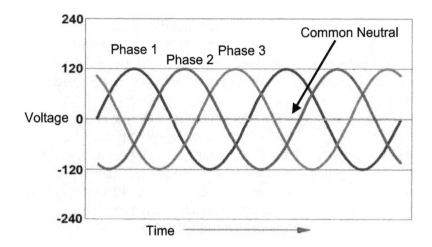

FIGURE 2-8: THREE-
PHASE POWER SINE
WAVE FORM

then one amp of current will return via the neutral conductor. One amp will then flow to the service neutral.

After turning on another one-amp load that is fed from the other service hot (phase 2). One amp will flow through the hot to the load and then return to the service panel via the neutral. But because the two phases are 180 degrees out of phase with each other, the two currents cancel each other out and no current will flow to the service neutral.

Imagine a situation where a home loses its service neutral. If the loads on each leg are about the same, each leg will remain at around 120 volts. However, if a large load is present on leg A, such as a microwave, the voltage on leg A will drop and the voltage on leg B will rise. While the loads are balanced, voltages will remain the same on each leg, with or without the service neutral. It's only when they are out of balance that current flows to the service neutral.

Three Phase Power

Many commercial and industrial customers receive their electricity in the form of **three-phase** power. In a three-phase system, the power received or generated is in the form of three sine waves, each 120° out of phase with the other, as illustrated in Figure 2-8.

THREE-PHASE

Three-phase power is most effective in driving large motors. Generally, three-phase motors generate about 1.5 times the output of similarly sized single phase motors.

Three-phase power is also more constant. In single phase circuits, the power pulsates. Due to the nature of the waveform, the power is zero three times in each cycle. Whereas, in **polyphase systems** (generally three-phase), the power delivered is almost constant when the loads are balanced, and never falls to zero.

POLYPHASE SYSTEMS

FIGURE 2-9: UTILITY
PROVIDED SINGLE-PHASE
POWER DIAGRAM

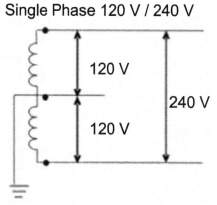

Single Phase 120 V / 240 V

120 V

240 V

120 V

When designing a PV system for a structure that receives three-phase power from the utility, it is important that the inverter match the utility power system.

For standard split-phase power, the two phases are exactly out of phase (shifted by 180 degrees), so that the voltage of the waveform becomes twice that of the phases: 2 x 120 Volts = 240 Volts (Figure 2-9) when both hot conductors are connected to the load.

But in a three-phase system, it is not quite so simple. Two selected phases are only 1/3 of the way out of phase (shifted by 120 degrees), so their peaks do not line up. The voltage of the resulting waveform is only 1.73 (the square root of 3) larger than the voltage of each of the phases: 1.73 x 120 volts = 208 Volts or 1.73 x 277 volts = 480 volts.

WYE CONFIGURATION

Transformers that generate three-phase power are configured in two ways. The **Wye configuration** (called Wye as the connection resembles the letter "Y") has three phases that connect to the neutral wire at the center point (four wires in all). These conductors are typically referred to as line 1 (phase A), line 2 (phase B), line 3 (phase C) and a neutral. In the US, the most common three-phase, four-wire Wye configuration voltages are 208/120 V and 480/277 V, as depicted in Figure 2-10.

DELTA
CONFIGURATION

There is also the **Delta configuration**, as illustrated in Figure 2-11. Named because it resembles the Greek symbol Δ (delta), only three conductors leave this configuration if it contains no neutral. A service of this type will only be able to service three-phase loads. This type of service is available in 208 V, 400 V, 480 V and 600 V. In a three-wire Delta configuration, the voltage when measured across two lines will always equal the voltage of a single phase.

FIGURE 2-10: WIRING
DIAGRAMS FOR TYPICAL
WYE TYPE 3 PHASE
ELECTRIC

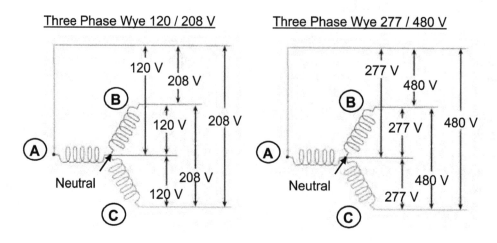

Three Phase Wye 120 / 208 V

120 V
208 V
B
120 V   208 V
A
Neutral
208 V
120 V
C

Three Phase Wye 277 / 480 V

277 V
480 V
B
277 V   480 V
A
Neutral
480 V
277 V
C

A four-wire Delta configuration (with a neutral) is also available and can power single-phase loads as well as three-phase loads. In a 120/208/240 V Delta configuration, when the voltage is measured between two lines, it will measure 240 V. When measured between the neutral and a single line, it will measure 120 V. This is similar to a traditional single-phase system, so it is possible to wire single-phase loads with this configuration.

However, when measuring the voltage between line 2 (phase B) and the neutral, the voltage will be 208 V. This conductor is referred to as the **high leg** (illustrated in Figure 2-11). Great care must be taken not to connect a single-phase 120 V load to the high leg, as that load will receive 208 V.

A five-wire variation of the Wye configuration adds an earth ground wire, usually connected at the same center point as where the neutral connects to the lines. This ground is then connected to the grounding system at the circuit breaker panel. This variation, however, is not common.

It is critical to know the voltage as well as the configuration (Wye or Delta) of the three-phase power provided by the utility in order to properly select and connect a three-phase inverter within a PV system.

Voltage Unbalance

Voltage unbalance occurs when the voltages of a three-phase system on the terminals of a three-phase load are not equal. Voltages on each phase should not vary more than 1%. The unbalance may result from too many single-phase loads placed on one phase of the system.

Single phasing may result when one phase of a three-phase system is completely lost. Common causes of single phasing are the result of a blown fuse, a switch failure or a lightning strike on the power lines.

Current Unbalance

Small voltage unbalance in a three-phase system may result in significant **current unbalance**. This occurs when the current on each phase is not equal. Current unbalances should never exceed 10%.

Three Phase Delta 3-Wire 208 V

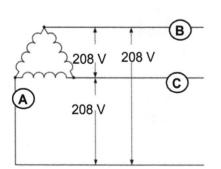

Three Phase Delta 4-Wire 120/208/240 V

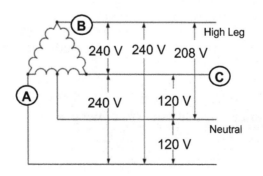

FIGURE 2-11: WIRING DIAGRAMS FOR TYPICAL DELTA TYPE 3 PHASE ELECTRIC

PHASE UNBALANCE

Phase Unbalance

In an ideal three-phase system, each phase is 120° out of phase with each other. When single-phase loads are applied unequally on the various phases, the phase separation can become more or less than 120°.

If all three phases are balanced, the return current for any one phase is carried by the other two. Again, the service neutral only carries current if the load is unbalanced.

Factors that may result in voltage unbalances can be classified into two categories: normal factors and abnormal factors.

Voltage imbalances due to normal factors, such as single-phase loads and three-phase transformer banks with open star-open delta connections, can generally be reduced by properly designing the system and installing suitable equipment and devices.

Abnormal factors include series and shunt faults of circuits, bad electrical contacts of connectors or switches, asymmetrical breakdown of equipment or components, asynchronous burnout of three phase power fuses, single-phase operation of motors, etc. These abnormal factors may result in critical damage of systems and/or equipment.

Who Owns the Grid?

The electric grid, which includes generation, transmission, and distribution, is owned by a quite a number of different players, in a number of different corporate forms.

INVESTOR-OWNED UTILITY (IOU)

As of 2017, there were 168 **investor-owned utilities (IOU)** that owned 38% of all net generation, 80% of the transmission infrastructure, and 50% of the distribution infrastructure. An IOU is a for-profit corporation owned by one or more investors. While smallest in number, IOUs serve over 71% of the electric utility customers in the US.

MUNICIPAL SYSTEM

RURAL ELECTRIC COOPERATIVE

There are about 2,900 publicly-owned utilities and cooperatives (**municipal systems** and **rural electric cooperatives**) that account for 15% of net generation, 12% of transmission, and nearly 50% of the nation's electric distribution lines.

Approximately 2,800 independent power producers account for about 40% of net generation (these would include large wind farms as well as utility-scale solar arrays).

The federal government owns 9 power agencies (such as the Tennessee Valley Authority) that own 7% of net generation and 8% of the transmission lines.

The 6,000 or so "owners" each control a small portion of a vast electrical system that is called the "grid". In order to operate effectively, there must be a substantial amount of oversight from some central authority to make sure it all operates smoothly.

State Regulation

Those who own the generating, transmission and distribution systems are regulated by individual state's **Public Utility Commission (PUC)** or the **Public Service Commission (PSC)**. These are regulatory agencies appointed by the state legislatures. These agencies approve the construction of generation facilities and also set electricity rates within their state.

PUBLIC UTILITY
COMMISSION (PUC)

PUBLIC SERVICE
COMMISSION (PSC)

Because it is more local in nature, the state PUC or PSC is largely responsible for regulating the generation and distribution portion of the grid within the borders of that state.

Regional Regulation

The hundreds of thousands of miles of high-voltage transmission lines within the US are designed to carry electricity from where it is generated to where it is needed. This vast assembly of poles, towers, transformers and stations is organized into three large regional networks.

These include the **Eastern Interconnection**, the **Western Interconnection**, and the **Electricity Reliability Council of Texas Interconnection (ERCOT)**, as illustrated in Figure 2-12.

EASTERN
INTERCONNECTION

WESTERN
INTERCONNECTION

ERCOT

The three large regions operate for the most part independently of each other, but there are limited transfers of electricity between them. Although they each operate at the same average frequency (60 hertz), the individual interconnections are not in synch with one another and therefore cannot be directly connected through high-voltage AC transmission lines.

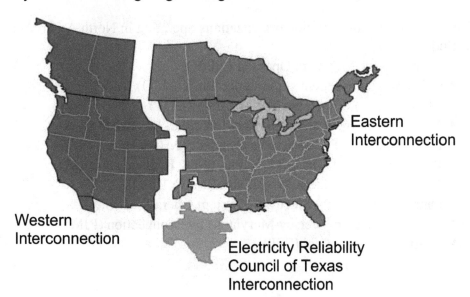

Eastern
Interconnection

Western
Interconnection

Electricity Reliability
Council of Texas
Interconnection

FIGURE 2-12: US
REGIONAL ELECTRICITY
REGULATING
AUTHORITIES

| HIGH-VOLTAGE DIRECT CURRENT |

| RECTIFIER |

Instead, **high-voltage direct current (HVDC)** transmission systems connect the various regional systems. These systems require a **rectifier** to convert from one region's AC power into DC. It is then transmitted to the next region, where an inverter converts the DC back to AC. Six DC ties link the Western Interconnection with the Eastern Interconnection within the US, with one additional tie in Canada. The Texas Interconnection is linked to the Eastern Interconnection by two DC ties.

| NERC |

These interconnection regions are overseen by the **North American Electric Reliability Corporation (NERC)**, a not-for-profit organization responsible for working with all those involved in providing power to the grid. Their role is to develop standards for power system operation, monitoring and enforcing compliance with those standards, assessing resource adequacy, and providing educational and training.

| FERC |

The NERC is in turn overseen by the **FERC (Federal Energy Regulatory Commission)** a US federal agency that regulates the transmission and wholesale sale of electricity, natural gas and oil over state lines.

| REGIONAL TRANSMISSION ORGANIZATIONS |

About 60% of the nation's bulk power systems are controlled by ten **Regional Transmission Organizations (RTO)**. RTOs are independent, non-profit organizations with members from independent power generators, transmission companies, load-serving entities, utilities, power marketers and energy traders that operate within the region.

The RTOs control, manage, monitor and coordinate grid operations within their jurisdiction. They typically handle the market transactions when one utility purchases power from another within the region, as well as handle transmissions between the various regions. They are also responsible for overseeing and planning the expansion and maintenance of the transmission grid within their region, as illustrated in Figure 2-13.

The ten regional transmission organizations operating in North America include:
- Alberta Electric System Operator (AESO)
- California independent system operator (CAISO)
- Electric Reliability Council of Texas (ERCOT)
- Midcontinent Independent System Operator, Inc. (MISO)
- New Brunswick Power System Operator (NBPSO)
- ISO (Independent Systems Operator) New England (ISO-NE)
- New York Independent System Operator (NYISO)
- Ontario Independent Electricity System Operator (IESO)
- PJM (Pennsylvania-Jersey-Maryland) Interconnection (PJM)
- Southwest Power Pool (SPP)

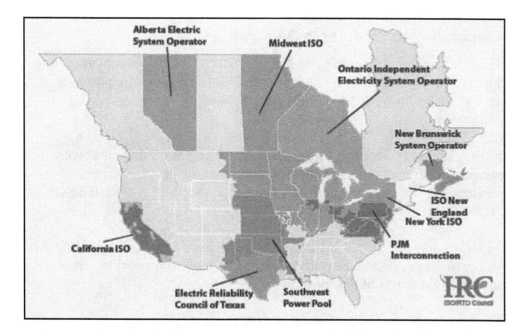

FIGURE 2-13:

JURISDICTIONAL BOUNDARIES OF THE TEN REGIONAL TRANSMISSION ORGANIZATIONS OF NORTH AMERICA

(FROM THE ISO/RTO COUNCIL)

Energy Provider versus Utility

For most of its history, the electrical utility grid has been fairly simple and straightforward. A regulated company produced electricity, then transmitted and sold that power to customers. That model, however, is changing.

The National Energy Policy Act of 1992 created an system to allow for wholesale electric generation competition. It created a new type of energy producer known as the **Exempt Wholesale Generator (EWG)** that did not have to follow the same rules or regulations as traditional utilities, making it simpler for them to enter the market.

In 1996 regulators required that utilities allow EWGs open access to transmission service, effectively separating generation from transmission.

Since that time, a number of states have allowed customers to choose their electrical power generator. These generating companies are known as **Retail Electric Providers (REP)** or **Competitive Retail Electric Service (CRES)** providers. Transmission and distribution services (getting the power from the point of generation to the customer) are still controlled by the public utility.

These utilities are often referred to as **Transmission & Distribution Service Providers (TDSP)** or **Electric Distribution Utilities (EDU)**. Occasionally they are also referred to as **Transmission and Distribution Utility (TDU)**.

TDSPs or EDUs are the companies who own and maintain utility poles and power lines. These utility companies are responsible for the physical delivery of electricity to homes and businesses.

EXEMPT WHOLESALE GENERATOR (EWG)

RETAIL ELECTRIC PROVIDER (REP)

COMPETITIVE RETAIL ELECTRIC SERVICE (CRES)

TRANSMISSION & DISTRIBUTION SERVICE PROVIDER

ELECTRIC DISTRIBUTION UTILITY (EDU)

TRANSMISSION & DISTRIBUTION UTILITY (TDU)

Responding to Changes in Demand

The electrical grid has little or no storage capacity. It operates by matching supply and demand on a second-by-second basis. When more power is needed, the utilities have traditionally responded by increasing energy production.

If they do not have enough capacity to meet the demand, they must then purchase additional power from other generating facilities. Typically this purchased power is much more expensive than the utility's normal power source.

As more customer-owned solar units come on line, control of the generation source of the provided electricity is increasingly taken away from the utilities and put in the hands of the consumer.

BASE LOAD

The **base load** supplied by the utility to its customers is the minimal amount of power required by the system throughout the daily cycle, as illustrated by Figure 2-14.

Traditionally this base load has been supplied by power plants that are slow to start generating power, but once operational, provide a consistent output. Examples of these type of plants would be coal-burning or nuclear power plants. A coal power plant can take from 10-20 hours to ramp up from a "cold start" to generating about 70% of its rated power. A nuclear power plant can take from 24-72 hours to restart after it has been shut down.

NAMEPLATE CAPACITY

Natural gas power plants are much quicker to restart. It may only take 2-3 hours for a dormant gas power plant to be generating at 70% of its **nameplate capacity**.

On most occasions, the fluctuation in daily load demand is fairly predictable. When demand is low, utilities simply turn down the generation capacity from their power supply. As demand increases, more responsive sources of power are added to the mix. As a safety margin, the industry typically maintains 14-15% more generating capacity than the typical highest usage of the year.

The intermittent nature of solar makes predicting demand much more difficult for utilities. As more and more customers install PV systems, much of the power they require is self-generated. But while their load demands may remain steady, from the utility's perspective the load demands will rise and fall dramatically as shifting clouds increase or decrease local power production.

In addition to increased moment-to-moment demand fluctuations, the utilities will also be forced to deal with shifting demand curves as illustrated by the duck curve that result as customer-owned production ramps up during mid-day, but falls off sharply at sunset.

Demand-Side Management

Demand-Side Management (DSM) is an attempt by energy providers to modify consumer demand for energy through financial incentives and changes in behavior. The objective of DSM is to achieve a balance between energy production and demand, since the imbalance between these makes the price of energy more expensive for the consumer (and less profitable for the utility).

Demand response (DR), on the other hand, pursues the temporary reduction of electricity consumption by the consumer (discretionary and limited in time) during periods of peak demand in exchange for economic incentives.

In the past, demand-side management by utilities has largely been conducted through **energy efficiency** programs. By incentivizing customers to be more efficient, the utilities could delay or eliminate costly infrastructure expansion.

Utilities increasingly realize that a more integrated approach to DSM is required to ensure the grid will be capable of handling a rapidly growing distributed energy system, electrification of vehicles and heating systems, integration of batteries, and the integration of behind-the-meter technologies.

Through a combination of DSM strategies, such as energy efficiency programs, **time-of-use pricing**, and the addition of utility-scale storage systems onto the grid, utilities hope to minimize the investment in infrastructure required to service a growing demand and the integration of intermittent renewable energy resources (such as wind and solar).

Additionally, energy providers can also deal with temporary demand fluctuations through a demand response strategy. When the demand is at its peak, utilities can control (turn off) water heaters, air conditioners, and pool pumps in large regions to stabilize the energy demand with supply. They can also control when electric vehicle (EV) batteries are charged - or even draw power from EVs to increase the local energy supply.

Time-of-Use Pricing

The time of day or the day of the week electricity is created and consumed has an impact on its cost. Wholesale electricity prices (the price a utility pays for electricity before reselling it) vary throughout the day based on demand at that particular moment. The higher the demand for the power being generated, the higher the price. The day of the week also plays a factor. Typically less electricity is consumed on weekends and holidays, when many businesses are closed.

Demand for electricity is also generally higher during the summer months when air conditioners add significantly to load demands. Increasingly utilities are shifting to time-of-use pricing models to encourage consumers to use less power during peak demand times. This tends to "flatten" the demand curve, placing fewer strains on utility infrastructure. Figure 2-15 illustrates a typical time-of-use pricing model.

Load Shifting

LOAD SHIFTING

Increasingly, programmable appliances can be brought into play to help customers reduce energy bills. The practice of **load shifting** uses timers to more closely align load demands with the production cycle of the PV array and low-cost energy from the utility.

Load shifting does not reduce the amount of energy consumed, it simply moves or shifts the time when that energy is consumed to periods when ample energy is available.

Many loads are not time sensitive. For example, if the array produces its maximum power at 1 pm, simply program the dishwasher to run at that time.

PEAK HOURS

OFF-PEAK HOURS

PV system designers can also incorporate storage devices (typically batteries) to shift energy consumption from the utility. Loads can be serviced from the batteries during **peak hours** (when prices are high) and recharged from the utility or from the array during **off-peak hours**.

Load Shedding

LOAD SHEDDING

Load shedding is a bit more complicated. With load shedding, loads are prioritized. If the total load of the facility reaches a certain level, a lower

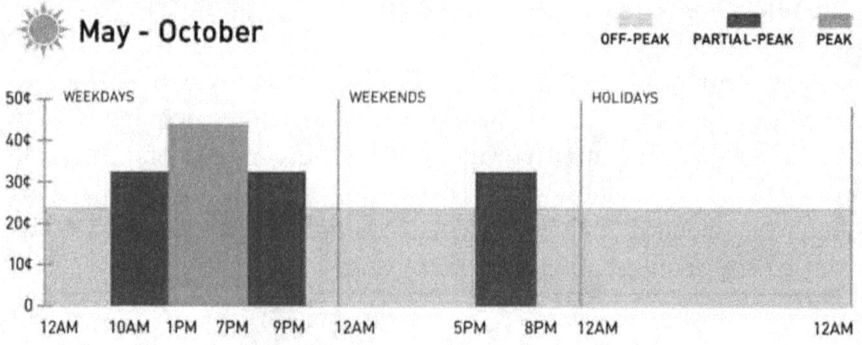

FIGURE 2-15: TIME-OF-USE PRICING STRUCTURE PUT IN PLACE IN 2016 BY PACIFIC GAS & ELECTRIC

☀ **May - October**

OFF-PEAK   PARTIAL-PEAK   PEAK

priority load, such as a freezer or hot water heater can be temporarily shut down for a period of time to reduce the total load.

Power management tools are available that incorporate this feature for commercial systems. It is a practice not often implemented in residential systems.

The practice of load shedding avoids any negative influences the utility's billing policies may have on the price of power, particularly in lowering **demand charges** - where the utility adds a multiplier to the total monthly bill based on the highest power draw experienced during any 15-minute interval during the month. This can increase the bill dramatically.

DEMAND CHARGES

Unlike in load shifting, load shedding does typically lower overall energy consumption.

Understanding Power

Electric utilities are often referred to as power companies. To the general public, they exist to provide energy to homes and businesses. This energy runs lights, motors, heaters and air conditioners.

But the system of energy delivery is not as simple as it may appear. There are a number of forms of power. It is necessary to understand several forms in order to understand how the grid operates.

In this quest, it is important to define the difference between:
- real power,
- apparent power,
- reactive power.

Real Power

Real power is the power required by a piece of equipment to operate. It is measured in watts (W). For example, a 60-watt light bulb will consume 60 W of real power when it is turned on. Real power is what the average consumer thinks of when (and if) they consider the concept of power. In a DC system, all power provided is real power.

REAL POWER

Apparent Power

Apparent power refers to all of the power that is supplied to the circuit that will ultimately power the loads. From the utility's perspective, this is the amount of power sent to the home or business. This power is measured in **volt-amperes (VA)**.

APPARENT POWER

VOLT-AMPERES (VA)

Reactive Power

Many loads are not 100% efficient in converting the power entering into power output. The generation of magnetic fields are required in AC reactive

FIGURE 2-16:
RELATIONSHIP BETWEEN
APPARENT POWER, REAL
POWER, REACTIVE
POWER AND THE POWER
FACTOR

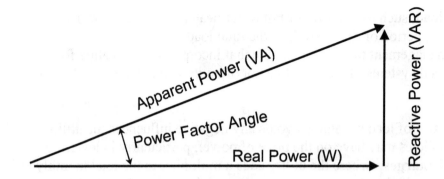

loads, such as motors or florescent lights. Creation of these magnetic fields cause the electrical current to "lag" the voltage, resulting in current that is not in phase with the voltage. As a result, a certain amount of power is required to operate the load but not all of it is available to power the load (more power in than power out).

REACTIVE POWER

IMAGINARY POWER

VOLT AMPS REACTIVE
(VAR)

Reactive power is often referred to as **imaginary power**, as it is required to run the load, but is not actually consumed by the load. This is the power "inefficiency" inherent to the load (the difference between the power input required by the load and the power that is actually used by the load). Reactive power is measured in **volt amps reactive (VAR)**.

While reactive power does not directly power the load, it supports the voltage necessary to turn on an AC motor or system and keep the real power balanced and allow a motor or system to operate efficiently.

Power Factor

The relationship between real power (W), apparent power (VA) and reactive power (VAR) is demonstrated in Figure 2-16. How efficiently the load converts the power coming in to usable (or real) power is known as the **power factor**.

POWER FACTOR

The power factor is the relationship between real and reactive power and measures how effectively electric power is being used. A power factor of 1.0 would indicate that 100% of the power entering a load is being used by the load (real power). A power factor of 0.95 indicates that only 95% of the power entering a load is used by the load (5% absorbed as reactive power).

A power factor above 0.95 is considered "good" when evaluating a typical commercial building. While power factors vary widely, a 2015 study in Austin, TX of 13,522 commercial customers found an average power factor of 92.6%.

Some inverters on the market today only produce real power. This can cause the power factor associated with a commercial customer to fluctuate dramatically, as power sources shift from the grid to the PV array to service the loads .

Utilities often require large commercial and industrial customers to maintain a power factor above a certain level. The power factor is a measurement of how efficiently the power entering the facility is being used or consumed.

FIGURE 2-17: VOLTAGE AND AMP WAVEFORMS ALIGNED - TRUE POWER

If 100% of the power entering was used to run loads, the facility would have a power factor of 1.0. A power factor of 1.0 is obtained when current and voltage are in phase, as in a circuit containing only resistive loads. A power factor of 1.0 is known as a **unity power factor**.

UNITY POWER FACTOR

Power factor is expressed as a ratio or percentage of real power (watts) that is used by the loads, divided by apparent power (VA usually expressed with the letter "S") or the amount of power supplied by the utility:

PF (power factor) = P (W) / S (VA)

If 100 VA of power is received by the factory, but only 90 W can be consumed by the load in the form of real power, then the system would have a power factor of .90 or 90% (PF = 90 W/ 100 VA).

AC power travels from the source (normally a utility's power plant) to the load in the form of a wave. It is often thought of as a single wave, but in reality is actually the combination of two wave forms, one for volts and the other for amps. When these waveforms are in perfect alignment, they are often referred to as **true power** (as illustrated in Figure 2-17).

TRUE POWER

Certain loads, such as incandescent light bulbs or the coils of a toaster are known as **resistive loads**. They do not cause a shift in the two waveforms of AC power. 100% of the power going into a load is used by the load. This would be measured as a load/power factor of 1.0.

RESISTIVE LOAD

But some loads can cause the waveforms to shift. This is known as **reactive power**. Reactive power introduces inefficiencies into the process. A load will not use as much power as is being supplied. An **inductive load,** such as a motor or a florescent light, will shift the voltage waveform ahead of the current waveform, creating positive reactive power. A **capacitive load** will cause the voltage waveform to lag behind the current waveform, creating negative reactive power as shown in Figure 2-18.

INDUCTIVE LOAD

CAPACITIVE LOAD

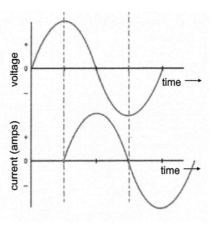

Positive Reactive Power – Voltage Leads Current

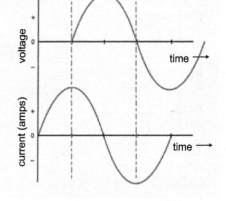

Negative Reactive Power – Voltage Lags Current

LEADING POWER FACTOR

LAGGING POWER FACTOR

The power factor at a site will always fall between 0 - 1 and is determined by the lead or lag of current with regard to voltage. In a capacitive load, the voltage waveform trails behind the current waveform, so it will create a **leading power factor** (because the current "leads" the voltage).

On the other hand, an inductive load will create a waveform where the voltage waveform comes before the current waveform, so it is said to have a **lagging power factor** (since the current "lags" behind the voltage).

In any system, it is the true power that is doing all the work. The reactive power is working against this process. Each load behaves just a bit differently. The combined effect of all the inefficiencies introduced into the power system because of the shifting of these waveforms is called the reactive volt-amps (VAR). The bottom line is that because of the inefficiencies caused by the reactive volt-amps (VAR), the utility must supply more power than is actually used by the loads (the true power, measured in watts).

The larger amount of power supplied by the utility is called the apparent power, measured in volt-amps (VA). For larger customers, utilities often factor in a reactive volt-amps (VAR) rate to recover the cost of the apparent power. How much inefficiency is in the system is calculated through the load/power factor.

The power factor is determined by dividing real power (measured in kW) by apparent power (measured in kVA). This can be thought of as a measure of efficiency - dividing the power used by the load by the amount of power supplied to the load by the generator.

Utilities typically seek to keep this power factor above 90%. If the power factor falls below this level, the utility may charge additional fees or apply a different rate schedule. Under certain circumstances, a PV system can reduce a facility's power factor as measured by the utility.

Inverters and Reactive Power

Inverters are typically designed to generate only real power. The more a business relies on power from the solar array, the greater the portion of reactive power that must be provided from the grid. This can dramatically shift the existing power factor of the customer.

While the solar array is generating real power to service the loads, the home or business is still drawing (and paying for) reactive power necessary for operating any inductive load from the grid. For the grid operator, this means that it must generate and deliver reactive power to supply an increasing need for variable energy.

Take for example a factory that draws 100 kW of power from the utility and operates with a power factor of 0.95. Of the 100 kW, 95 kW is real power and 5 kW is reactive power.

This factory then installs a large PV array. Assume half of the load is serviced by the array at a given moment (50 kW). All of the power from the array is produced in the form of real power. The loads of the factory still need 5 kW of reactive power, all of which must be supplied by the utility.

Yet the factory is now only drawing 50 kW from the grid (45 kW used as real power and 5 kW as reactive power), boosting the power factor to 0.90. If the array produced even more of the factory's power needs (say 90 kW), then the power factor would climb even more (5 kW of reactive power from the 10 kW provided by the utility, or a power factor of 0.50).

Inverters with reactive power control can be configured to produce both active and reactive power. In this way the power factor for the load can be managed and kept within reasonable limits. Businesses that experience a low power factor (and therefore a higher cost of electricity) might be able to use their solar array to actually decrease the power factor experienced from the grid and bring down the cost of their power.

Inverter manufacturers can offer guidance on how to minimize the impact of changes to the load/power factor. Most inverters can create and/or absorb reactive power, but these capabilities are normally disabled as a default setting.

Maintaining Power Quality

The grid as it exists today did not anticipate the widespread development of distributed energy systems. It was designed assuming a central power source, delivering controlled power long distances to remote customers. Adding distributed energy systems such as PV greatly complicates this already complex system.

Voltage Issues

When operating properly, utilities provide power within an acceptable voltage range. Voltages falling outside this range can damage equipment that is connected to the grid. In a 120 V (nominal) system, the acceptable voltage range is between 114 V-126 V. During periods of time when load demand is high, voltages near the substation (near the source) are typically higher than voltages tested some distance from the substation.

Utilities can adjust the voltage on the grid either by increasing generation, or by supplying reactive power (VAR), normally accomplished by switching on capacitors during high demand and switching them off when load demand falls. Over the years a number of technologies have been developed to assist utilities in **voltage optimization** (voltage correction, stabilization, or reduction).

> **VOLTAGE OPTIMIZATION**

The voltages present on any electrical system vary from second to second within an acceptable range. Most electrical loads are designed to operate within (and often even a bit beyond) these ranges. Higher voltages, or **overvoltage**, can waste power, and cause loads such as motors to convert this wasted energy into heat, reducing the life of the motor over time.

> **OVERVOLTAGE**

The voltage present on the system is also affected by nearby load demand. If, for example, a nearby factory turns on and off a large motor, this action can lead to brief spikes and dips in the voltage available to nearby buildings.

> **TRANSIENTS**
> **SURGES**
> **VOLTAGE SWELL**
> **DIPS**
> **VOLTAGE SAG**

These are known as **transients**. Transient voltage that is higher than normal are often called **surges** or **voltage swell**, while lower voltages are referred to as **dips** or **voltage sag**. Transients can also be caused by lightning strikes, power generators coming on or offline, or, as mentioned, fluctuating demand.

A voltage swell may be caused by loads near the substation, incorrectly wired transformer taps, or very large loads that are suddenly turned off.

A voltage sag may be caused by over-loaded transformers, undersized wire, too many loads on a circuit, or very large loads that are suddenly turned on.

Frequency Issues

When there is a sudden drop in generating capacity (such as a power plant going off line), the **frequency** of the power on the grid can be affected. In the United States, the frequency of the electrical grid operates at 60 hertz. This means that the AC sine wave is designed to rise and fall 60 times each second.

> **FREQUENCY**

Irregular and/or higher and lower frequency waveforms are called **harmonics**. When the frequency of the power on the grid falls outside of the

> **HARMONICS**

normal limits, PV systems are designed to shut down (to avoid damaging equipment connected to the grid).

Power comes from the utility in the form of a clean sine wave. As it goes through different types of loads, the voltage and current can be distorted by certain loads.

Loads that draw power along the provided or fundamental sine wave are referred to as a **linear load.** Examples of linear loads include transformers, motors and capacitors.

LINEAR LOAD

Non-linear loads, such as UPS equipment, computers, variable-speed drives, EV charging stations and electronic fluorescent lighting ballasts can introduce harmonic distortion into the electrical signal.

NON-LINEAR LOAD

The **total harmonic distortion (THD)** is a measurement of how much the voltage or current waveform is "distorted" or changed from its conventional sine wave shape (Figure 2-19).

TOTAL HARMONIC DISTORTION (THD)

THD is generally expressed as a percentage of deviation from the ideal or fundamental sine wave (illustrated in Figure 2-20).

Harmonics are not generally a problem at low levels, but very high levels may cause conductors to over heat or disturbances in some equipment. While there is no firm limit on THD limits, IEEE 519 recommends that systems like computers and related equipment have no more than 5% total harmonic voltage distortion with the largest single harmonic no more than 3% of the fundamental voltage.

In systems where a large part of the power is supplied by solar, this will cause additional stress, throwing the frequency even further outside of normal operating limits. The effect could be that a localized single power outage may cascade throughout the system as more and more PV systems go offline.

A **harmonic mitigating transformer (HMT)** is a transformer designed to reduce the harmonics in a power distribution system. Some styles of HMTs are referred to as phase-shifting transformers. An HMT works best when

HARMONIC MITIGATING TRANSFORMER

FIGURE 2-19: HARMONIC DISTORTION

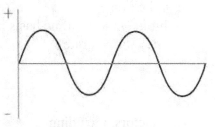

Linear Load

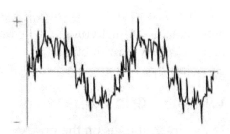

Non-Linear Load

FIGURE 2-20: HARMONIC
DISTORTION

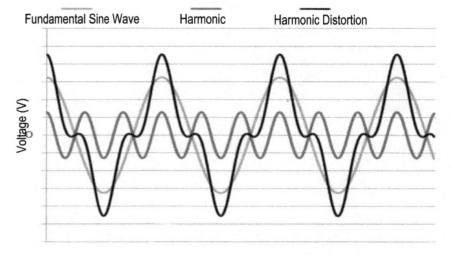

located close to the load. This generally means that HMTs are located at
scattered locations throughout a facility where harmonics have become an
issue due to a high concentration on non-linear loads.

The utility industry is concerned with the lack of frequency and voltage ride-
through requirements for solar facilities. Most inverters are designed to shut
off and then reconnect a short time later during even a momentary disruption
of the grid (higher or lower than normal voltages or frequency).

If enough PV systems are connected to the system, small problems can
quickly become large problems and significant portions of the grid turn off
and then come back on line at the same instant. It would be better for the grid
if inverters were designed to accommodate temporary fluctuations in the
grid's power profile. As a result, many utilities are beginning to require the
use of **smart inverters** that incorporate these voltage and frequency ride-
through capabilities.

SMART INVERTER

How Utilities Control Power Quality
In the grid as it has operated for the last century or so, utilities have controlled
power quality through the use of **step-down transformers** (also called a
voltage-reducing or "tap-down" transformer). Higher voltages from the power
plants are reduced in voltage at sub-stations. If the voltages entering are too
high, the **tap-setting** (the ratio between incoming and outgoing voltage) can
be adjusted to best meet the needs of nearby customers.

STEP-DOWN
TRANSFORMER

TAP-SETTING

Utilities also incorporate **voltage regulators** within the system that
automatically adjust voltages to within acceptable limits on a real time basis in
response to system fluctuations. These regulators may incorporate
capacitors, or be more electronic in nature.

VOLTAGE REGULATOR

When the Grid Goes Down

Power interruptions on the grid are caused by many factors, including
weather, vegetation (trees falling on lines), and utility practices. Most outages

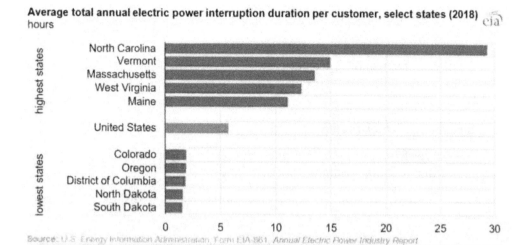

Average total annual electric power interruption duration per customer, select states (2018)
hours

highest states
North Carolina
Vermont
Massachusetts
West Virginia
Maine

United States

lowest states
Colorado
Oregon
District of Columbia
North Dakota
South Dakota

0   5   10   15   20   25   30

Source: U.S. Energy Information Administration, Form EIA-861, Annual Electric Power Industry Report

last for a relatively short period of time. In 2018, power outage durations for U.S. electricity customers averaged 5.8 hours per customer.

As indicated in Figure 2-21, the average U.S. home or business experienced about six grid power outages during 2018.

After the issue that caused the grid to fail (such as lines down in an ice storm) has been addressed and/or repaired, restoring power to the grid is not as simple as flipping a switch to start up the generators. It involves an often complex process referred to as a **black start**.

BLACK START

For outages that are limited in scope, the electric power used to restart the system is provided from the station's own generators. If all of the plant's main generators are shut down, power must be drawn from other generating stations from the grid through transmission lines.

However, during a wide-area outage, off-site power from the grid may not be available. In the absence of grid power, a black start needs to be performed to **bootstrap** the power grid into operation. Bootstrapping refers to a self-starting process that restarts the grid without external power input.

BOOTSTRAP

To provide a black start, some power stations have small diesel generators, which can be used to start larger generators, which in turn can be used to start the main power station generators. Generating plants using steam turbines require station service power of up to 10% of their capacity for boiler feedwater pumps, boiler forced-draft combustion air blowers, and for fuel preparation. It is often uneconomical to provide such a large standby capacity at each station, so black-start power must be provided over designated tie lines from another station.

A typical black start process might be as follows:

- A battery starts a small diesel generator installed in a generating station.

- The power from the diesel generator is used to bring that generating station into operation.

- Specific transmission lines between the station and other generating stations are energized.

- The power from the black start station is used to start one of the nuclear/fossil-fuel-fired base load plants.

- The power from the base load plant is used to restart all of the other power plants in the system.

- Power is finally re-applied to the general electricity distribution network and sent to the consumers. Often this will happen gradually, since starting the entire grid at once may be unfeasible. High initial load demand might overtax the system and cause the grid to fail at startup.

Widespread deployment of solar energy systems makes this process more complicated. When the grid operator was the only source of energy on the system, they could predict load demand fairly accurately, ensuring there was enough power supplied to handle the restart.

But solar hides much of the load demand from the grid operator, as power from the array is hidden behind the meter - servicing loads that are not accounted for by the grid operator. Since inverters are designed to wait a period of time (usually about 5 minutes) before turning back on after the grid signal is restored - the grid operator may experience a higher than anticipated load demand during the initial moments after restoring power to the customers.

Energy Storage on the Grid

Until recently, storage of energy on the grid has been limited and existed largely in the form of **pumped hydroelectric storage** and **compressed air energy storage (CAES)**.

PUMPED HYDRO-
ELECTRIC STORAGE

COMPRESSED AIR
ENERGY STORAGE
(CAES)

Pumped hydroelectric storage normally incorporates an upper reservoir where water is stored. During periods of high energy demand, water is released from this reservoir and powers generating turbines. During periods of low energy demand, low-cost power (from a nearby hydro plant or wind turbine, for example) is used to replenish the upper reservoir.

Compressed air energy storage (CAES) is very similar in concept to the pumped hydroelectric storage. But instead of pumping water to a high reservoir, air is pumped and compressed into an underground cavern. Then during periods of high energy demand, this air is released to drive turbines.

Prior to 2009, the cost of battery systems to store electricity made them too expensive and impractical to implement on a large scale in storing power for use on the grid.

In recent years, falling costs and government incentives have combined to promote the integration of battery storage on the grid.

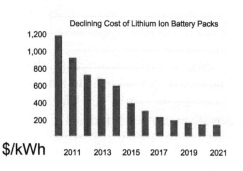

Declining Cost of Lithium Ion Battery Packs

$/kWh

Lithium-ion battery pack prices, which were above $1,100 per kilowatt-hour in 2010, have fallen 89% in real terms to $137/kWh in 2020 as shown in Figure 2-22. BloombergNEF forecast battery costs falling under US$100/kWh in 2024 and hitting around US$60/kWh by 2030.

The grid still only has the capacity to store only a tiny amount of the potential load demand (about 2.2%).

While still a relatively small portion of the mix, grid battery systems have grown rapidly in recent years. In 2010, the United States had seven operational battery storage systems, which accounted for 59 megawatts (MW) of power capacity (the maximum amount of power output a battery can provide in any instant) and 21 megawatt hours (MWh) of energy capacity (the total amount of energy that can be stored or discharged by a battery).

By the end of 2018, the United States had 125 operational battery storage systems, providing a total of 869 MW of installed power capacity and 1,236 MWh of energy capacity.

By 2020 there was a combined capacity of 23.2 gigawatts (GW) of power storage on the US grid. In 2021 alone an additional 12.4 GW of battery storage was added to the grid.

The U.S. Department of Energy announced in 2021 a goal to reduce the cost of long-duration energy storage by 90 percent by 2030. This goal covers technologies that can discharge electricity for at least 10 hours on a charge.

Global energy storage deployments, including customer-owned storage, will reach 358 GW/1,028 GWh by the end of the decade — a twentyfold increase over 2020 capacity — according to an analysis by BloombergNEF.

Cost of Energy to Utilities

In recent years, the **levelized cost of energy (LCOE)** generated by solar has declined dramatically, down over 100% from 2009. LCOE is a measure of

LEVELIZED COST OF ENERGY (LCOE)

the average net present cost of electricity generation for a new generating plant over its lifetime.

Over the past decade, electrical production in the US has shifted from one based largely on fossil fuels, to a more diversified mix of fossil fuel and renewable energy. Most new electrical generating plants constructed in the past decade have been wind, solar and natural gas, driven by the shifting LCOE.

According to a 2020 study by the financial advisory firm Lazard, the LCOE of unsubsidized (not including any government incentive programs) utility-scale solar was between $0.028 - $0.041 per kWh, making it far and away the least expensive form of energy. A possible exception is wind generated power, which has a generation cost of between $0.026 - $0.05 per kWh.

This compares to a LCOE of between $0.045 - $0.074 per kWh for combined cycle natural gas plants, between $0.065 - $0.152 per kWh for a coal powered plant, between $0.131 - $0.204 for a nuclear power plant, and between $0.151 - $0.196 per kWh for a natural gas peaker plant.

Even the cost of generating power from a fully depreciated coal power plant is still about twice that of building a brand new solar array, averaging about $0.042 per kWh.

COMBINED CYCLE

Combined cycle natural gas turbines burn natural gas in one cycle and in another cycle the system's exhaust heat is recaptured and used to heat water into steam that drives the turbine. To be cost effective, combined cycle plants need to run 30% to 70% of the time.

PEAKER PLANT

Peaker plants (normally natural gas) are usually only used when energy demand is high. They are designed to run less than 10% of the time, and are generally more expensive and less efficient to operate.

In recent years utilities have sought to offset high priced peaker plants by adding battery storage to the grid, which can be easily and quickly dispatched during periods of peak load demand.

IN-FRONT-OF-THE-METER

In 2020, the LCOE of a utility battery storage system (**in-front-of-the-meter**) was between $0.055 - $0.094 per kWh. This is about one-third the cost of building a natural gas peaker plant, which makes utility-scale storage a very attractive alternative. As a result, utility-scale storage has grown dramatically as illustrated in Figure 2-23.

In addition to storing power to meet load demands, batteries are also increasingly used on the grid to clean power. Harmonic distortions in frequency can be scrubbed from the system by running AC power through DC

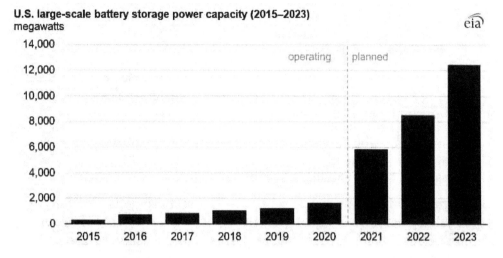

U.S. large-scale battery storage power capacity (2015–2023)
megawatts

eia

operating | planned

14,000

12,000

10,000

8,000

6,000

4,000

2,000

0

2015   2016   2017   2018   2019   2020   2021   2022   2023

FIGURE 2-23: GROWTH IN LARGE-SCALE BATTERY STORAGE

(FROM US ENERGY INFORMATION ADMINISTRATION)

batteries. The inverted AC power leaving the system is then free of any distortions accumulated up to that point during distribution.

Electricity Pricing

For many years utilities have relied on a flat rate, or volumetric rate when charging customers for power. Customers paid a set rate, for example, $0.12 per kWh, for their electricity, regardless of how or when they consumed the power.

Yet the cost of producing that power can vary significantly depending upon how and when it is produced. During periods of peak demand, utilities may be forced to use inefficient and high cost generators, or purchase needed power on the spot market. And customers that use a lot of power for a short period of time tax the infrastructure more than a customer that uses the same amount of power, but at a uniform rate over a longer period of time.

In response to these realities, many utilities have begun to institute a time-of-use rate structure, charging more per kWh for electricity consumed during peak load periods when power costs the utility more to produce.

Other utilities institute **demand charges**, that seek to recover higher infrastructure costs incurred by customers (generally commercial or industrial users) who use large amounts of power for short periods of time.

DEMAND CHARGES

A number of factors influence the cost of electricity. These include:
- Power plant costs: Each power plant has financing, construction, maintenance, profits to investors and operating costs.

- Fuel prices, especially for natural gas, coal and petroleum fuels. These fuels vary in price over time (and seasonally) and may increase during periods of high electricity demand and when there are fuel supply constraints or disruptions.

- Transmission and distribution system: The transmission and distribution systems that connect power plants with customers have construction, operation, and maintenance costs.

- Weather conditions: Extreme temperatures can increase demand for heating and cooling, and the resulting increased demand can push up fuel and electricity prices.

- Time of day: Utilities generally run their least expensive power plants most often. So when demand is high, higher cost peaker plants must be dispatched, which will increase the cost of power.

- Regulations: In some states, public service/utility commissions fully regulate prices, while other states have a combination of unregulated prices (for generators) and regulated prices (for transmission and distribution).

As a result of these factors, electricity costs can vary widely from state to state and utility to utility.

In 2020 the average US retail price for electricity (includes all customers - residential, commercial and industrial) in the US was 10.59 cents per kWh. Prices ranged from a high of 27.55 cents per kWh in Hawaii, to a low of 7.51 cents per kWh in Louisiana.

2021 saw a dramatic increase in electric prices nationwide, rising to an average of 11.21 cents per kWh. This represents an annual price increase of about 6%. In 2021 the average residential rate was 14.12 cents per kWh, the average commercial rate was 11.33 cents per kWh, and the average industrial customer rate was 7.47 cents per kWh.

Bear in mind, these prices represent only the delivered cost of the power and may not include access fees and other fees often added to utility bills.

Generating Capacity

There is often a difference between how much power a generating source is capable of producing (if it ran 24/7 at its maximum output level) and how much it produces in practice.

CURTAILMENT

Some power plants operate nearly all the time once energized (like nuclear), and some can only operate when outside resources are available - such as wind for wind turbines and sunshine for solar. Other generators are designed to handle only peak load demands, so they are turned off, or **curtailed**, when power is not needed - such as natural gas peaker plants.

There are typically three types of capacity measures according the U.S. Energy Information Administration (EIA):

- **Nameplate generation capacity** – Determined by the manufacturer of the generator

NAMEPLATE
GENERATION CAPACITY

- Net summer generation capacity – Determined by performance tests during peak demand between June 1 – September 30

- Net winter generation capacity – Determined by performance tests during peak demand between December 1 – February 28.

The **capacity factor** of a fuel type is determined by dividing actual historic generation by the total amount of generation possible if the plant ran at maximum every moment of every day throughout the year.

CAPACITY FACTOR

Capacity factors can and do vary over time as technologies and utility practices change. The capacity factors for various fuel sources are illustrated in Figure 2-24.

Curtailment

As more and more renewable energy sources are connected to the grid, the management of these resources becomes increasingly difficult. Since the electric grid must always be balanced so that generation exactly equals usage, inevitably there are times when there is more electricity available than required.

Since starting and shutting down nuclear and coal power plants takes a great deal of time, this excess of electricity often results in the curtailment of renewables. Curtailment varies greatly by month, and is increasing as more renewable sources are added to the grid - as illustrated in Figure 2-25.

According to the Energy Information Administration (EIA), curtailments of solar-powered electricity generation have increased significantly in recent years.

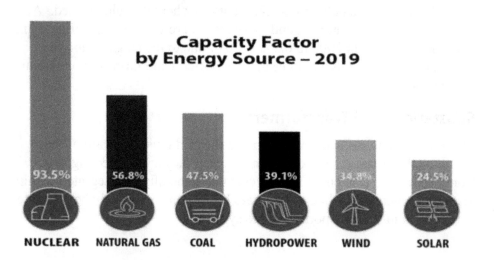

FIGURE 2-24: CAPACITY FACTOR BY ENERGY SOURCE (2019)

(DATA FROM U.S. Energy Information Administration)

FIGURE 2-25:

RENEWABLE ENERGY
CURTAILMENT -
CALIFORNIA

(FROM EIA)

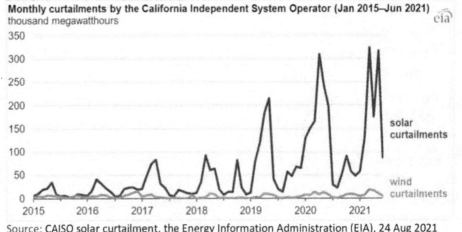

Monthly curtailments by the California Independent System Operator (Jan 2015–Jun 2021)
thousand megawatthours

Source: CAISO solar curtailment, the Energy Information Administration (EIA), 24 Aug 2021

In 2020, solar curtailments accounted for 94% of the total energy curtailed in CAISO (the California Independent System Operator), with the grid operator curtailing 1.5 million MWh of utility-scale solar, or 5% of its utility-scale solar production.

Solar curtailments tend to be most pronounced in the cool but sunny spring months when electricity demand is relatively low. The growth of rooftop solar results in increased utility-scale solar curtailment, as distributed production lowers utility power demands even further.

There are two main reasons behind renewable energy curtailment: system-wide oversupply and local transmission constraints.

- System-wide oversupply is when there is simply not enough demand for all the renewable electricity that is available. Because renewable energy is variable in nature, there are periods of time throughout the day when supply can easily exceed demand.

- Local transmission constraints are a growing cause of renewable energy curtailment. This occurs when there insufficient local transmission infrastructure to deliver that electricity to where it could be used. An example of this can be found in Texas, where wind energy curtailment fell from 17% in 2009 to 0.5% in 2014 due to the construction of additional transmission lines that connected wind farms to population centers.

Substations and Transformers

Those wishing to connect PV systems to the grid must be aware of the operational limitations of the system to which they are connecting. Commercial and residential PV systems will generally be integrated within the distribution network, while utility scale PV systems will likely be integrated within the transmission portion of the system.

The transmission grid is often called the **bulk power system**. Typically, transmission lines operate at voltages above 138 kV. Sub-transmission substations will then step down the voltages to 33 kV- 138 kV before it enters the distribution network.

BULK POWER SYSTEM

Distribution Substations

Distribution substations use transformers to step down the voltages even further (usually between 4 kV - 36 kV) to be feed directly to customers. The size of a distribution power transformer typically vary from 16 MVA to 63 MVA. The power output is typically a three-phase.

Wire size leaving the distribution substation will vary depending on the amount of load that must be serviced. Generally the utility will use steel reinforced aluminum wire (ranging in size from #4 AWG - #1/0 AWG) are used for short distribution runs to farms, homes and small businesses. Wires #4/0 AWG and larger are used for bulk distribution.

Distribution Voltages

Electricity leaves the distribution substation at voltages too high for the typical end user to use to service their loads. These are commonly referred to as **primary line voltages**.

PRIMARY LINE VOLTAGES

Common primary line voltages in the US are 2,300, 4,160, 12,470, 13,800, 25,000 and 34,500 volts, based on the need and preference of the local utility.

At or near the customer's premises, these primary voltages are stepped down through a **distribution transformer**. Power on the low-voltage side of the distribution transformer is called **secondary distribution lines**.

DISTRIBUTION TRANSFORMER

SECONDARY DISTRIBUTION LINES

Common secondary line voltages are 120, 208, 240, 277 and 480 volts.

Distribution Transformers

Residential service generally utilizes single-phase 240 volt voltages. Several residential locations can be served from a single transformer. The transformer must be sized to meet the needs of the total load of all of the customers connected to it.

The most common type of distribution transformer used in North America to service residential customers are single-phase oil-filled, pole-mounted transformers, normally referred to as an overhead or **pole-top transformers**

FIGURE 2-26: PAD-MOUNT TRANSFORMER

POLE-TOP TRANSFORMER

PAD-MOUNT
TRANSFORMER

Customers serviced from underground distribution lines receive power from **pad-mount transformers,** as pictured in Figure 2-26. These are electrically similar to pole-top units, but are packaged in a box-like, oil-filled metal enclosure and installed on a ground-level concrete foundation.

Businesses and industrial plants generally do not share transformers with other customers and require larger transformers to meet the high load demands of the facility.

Most industrial facilities utilize 480-volt three-phase power, but some may require primary line voltages due to very high energy needs.

Common capacity for distribution transformers range from 3 kVA to 1,000 kVA. The size required will be based on the total load serviced by that transformer. Unless load demands are changing significantly, adding a PV array to an existing facility should not impact the load capacity of the transformer connected to the system.

Transformers are bidirectional devices. Power can flow in both directions, both from the utility to the load, and from the PV system to the utility. In fact, transformer can pass real power from the primary side of the network to secondary (customer) side while simultaneously passing reactive power from secondary to the primary.

PV Installation Impact on the Utility Distribution System

The amount of power that can flow through the distribution system is limited by the size of the wire and the voltage of the system, as well as the capacity of the equipment (transformers, for example) integrated into it.

Prior to connecting a large PV system, it must be determined by the utility that the additional generation source will not exceed the capacity limits of the current infrastructure.

Under normal circumstances, customer-owned PV systems are installed to offset existing loads. So the addition of a PV system will not increase the amount of energy on the lines, simply service existing loads from a more local generation source (so the addition of PV will actually decrease the amount of energy flowing on the local distribution system).

However new generation sources that are not directly tied to local load demand (such as a utility-scale solar installation) will require that the utility balance the new generation with the existing infrastructure.

In situations where several customers are serviced by a single transformer, the addition of a PV system into the network may require that the transformer be resized to accommodate the additional generating capacity.

For example, an office park may be serviced by a 50 kVA transformer. One tenant of the park has already installed a 30 kW solar array. A second tenant now wants to install a 35 kW solar array.

It must be assumed (however unlikely that may be) that each array is capable of backfeeding its entire generating capacity to the grid. So the combined generating capacity of both arrays would be 65 kW, which exceeds the limitations of the existing distribution transformer. There may also be issues with the ampacity limits of the existing wire. Who pays for these upgrades will be a matter of negotiation between the business and the utility.

Virtual Power Plants

Utilities have traditionally obtained energy from generating plants that they either own, or they purchase power from plants owned by others through a power purchase agreement.

A **power purchase agreement (PPA),** or electricity power agreement, is a contract between two parties; one party generates the electricity (the seller) and one party purchases that electricity (in this example, the utility). Contractual terms of a PPA may last anywhere between 5 and 20 years.

POWER PURCHASE AGREEMENT (PPA)

A **virtual power plant (VPP)** is an arrangement where the utility purchases power from multiple sources, and then coordinates and controls that power though a centralized management system. The interconnected units are dispatched through the central control room of the VPP, but remain independent in their operation and ownership.

VIRTUAL POWER PLANT (VPP)

While virtual power plants have been around for a number of years, they were traditionally comprised of networks of decentralized, medium-scale power generating units such as wind farms, solar parks, and **combined heat and power (CHP)** plants.

COMBINED HEAT AND POWER (CHP)

But as more distributed solar with storage is dispatched, utilities are testing VPP systems that can draw power from thousands of homes and even electric vehicles.

In 2021, for example, Hawaiian Electric launched a VPP pilot project where they will combine approximately 6,000 behind-the-meter solar-powered home batteries to create an aggregated virtual power plant. The utility will then use a portion of the homeowner's solar-generated power and storage to handle short term variations in grid demand.

In exchange for agreeing to allow the utility to periodically access a portion of their available power, each homeowner that participates will be paid up to $850 per kW for discharging their solar charged battery for up to 2 hours at full power through evening peak periods. They will also be compensated under existing solar+storage tariffs outside of those periods.

Virtual Utilities

In recent years, large corporations have invested heavily in transitioning to renewable energy sources, primarily solar.

Accounting for both on-site and off-site solar installed through the end of 2019, Apple takes the top spot with 398.3 MW installed. Amazon holds the second spot with 369 MW installed, followed by Walmart with 331 MW and Google with about 250 MW of solar.

All these corporations have made very public commitments to powering their operations through renewable energy. Another thing they all have in common is that they have all received a federal designation for their energy subsidiaries to operate as a wholesale seller of electricity. In other words, they are all utility companies.

To this point, each of these companies has sold power only to themselves, but that may (and likely will) change.

As more and more "silicon valley" firms get involved in the electrical utility market, it is easy to envision a time when the largest utility in the nation will own no generating capacity (relying on PPAs and VPPs) and no power lines (leasing distribution and transmission infrastructure from more traditional providers).

VIRTUAL UTILITY

Such a **virtual utility** will not be constrained by geography (as it is virtual) and may fall outside the normal regulatory framework. It may be that they will not even sell energy as a commodity (in the form of kWhs) but as energy services.

The Utility of the Future

The electric grid is currently undergoing changes nearly as dramatic as were experienced by the communications systems several decades ago as they transitioned from "plain old telephone" to the integration of the Internet, wireless communications, cloud storage and more.

Distributed energy systems such as flexible demand, distributed generation, energy storage, the widespread adoption of the electric car, and advanced power electronics and control devices are redefining a utility landscape that has largely remained unchanged for a century.

Traditionally, power systems have been designed to meet infrequent peaks in demand and incorporate generous safety margins. They have also been encumbered by a plodding regulatory system that is generally incapable of responding to changes in technology in a timely fashion.

The financial incentives in a traditional electric utility are also undergoing changes. Traditionally, electric utilities determine their revenue based on the volume of electricity sold. In this model, utilities have an incentive to expand, or at least not reduce, sales. They can be reluctant to support approaches that reduce overall sales volumes, including widespread adoption of distributed solar.

Decoupling is a pricing model designed to remove this disincentive by allowing utilities to recover revenue independent of their sales volumes. Specifically, decoupling allows a utility to assess a small rate surcharge if the utility's sales fall short of expectations. In this way, utilities become indifferent to losing sales and more likely to support energy efficiency and distributed solar.

> DECOUPLING

Challenges facing the electric industry include:

- Developing ways to better utilization of existing infrastructure and smarter energy consumption,

- effectively integrating distributed energy systems into the grid,

- effectively integrating the expansion of the electric vehicle market into the grid,

- addressing cyber-security, privacy and data transport concerns as the grid incorporates "smart" appliances and systems,

- reacting to a shifting load demand pattern as more batteries and distributed energy systems are integrated onto the grid,

- revamping the regulatory market to be more responsive and adaptive to changes in technology,

- determining how virtual utilities will be regulated and operated,

- establishing an equitable method of paying for additional transmission capacity that must be integrated into the grid,

- evolving the energy pricing models to more closely reflect the complex relationship between electric generation and electric consumption patterns.

Chapter 2 Review Questions

1) High voltage utility transmission lines generally terminate at:
   a) a distribution sub-station
   b) the point of common coupling on the customer's premises
   c) a branch circuit
   d) a polyphase transmission station

2) A _____ is generally used to step down or step up the voltage within an AC power system .
   a) transformer
   b) capacitor
   c) load resistor
   d) diode

3) Most residential homes in the U.S. receive:
   a) single-phase/split phase power
   b) power at a frequency of 60 Hertz
   c) a 240 volt signal consisting of two 120 volt signals operating at 180 degrees of separation
   d) all of the above

4) Both phases of a single-phase/split phase electrical system normally share a common neutral?
   a) true
   b) false

5) Which of the following is **NOT** a common three-phase wiring configuration installed in the U.S.?
   a) 120 / 208 V Wye configuration
   b) 277 / 480 V Wye configuration
   c) 120 V four-wire Delta configuration
   d) 208 V three-wire Delta configuration

6) The situation that occurs when the voltages on the conductors of a three-phase system are not equal is called:
   a) current unbalance
   b) phase shifting
   c) voltage unbalance
   d) harmonic distortion

7) Which of the following agencies is **NOT** involved in regulating the U.S. electrical grid?
   a) Interstate Renewable Energy Council (IREC)
   b) Public Utility Commission (PUC)
   c) North American Electric Reliability Corporation (NERC)
   d) Federal Energy Regulatory Commission (FERC)

8) The amount of energy a generator is capable of producing is known as its:
   a) baseload
   b) nameplate capacity
   c) apparent power
   d) reactive power

9) Which of the following is **NOT** a tool that utilities use in demand side management?
   a) power factor correction
   b) energy efficiency programs
   c) time-of-use pricing
   d) load shifting

10) The energy, measured in watts, that is consumed by an appliance is known as:
   a) the power factor
   b) real power
   c) apparent power
   d) reactive power

11) If a factory receives 1000 kVA from the power company and consumes 850 kW in all its equipment, then:
   a) the factory has a power factor of .85 or 85%
   b) the factory has a load factor of 850
   c) the factory consumes 1,000 kVA of real power
   d) all of the above

12) Which of the following will likely cause a negative impact on the power factor of a commercial utility consumer?
   a) an increase in resistive loads
   b) a decrease in resistive loads
   c) an increase in inductive loads
   d) a decrease in inductive loads

13) The waveform associated with an Inductive load has a:
   a) leading power factor
   b) lagging power factor
   c) current unbalance
   d) voltage unbalance

14) Utilities generally strive to keep a facility's power factor:
   a) above 90%
   b) below 90%
   c) at 100%
   d) It is a customer concern, not an issue utilities deal with.

15) A measurement of how much the voltage or current waveform differs from a normal sine wave is known as :
   a) voltage sag
   b) voltage surge
   c) non-linear load migration
   d) total harmonic distortion

16) Voltage sags or voltage swells are known as:
   a) harmonics
   b) lagging or leading power factors
   c) reactive power
   d) transients

17) The process utilities must undergo to restart power after the grid fails is known as a:
   a) bootstrap protocol
   b) black start
   c) polyphase regeneration process
   d) curtailment response protocol

18) Most storage capacity on the grid today is in the form of:
   a) lithium-ion battery banks
   b) lead acid battery banks
   c) pumped hydroelectric
   d) compressed air

19) Between 2010 and 2020, the price of lithium-ion battery packs have:
   a) increased dramatically
   b) remained relatively constant
   c) decreased dramatically
   d) become regulated through legislation

20) Natural gas generating turbines that recapture the system's exhaust heat to create steam to drive a turbine are known as:
   a) combined cycle
   b) peaker plants
   c) dual-activated generators
   d) load-leveling generators

21) Fee adjustments charged customers by utilities that seek to recover the cost of infrastructure required to provide large amounts of power for short periods of time are known as:
   a) demand charges
   b) access charges
   c) distribution charges
   d) capacity charges

22) Which of the following generation sources has the highest capacity factor (as of 2019)?
    a) nuclear
    b) natural gas
    c) coal
    d) solar

23) In recent years the levelized cost of energy (LCOE) to utilities has:
    a) increased dramatically
    b) remained relatively constant
    c) decreased dramatically
    d) become regulated through legislation

24) Turning off a power generator in response to low demand is known as:
    a) the system's capacity factor
    b) demand charges
    c) curtailment
    d) a step-down transformer

25) The power lines that feed energy from the distribution transformer to the customer are known as:
    a) primary distribution lines
    b) secondary distribution lines
    c) load-side distribution lines
    d) low-voltage distribution lines

26) A contract where one party generates power and another purchases it for its own use or for resale is known as:
    a) virtual power plant
    b) secondary distribution agreement
    c) decoupling
    d) power purchase agreement

27) Challenges facing the utility company of the future include:
    a) how to better utilize existing infrastructure
    b) addressing cyber-security, data transport and privacy issues
    c) reacting to shifting load demand patterns
    d) all of the above

Chapter 3

Costs, Ownership Options & Permitting

When a customer decides to investigate installing a PV system on their home or business, it is largely a financial decision.

While there may be non-financial reasons to install solar, most decisions ultimately come down to whether or not the investment makes sound financial sense.

Prior to the actual design and installation of a system, a number of questions must be answered.

- What size system is required given the current and future energy needs of the home or business?

- What will be the initial cost of the system and where will the money come from to pay for it?

- What incentives are available to help offset the cost of the system?

- What will be the ongoing operational and maintenance costs of the system?

- Who will own and operate the system once it is installed?

- What rules and regulations govern the installation of a solar array in the location where it is to be installed?

- How much money will the system save, both now and into the future?

Load Assessment

LOAD ASSESSMENT

Every project begins with determining just how much electricity the client wishes or needs to generate. This is referred to as a **load assessment**.

For existing homes and businesses, a load assessment may be as simple as reviewing current utility bills. For new structures, there are a number of options to use when trying to estimate what future electrical use will be.

Residential Construction Estimates

Estimating load demand for a building under construction can be a bit difficult, as there is no history to base decisions upon and the future occupant may be unknown.

Many contractors simply use a 2 watt per usable square foot "rule of thumb" when estimating the size of the PV array. So if building a 1,500 square foot home, they would install a 3 kW array (1,500 sf x 2 W).

But this method does not take into account climate, variations in electric usage, heating and cooling methods (are they installing a gas furnace, or a heat pump?), etc.

Another method used to estimate the array size is to take national or state electrical use averages and adjust for local solar conditions and the expected efficiency of the system.

According to the EIA (US Energy Information Agency), in 2019 the average US home used 877 kWh of electricity per month - or 29.17 kWh per day.

The typical American home uses 41% of their electricity on space heating, and 35% on appliances, electronics and lighting. However, how much is consumed varies significantly by state.

The highest average electrical consumption can be found in Louisiana, where the average home consumes 1,273 kWh per month. The lowest average consumption rate can be found in Hawaii, at just 515 kWh per month.

Using this method, a home in St. Louis, MO, where the contractor intends to install a 90% efficient PV system, would expect to need an array sized at:

Array Size (kW) = [1,086 kWh per month (average for MO) / 30.5 days per month] / 4.99 hrs insolation (obtained from PV Watts) / .90 (derate efficiency of system) =
35.6 kWh per day / 4.99 hr insolation/ .90 derate=
7.93 kW array

Commercial Construction Estimates

According to the Department of Energy (DOE), the average electrical use per square foot per year for a commercial building is approximately 22.5 kWh.

This estimate breaks down as follows:
- 8 kWh/square foot for refrigeration & equipment
- 7 kWh/square foot for lighting
- 3 kWh/square foot for cooling equipment (AC)
- 2 kWh/square foot for heating equipment
- 2 kWh/square foot are consumed by ventilation
- .5 kWh/square foot for hot water heating.

So it could be estimated that the average 10,000 square foot commercial building would consume 225,000 kWh per year (10,000 square feet x 22.5 kW) or about 18,750 kWh per month (225,000 kWh / 12 months).

But energy use estimates can vary widely, depending on the type of commercial use. According to the DOE:
- a food service facility (restaurant) consumes approximately 56 kWh/square foot,
- a retail mall consumes approximately 23 kWh/square foot on average,
- a large office building consumes about 15 kWh/square foot,
- a warehouse consumes only about 9 kWh/square foot.

California Mandate Calculations

In an effort to draw 100% of state electricity from renewable resources, the state of California began requiring that solar panels be installed on all new residential buildings of 3 stories or less.

As of Jan 1, 2020, solar panel requirements outlined in Assembly Bill 178 are enforced on all new structures built in the state of California.

Advocates argue that adding solar in new construction adds only about $8,400 to the overall cost of the structure. And since the cost is incorporated into a mortgage (for new construction), the added cost results in increasing mortgage payments by about $40 per month while saving approximately $80 per month in electricity costs.

Building Climate Zones

Building Climate Zones

County Boundary

Source: California Energy Commission

FIGURE 3-1: CALIFORNIA BUILDING CLIMATE ZONES

(SOURCE: CALIFORNIA ENERGY COMMISSION)

The law requires that all electrical use within the building be offset by solar production. This amount, however, may be difficult to estimate since the building has not yet been built. So the state has come up with a rather complex method of trying to estimate electrical use.

The method, at its core, is to multiply the usable square footage of the building by a factor determined by the climate where it sits - times the number of dwelling units (for multi-tenant buildings) multiplied by another predetermined factor.

The state has been divided into 16 different climate zones as indicated in Figure 3-1.

The formula is:

$$\text{kW PV required} = (\text{CFA} \times A) / 1000 + (\text{NDwell} \times B)$$

WHERE:

    kW PV = kWdc size of the PV system
    CFA = Conditioned floor area
    NDwell = Number of dwelling units
    A = Adjustment factor from Table 3-1
    B = Dwelling adjustment factor from Table 3.1

For example, assume a builder is about to construct a 2,500 square foot single-family home in Redding, California. They determine that the building site is considered to be within climate zone 11.

The minimum size of the PV system would be determined as follows:

$$\text{kW PV} = [2,500 \text{ (SF)} \times 0.836 \text{ (factor from table)} / 1,000] + [1 \text{ (single family)} \times 1.44]$$
$$\text{kW PV} = (2,090 / 1,000) + 1.44 = 2.09 + 1.44 = 3.53 \text{ kW}$$

This is the **minimum** size required.

TABLE 3-1: CALIFORNIA MANDATE ADJUSTMENT FACTORS

(*SOURCE: CALIFORNIA ENERGY COMMISSION*)

Climate Zone	A - CFA	B - Dwelling Units
1	0.793	1.27
2	0.621	1.22
3	0.628	1.12
4	0.586	1.21
5	0.585	1.06
6	0.594	1.23
7	0.572	1.15
8	0.586	1.37
9	0.613	1.36
10	0.627	1.41
11	0.836	1.44
12	0.613	1.40
13	0.894	1.51
14	0.741	1.26
15	1.56	1.47
16	0.59	1.22

Using the 2 W per square foot rule of thumb, the contractor would install a 5 kW array (2,500 square feet x 2 W).

Calculating based on state electrical consumption averages (California homes average 557 kWh per month), the contractor might size the array as follows:

kW = [557 kW per month / 30.5 days per month] / 5.5 hrs insolation (average for this zone) / .90 (efficiency of the system) = 3.32 kW / .9 = 3.7 kW

Since this calculation results in an array larger than the minimum as determined by the state law formula - it would be permitted.

There are exceptions outlined under the law where new homes are not required to install solar.

These include:

- Shading. No PV is required if there is less than 80 contiguous square feet of unshaded roof space.

- Roof Space. In climate zone 15, the required PV size may be reduced if there is inadequate space on the roof to accommodate the PV size specified, but cannot be less than 1.5 watts DC per square foot of conditioned floor area.

- Two Stories. For two-story residential buildings, the required PV size may be reduced if there is inadequate space on the roof to accommodate the PV size specified, but can be no less than 1.0 watt DC per square foot of conditioned floor area.

- Three Stories. For three-story residential buildings, the required PV size may be reduced if there is inadequate space on the roof to accommodate the PV size specified, but can be no less than 0.8 watts DC per square foot of conditioned floor area.

- Battery Storage. For buildings with a battery storage system, the required PV sizes may be reduced by 25 percent if a battery storage system is installed. For single family building, the minimum capacity of the battery storage system must be at least 7.5 kWh. For multifamily buildings, the battery storage system must have a minimum total capacity equivalent to 7.5 kWh per dwelling.

As of May 2021, California is the only state in the US to require solar on all new homes. Environment America, a national network of 29 environmental groups, is launching a campaign calling on at least 10 additional states across the country to set similar standards. These states include: Colorado, Maryland, Massachusetts, Michigan, Minnesota, Nevada, New Mexico, North Carolina, Pennsylvania and Texas. The campaign's intention is to introduce bills in 10 states by 2022.

Future-Proofing

A solar array, once installed, is expected to remain in service for at least 25 years. However, a lot can change during that period of time. The occupants of the building may change, load demands will certainly change, and new technologies may increase or decrease load demand.

FUTURE-PROOFING

It is much less expensive to incorporate flexibility into the system at the time of initial installation. Adding infrastructure for future expansion or flexibility within the system design is referred to as **future-proofing**.

Some common examples of future-proofing may include:

- For roof mounted systems, install wire of sufficient size to handle the current required if the entire roof area was covered in solar panels, rather than simply the size of the array installed to meet current needs.

- For ground mounted systems, install larger than required wire or place an empty conduit in the trench for later expansion.

- Install disconnects that are rated for the maximum current any future expansion may require.

- Install a "battery ready" inverter, even when no battery system is currently considered.

Electric usage at the building may increase for any number of reasons.

Common reasons include:

- Life changes of the owners (expansion of the family or business).

- Change in ownership.

- Electrification of the heating system. If the homeowner converts a gas furnace to a heat pump, for example, it will add to the electric load demand. A heat pump used in the winter months will add about as much load demand as air conditioning consumes in the summer months.

- Electrification of vehicles. Future decades will see a mass transition from oil-based transportation to electric. The average electric vehicle requires 30 kilowatt-hours to travel 100 miles. Studies show the average American drives about 29 miles each day. So a fair assumption would be that each vehicle at the home or business will add about 10 kWh to the daily load demand.

Of course, adding extra capacity to the system will increase the cost of the initial installation. It will save money over the life of the system, but will result in a higher bid for the initial installation. It is a good idea, in a competitive bid situation, to offer two alternatives - one that includes future-proofing and one that does not.

Conservation and Efficiencies

Those considering installing a PV system on their home or business are often surprised at the initial cost - especially if the system design includes storage. After all, they are essentially prepaying their electric bill for a number of years.

The most immediate and cost-effective way to reduce the pricetag of a PV system can be achieved by reducing load demand. For larger facilities, a formal **energy audit** might be beneficial before designing and installing a solar electric system.

ENERGY AUDIT

An energy audit may recommend:

- **Retro-commissioning.** This process involves an in-depth inspection of all building systems to identify worn components and inefficient configurations. Building systems are cleaned, repaired or replaced. System configurations are modified as needed. Payback for this process is generally one year or less.

RETRO-COMMISSIONING

- Lighting upgrades. Converting lighting to LED within the building is simple and generally will pay for itself within one to two years.

- **Submetering**. Buildings with multiple tenants often share a common utility connection billed to the landlord and electric use is simply incorporated into the rent. Replacing a common meter with meters billed directly to each tenant does not save energy directly. However, tenants tend to consume less energy when they are submetered. Separate metering creates a greater incentive for savings, since each tenants pays directly for the energy they consume. Inefficient energy users pay the full cost of wasting energy, while efficient users keep the savings.

SUBMETERING

- HVAC controls. Major upgrades to the heating and cooling systems of a building are a major efficiency project - but will result in a healthy return on investment. Motor replacements, heating upgrades and air conditioning upgrades result in payback periods typically around 5 years.

- Major HVAC upgrades, renewable generation and building envelope improvements will pay for themselves in 7-8 years on average.

- Easily obtained efficiencies, however, can be achieved through an inspection and upgrade of control systems. HVAC control systems are seldom adjusted to optimize energy efficiency while providing appropriate temperature control and ventilation. Older control systems are simply incapable of producing optimum HVAC operation. Few control systems are continually "commissioned" so they tend to drift out of adjustment. Efficiency losses can exceed 25 percent

- **Power factor correction.** Not all the power drawn by a building from the grid is actually consumed. The component that is used is called real power, but there is also a fluctuating component called the reactive power. If the power factor falls below 95% (.95), the utility will generally charge extra to compensate for the added unused energy.

POWER FACTOR CORRECTION

Improving Power Factor

The primary cause of an increased power factor is the presence of inductive loads. Typical inductive loads include: motors, pumps, air conditioning units, refrigerators, florescent lights.

FIGURE 3-2: 10 HP BALANCED 3 PHASE ROTARY CONVERTER PANEL WITH CAPACITORS

CAPACITOR

Power factor correction can be achieved by adding **capacitors** to counter-balance the inductive component. Theoretically, capacitors could reduce 100% of needed reactive power from the grid. However in practice, a power factor correction to approximately 95% provides maximum benefit.

Power factor correction capacitors increase system current-carrying capacity. Raising the power factor on a kW load reduces kVA. Therefore, by adding capacitors similar to those shown in Figure 3-2, additional kW may reach the load without altering the kVA provided by the utility.

Adjusting the power factor may also help in buildings with undersized infrastructure. Increasing the power factor from 75% to 95% on the same kW load results in 21% lower current flow. In other words, it takes 26.7% more current for a load to operate at 75%, and 46.2% more current to operate at 65%.

Including power capacitors in new construction and expansion of facilities can reduce the required size of transformers, bus and switches, resulting in lower overall project costs.

By reducing the power factor to 95% through the use of capacitors, the building owner will:
- reduce their electric utility bills,
- increase system capacity,
- improve system voltage while reducing current,
- reduce system losses.

There are two basic types of capacitor installations:
- individual capacitors on specific inductive loads,
- or banks of fixed or automatically switched capacitors at the feeder or substation.

Calculating the Cost of Electricity

The market for electricity is becoming more complex and unpredictable.

From 2000 to 2010 the average retail price of electricity in the U.S. rose from 6.81 cents per kilowatt-hour to 9.83 cents per kilowatt-hour. This is a 44% increase in price over 10 years. From 2010 to 2020 the price rose from 9.83 cents per kilowatt-hour to 10.66 cents per kilowatt-hour - only an 8% increase over a decade. Will energy prices continue to rise at this rate? Or will they fall - or stay the same?

And the retail price of electricity is just a portion of what appears on an average electric bill. There are more than 3,300 electric providers in the United States and almost as many ways of charging their customers for power.

But most commonly, charges fall into several broad categories. These include:
- **Energy charge** - the cost of the actual electrons produced.
- **Transmission charge** - costs associated with transporting electricity via high-voltage lines from the generating plant to local substations.
- **Distribution charge** -the cost of getting the power from the substation to the customer.
- Demand charge - the price utilities charge larger customers to ensure there is capacity available to meet their electrical needs.
- Basic monthly charge - usually a fixed fee for hooking to the grid, whether any power is used or not.

Other charges that may appear on a typical electric bill can include: taxes, incentive program fees, educational fees, fees associated with complying with renewable energy requirements, and many many more.

Energy Charges

When people think of the cost of electricity, it is the cost of electrical generation that typically comes to mind. Whether the power is produced by burning coal, burning natural gas, a nuclear or wind or solar or hydro power plant - there are costs involved in its production. These costs are passed along to the consumer, along with a profit margin for the utility in the form of energy or **generation charges**.

The cost of generating electricity has declined dramatically in recent years, largely due to the widespread addition of wind and solar resources, as well as the relatively low cost of natural gas.

Distribution Charges

Utilities are increasingly identifying and separating charges associated with generating the electricity from those of delivering it to their customers.

In states that allow competition between providers, this is important, as consumers have a choice in selecting the company they wish to purchase power from, but typically there is no choice in who delivers that power (the local provider owns the grid connected to the home or business).

Distribution charges compensate the local utility for the use of local wires, transformers, substations, meters, and other equipment used to deliver electricity to end-use consumers from the high voltage transmission lines.

Transmission Charges

Prior to the deregulation of the energy industry, all costs were incurred by a single company in bringing power from the generating plant to the customer. But in today's market, many entities may be involved in this process.

A charge may be added to a customer's electrical bill that indicates the cost of transmitting electricity over the transmission grid between the generating facility and the local utility's distribution facilities (typically a substation). Transmission charges may be rolled into other charges, but if they are billed separately, they will appear as a line item charge on a customer's bill.

Demand Charges

Energy on the grid is not typically stored (although this is slowly changing). When a motor or a light is turned on, the grid must instantaneously react, providing power for that load. There is a cost associated with building and maintaining the capacity to meet load demands. The challenge for utilities is to provide enough capacity to meet all the needs of their customers, but most of the time this capacity will not be used.

If a customer requires 100 kW of power at any given moment, the utility must create an infrastructure capable of delivering 100 kW of power. If that customer consumes 100 kW of power over a long period of time (say at a constant rate for 12 hours-per-day, 7 days per week), the price of the energy will cover the cost of creating the delivery infrastructure.

But the utility experiences the same infrastructure costs to deliver the peak amount of power to a customer, even if they consume it for only a short period of time. The utility had to invest in the capacity, but might never recover the cost of that investment.

The utility tries to account for this variation by assessing demand charges - charging a higher rate for the entire month's energy bill based on the highest power draw from the customer.

Demand charges are normally only assessed against large users, such as businesses and industry. They often use a 2,000 kWh per month consumption level to determine whether these charges apply. Demand charges can be significant, often 30-70% of the entire bill.

Demand charges are based on the largest amount of power used over a 15-minute period of time during the billing cycle. The utility monitors how much power is being used by the business at any given time. To avoid the momentary effect of spikes and surges, they determine that the use of this power must be maintained for a minimum of 15 minutes.

A fee is then assessed to the customer based on the maximum power level used over the course of the month. The higher the peak power level as compared to the average power use, the higher the fee.

Demand charges are calculated in the following manner.

Assume for example, a utility offers the following rate schedule to its commercial customers:

Basic Service Charge $22.00
Demand Charge per kW:
June through September $13.02
October through May...................... $9.02
Energy Charge per kWh: $0.03411

A local dairy farm consumes on average 3,900 kWh of electricity per month.

All the lights and equipment draw a consistent load of 5 kW at any particular moment. But the farm has a large pump that runs for about 30 minutes each day. This pump draws 20 kW, raising the maximum load demand for any 15-minute increment of the farm to 25 kW. So the bill for the month of July would be:

Basic Service Charge = $22.00
3,900 kWh x $0.03411 per kWh (energy charge) = $133.03
25 kWh x $13.02 per kWh (demand charge) = $325.50
Total = $480.53

Note that the demand charge is over 67% of the entire bill.

Assume now that the pump is operated from a battery system, recharged evenly from the grid each day. The maximum load demand would now only be 5 kW. The monthly bill would then reflect this lower demand cost:

Basic Service Charge = $22.00
3,900 kWh x $0.03411 per kWh (energy charge) = $133.03
5 kWh x $13.02 per kWh (demand charge) = $65.10
Total = $220.13

Note that the demand charge is now only 29% of the entire bill. In this example, incorporating a battery dedicated to the pump will save the customer

$260.40 each month due to the way demand charges are calculated. The total amount of energy used has not changed, just the pattern of how it is drawn from the grid.

When assessing demand charges, utilities will often refer to a customer's **load factor**.

The load factor is calculated by finding the ratio of total energy (KWh) used in the billing period, divided by the possible total energy that might have been used within the period if energy were consumed at the highest rate of consumption measured at the peak demand.

Load Factor = Total kWh for the billing period /
Peak Demand x # of Days x 24 Hours

For example, if a building consumed 3,000 kWh of power over a month, and the power was used at a constant rate (no variation) the **average rate of consumption** would be 3,000 kWh / 30 days x 24 hours per day = 3,000 kWh / 720 hr = 4.167 kW. In this case, peak demand would match the average rate of consumption (since there was no variation in the load).

So the load factor would be:

Load Factor = 3,000 kWh / 4.167 kW (peak demand) x 30 days x 24 hours =
3,000 kWh / 3,000 kWh = 1.0

Since load factor is expressed as a percentage, multiply x 100. So the Power Factor = 1.0 x 100 = 100%.

If, however, a motor ran for one hour during the month, resulting in a peak demand of 50 kW of power, the the power factor would be:

Load Factor = 3,000 kWh / 50 kW (peak demand) x 30 days x 24 hours =
3,000 kWh / 36,000 kWh = 0.083 x 100 = 8.3%

Generally, the lower the load factor, the greater the impact of demand charges on the monthly electric bill. Load factor ratios above 75% are considered reasonably efficient for commercial customers and demand charges will not have a serious effect on their electric bill.

In designing a PV system, especially for industrial or commercial facilities, reducing the maximum power draw of the system can mean significant savings to the customer by reducing the demand charge.

This can often be accomplished by incorporating batteries into the system that kick in when power needs are high, and recharge when power demands are low. This process is known as **load leveling** (sometimes referred to as **peak load shaving**).

LOAD LEVELING

PEAK LOAD SHAVING

Another closely related concept often confused with the load factor of a building is the **demand factor**. Sometimes these terms are used interchangeably - but they are not the same. The demand factor is a measurement of how close to capacity a system is operating at when it hits peak load.

DEMAND FACTOR

Essentially a demand factor is calculated by dividing the peak load (in kW) by the theoretical maximum power draw of a given system.

For example, if all the equipment in a building has a **load capacity** of 200 kW (if everything was turned on at the same time), and the peak demand for the system was 50 kW during a given month - then the demand factor for that time period would be:

LOAD CAPACITY

demand factor = maximum load in given time period / load capacity (maximum possible load)
= 50 kW (peak load demand) / 200 kW = .25 = 25%

Demand factors are often used in calculating the size of feeder circuits. Circuits rarely need to supply everything that is connected at one time. Demand factors for buildings typically range between 50 and 80 % of the connected load.

Demand Adjustment

Any inductive load, such as a motor of florescent lights, will decrease the power factor within the facility. The power factor is the difference between the amount of power consumed by the loads (real power) and the amount of power supplied by the utility that is required to operate the loads (apparent power).

Generally the utility assumes a standard power factor - usually about 95% or .95. If the facility's power factor falls below this number (because they operate a large number of motors - for example), then the utility will add additional charges to the bill. This is often referred to as a **demand adjustment**.

DEMAND ADJUSTMENT

Access Charges

Most utilities charge a basic fee, billed whether or not any power is used. This **access charge** is the fee for connecting the facility to the grid.

ACCESS CHARGE

Utilities argue that the fees are necessary to cover the cost of the meter, wire drops to the home or business, as well as the cost of billing. In recent years, however, utilities have sought to increase the grid access fee as more and more households install solar electric systems.

The utilities typically argue that the cost of maintaining the grid is fixed, and that solar transfers those costs to fewer and fewer customers. Since the utility is not selling the same volume of electricity to the customer with a PV system installed, they should be asked to pay their "fair share" of maintaining the grid through fixed fees.

Solar advocates counter that solar provides power to the system when it is needed most, during peak demand periods. A home or business with solar that is connected to the grid actually saves, they argue, rather than costs the utility money.

Other Common Charges

The regulatory nature of electricity and the imagination of utility companies can result in a whole host of miscellaneous charges that may appear on a commercial utility bill. These include but are not limited to:

Energy Efficiency Charge - Some utilities refer to this as Energy Efficiency while others call it Energy Conservation. Regardless of the name, this charge funds energy efficiency programs designed to help consumers lower their energy consumption, cost, and carbon emission.

Renewable Energy Charge - There are 29 states with a Renewable Portfolio Standard (RPS). States with an RPS collect funds to attain energy derived from renewable generators. Some utilities have an additional distribution charge to run programs that support the development of renewable resources.

Sales Tax Surcharge - Monthly charge or credit to reflect changes in various state taxes. The surcharge may vary by bill component and in certain states the sale of electricity is exempt from sales tax.

TRANSITION CHARGES

Transition Charges -Before markets were deregulated, utilities maintained the infrastructure and owned the facilities that generated power. Regulators determined that utilities would encounter additional costs during the transition to a more competitive market - and allowed them to recover some of these costs from consumers.

These charges may appear as: Advanced Metering Infrastructure, Delivery Capital Recovery Rider, Distribution Modernization Rider, Phase-In Recovery Rider, or a host of other terms that basically describe costs associated with an industry in transition.

Government Energy Programs - Often government collects funds to run energy-associated programs with surcharges on electric bills. These charges may include low-income energy subsidy programs, consumer education programs, or even refunds resulting from lawsuits filed against the utility.

NON-BYPASSABLE CHARGES

Non-Bypassable Charges- Most charges on the utility bill are tied directly to consumption of energy; the more energy purchased from the utility, the higher the cost of each item. When the amount of energy purchased from the utility is reduced by the local distributed energy source, the charges are reduced by a similar amount.

However, increasingly, some charges levied by utility companies are non-bypassable. In other words, charges are assessed not only on the amount of energy purchased by the consumer, but also assessed on the amount of energy produced and sold back to the utility company.

Utility Bill Review

Aside from standard information such as the utility's contact information, the customer address and account number - the various charges associated with the account will appear on the monthly bill.

It may be helpful to explore how these charges might be presented with a review of an example, as shown in Figure 3-3.

Note that in this example, the company (Acme Enterprises) has used 56,780 kWh of electricity over the course of the month. Their highest load demand (for any 15 minute period during the month) was 120 kW. The power factor

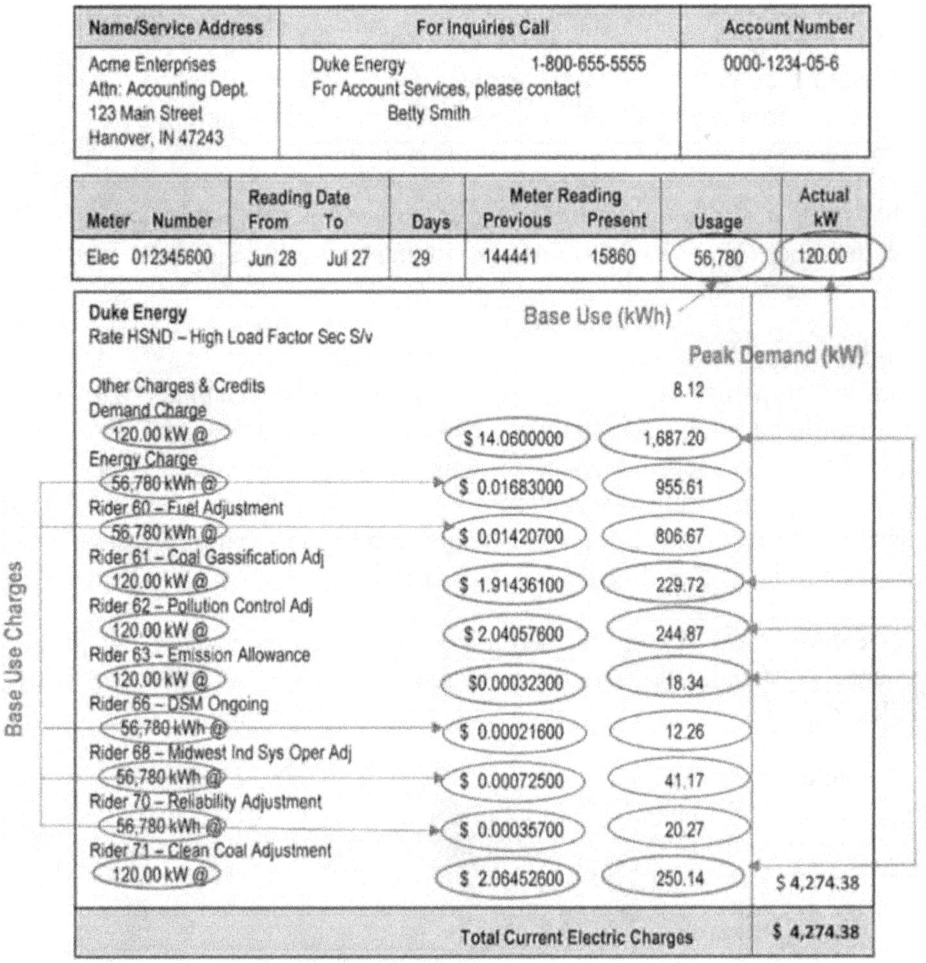

Name/Service Address	For Inquiries Call		Account Number
Acme Enterprises Attn: Accounting Dept. 123 Main Street Hanover, IN 47243	Duke Energy For Account Services, please contact Betty Smith	1-800-655-5555	0000-1234-05-6

Meter Number	Reading Date From	To	Days	Meter Reading Previous	Present	Usage	Actual kW
Elec 012345600	Jun 28	Jul 27	29	144441	15860	56,780	120.00

Duke Energy
Rate HSND – High Load Factor Sec S/v

Other Charges & Credits		8.12	
Demand Charge 120.00 kW @	$ 14.0600000	1,687.20	
Energy Charge 56,780 kWh @	$ 0.01683000	955.61	
Rider 60 – Fuel Adjustment 56,780 kWh @	$ 0.01420700	806.67	
Rider 61 – Coal Gassification Adj 120.00 kW @	$ 1.91436100	229.72	
Rider 62 – Pollution Control Adj 120.00 kW @	$ 2.04057600	244.87	
Rider 63 – Emission Allowance 120.00 kW @	$0.00032300	18.34	
Rider 66 – DSM Ongoing 56,780 kWh @	$ 0.00021600	12.26	
Rider 68 – Midwest Ind Sys Oper Adj 56,780 kWh @	$ 0.00072500	41.17	
Rider 70 – Reliability Adjustment 56,780 kWh @	$ 0.00035700	20.27	
Rider 71 – Clean Coal Adjustment 120.00 kW @	$ 2.06452600	250.14	$ 4,274.38
	Total Current Electric Charges		$ 4,274.38

FIGURE 3-3: SAMPLE COMMERCIAL ELECTRIC BILL

(EXAMPLE FROM BNP Media)

for this month is within the limits of their contracted rate - so there are no demand adjustments that appear on this bill.

Demand Charges

The first charge that appears is the demand charge. This utility under this rate structure charges $14.06 per kWh for demand charges. Since the customer consumed 120 kWh for at least a 15-minute period during the month - then the demand charges will be 120 kWh x $14.06/kWh = $1,687.20.

Had the customer consumed the same amount of energy (56,780 kWh) at a constant rate over the entire month (31 days x 24 hrs/day = 744 hrs) then the peak demand would have been 56,780 kWh / 744 hrs = 76.31 kWh. The demand charges under these conditions would only be 76.31 kWh x $14.06/kWh = $1,073.

Energy Charges

The next item on the bill is for the generation charge of the gross amount of energy used during the month. In this case the utility is charging $0.01683 per kWh or around 1.7 cents. The utility might then claim they charge very little for electricity (1.7 cents per kWh), but clearly with demand charges and other various charges added in - the cost is much higher (actually $4,274.38 / 56,789 kWh = $0.0753 per kWh).

The balance of the charges are for various riders and fees, generally assessed based on the amount of energy consumed - lowering consumption by installing a PV system would lower these fees as well.

Note that some of the added costs are based on total use and some are based on peak demand. Those based on peak load demand could also be offset through a strategy that focuses on load leveling.

Rate Codes:

Most utility companies offer a mind boggling number of rate plans, with options within the options, that make it quite difficult (some would say intentionally so) to determine just what will end up being charged. For example, American Electric Power (AEP) publishes a 220-page document that explains to customers the various plan options and riders that might appear on their electric bill.

RATE CODE

TARIFF CODE

Each **rate code** or **tariff code** will offer a different pricing scheme - varying the generation rates, transmission rates, distribution rates, time-of-day pricing schedules, demand charges, etc based on the option selected.

In the above example, the customer has selected Rate HSND - High Load Factor. This may, for example, be the rate schedule that the utility has set up for commercial facilities that use a minimum of 20,000 kWh per month.

A representative sample of code options can be seen in the below list from the Ohio Power Company (April 2021).

RS	Residential Service
RS-ES	Residential Energy Storage
RS-TOD	Residential Time-of-Day
RDMS	Residential Demand Metered Service
RSDM	Residential Service – Demand Metered
GS-1	General Service – Non-Demand Metered
GS-2	General Service - Low Load Factor
GS-TOD	General Service – Time-of-Day
GS-3	General Service – Medium/High Load Factor
GS-4	General Service – Large
COGEN/SPP	Cogeneration and/or Small Power Production
SBS	Standby Service

Energy Offset Goals

There may be a number of factors that individually, or in combination, impact the size of an array designed and installed at a specific site.

These may include:

- Project Budget. The customer may wish to install a system large enough to offset their entire load requirements, but simply does not have enough money to allocate to the project. The budget may then determine the size of the array.

- Available space. If the only suitable location for the array is on the roof of the structure, then the size will be restricted by the amount of usable space available for the array.

- State restrictions. Many states have set limits on the size of arrays consumers are allowed to install and still fall within the guidelines of the state's net metering laws. The state of Ohio, for example, limits the generating capacity of an array to 120% of the customer's average annual electric usage at the time the facility is connected to the electric grid. The state of Arizona allows up to 125% of the customer's total connected load.

- Utility restrictions. Utilities often set limits on the size of the array a customer may connect to the grid.

  These restrictions may be based on the type of service provided. For example, customers receiving 200 amp service may be restricted to arrays no larger than 15 kW.

  Most utilities pay lower rates (and some pay nothing) for power generated that exceeds consumption. This discourages sizing an array larger than the anticipated load demand.

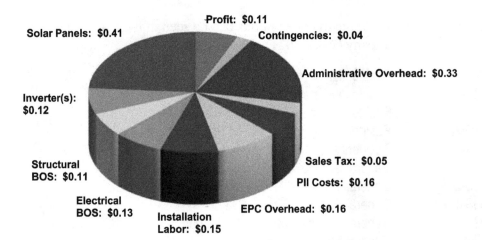

And most permitting fees are based on the size of the array. For example, a permit may cost $450 for a system 15 kW or less. For larger systems the fee would be $500 plus $15 per kilowatt for every kilowatt above 15 kW.

System Costs

Levelized Cost of Energy

LEVELIZED COST OF ELECTRICITY

The cost per kilowatt-hour of building and operating a generating plant over its anticipated productive life is referred to as the **levelized cost of electricity** (LCOE). Just as a utility must calculate these costs, a homeowner or commercial customer must include in a number of factors when calculating the true cost of their solar generating system.

Inputs included in calculating the LCOE include: capital costs, fuel costs, fixed and variable operations and maintenance (O&M) costs, financing costs, and an assumed utilization rate for each power plant.

Initial System Costs

In recent years the cost of a PV system has decreased dramatically. As of the end of 2020, the National Renewable Energy Laboratory calculates the average installed cost of a residential PV system in the United States was $2.71 per watt. This is down from $7.53 per watt in 2010.

ECONOMIES OF SCALE

Commercial systems of 200 kW or larger benefit from **economies of scale** (volume discount on products, specialized equipment, soft costs spread over a larger project, etc.), and can therefore be installed at a substantially cheaper cost per watt. In 2020 the average cost of a commercial system in the US was $1.72 per watt, down from $5.57 per watt a decade earlier.

DIRECT CAPITAL COSTS

The cost breakdown per watt in 2020 for a commercial system is illustrated in Figure 3-4. Note that less than half the cost of an installed system is in the cost of its components, or the **direct capital costs**. Direct capital costs typically include the cost of the solar panels, the inverter(s), the structural balance of systems (BOS) (such as the racking, hardware mounts, trenches, etc), the electrical balance of systems (BOS) (such as the wire, disconnects, conduit, etc) and the **supply chain costs** (such as distributor profits, transportation, etc.).

The **indirect capital costs**, such as installation, sales tax, permitting, administrative costs, profit, etc. made up about 55% of the costs involved in installing a typical commercial PV system in 2020.

SUPPLY CHAIN COSTS

INDIRECT CAPITAL COSTS

Operation and Maintenance

One of the attractive features of a PV system is that they require very little maintenance over their lifetime. However, some maintenance is required, such as tightening electrical connections, replacing fuses, repairing broken or crushed conduit and fittings, locating ground faults, resealing leaking electrical boxes, and repairing or replacing inverters and modules.

NREL estimates that the ongoing operation and maintenance costs of a midsized (10 to 100 kW) PV system will average about $0.19 per watt per year. So the owner of a 10 kW system should budget about $190 per year (10,000 watts x $0.19/w) to cover the costs of ongoing operation and maintenance of the system.

Cost of Money

The purchase of a solar array is a large investment that somebody has to pay for. The business or homeowner may have enough money, or **capital** on hand or they may have to borrow all or a part of the system cost. There is always a cost associated with borrowing this money.

CAPITAL

Even if the client pays cash for the system from funds they have on hand, there is an **opportunity cost**, or the value of the money or the **return on investment** they might have received if they had put the money into another investment.

OPPORTUNITY COST

RETURN ON INVESTMENT (ROI)

But if they had to borrow the money, they will likely have to pay interest on those funds. The **interest rate**, or amount of interest paid varies based on a number of factors.

INTEREST RATE

These include:

- Inflation - if prices in general are going up, the cost of money goes up as well, as money in the future is worth less than money in the present. So lenders increase the interest rate to compensate for this.

- Investment risk - if lenders think that the investment may not pay off, they will charge more to compensate for this increased risk.

- Credit worthiness - if the borrower has shown in the past that they will pay back money loaned, then the risk to the lender decreases.

- Demand for money - if the economy is growing or the government has cut back on the money supply to try to curb inflation, then there is less money to lend, so prices for the limited supply (interest rates) go up.

Project Financing

When developing a large solar array, there are not only different phases in the project development process (such as selling the project, designing it, permitting, installation, etc), but there are often different types of financing involved depending on the stage of the project.

For large solar projects, it is useful to classify debt primarily in relation to the project's life cycle. There are three broad categories of debt for solar projects.

These include:
- development-stage debt for the pre-construction period,
- construction debt to finance the period of active installation work, and
- permanent debt that remains in place after the project is operational and development work is complete.

Development Loans

DEVELOPMENT LOAN

In the very early stages of a project, the owner or developer of the project may need to borrow money to get the project started.

SITE CONTROL

Costs may include: up front interconnection deposits, PPA deposits, solar resource studies, permitting, and site control costs. **Site control** refers to an agreement to use land or a building surface for the construction and operation of the array. Site control most often comes in the form of a lease or an option to purchase land or use a structure.

Development loans can also be a bridge to future funding. They are normally relatively informal agreements set for a short period of time, at a high interest rate, with very little flexibility for the developer without the lender's approval. There is also often a promise granted giving the lender "first right of refusal" to finance the project should it turn out to be promising.

Construction Loans

CONSTRUCTION LOAN

During the construction of a project, a very large portion of the total project's budget will be spent. There are costs for: materials (panels, inverters, racking, etc), labor, engineering services, consultants, equipment and more.

But all these expenses don't happen all at once, and lenders don't generally want to turn over all the cash for the project until they have been assured that the money is spent on the specific items agreed upon in the contract.

Payment streams must be managed carefully. For this reason, construction loans tend to be very complex and risky. Lenders will generally require that the developer bear part of the risk by investing some of their own money (so the lender does not shoulder all the risk of the project).

Construction loans are normally on a relatively short timetable and they're dependent on the completion of the project. The lender is presented with a construction timeline, detailed plans and a realistic budget.

Once approved, the borrower will be put on a draft or **draw schedule** that follows the project's construction stages. As each stage of the project is completed, the lender releases funds to pay for that stage and/or the next stage of the project. These draws tend to happen when major milestones are completed. The developer will typically be expected to make only interest payments during the construction stage.

DRAW SCHEDULE

Permanent Loans

Once all development and construction has been completed, the financing shifts from the short term, expensive and restrictive terms of development and/or construction loans, to longer term or **permanent loans**.

PERMANENT LOAN

In a large solar project, the milestone which marks this transition is often referred to as the project's **commercial operation date (COD)**. Typically this is the day that the system becomes fully operational and can begin providing power to the building owner or sell power under the terms of a power purchase agreement (PPA).

COMMERCIAL OPERATION DATE

Owned systems (including those where the business paid cash for the system) made up only 35 percent of the nonresidential solar market in 2015, and fell to only about 25 percent of all nonresidential systems by 2020 (according to GTM Research). The vast majority of large solar projects fall under the **third-party ownership (TPO)** model.

THIRD-PARTY OWNERSHIP (TPO)

Property Assessed Clean Energy (PACE) Financing

State and local governments increasingly are offering a financing option for PV systems where the costs are directly tied to the property rather than the owner. Under the **property assessed clean energy (PACE)** program, the property owner applies to the government for funding the construction of a PV system. The government then provides 100% of the cost of the project in the form of a long term loan (typically 20 years). The loan is then paid back through property tax assessments (on the regular tax bill).

PROPERTY ASSESSED CLEAN ENERGY

If the building owner sells the property, the liability (the tax assessment) stays with the property. This program is normally available only to commercial customers (often called PACE-C), but is increasingly being offered to residential (PACE-R) customers as well.

When it works as designed, this program offers 100% financing for PV where the energy savings often exceed the cost of the system. It also offers flexibility when real estate is transferred from one owner to another.

It should be noted, however, that when a PACE loan is secured, a lien is placed on the property until the loan is paid off. Many lenders will not issue a mortgage on a property with an existing PACE loan in place, because PACE loans are structured to take precedence over the mortgage.

On-Bill Financing

ON-BILL FINANCING

On-bill financing of renewable energy systems is a method of financing that offers loans for systems that are then repaid through utility bills. This means that the loan is tied to the electric meter rather than the individual. No money is paid up front, with costs amortized over the life of the system. This system allows renters to participate in renewable energy programs even when they pay utilities directly (as system costs are built into the cost of electricity).

As of 2019, 30 states have utilities offering on-bill financing or legislation is in place related to on-bill financing.

Ownership Options

Most people assume that home owners or businesses that have a PV system, paid for and own that system. It is perhaps surprising to find that only about 25% of non-residential PV systems installed in the US are in fact owned by the customer using the solar power.

Third-party ownership of solar PV systems, either leased to or power sold to customers, has become the dominant financing model.

Direct Ownership

DIRECT OWNERSHIP

Under the **direct ownership** model, the homeowner or business that uses the solar power, pays for and owns the PV system.

There are advantages to ownership. The owner can:
- take advantage of federal tax credits or other incentive programs, own and sell any SRECs the system may generate.

There are disadvantages as well. The owner must:
- pay for insurance for the system,
- pay to maintain the system,
- pay the entire cost of the system up front, or borrow money to do so,
- repair any damages to the system.

Third-Party Ownership

Tenant-landlord relationships and building lease terms add layers of complexity to solar financing. Customers that lease property will likely need to work with the property owner in order to install solar on their home or business.

Differences between building lease terms (for example they may have only a 5 year lease) and the lifetime of a solar array (20-plus years) are another challenge that solar consumers will need to consider when obtaining solar financing.

Another common reason customers may opt for a third-party ownership alternative is that the tax benefits would be of no value to them. Non-profit organizations, such as churches and schools pay no federal income tax, so the investment tax credit would not apply to their purchase. A for-profit third party could develop and own the system, taking advantage of the tax benefits and passing the resulting savings along to the end user.

Generally speaking, the same benefits and disadvantages of third-party ownership versus direct ownership of solar generating plants apply as a customer might experience in owning or renting the building from which they operate.

Third-party ownership reduces the up-front costs as well as operating risks associated with the system, but generally the customer will pay a higher rate for their energy than they would if they owned the system outright.

Solar Leases
Under the **solar lease** model, a third party pays for and installs a PV system. They then lease that system to a customer for a fixed amount (usually paid monthly). The developer is essentially renting the solar equipment to the end user, and the end user receives the energy that is generated by the system.

> SOLAR LEASE

The amount paid under a solar lease is the same regardless of how much energy is produced during the time period. Lease agreements are usually 20-25 years in duration.

The advantages to the customer include:
- no up front costs,
- no insurance requirements,
- no maintenance costs (depending on the lease agreement),
- customers with poor credit may qualify when they would not qualify for a loan,
- the customer is protected from utility rate increases.

Disadvantages to the customer include:
- the system owner takes advantage of all tax credits, SRECs and other associated incentives,
- the value of the electricity generated will vary based on monthly production.

FIGURE 3-5: STATES THAT ALLOW OR RESTRICT THIRD-PARTY POWER PURCHASE AGREEMENTS (2021)

FROM WWW.DSIREUSA.ORG

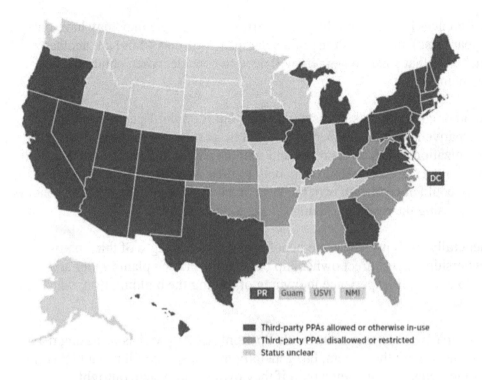

■ Third-party PPAs allowed or otherwise in-use
▩ Third-party PPAs disallowed or restricted
▨ Status unclear

Power Purchase Agreements (PPA)

Under a solar **power purchase agreement (PPA)**, a solar investment company buys, installs, and maintains the PV system on a homeowner's property. The homeowner purchases the energy generated by the system on a per-kilowatt-hour basis through a long-term contract. Under this option, the customer pays for the power, they do not lease the equipment.

PPAs are a prominent solar financing tool but are not available in all locations. Some states limit or prohibit PPAs. These limitations and restrictions generally center around how a state views third-party ownership of distributed energy systems that sell electricity to customers and how such agreements are in direct competition with existing electric service utilities.

As of 2021, there are currently fifteen states that have enacted legislation to authorize and/or regulate PPAs. The following states allow power purchase agreements: Arkansas, Colorado, Connecticut, Delaware, Hawaii, Iowa, Michigan, Montana, Nebraska, New Hampshire, New Jersey, Oregon, Rhode Island, Virginia, Washington. An additional eleven states allow PPAs to operate in some jurisdictions or with certain restrictions. Nine states have laws that restrict access to PPAs, as indicated in Figure 3-5.

The advantages of PPAs to the customer include:
- no up front costs,
- no insurance requirements,
- no maintenance costs (depending on the lease agreement),
- they provide a long-term hedge against fluctuating energy costs and can assist in more predictable budgeting,

POWER PURCHASE AGREEMENT (PPA)

- they may offer more options in vendors to supply power (rather than simply the local utility), driving down costs through competition,
- they are a quick and inexpensive way to achieve corporate sustainability goals.

Disadvantages to the customer include:
- the system owner takes advantage of all tax credits, SRECs and other associated incentives,
- the cost of energy may be higher than under the direct ownership model.

Non-profit organizations (such as schools and churches) may find PPAs to their advantage, as they do not qualify for tax credits so the cost of ownership may actually be greater than if they obtain power through a PPA.

There are a number of different types of PPAs. These include:
- Physical Power Purchase Agreement
- Virtual Power Purchase Agreement
- Sleeved Power Purchase Agreement

Under a **physical PPA** agreement, the corporate buyer is responsible for the electrons produced (the actual electricity) as well as the sale of those electrons.

> PHYSICAL PPA

A company signs a long-term contract with a third-party seller who agrees to build, maintain, and operate a renewable energy system either on the customer's property (on-site) or off-site. What happens to the power generated is entirely up to the customer.

In most cases the purchaser uses the generated power for their own operations, but not always. They may decide to sell all or part of the energy to another party. Depending on the contract involved, the buyer may also have to pay any transmission charges.

Under a **virtual PPA**, the corporate buyer is not responsible for the electrons produced. The buyer simply enters into a long-term contract (typically about 20 years) to purchase renewable energy from the seller at a fixed price. If the market price of electricity goes up, the buyer benefits from the savings. If the market price of electricity goes down, then the buyer may pay more for power than they would have otherwise had they not locked in the long term rate.

> VIRTUAL PPA

In a **sleeved PPA**, a utility company handles the transfer of money and energy to and from a solar project on behalf of the buyer. The utility takes the energy directly from the array and "sleeves" it to the buyer, for a fee.

> SLEEVED PPA

If the purchased renewable energy isn't enough to meet the buyer's energy needs, the utility is also generally responsible for supplying the additional power.

A sleeved PPA option may be preferred for corporations that do not wish to deal with wholesale power market fluctuations, or are located in a region that restricts or prohibits other forms of power purchase agreements.

Community Solar

It has been estimated that as many as 80% of homes and businesses are not suitable candidates for solar to be installed on their facility. Reasons may include: shading, existing lease agreements, bad credit scores, regulatory restrictions and more.

COMMUNITY SOLAR

Community solar is a model where a group of homeowners/businesses can share the benefits of a larger solar array that is located off site of the customer's property. They usually are offered in one of two formats.

OWNERSHIP MODEL

The **ownership model** is where each participant purchases a share of the overall project and receives power based on the portion they own. For example, if ten homeowners each contributed equally to a community solar project, then each would receive ten percent of the array's production.

FIGURE 3-6: STATES WITH VIRTUAL NET METERING POLICIES

(FROM INSTITUTE FOR LOCAL SELF-RELIANCE)

Available
Limited by tech or customer type
Utility option to offer

ILSR

In ownership community solar programs, participants may not purchase more shares than necessary to meet their annual electricity usage. A matching percentage of the project's output will be credited to the customer through their electricity bill.

Such a system obviously requires the participation

VIRTUAL NET METERING (VNM)

of the local utility. In states that have adopted **virtual net metering (VNM)** policies as illustrated in Figure 3-6, utilities are required (to a greater or lesser degree) to accommodate community solar projects.

Under the ownership model of community solar, the owner retains their allocated portion of the federal tax credits, and SRECs sold, and any other incentives enjoyed by the project.

Ownership models of community solar are complex and difficult to set up and administer. Also, participation is limited only to those who have the up front capital to pay for their portion of the system.

Another option is the **subscription model** of community solar. Under this model, participants simply pay a solar developer for power generated from the system. Typically there are no up front costs, and membership can be quite fluid (customers can join and cancel as they see fit).

SUBSCRIPTION MODEL

Peer-to-Peer Sales
One concept that is still in its infancy, but shows tremendous promise, is the **peer-to-peer sale** of electricity, where an owner of a solar array can sell directly to another retail customer, bypassing the utility company altogether. Early examples of this concept, such as the Brooklyn Microgrid, use blockchain to manage and automate transactions between producers and consumers.

PEER-TO-PEER SALES

Blockchain is a secure electronic ledger system where transactions are recorded. It forms the foundation of crypto currencies such as Bitcoin, and can verify small transactions between energy users and producers.

BLOCKCHAIN

Blockchain can manage large volumes of transactions quickly, securely, and at a relatively low cost. The ledger system can also dramatically reduce the overhead costs of using intermediaries, such as clearinghouses.

Financial Incentives Programs

A number of tax credits, grants, loans and other programs exist designed to encourage the development of solar within the nation and/or within specific geographic areas. A good source for up-to-date information regarding programs that exist in a specific location can be found at www.dsireusa.org (Database of State Incentives for Renewables and Efficiency).

When planning a PV system, maximizing the use of available incentive programs can have a significant impact on the net cost of the project.

These incentives include:
- the Federal Business Energy Investment Tax Credit (ITC),
- **modified accelerated cost-recovery system (MACRS),**
- net energy metering (NEM),
- renewable energy credits (RECs),
- renewable energy grants,
- favorable loan programs,
- utility incentive programs,
- sales tax exemptions (where the purchase of the equipment used in the PV system may be exempt from state and/or local sales taxes),

MODIFIED ACCELERATED COST-RECOVERY SYSTEM

- property tax exemptions (some jurisdictions do not increase the property assessment based on the added value of an installed solar array).

Federal Business Energy Investment Tax Credit (ITC)

FEDERAL BUSINESS ENERGY INVESTMENT TAX CREDIT (ITC)

Originally established in the Energy Policy Act of 2005, the **Federal Business Energy Investment Tax Credit (ITC)** is one of the most significant renewable energy incentives. The credit originally allowed individuals and businesses to deduct 30% of the cost of a PV system directly from their tax bill.

For example, if a home owner pays $20,000 to install a PV system, they could claim a $6,000 tax credit. This is different than a deduction, which just reduces the amount of their taxable income. A tax credit can be deducted directly from their tax bill.

This provision was originally scheduled to end in 2016. But it was extended for three years, stepping down from 30% to 26% to 22% and then eliminated for residential customers. In December 2020 the tax credit (then at 26%) was extended by Congress for another 2 years, as indicated in Table 3-2.

There was always a bit of confusion around when a project would be eligible to claim the ITC. Did the project need to be completed and commissioned before the end of the year in order to qualify? Was the issuing of a permit satisfactory, even though the project was not yet completed?

In June 2018 the IRS issued guidance regarding when a project was eligible for the ITC based on a "commence construction" standard.

TABLE 3-2: FEDERAL BUSINESS ENERGY INVESTMENT TAX CREDIT SCHEDULE FOR PHOTOVOLTAICS

Year	Residential	Business
2021	26%	26%
2022	26%	26%
2023	22%	22%
2024	0%	10%

The IRS ruled that a taxpayer may use one of two methods to establish that construction of a qualified solar facility has begun for purposes of claiming the solar investment tax credit (ITC). These include:
- starting physical work of a significant nature (**physical work test**), or
- meeting the so-called **5% safe harbor test** (i.e., paying or incurring five percent or more of the total cost of the facility in the year that construction begins).

PHYSICAL WORK TEST

5% SAFE HARBOR TEST

Both methods require that a taxpayer make continuous progress toward completion of the project once construction has begun. Commercial and utility-scale projects that have commenced construction before December 31, 2023 may still qualify for the 26 or 22 percent ITC if they are placed in service before January 1, 2026.

Modified Accelerated Cost-Recovery System (MACRS)

All things eventually wear out. The tax code recognizes this fact, and allows individuals and businesses to deduct the portion of the value of an investment from their taxable income to account for this. This is known as **depreciation**.

DEPRECIATION

In its simplest form, the amount that can be deducted is simply calculated by taking the cost of the item and dividing it by the number of years it will take that item to wear out - or become of no value. If a PV system cost $20,000 to install, and is expected to last 25 years, using this **straight-line depreciation** method the owner would calculate depreciation as follows:

STRAIGHT-LINE DEPRECIATION

Depreciation = $20,000 (cost)/ 25 years (life of asset) = $800

The owner could then deduct $800 from his/her annual taxable income, slightly reducing their tax bill.

The IRS, however, allows for investors in solar PV systems to depreciate the cost of the system more rapidly. That way they will experience greater tax savings in the early years of the investment.

However, if a taxpayer opts for the accelerated depreciation option, they must deduct half of the federal investment tax credit from the **basis** (cost of the asset used for calculating the taxes). For example, if claiming the 26% ITC, the depreciable portion of the system must be reduced by 1/2 the tax credit ($20,000 * .87 = $17,400).

BASIS

In response to the economic downturn of 2008, Congress took action to encourage capital investment by accelerating the MACRS depreciation schedule. The Tax Relief, Unemployment Insurance Reauthorization, and Job Creation Act of 2010 allowed companies to claim 50% of the depreciation in the first year on qualifying capital equipment (solar included) purchased and placed in service by December 31, 2011.

Year	Depreciation Rate	Basis	Deduction
1	20.00 %	$ 17,400	$ 3,480
2	32.00 %	$ 17,400	$ 5,568
3	19.20 %	$ 17,400	$ 3,341
4	11.52 %	$ 17,400	$ 2,004
5	11.52 %	$ 17,400	$ 2,004
6	5.76 %	$ 17,400	$ 1,002

TABLE 3-3:
ACCELERATED DEPRECIATION RATE SCHEDULE FOR $20,000 PHOTOVOLTAIC SYSTEM

In 2017, the depreciation allowed in the first year was increased to 100% for capital expenditures purchased before Jan. 1, 2023. After that, first-year bonus depreciation goes down as follows:

- 80% for property placed in service after December 31, 2022 and before January 1, 2024.
- 60% for property placed in service after December 31, 2023 and before January 1, 2025.
- 40% for property placed in service after December 31, 2024 and before January 1, 2026.
- 20% for property placed in service after December 31, 2025 and before January 1, 2027.

The expanded first year deduction does not apply to state taxes. Calculations of the MACRS for a system costing $20,000 are detailed in Table 3-3.

Net Energy Metering (NEM)

Most states have enacted legislation designed to outline the rules that apply to utilities when a customer connects a PV system to the grid. In most cases these rules have been designed to encourage the development and expansion of solar within the state.

As of March 2020, 34 states had mandatory net metering rules. Two states do not have any mandatory **net metering** rules, but have utilities that allow net metering (Idaho and Texas); six states have statewide compensation rules other than net metering (Arizona, Georgia, Hawaii, Louisiana, Mississippi, and Utah); and three states have no net metering in place (Alabama, South Dakota, and Tennessee). Five states (Illinois, Indiana, Kentucky, Michigan, New York) do currently have net metering credits, but they are transitioning into different forms of compensation, as indicated in Figure 3 -7.

FIGURE 3-7: STATES WITH MANDATED NET METERING RULES

(FROM SOLAR POWER WORLD MAGAZINE)

NET ENERGY METERING (NEM)

BI-DIRECTIONAL METER

At its most basic, net metering allows solar electric customers to direct excess energy production back to the grid through a **bi-directional meter**. The meter keeps track of how much energy has been "stored" on the grid. The amount is then used as a credit to offset electricity drawn from the grid when the load demand of the structure is greater than the amount of energy produced by the solar array.

Studies indicate that only about 20% - 40% of the energy produced by a typical solar array finds its way onto the grid. The remainder is used by the home or business directly.

While the rules can vary significantly from state to state, most net metering laws define:

- Which utilities must purchase excess energy from the owners of PV systems. In most cases electrical co-operatives and municipal-owned electrical systems are exempt.

- How much the utility must pay for this energy. Does the utility have to pay the full retail price for the power from the PV system? Do they credit only the generation costs, but still charge the distribution fees?

- What happens if the customer generates more power than they consume? Often this moves the customer from a consumer to a power producer, and the net metering law no longer applies. Designers must take great care in these cases not to oversize the system.

- The **true-up period.** Generally this will either be at the end of each month, or at the end of the year. At the end of each true-up period, any accumulated energy credits are lost and the calculations start again at zero. If excess generation can be carried forward from month to month, this practice is often referred to as **kWh banking.**

TRUE-UP PERIOD

KWH BANKING

- What interconnection charges are allowed. These are either fixed grid-access charges, or fees assessed by the utility for connecting the system to the grid.

- Any non-bypassable charges. These would include charges that are added to the electric bill (such as educational program fees, or renewable energy compliance fees) that cannot be offset by energy savings from the PV system.

In recent years a number of states have begun to weaken net metering laws as more solar arrays are connected to the grid. As distributed systems become a more and more substantial portion of the grid's energy mix, many utilities are seeing net metering policies as a threat to their profitability.

More and more utilities are seeking to weaker net metering benefits through:

- excess generation credits. Utilities are increasingly shifting from annual to monthly true-up schedules.

- fixed energy charges that cannot be offset with solar energy credits. Many utilities are doubling or tripling the fixed access charges for customers who install solar on their property.

- reduction in compensation per kWh. Traditional net metering policies paid retail for any excess power pushed onto the grid from the solar array.

Utilities are pushing to change this compensation rate, typically paying only wholesale generation rates.

For example, in 2021 the California Public Utility Commission proposed a new net metering program, referred to as NEM 3.0, which would charge a grid access fee of $8/kWh of installed solar (the average home with solar would pay about $48 per month in access charges) and significantly reduced the array owner's compensation for energy sent to the grid.

Industry analysts estimated that this policy change would more than double the average payback period for a solar array installed in California from 5-6 years to between 14-15 years.

Public backlash was so great that in 2022 the California Public Utility Commission announced that they would suspend action of the changes "indefinitely."

Solar Renewable Energy Certificates (SRECs)

When a state establishes a renewable portfolio standard (RPS), the process normally requires that utilities must pay a penalty when they fall short of the set goals. As a result, utilities often purchase RECs (renewable energy certificates), or in the case of solar, SRECs (solar renewable energy certificates) to assist in achieving these goals.

The purchase of a REC allows the utility to claim the power produced as part of their portfolio, even though they do not use or own that power. Rather than negotiating prices directly with each system owner, REC markets develop within a number of states. As of 2022, only six states (New Jersey, Massachusetts, Pennsylvania, Maryland, Delaware, and Ohio) and Washington DC have active SREC markets. Illinois has a slightly different SREC market that operates under its Adjustable Block Program.

Prices for SRECs are influenced by the aggressiveness of the RPS goals, the size of penalties established by the RPS, the amount of solar installed in the area, and any other number of constantly shifting factors.

One SREC equals one megawatt-hour (1 MWh) of energy produced by a solar electric system. A typical 10 kW array will produce about 12 SRECs each year.

The value of an SREC can exceed the value of the energy produced by a system and has tremendous implications for developers of solar arrays.

For example, on March 1, 2022 SRECs were selling for $277 in the state of New Jersey. A commercial solar developer who owns a 100 kW array could expect to generate 120 SRECs each year. If sold at market price, this would generate an additional $33,240 of revenue each year. Sale of the power generated from the array, even at a full retail price of $0.08 per kWh, would only generate about $9,600 in revenue.

Those wishing to sell SRECs can either:
- advertise credits on the **GATS (Generation Attribute Tracking System)** Bulletin Board or other similar services,
- check the GATS Buyer's Bulletin Board for specific purchase requests,
- work with an **aggregator** or broker to either purchase the SRECs directly, or to assist the SREC owner in finding a buyer.

GENERATION ATTRIBUTE TRACKING SYSTEM (GATS)

AGGREGATOR

GATS is owned and managed by PJM, a regional transmission organization (RTO) that coordinates the movement of wholesale electricity in all or parts of Delaware, Illinois, Indiana, Kentucky, Maryland, Michigan, New Jersey, North Carolina, Ohio, Pennsylvania, Tennessee, Virginia, West Virginia and the District of Columbia. Other similar REC trading organizations exist in other parts of the country.

Most smaller system owner, however, generally choose to work with an aggregator who is skilled in managing the paperwork involved. The aggregator takes a fee (usually between 2-10%) for these services.

All solar energy systems eligible to earn SRECs must report system production based upon readings from a **revenue-grade meter** that meets the American National Standards Institute (ANSI) Standard C12.1-2008. This meter is in addition to the electric meter installed by the local utility to measure the home or business' electric consumption. Many newer PV systems incorporate a revenue-grade production meter within their inverters.

REVENUE-GRADE METER

REAP Grants & Loans

The **Rural Energy for America Program (REAP)** is a program administered by the USDA (United States Department of Agriculture). The program provides guaranteed loans and grants ($2,500 minimum - $500,000 maximum) to agricultural producers and rural small businesses for renewable energy systems or energy efficiency improvements.

REAP PROGRAM

The program is designed to assist agricultural producers with at least 50 percent of their gross income coming from agricultural operations and small businesses located in rural areas (located in towns or villages with populations less than 50,000).

The program offers:
- loan guarantees on loans up to 75% of total eligible project costs,
- grants for up to 25% of total eligible project costs,
- combined grant and loan guarantee funding up to 75% of total eligible project costs.

Feed-In Tariffs (FIT)

A **feed-in tariff (FIT)** is a policy tool designed to promote investment in renewable energy sources. This usually involves the payment of above-market prices for renewable energy delivered to the grid.

Feed-in tariffs usually involve long-term agreements (typically 15-25 years) and prices tied to the cost of production of the energy, rather than market prices. The long-term contracts and guaranteed prices minimize the risks inherent in energy production projects, encouraging investment and development that otherwise might not take place.

Anyone who produces renewable energy is eligible for a feed-in tariff, but they are most common in utility-scale projects. Generally, feed-in tariffs offer:

The **Public Utilities Regulatory Act of 1978 (PURPA)** requires utilities purchase renewable energy from producers known as **qualifying facilities (QFs)**. The act requires electric utilities to purchase electric energy from these qualifying facilities (of 80 MW or less in size) at a rate that does not exceed the cost to the electric utility should they purchase the power from another source or generate it themselves.

FITs are generally financed through a fee assessed to all utility customers incorporated into their utility bill.

Community Choice Aggregation (CCA)

Another tool sometimes used to expand the reach of renewable energy within the energy mix on the grid is **Community Choice Aggregation (CCA).**

Also sometimes referred to as municipal aggregation, CCA allows local government bodies (or multiple jurisdictions working in partnership) to purchase, as a block, power from a third party supplier while still utilizing the transmission and distribution infrastructure from the local utility.

This option was originally envisioned as a way for local authorities to negotiate better prices for residents - however in recent years it has also been used as a tool to secure power from renewable energy sources (and often these two goals may be achieved in tandem).

As of May 2019, eight states – California, Illinois, Massachusetts, New Jersey, New York, Ohio, Rhode Island and Virginia – have enacted CCA legislation.

Calculating Return on Investment (ROI)

It might seem a pretty straightforward calculation to determine the **return on investment (ROI)** of a photovoltaic system. Simply calculate the cost of the system, then divide it by the value of the electricity it produces. This will determine how many months it will take for the system to pay for itself. But it is not quite that easy.

Besides the initial cost of the system and the value of the energy it produces, there are a number of other items that should be considered.

These include:

- The time value of money. If the money used to build the the system is borrowed, the interest paid must be factored in. If the money used is not borrowed, then what interest return could be obtained if it was invested into some other product (such as a certificate of deposit)?

- The expected life of the system components. If the inverter is only expected to last 10 years, then the cost of replacing it during the life of the system should be anticipated and added into the cost of the system.

- Ongoing **operation and maintenance (O&M) costs**. While required maintenance on a solar system is low, it is not zero. Some costs should be anticipated to keep the system operating efficiently over its expected life.

O&M COSTS

- The decay of the system. As panels and inverters age, they become less efficient. It should be anticipated that the system will produce less electricity as it gets older. Many companies factor in a .5% annual decline in energy production.

- The true price of the electricity offset, as well as the future price of electricity. Historically the price of electricity has increased over time, but this is not certain. And if it does increase, by how much?

- Local, state and federal **incentives**. Are there programs in place that will help offset the initial cost of installing a system?

INCENTIVES

Average Blended Cost vs Avoided Cost

Clearly there is a substantial amount of complexity integrated into even the simplest electric bill. So just what is the cost of electricity? Many sources reference only the cost of generation, which clearly understates the true cost of the power consumed.

A simple calculation results in the **average blended cost** of electricity. At its core, it is the total cost involved in obtaining the power (**total annualized spend**) / the number of kWh consumed over a period of time (typically a year). Most customers don't care about the details of how an electric bill is calculated. They simply want to know what the final bill will be.

AVERAGE BLENDED COST

TOTAL ANNUALIZED SPEND

Likewise, when considering whether or not to invest in a PV system, the average customer wants to know how much the project will save them each year. This is referred to as **avoided cost**, or **annual blended savings**.

AVOIDED COST

ANNUAL BLENDED SAVINGS

To calculate this number, simply take the total energy savings that result from the project (how much was spent each year before the system was installed minus how much will be spent each year after the project is completed) / the number of kWh produced by the system. This represents how much the energy produced by the system is worth per kWh.

Because of the rate structures employed by most utilities, the average blended cost and the avoided cost will almost never be the same. The avoided cost per kWh will almost always be lower due to various fixed costs and demand charges that impact the rate paid.

If a financial analysis of a project represents the average blended cost as the avoided cost, then the financial benefits of the system will likely be over stated - perhaps significantly.

FUTURE COST

Another factor to consider is the **future cost** of electricity. Many financial evaluation models anticipate an estimated annual percentage increase in the cost of electricity. However, just as prices for PV systems are falling for consumers, the cost of producing electricity may also fall for producers. Predicting future prices is always a risky business.

Increased Value of Property

One economic benefit that is often overlooked when calculating the financial return on the installation of a solar array is the increased value the system adds to the home or business.

A 2021 Zillow (an online real estate marketplace) study noted that homes with solar installations tend to sell for about 4.1% more than homes without. Some locations show a higher value add (5.4% for New York City), and some show lower (2.7% for Riverside, California). An older study from Lawrence Berkeley National Laboratory revealed an increase in resale value of about $5,900 for each kilowatt of solar power that's installed.

Payback Period

PAYBACK PERIOD

Customers often want a simple answer to a very complex question. It is common, therefore, to summarize the economics of solar in terms of the system's **payback period**. In other words, how long will it take for the investment to pay for itself?

The payback calculation is:

Payback = Initial net cost ($) / (Annual Blended Savings - O&M costs)

For example, assume a dairy farm installs a 30 kW system at a cost of $2.50 per watt. The initial pre-incentive cost of the system would be $75,000 (30,000 W x $2.50 per watt).

Assume grants and incentives for this project include:
- 26% federal investment tax credit = $75,000 x .26 = $19,500
- 25% grant from the USDA (REAP program) = $75,000 x .25 = $18,750
- MACRS = $75,000 x .87 (half of the ITC cannot be depreciated) x .21 (assumes tax rate of 21%) = $13,700

So the final net cost of the system is:

$75,000 - $19,500 (ITC) - $18,750 (REAP) - $13,700 (MACRS) = $23,050

If the system is expected to generate 39,000 kWh per year, and the owner of the dairy pays 9 cents per kWh, but it is anticipated that the operating and maintenance costs of the system will be $150/year, then the avoided cost or annual blended savings is:

39,000 kWh x $0.09 /kWh = $3,510 - $150 (O&M costs) = $3,360 per year

The payback period of the array can then be calculated as:

Payback = $23,050 / 3,360 per year = 6.86 years

Completing the Financial Analysis

However the payback period does not tell the whole picture when determining if an investment in PV is a financially sound decision.

A complete financial evaluation should consider:
- the initial system cost (parts, permits and labor),
- operation and maintenance costs,
- insurance costs,
- interest payments on loans used,
- and depreciation.

less any...
- federal tax credits,
- SRECs if available,
- and grants.

The final adjusted cost is then divided by the amount of energy the system will produce, calculated:
- based on the current electric rate per kWh factoring in an escalating rate for future electricity,
- adjusted for inflation,
- and adjusted for some level of **system degradation** (over time the system will produce less power as parts age).

$\boxed{\text{SYSTEM DEGRADATION}}$

Clearly, determining the financial implications of a specific PV system, especially large commercial systems, can be a complicated and daunting task.

Fortunately there are many tools available on the market to assist in making PV system financial calculations. Most of these tools import rate schedules and usage details from utility databases.

Authorities Having Jurisdiction (AHJ) and Utility Restrictions

Part of any complete site assessment is determining what is and what is not allowed at a specific location.

AUTHORITY HAVING JURISDICTION (AHJ)

There are many entities that may have a say in how the system is designed and installed. These entities are collectively referred to as the **authorities having jurisdiction (AHJ)**.

These may include, but are not limited to:
- city or county building departments,
- state rules and regulations,
- sub-division or office park rules and covenants,
- planning and zoning restrictions,
- historical preservation requirements,
- and utility rules and restrictions.

PERMITS

LICENSES

For a grid-connected system, the first step in the approval and permitting process should be to contact the electric utility that serves the property. They will likely be able to help guide the designer to the right folks to speak with regarding **permits** and any **licenses** that may be required. But they will also have a few requirements of their own.

Utility

Most utilities have created standard forms that are required from homeowners who intend to install a PV system. Bear in mind that there will likely be fees associated with each of these requirements.

These include:

INTERCONNECTION AGREEMENT

- **Interconnection Agreement**
  Prior to construction, the project developer must obtain a utility review and approval for the proposed system. A formal contract is then signed with the utility. This document sets forth all the terms and conditions under which the system can be connected to the utility grid. It includes information about the system owner's obligation to obtain permits and insurance. It also outlines how the system must be operated and maintained. Typically this agreement will require that the installed system meet the **Institute of Electrical and Electronics Engineers (IEEE) Standard 1547**, *"Standard for Interconnecting Distributed Resources*

IEEE 1547

with Electric Power Systems," the **National Electrical Code (NEC)**, all applicable local codes - and that the equipment installed comply with **UL Standard 1741**.

NATIONAL ELECTRICAL CODE

UL 1741

- **Net Metering Agreement**
  This document, often called the "sale/purchase agreement", spells out the conditions under which the excess power from the system will be purchased by the utility, and the rates that will be charged to the homeowner for the power purchased from the utility.

NET METERING AGREEMENT

- Insurance Requirement
  Most utilities require the homeowner provide insurance to protect the utility's system and personnel from any problems that might be the result of connecting the photovoltaic array to the grid. Basic homeowner's insurance may already be adequate, or a rider may need to be purchased to meet this requirement.

Utility interconnection to smaller systems is generally a faster process than for larger projects. A 5-kW residential rooftop system might require only a few days prior to and after construction for utility approvals. A larger commercial or utility-scale system might, however, require months of reviews, supplemental studies, and negotiations before approval is granted.

During construction the utility may require periodic inspections. A final utility inspection will also likely be required before they grant permission to operate the system.

The property is connected to the grid through a utility **transformer**, which steps down the voltage and current to supply the appropriate power to the building. The project developer must coordinate with the utility to ensure that the transformer in place can handle the maximum bi-directional flow of the array.

TRANSFORMER

If the transformer needs to be upgraded to support the project, this may result in significant delays and costs, as increasingly the utility is requiring that the solar developer pay the cost of the transformer upgrade.

It will be necessary to determine which governmental agency or agencies are in charge of issuing a permit for the project. It may be the city, or the county or the state - or there may be no governmental department overseeing the installation of PV in the area.

County or City Building Department

Requirements vary widely from place to place, as will the fees charged. But applying for a permit requires preparation. Typically a jurisdiction will require:

- an **electrical permit** (assessing the system from an electrical perspective, such as wiring size, bonding and grounding, equipment ratings, etc) .

- a **mechanical permit** (assessing the structural elements such as the racking system design, effects of the PV load on the structure of the home, etc.) Special streamlined permitting processes and lower fees might be in place for small systems in some locations.

- licenses and/or certifications may also be required by the local jurisdiction.. It may be necessary to check with the state's licensing board to determine what licenses are required to install PV systems. For example, a licensed electrician must install the wiring portion of the system. Or the municipality may require that the system be designed by a certified professional (certified in PV design through an organization such as ETA or NABCEP).

- once the system is installed, it is often subject to inspection by a code official from the city and/or county.

SolarAPP+

One major obstacle to the expansion of residential and commercial PV within the US is the reality that the permitting and inspection practices are inconsistent and time consuming across various jurisdictions.

While the direct costs associated with permitting (currently estimated at about $0.13/watt) are high, the indirect costs of permitting can be much higher (the Solar Energy Industries Association estimates as much as one dollar per watt).

These indirect costs include:

- Multiple inspections by multiple authorities (city, utility, contracted engineers, etc). Applications often undergo a succession of reviews by multiple departments, which then commonly conduct their own inspections.

- A complicated application process with multiple requirements - each unique to every jurisdiction.

- Delays in projects due to permitting and inspections. Initial permits will add 2-8 weeks to the project. Another 1-4 weeks will pass waiting for inspections, and another 3-6 weeks delay can be expected as the utility determines the site is ready to produce power.

FIGURE 3-8:
COMPARISON BETWEEN US AND GERMANY SOLAR PV PERMITTING COSTS - 2013

(FROM ROCKY MOUNTAIN INSTITUTE)

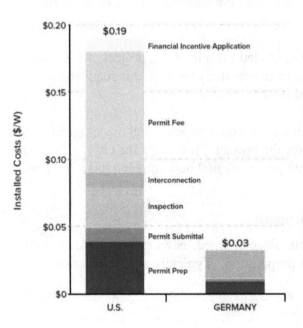

Nations such as Germany and Australia have standardized and streamlined their application process - reducing the time involved and costs of installing a residential solar system. As a result, the cost of permitting has been dramatically reduced, as indicated in Figure 3-8.

In Germany, for example, it's not uncommon for a homeowner to contact a solar installation company and have a system installed on their roof in less than a week.

A streamlined approach can dramatically reduce the cost of the overall system. In Australia, for example, residential solar systems installed in August 2020 cost about AUD $1 (about USD $0.70) per watt - including installation. This compares with an average cost of $2.69 per watt in the U.S. during the same time period, according to Wood Mackenzie in a study conducted for the Solar Energy Industries Association.

In 2018, in an effort to streamline the US permitting process, the Solar Energy Industries Association, the Solar Foundation and NREL launched the Solar Automated Permit Processing initiative known as **SolarAPP+**.

SOLARAPP+

The program envisions the creation of standardized online permitting and interconnection tools that results in instantaneous permitting for eligible installers on qualifying solar projects.

Key elements of the proposed SolarAPP+ process:

- provides a simple, standardized, online permitting platform to local AHJs at no cost to them (paid for by a fee paid by the installer).

- performs an automated plan review with compliance checks built in to the system, enabling instant approval for qualified systems. The system would also block noncompliant applications from entering AHJ workload.

- incorporates a centralized library of resources and training materials from code bodies and expert organizations.

- establishes equipment standards, system designs and/or certified equipment lists for solar and storage projects installed through the SolarApp+.

While still in the testing phase of development, in May 2021 NREL turned over the ongoing administration of the system to Underwriters Labs (UL). The stated goal is to have 90% of all solar permits in the US handled through the SolarAPP+ system by 2030.

Home Owners Associations

Many residents (53% of all US households according to industry reports) who live in a planned development or condominium belong to a **homeowners**

HOMEOWNERS
ASSOCIATION (HOA)

association (HOA) that establishes rules for a neighborhood's aesthetics and manages shared amenities (like pools and green areas).

Historically, many HOAs have established rules aimed at restricting where and how a PV system may be installed on a member's property. Many even prohibit the installation of solar within the development.

In response, a number of states have enacted laws designed to protect homeowners' rights to generate solar power. These laws generally fall under two categories: solar access laws and solar easements.

SOLAR ACCESS LAWS

Solar access laws generally allow HOAs to impose reasonable restrictions, however prohibit them from rules designed to prevent the installation of solar on member properties. The HOA may require permission prior to installation, inspection and approval of the design, and inspection and approval of the installed system.

SOLAR EASEMENTS

Solar easements are voluntary agreements that individual property owners enter into with their neighbors or the HOA that are designed to ensure that the installed system gets enough sunlight once installed. An easement can specify a number of provisions, such as requiring that nearby trees are trimmed or that no structures may be built that would block the sun from reaching the solar array.

Historical Concerns

When installing solar on an older structure or a building of significant historical significance, there is a tension between preserving architectural landmarks and increasing energy efficiency.

Most historical commissions will require that any new fixture (and this includes a solar array) must be "appropriate" which is generally defined as something that does not profoundly impact the historical appearance or nature of the building.

Historic preservation encompasses not only individual buildings, but also a broad range of historic places including historic districts, cultural landscapes, and archeological sites. A number of agencies and organizations administer and advocate for historic preservation.

NATIONAL PARK SERVICE (NPS)

The **National Park Service (NPS)** is the principal federal agency responsible for preservation programs and activities. The NPS administers the National Register of Historic Places.

ADVISORY COUNCIL ON HISTORIC PRESERVATION

The **Advisory Council on Historic Preservation (ACHP)** is another public preservation agency at the national level. The ACHP reviews projects that affect properties determined eligible for listing on the National Register of Historic Places.

State Historic Preservation Offices (SHPO) provide oversight of historic preservation programs in each of the 50 states and territories. **Tribal Historic Preservation Offices (THPO)** may assume any or all SHPO functions on tribal lands. Local historic preservation commissions may also be established to review projects under local preservation ordinances.

STATE HISTORIC
PRESERVATION
OFFICES (SHPO)

TRIBAL HISTORIC
PRESERVATION
OFFICES (THPO)

Most review activity will take place at the local level. Local historic preservation commissions may be empowered to approve or deny proposed alterations to a designated property. Local review processes vary widely, so check with local planning or historic preservation staff if the site appears to be of historical significance or is located within a historical preservation district.

Identify Customer's Concerns

There are as many reasons a potential customer might be hesitant to install solar on their home or business as there are potential customers.

But common concerns generally fall into four main categories.

- Cost. There is an assumption that the project will involve high up-front and out-of-pocket costs and long payback periods.

- Reliability. Most individuals are only vaguely aware of solar power technologies and confusion about its performance and capabilities create concerns about the reliability of solar technology.

- Complexity. The time consuming and complex nature of purchasing and installing solar energy systems discourages many potential customers.

- Inertia. The lengthy decision-making process and financial complexity of the process can cause many to simply "put it off until later." Generally the installation of solar PV on a facility is not an urgent business decision.

Chapter 3 Review Questions

1) A residential home located in Georgia is found to have a monthly average electric bill of 1,375 kWh. The site has been assessed and found to have 4.24 hours of insolation per day (on average) and the system to be installed has been derated at 87%. What size array should be installed at this site to provide 95% of the annual energy use?
   a) 12.22 kW
   b) 11.61 kW
   c) 9.25 kW
   d) 8.79 kW

2) According to the DOE, the average annual electrical use per square foot for commercial property in the US is about:
   a) 8 kWh
   b) 15 kWh
   c) 22.5 kWh
   d) 30.5 kWh

3) As of Jan 1, 2020 California law requires that:
   a) solar panels be installed on all new residential buildings of 3 stories or less
   b) solar installed on all new residential buildings must offset a minimum of 50% of the anticipated usage for that facility
   c) for roofs with less that 80 contiguous square feet of unshaded roof space available, a ground mounted system must be installed
   d) all of the above

4) Installing disconnects that are rated fro the maximum current any future expansion of the system might produce is an example of:
   a) decoupling
   b) expansion fitting
   c) retro-commissioning
   d) future-proofing

5) The process where an in-depth inspection of all building systems is performed to identify worn components and inefficient configurations is known as:
   a) decoupling
   b) expansion fitting
   c) retro-commissioning
   d) future-proofing

6) A building owner can install _____ to correct a low power factor caused by excessive inductive loads.
   a) capacitors
   b) resistors
   c) inductors
   d) transformers

7) The portion of the energy bill that identifies charges associated with delivering power from the substation to the customer is known as the:
   a) energy charge
   b) transmission charge
   c) distribution charge
   d) demand charge

8) Incorporating a battery in a system designed to operate a high-energy load for a brief period of time will likely result in lowering the customer's:
   a) energy charge
   b) transmission charge
   c) distribution charge
   d) demand charge

9) A customer has a peak load demand of 20 kW (for a minimum of 15 minutes) for the month of September. The office building consumed 2,500 kWh of energy that month. What is the customer's load factor?
   a) 0.008 or 0.8%
   b) 0.1736 or 17.36%
   c) 0.24 or 24%
   d) 0.8333 or 83.33%

10) If all the loads in a given facility were turned on at the same time, this is known as that facility's:
    a) demand factor
    b) load factor
    c) energy factor
    d) load capacity

11) If a factory has a load capacity of 305 kW and experiences a peak load demand of 155 kW during a billing cycle, that facility has a demand factor of:
    a) 155 kW
    b) 305 kW
    c) 50.8 %
    d) 196.8%

12) Generally load factors above _____ are considered reasonably efficient for commercial customers.
    a) 50%
    b) 65%
    c) 75%
    d) 90%

13) Charges assessed not only on the amount of energy purchased from the utility, but also assessed on energy produced and sold back to the utility are known as:
   a) demand charges
   b) access charges
   c) transition chargers
   d) non-bypassable charges

14) The cost of building and operating a generating plant over its anticipated productive life is known as:
   a) Indirect capital costs
   b) levelized cost of energy
   c) return on investment
   d) non-bypassable charges

15) The cost of a PV array's racking system would be an example of a:
   a) direct capital cost
   b) levelized cost
   c) supply chain cost
   d) non-bypassable charge

16) Which of the following is **NOT** a typical financial instrument used during the construction and operation of a large commercial solar array?
   a) development loan
   b) construction loan
   c) procurement loan
   d) permanent loan

17) A government-sponsored financing option that creates a loan directly linked to the property (not the owner) and is generally paid for on the tax assessment is known as:
   a) property attached commercial energy (PACE)
   b) property assessed clean energy (PACE)
   c) property attached construction encumbrance (PACE)
   d) program to assign charges equitably (PACE)

18) Which of the following is **NOT** true with regards to power purchase agreements (PPA)?
   a) The customer pays only for power, not the equipment to produce the power.
   b) A PPA is the most common way to finance large commercial systems and are regulated under the Energy Policy Act of 2005.
   c) PPAs are often used by non-profit organizations since they (the organizations) do not qualify for ownership tax credits.
   d) They are a quick and relatively inexpensive way to attain corporate sustainability goals.

19) Where a group of homeowners/businesses purchase a share of a large solar array and receive energy credit on their electric bill equal to the amount produced by the portion of the array they own is known as:
a) ownership model community solar
b) subscription model community solar
c) virtual net metering
d) a power purchase agreement

20) An incentive program where the owner of a recently constructed solar array can receive a tax refund for a portion of the cost of installing the array is known as:
a) modified accelerated cost-recovery system (MACRS)
b) levelized cost of energy (LOE)
c) return on investment (ROI)
d) investment tax credit (ITC)

21) Studies show that in a grid-tied net-metered system (without battery backup), approximately _____ of the energy produced by the PV array is used directly by the home or business (does not pass through the meter to the grid).
a) 10% - 30%
b) 20% - 40%
c) 60% - 80%
d) 80% - 90%

22) If excess energy generation can be carried forward from month to month on a system owner's utility bill, this is known as:
a) kWh banking
b) virtual net metering
c) the true-up period
d) peer-to-peer sales

23) The system where renewable energy credits are bought and sold is known as:
a) GATS (generation attribute tracking system)
b) MACRS (modified accelerated cost-recovery system)
c) REAP (renewable energy aggregator program)
d) BASS (blockchain aggregator sales system)

24) Which of the following would **NOT** generally be factored in when calculating a system's return on investment (ROI)?
a) operation and maintenance costs
b) direct capital costs in constructing the array
c) availability of PACE financing
d) the time value of money

25) The amount of time a system will take to pay for itself in energy savings is known as its:
a) average blended cost
b) annual blended savings
c) return on investment
d) payback period

26) A 26 kW array is to be built on a commercial farm. The installation cost per watt is $2.00. The following apply to this array:
- it qualifies for a 25% REAP grant
- it qualifies for accelerated depreciation (at a tax rate of 21%)
- it also qualifies for a 26% investment tax credit
- it is estimated that the O&M costs will be $280 per year
- assume the cost of electricity at the site over the next 10 years will   average $0.11 per kWh
- the array will generate about 35,770 kWh of energy per year

What is the payback period for this array?
a) 4.37 years
b) levelized cost
c) supply chain cost
d) non-bypassable charge

27) Launched in 2018, a national effort to streamline the solar permitting process in the US is known as:
a) net metering
b) NREL (National Renewable Energy Licensing)
c) PURPA (Providing Urgent Response for Permit Authorization)
d) SolarAPP+

28) Approximately what percentage of US households live in planned developments that come under the jurisdiction of homeowner's associations?
a) 10%
b) 26%
c) 53%
d) 68%

Chapter 4

System Options

Determining the System Configuration

There are a number of ways a photovoltaic system can be configured to best meet the needs of a particular customer.

Some questions that need to be answered to help determine the system that best suits the situation include:

- Is the electrical grid available?

- How reliable is the grid? Are there frequent outages, for example?

- How critical are the loads being serviced by the system? For example, is the system being mounted on a hospital where power is literally a matter of life and death?

- Is shading an issue?

- How much space is available for the array?

- What is the billing structure from the utility, for example, is time-of-day pricing in place that would make battery systems attractive? Are there demand charges that could be offset with integrated storage?

Grid-Tied Systems

By far the most common system configuration installed in developed countries is the **grid-tied system**.

GRID-TIED SYSTEM

This configuration essentially uses the grid as a storage device. When more energy is generated by the system than is required by the load demand, the excess power is fed to the grid. When more load is

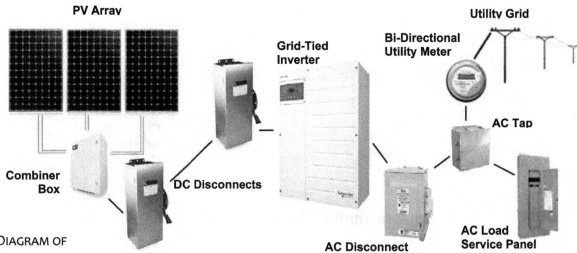

PV Array

Utility Grid

Grid-Tied
Inverter

Bi-Directional
Utility Meter

Combiner
Box

DC Disconnects

AC Tap

AC Disconnect

AC Load
Service Panel

FIGURE 4-1: DIAGRAM OF
A GRID-TIED PV SYSTEM
WITH STRING INVERTER

required than the system is producing, the excess load demand is met by power drawn from the grid.

In effect, the electrical grid serves as a battery. "Storing" excess energy and then providing it when it is needed. This avoids the cost of a battery system (often more than half of the total system cost) and also avoids the maintenance issues required by battery banks.

A basic grid-tied system, can utilize a string inverter, such as the system depicted in Figure 4-1, or increasingly, incorporate microinverters or power optimizers that work in tandem with a fixed-voltage inverter.

Regardless of how it is configured, grid-tied systems have the advantage of avoiding the cost and maintenance issues involved when incorporating a battery backup system.

ISLANDING

One disadvantage, however, is that grid-tied photovoltaic systems are designed to shut down when the grid loses power. This avoids a situation where workers repairing the lines assume there is no power, only to find that the PV system is pumping electricity onto supposedly "dead" lines (known as **islanding**). In the past, workers have been killed or severely injured when a distributed energy system continued to operate while connected to a grid under repair.

As a result, a typical grid-tied system will only be as reliable as the electrical grid to which it is connected.

Rapid Shutdown of PV Systems on Buildings

Perhaps the most dramatic change in the 2014 NEC, from the perspective of PV design, was the incorporation of a provision (in Section 690.12) that all rooftop arrays must incorporate a method where they can be effectively shut down at the source.

The reason for this provision comes from the increasing risk faced by first-responders when responding to a fire at a structure where a PV system is installed. This risk is present in all occupied buildings - but not for ground mounted systems. So rapid shutdown requirements do not apply to ground mounted systems.

Historically, when a first responder disconnects power from the grid (by pulling the meter, for example), they can safely assume that they will not come into contact with any live electrical wires within the building.

However, if a PV system is present and the sun is shining, wires within the structure may still be energized, even when the main **AC disconnect** has been opened and the system is no longer operating (power can still be present from the panels to the string inverter where the anti-islanding feature has shut down the system).

AC DISCONNECT

2014 NEC Rapid Shutdown Requirements
To prevent this situation, the 2014 NEC required that when the PV system disconnect is turned off:

- conductors more than 1.5 meters (5 feet) inside the building structure and no more than 3 meters (10 feet) from the array be limited to a maximum of 30 volts and 240 watts within 10 seconds of system shutdown. 30 volts is considered "touch safe" in a wet environment,

- systems with rapid shutdown should be labeled as such,

- equipment that performs the rapid shutdown should be listed and identified as meeting the rapid shutdown requirements.

System designers could comply with this 2014 provision in a number of ways.

These include:

- use of microinverters, which disconnect at the panel when the grid is not present,

- use of power optimizers, which also disconnect at the panel when the grid is down,

- use of a **disconnecting combiner box** (must be located within 10 feet of the array) that is wired to an emergency shutoff switch located near the utility service entrance, an example is shown in Figure 4-2,

- or locate the string inverter within 10 feet of the array.

DISCONNECTING COMBINER BOX

FIGURE 4-2: EMERGENCY DISCONNECT SWITCH CONNECTED TO COMBINER BOX

(FROM BENTEK SOLAR)

2017 NEC Rapid Shutdown Changes

The 2017 NEC added some additional requirements. These include:

- conductors within one foot of the **array boundary** (rather than 10 feet) must be energized to no more than 30 volts within 30 seconds (rather than ten seconds) of the main disconnect being turned off.

- the specific component parts used must be listed (by UL or some other listing agent) that they comply with rapid shutdown provisions (**rapid shutdown equipment**, or PVRSE) or as a system, when designed to work together (**rapid shutdown system**, or PVRSS),

- or, the array has no exposed wiring methods or conductive parts and is more than eight feet away from any grounded metal,

- or, within the array boundaries, there is no conductor with a voltage higher than 80 V when rapid shutdown is initiated. Under the 2014 rules, DC conductors could be up to 1,000 V inside the boundary of the array.

At the time, no standard existed that allowed compliance with these provisions. Also, few product systems were available that contained all wiring from the panel to the junction box in nonconductive raceways (a few non-metallic solar shingle systems).

The effect of these changes was that after 2018, all roof-mounted arrays must incorporate some type of **module-level power electronics (MLPE),** such as power optimizers or microinverters, that reduced the conductor voltages to less than 80 V within the array boundary once rapid shutdown was initiated.

2020 NEC Rapid Shutdown Changes

In the 2020 NEC, rapid shutdown inside the array boundary was revised to address "PV hazard control systems". This is a change in terminology that replaced the rapid shutdown system provision as outlined in the 2017 code.

First published in December 2020, *ANSI/CAN/UL 3741: Standard for Safety for Photovoltaic Hazard Control* provides a means of evaluating photovoltaic (PV) hazard control components, equipment and systems that comply with the rapid shutdown requirements.

DC Coupled: Grid-Tied with Battery Backup

One of the critical disadvantages of a grid-tied PV system is that when the grid goes down - the system is designed to shut down due to islanding. To avoid the problem of loss of power when the electrical grid goes down, some grid-tied systems incorporate a battery backup system into their design.

This design, often referred to as a **DC coupled system**, as seen in Figure 4-3, might be practical if the installation is located in an area with an unreliable grid, or if there are **critical loads** within the building that absolutely must have power all the time (such as within a hospital, for example).

Sidebar terms:

- ARRAY BOUNDARY
- RAPID SHUTDOWN EQUIPMENT (PVRSE)
- RAPID SHUTDOWN SYSTEM (PVRSS)
- MODULE-LEVEL POWER ELECTRONICS
- UL 3741
- DC-COUPLED SYSTEM
- CRITICAL LOADS

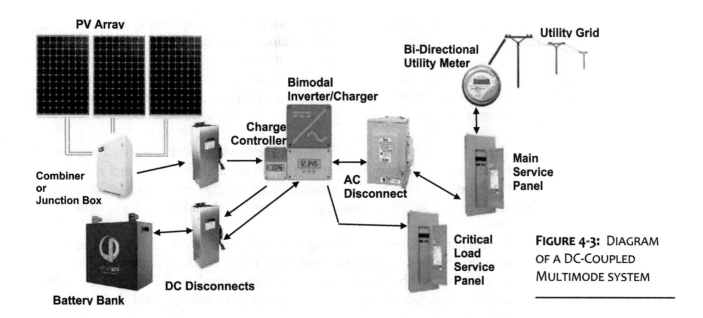

PV Array

Combiner
or
Junction Box

Battery Bank

DC Disconnects

Charge
Controller

Bimodal
Inverter/Charger

AC
Disconnect

Bi-Directional
Utility Meter

Utility Grid

Main
Service
Panel

Critical
Load
Service
Panel

FIGURE 4-3: DIAGRAM OF A DC-COUPLED MULTIMODE SYSTEM

For most facilities, there are two further classes of load. **Essential loads** provide secondary support services that may still be required for health and safety reasons, such as emergency lighting. These loads must still have some form of backup but do not require uninterrupted power, so can be allowed to fail or ride through the time it takes for a generator to start.

Finally, there are **non-essential loads** that are not required during brief periods when the grid is down, such as ceiling fans or printers.

When designing these systems, it is typical that specific critical circuits be identified to receive power from the battery bank (rather than the entire building), when the grid is down. These circuits must be disconnected from the grid (either physically, or electronically) before they can be energized.

This is normally accomplished through the integration of a **critical load panel** - essentially a second service panel that connects to all critical loads but is not directly connected to the utility grid.

The main service panel and the critical load panel are connected to the bimodal inverter. During normal operations, both the main panel and the critical load panel are connected together to the array, battery bank and the grid through the inverter.

When the grid goes down, the bimodal inverter disconnects from the main service panel (isolating the system from the grid) through the use of an integrated **transfer switch**. It then redirects the system's power (array and battery bank) to the critical load panel only.

ESSENTIAL LOADS

NON-ESSENTIAL LOADS

CRITICAL LOAD PANEL

TRANSFER SWITCH

Many commercially available systems, such as the system from SolarEdge, pictured in Figure 4-4, integrate multiple components into the inverter. For example, in this system the charge controller function and DC disconnect are integrated into the inverter unit. An added **autotransformer** unit must be connected to the inverter to monitor the grid and act as an anti-islanding transfer switch.

The inverter unit has two DC inputs (one from the array and one from the battery bank) and two AC outputs (one to the main service panel and one to the critical load panel. The monitoring (metering) system is handled in the cloud or an additional consumption meter may be added to the system..

Some charge controllers allow system owners to retrofit existing string-inverter grid-tied systems to incorporate battery backup (creating a DC-coupled system) by incorporating a charge controller with a manual transfer switch that avoids the necessity of replacing the existing grid-tied string inverter.

Incorporating a battery bank into a typical grid-tied system will add substantially to the overall cost and maintenance requirements of the system. However, as battery prices decline and the grid viewed as unreliable, grid-tied systems with battery backup have become increasingly popular. In 2020, over 20% of all systems installed in the US incorporated some sort of battery backup.

Other situations where DC-coupled systems may be appropriate include:
  ▪ time of use shifting (load shifting),

FIGURE 4-4: DIAGRAM OF DC COUPLED RESIDENTIAL INSTALLATION

(FROM SOLAREDGE)

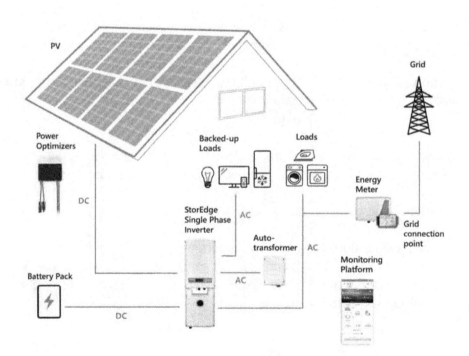

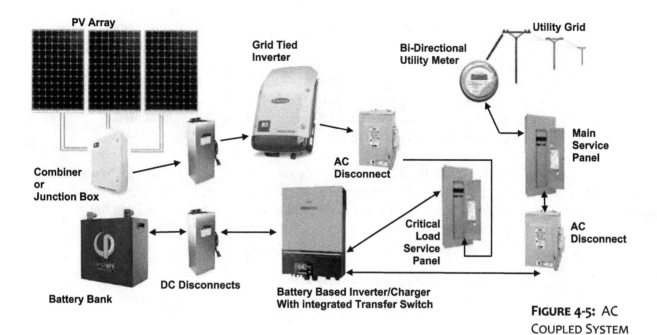

PV Array

Grid Tied
Inverter

Bi-Directional
Utility Meter

Utility Grid

Combiner
or
Junction Box

AC
Disconnect

Main
Service
Panel

Critical
Load
Service
Panel

AC
Disconnect

Battery Bank

DC Disconnects

Battery Based Inverter/Charger
With integrated Transfer Switch

FIGURE 4-5: AC
COUPLED SYSTEM

- peak demand reduction (load leveling or peak load shaving),
- where net metering isn't permitted.

AC-Coupled Multimode Systems

Systems that convert the DC power of an array into AC power, and then convert the AC power back to DC to charge a battery bank, are gaining in popularity.

At first glance, this may seem an unnecessary step and added complexity, but there are a number of advantages.

AC-coupled systems allow owners of existing PV systems to add a battery backup without changing their installed system configuration.

(AC-COUPLED SYSTEM)

In AC-coupled system illustrated in Figure 4-5, the grid-tied inverter is connected to the critical load panel (rather than the main service panel). A battery-based inverter/charger is also connected to the critical load panel, and then connected to the battery bank.

The battery-based inverter/charger can take AC power from the grid-tied inverter and/or from the grid and charge the batteries (converting it from AC to DC). It can also take DC power from the batteries (in the event of a power outage, for example) and convert it to AC power that is distributed through the critical load panel.

When the grid is operating, power flows from the critical load panel to the main load panel (and all the loads are energized and excess power can flow to the grid). When the grid goes down, an integrated transfer switch within the inverter disconnects from the main service panel, isolating the system from the grid.

There are a number of integrated systems on the market today (such as the Enphase Enpower system or the Tesla Powerwall 2) that offer components designed to work together and combine the battery bank with the inverter/charger in one unit.

Note that in all grid coupled systems (both AC-coupled and DC-coupled), a transfer switch must be located within the system. This transfer switch will sense when the grid goes down and disconnect the system from the grid to avoid islanding. In some cases the transfer switch will be a separate unit, or it may be integrated within the inverter.

Designing AC Coupled Battery Bank Systems

AC coupled systems may be installed at a location for a number of reasons. In residential settings, these normally include:

- the originally installed system did not incorporate battery backup to serve critical loads when the grid fails.

- net metering isn't permitted at the location. A battery bank can be set to store excess energy (since it cannot be exported to the grid), and then offset power that might otherwise be purchased from the grid when the array is not producing sufficiently to service the loads (such as at night, for instance).

In commercial situations, utility billing practices may make AC coupled systems an attractive alternative for additional reasons that may or may not be a factor in a residential setting. These systems may or may not incorporate a solar array as part of their energy strategy.

FIGURE 4-6: LOAD SHIFTING FOR HOUSEHOLD LOCATED WHERE EVENING POWER FROM THE UTILITY COSTS MORE THAN AFTERNOON POWER

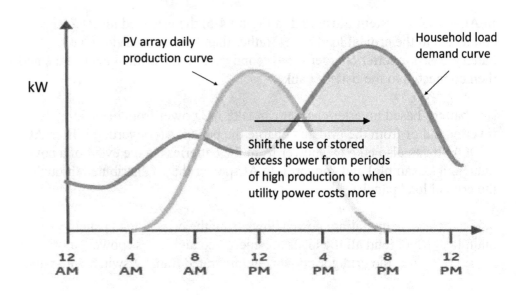

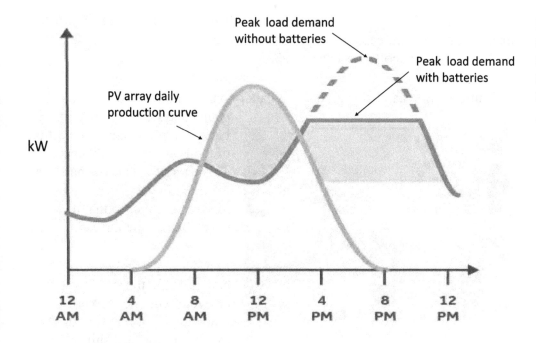

PV array daily production curve

Peak load demand without batteries

Peak load demand with batteries

kW

12 AM | 4 AM | 8 AM | 12 PM | 4 PM | 8 PM | 12 PM

These reasons include:

- time of use shifting. If the utility pricing scheme charges more for power during periods of high demand, the customer can shift their consumption by storing excess power generated by the PV array (rather than selling it back to the utility) and then using the stored power during periods of high-cost power (rather than purchasing it from the utility). This process is also known as **load shifting,** as illustrated in Figure 4-6.

- Peak demand reduction, commonly called **peak shaving**. Utilities often charge commercial customers a rate based on the 15-minute interval within the month where the most power was used. The higher the use, the higher the bill. Customers can reduce their peak usage, offsetting it with power from the battery bank, as illustrated in Figure 4-7. This can dramatically reduce their monthly bill from the utility company.

> LOAD SHIFTING

> PEAK SHAVING

PV systems that incorporate batteries designed to deal with load shifting and/or peak shaving are often referred to as **self-consumption grid-tied** systems.

> SELF-CONSUMPTION GRID-TIED

Current Transformers

The sizing of self-consumption battery banks generally involves obtaining a detailed load-versus-time profile of home energy consumption with the use of energy-monitoring equipment.

Current transformers (CTs) are installed around the hot conductors in the solar production circuit (normally within the service panel). The arrow on the CT must be pointing toward the load, as illustrated in Figure 4-8. Load consumption data is collected and sent to a monitoring system.

> CURRENT TRANSFORMERS

The data from the solar array must also be collected to determine how much excess power is sent back to the grid during peak generation times. Most grid-tied inverters collect and report this data.

This information can be used to size a battery bank within an AC or DC-

FIGURE 4-8: INSTALLED CURRENT TRANSFORMER (CT)

coupled system. The battery bank is sized to store the portion of the PV array's daily energy. This energy would normally be exported to the grid in a net-metered system, so that it can be consumed onsite instead.

In order to properly size a battery bank, the system designer will need to know how much load will need to be offset to account for load shifting or peak shaving requirements, or to provide power during a grid outage. Designers often oversize battery banks, assuming power outages will last longer than they actually do.

Sizing Battery Bank for Power Outages

Eaton's *2015 Blackout Tracker* report found that of the more than 3,500 outages in the U.S., the average duration was only 49 minutes. The Electric Power Research Institute also estimated that 57% of U.S. power outages last less than five minutes. Depending on the client's system availability requirements, a relatively small battery bank can handle most grid outages.

For example, a typical home in the U.S. consumes about 30 kWh per day. This power is not consumed at a uniform rate (30 kWh / 24 hrs). An hourly load assessment could be conducted, but for this example, assume during waking hours the client consumes 2 kWh per hour.

A lithium ion battery bank designed to provide one (1) hour of emergency backup would be sized:

load demand / system voltage / depth of discharge / inverter efficiency, or
2 kWh / 48 volts = 41.67 Ah / 95% DOD = 43.86 Ah / 97% = 45.2 Ah

AC coupled systems are marketed in terms of kWh rather than the more traditional Ah rating of battery systems, and the DOD and inverter efficiency is already calculated into this rating. This system would need a 2 kWh battery bank to deal with any power outages less than one hour in duration.

Effectively, this system acts as an **uninterruptible power source (UPS)** for the entire house.

UNINTERRUPTIBLE POWER SOURCE (UPS)

Most AC coupled systems on the market are essentially plug and play. Follow the manufacturer's instructions. Some systems, such as Tesla's Powerwall, require they be installed by an installer that has been certified by the manufacturer.

Designing AC-Coupled Systems using Lead Acid Batteries

While most **energy storage systems (ESS)** available on the market for AC-coupled systems incorporate lithium ion batteries, it is possible to design an AC-coupled system using lead acid batteries.

ENERGY STORAGE SYSTEMS (ESS)

An AC-coupled system of this type has significant advantages over incorporating a generator into the system to deal with periodic power outages.

These include:
- reduced noise (generators can be very loud),
- reduced wear and tear on the generator, which must run the entire time the grid is down. Incorporating a battery bank into the system reduces significantly the amount of time a generator must operate during extended power outages.

Prior to adding a battery-based inverter and battery bank to an existing grid-tied system, it is common to add a critical load panel so the battery bank need not supply power to the entire load when the grid goes down.

However, the existing solar array and the existing grid-tied inverter may have been sized to provide enough power to service all daily loads.

As a result, when designing an AC-coupled system, care must be taken to avoid overcharging the battery bank when production from the array exceeds load demand and the grid is not available to absorb any excess production.

If all the power flowing through the grid-tied inverter is to be captured, then the battery bank must be sized based on the grid-tied inverter's output. Generally this requires about 100 Ah per 1 kW of PV on a 48 Vdc system. Such a large battery bank may be much more than is required to service only critical loads during short term and/or infrequent power outages.

The battery bank required to service critical loads would be sized in a manner similar to sizing a battery bank for a stand alone system, with the daily critical load substituted for the total daily load demand.

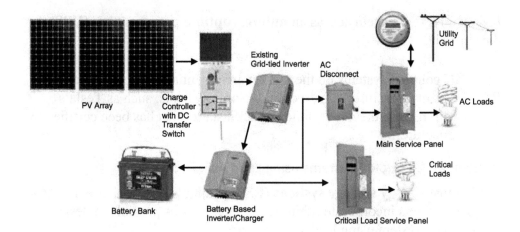

If a smaller battery bank were installed, however, then the power flowing from the array through the grid-tied inverter might severely overcharge the battery bank or charge it too quickly. It should be noted that charging rates faster than C/5 (from empty to full in 5 hours) can be harmful to lead-acid batteries and shorten their functional life.

Designers can avoid this problem by incorporating a diverted load (such as a hot water heater) in a manner similar to that used when designing a stand-alone system.

Or a charge controller with a DC transfer switch can be incorporated into the system. When the grid is operational, power flows through the charge controller from the PV array to the grid-tied inverter, as indicated in Figure 4-9.

However, when the grid goes down, the transfer switch within the charge controller redirects the array's power to the battery-based inverter, as demonstrated in Figure 4-10. The charge controller then limits the amount of power going to the battery bank, avoiding overcharging.

FIGURE 4-10: POWER
FLOW OF AC-COUPLED
SYSTEM WITH CHARGE
CONTROLLER WHEN
GRID IS DOWN

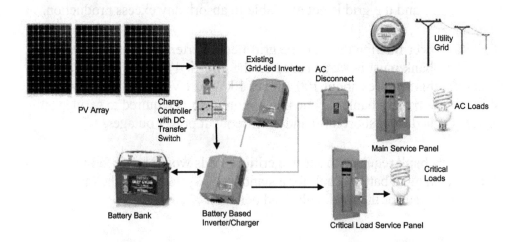

Rapid Shutdown Issues with Battery Systems

The rapid shutdown provisions of the NEC are designed to ensure that power is not present within the building when the main PV disconnect is turned off (disconnected from the grid).

However, one of the main advantages of incorporating batteries into a PV system is to ensure the array remains functional and power is available, even when the grid goes down. Obviously these two goals are in conflict.

In grid-tied systems that do not incorporate batteries, the AC disconnect is considered the **rapid shutdown initiator (RSI)**. In other words, when the main AC disconnect is opened (turned off), shutdown takes place at the array. With systems that incorporate batteries, a second RSI is required.

RAPID SHUTDOWN INITIATOR (RSI)

Most AC-coupled and DC-coupled systems incorporate a manual RSI with the battery-based inverter unit. However, since the RSI must be accessible by first responders, this means the inverter must be mounted outside (normally within 10 feet of the meter), or an auxiliary RSI (for the battery system) must be installed.

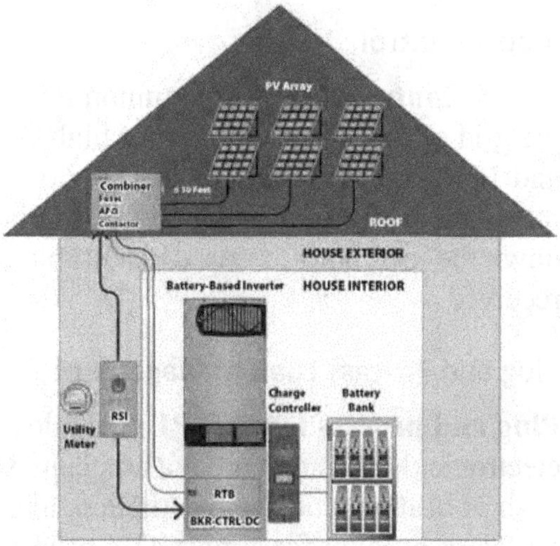

FIGURE 4-11:
REMOTE BATTERY RAPID SHUTDOWN INITIATOR

FROM OUTBACK POWER

Most battery-based inverters will offer a remote disconnect switch designed to integrate into their unit, such as the optional switch offered by Outback Power for their system, as illustrated in Figure 4-11.

Load Management

Batteries are often introduced into a system as a tool that allows better management of the load. Load shifting, peak load shaving and power outages are all reasons cited for incorporating batteries at a site. But batteries are expensive, so load management devices are often incorporated to reduce the size of the battery bank required to accomplish these goals.

Load management, often called demand-side management (DSM), is the process of balancing the supply of electricity available with the electrical load by adjusting or controlling the load rather than the supply.

LOAD MANAGEMENT

This can be achieved by the direct intervention of the utility in real time, or by the consumer managing how they use loads either manually or through a number of automated devices.

A very early load management device might be a timer placed on a water heating circuit to turn off the heater during periods of peak load demand. Over the years, the technical nature of these load management devices has changed dramatically.

Frequency-based Decentralized Demand Control

Excessive loads on the grid physically slow the rotors of a grid's synchronized generators. This causes service throughout the grid to have a slightly reduced frequency.

Inexpensive electronic devices can easily and precisely measure the frequency present and turn off sheddable loads. Most electronic electric power meters internally measure frequency, requiring only simple demand control relays to turn on and off equipment.

Ripple Control

Ripple control is another common form of load control. With ripple control, the grid operator superimposes a high-frequency signal (usually between 100 and 1600 Hz) onto the standard 50–60 Hz of the main power signal. A receiving device attached to non-essential loads receives this signal, shutting down the load until the signal is disabled or another frequency signal is received.

Plug and Process Load Management

Plug and process loads (PPL) include all plugged-in and hardwired electronic devices that are not associated with other major building end uses such as heating, cooling, ventilation, and lighting. PPLs in commercial buildings account for almost 47% of U.S. commercial building electricity use.

Automated systems exist for homeowners to control and manage energy consumption at the appliance level. These systems rely on the technology inherent in the Internet of Things (IoT) that provides the ability of devices to send and receive data via the Internet.

However systems required to provide effective load control within commercials structures are much more complex. Commercial buildings generally have multiple occupants, many more devices, multiple impressions of what is or is not a critical load - so uniform management systems are often quite difficult to implement.

An effective load management system must have five main capabilities:
- location identification of the load,
- communication processes,
- control of the load,
- energy metering, and
- data storage.

One PPL solution is to install a "smart outlet." A **smart outlet** can be installed at the electrical outlets of a building either as plug-through receptacle or embedded into the outlet itself, such as the example pictured in Figure 4-12.

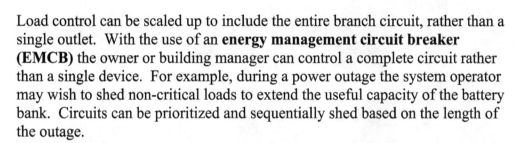

FIGURE 4-12:
COMMERCIALLY
AVAILABLE SMART
OUTLET

SMART OUTLET

Typically, a smart outlet measures the power consumption of the device that is plugged into it and transmits the data wirelessly to a central monitoring system. Building managers can view the data and turn devices on or off, either manually or through pre-determined settings.

Load control can be scaled up to include the entire branch circuit, rather than a single outlet. With the use of an **energy management circuit breaker (EMCB)** the owner or building manager can control a complete circuit rather than a single device. For example, during a power outage the system operator may wish to shed non-critical loads to extend the useful capacity of the battery bank. Circuits can be prioritized and sequentially shed based on the length of the outage.

ENERGY MANAGEMENT CIRCUIT BREAKER

Larger Systems Using Microinverters

For larger arrays that incorporate microinverters, an AC-rated combiner box will be required.

For smaller systems, the PV output circuit can run (in conduit) directly to the building, connecting to either a meter or an AC disconnect (or both). Increasingly larger PV installations are incorporating microinverters.

Advantages of this system design include:

- zero risk of **arc fault** as the entire system incorporates standard AC wiring. All modern inverters incorporate arc fault detection, however it remains a risk with high voltage DC systems.

ARC FAULT

- automatic rapid shutdown compliance, as the microinverter ensures the current is terminated within the array boundary since the inverter is connected directly to the panel.

- increased system efficiency and shading mitigation.

- increased system reliability as there is no single point of failure, as in a larger string inverter system.

- increased power quality. microinverters will automatically correct **phase imbalance** within a three-phase system. Voltages at the site can become unbalanced due to the unequal system impedances, the unequal distribution of single phase loads, asymmetrical three-phase equipment

PHASE IMBALANCE

and devices, unbalanced faults, or bad electrical connections. An unbalanced three-phase system can cause three-phase motors and other three-phase loads to experience poor performance or premature failure.

AC Combiner Box for Microinverters

Since microinverters generate AC current at grid voltage (240 Vac single phase or 208 Vac three phase) rather than DC, when connected together they are connected in parallel rather than series. So multiple microinverters connected together are a **branch circuit,** rather than a string. Each microinverter added increases the amps on the circuit.

BRANCH CIRCUIT

The limiting factor on the number of microinverters in each branch circuit is the maximum ampacity of the proprietary cabling used in the system (generally limited to 20 amps).

For example, the Enphase IQ7+ microinverter generates 290 VA of continuous power. Each microinverter in a single phase system will add 1.21 A to the branch circuit (290 VA / 240 V) and 1.39 A in a three phase system (290 VA / 208 V). So branch circuits are limited to 13 microinverters for a single phase system (13 x 1.21 A= 15.73 A x 1.25 safety margin = 19.66 A) to stay under the 20 A limitation of the cable. Three phase systems are limited to 11 microinverters for each branch circuit.

When designing a system that incorporates more microinverters than can be accommodated in a single branch circuit, a combiner box is required.

Enphase, the industry leader in microinverters, offers a combiner box as shown in Figure 4-13 that integrates overcurrent protection as well as the monitoring hardware for the system.

This combiner box has space for four 20 A double-pole circuit breakers connected to four branch circuits from the array or battery bank. The monitoring hardware is also incorporated into the unit and can be paired with the site's wireless Internet service (or to a mobile phone network).

Multiple combiner boxes can be used for very large systems.

Battery-less Coupled Systems

Enphase made headlines in early 2022 with the announcement of their IQ8 series of microinverters. The groundbreaking feature of these systems is that they can provide power to critical loads even without a battery attached to the system.

When the grid goes down, the system will disconnect from the grid in a manner similar to all AC-coupled systems. Then the array will provide power directly to the loads, but only to the extent that solar power is available at any given instant.

Due to the variability of solar power (clouds passing overhead, for instance) the available power rises and falls from moment to moment. With no battery incorporated to even out this variability, the system is designed to shut down if the load demand is too high.

The system incorporates a load controller to manage loads, shedding predetermined circuits as needed.

While this is the first product to incorporate battery-less backup capability, it is highly likely that more systems will begin to incorporate similar features.

Commercial Systems

In many respects, most of the same design issues that apply to smaller residential systems also apply to larger commercial systems. The same components are utilized, but scaled up for larger systems.

The chief difference when determining the design options for a larger system (10 kW and up - in 2016 the average commercial system was 217 kW) lies in the selection of the inverter and how it is connected to the electrical grid.

The designer of a commercial PV system must decide whether to install one large inverter, capable of handling the power generated by the entire array, or to install a number of smaller inverters and then combine their AC output.

Note that many of the advantages/disadvantages between a single large inverter and multiple string inverters in a commercial installation are quite similar to the issues involved when determining whether or not to use microinverters or a string inverter in a residential installation.

Large commercial inverters typically have connection points for multiple **subarrays**, as indicated in Figure 4-14. A subarray that has two output conductors, one positive and one negative (which is typical) is referred to as a **monopole subarray**.

SUBARRAY

MONOPOLE
SUBARRAY

FIGURE 4-14: SYSTEM DESIGN WITH SINGLE COMMERCIAL STRING INVERTER

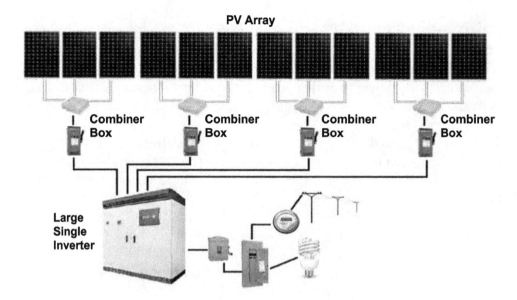

Larger systems can alternatively be designed to incorporate many smaller string inverters. These are essentially smaller PV systems combined together on the AC side of the inverters, as shown in Figure 4-15.

Advantages and disadvantages of these configuration options are detailed in Table 4-1.

Larger Power Optimizer Systems

Many larger commercial installations are moving away from a single large inverter to installations that feature multiple optimizer-based sub-arrays coupled together.

The advantages of this design choice include:
- no single point of failure within a large inverter,
- module level monitoring and efficiency,
- a greater workforce is available to install and service the smaller systems, as large inverter systems may require specialized training.

FIGURE 4-15: LARGE SYSTEM DESIGN WITH MULTIPLE STRING INVERTERS

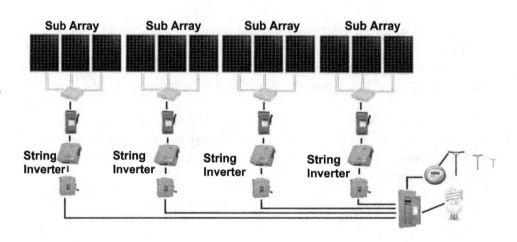

	Single Inverter	Multiple Inverters
Equipment Cost	Less Expensive	More Expensive
Installation Cost	Less Expensive	More Expensive
DC Wiring	More Complex	Less Complex
AC Wiring	Less Complex	More Complex
Unit Weight	Very Heavy, requires lifting equipment	Lighter, no special equipment required
System Availability	Single point of failure	Entire system is not affected when one inverter goes down
MPPT	Single MPPT for entire array	MPPT adjusted for each inverter
Array Orientation	All panels in the array must be oriented in the same direction	Each inverter can have unique orientation
Array Configuration	Each string must be of the same length	Each inverter can have unique configuration
Module Selection	All modules in the array must be identical	Each sub-array can have unique modules
Fault Detection	Difficult	Less Difficult
Performance Monitoring	Difficult	Less Difficult
Output	—	1% to 1.5% higher
Grid Connection	Must match grid exactly	Often field configurable
Warranty	Usually 5 years	Usually 10 years
Service	By trained technician	By installers

TABLE 4-1: ADVANTAGES AND DISADVANTAGES OF A SINGLE COMMERCIAL STRING INVERTER COMPARED WITH MULTIPLE STRING INVERTERS

Products have recently come on the market that seek to capitalize on the advantages offered by both systems. These products incorporate multiple string inverters in a single cabinet, enabling the installation at a single point (like a centralized inverter) but with the modularity of multiple inverters.

Bipolar PV Systems

While rare, **bipolar PV systems** do exist and present a number of challenges to the installer/designer when and where they are employed.

BIPOLAR SYSTEM

In PV systems, the DC power output from the array generally arrives at the inverter on two conductors, one positive and the other negative. There may be multiple pairs of power output from the array, but they leave and arrive in this familiar pattern.

A bipolar system, however, "has two outputs, each having opposite polarity to a common reference point or center tap." (NEC 690.2) So what does this mean?

FIGURE 4-16: BIPOLAR
PV SYSTEM
CONFIGURATION

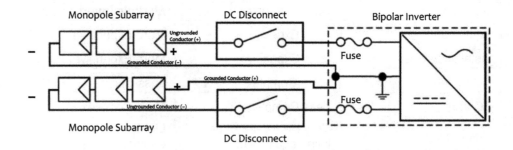

A subarray that has two output conductors, but their output polarities are in reference to a common (neutral), is called a **bipolar subarray**. This wiring configuration is similar to service coming from the utility to a home in a 120/240 Vac split-phase system. In that system there are two hots, each sharing a common or neutral. In a bipolar array, the positive and the negative share a common neutral.

Outputs from two monopole subarrays can be combined in a combiner box, or, if by combining the voltage the system would exceed the ratings of the conductors and/or equipment located outside the inverter, then the conductors from each subarray must run separately to the inverter for termination, as illustrated in Figure 4-16.

In a bipolar system, the subarrays are effectively connected in series, increasing the voltage of the system above the limitations of each array.

For example, if each subarray had a voltage limit of 600 Vdc, then the output from the combiner box when the two subarrays are combined in a bipolar configuration would be 1,200 Vdc.

Such a configuration can only be used with combiner boxes and inverters that are specifically designed for bipolar systems. The monopole subarrays feeding the combiner box must also be balanced (configured in an identical manner).

In general, the higher the voltage of a system, the lower the cost (smaller wire, disconnects, breakers, etc). The NEC currently limits residential systems to 600 volts DC. PV system DC circuits on or in commercial and multi-family buildings are limited to a maximum voltage no greater than 1000 volts. While there is no set limit on ground-mounted commercial systems, the availability of product effectively limits commercial systems to 1,000 Vdc. By configuring a system using bipolar subarrays, the designer can raise the system's voltage while still using products with lower-voltage ratings within the monopole subarrays.

System Monitoring

One big advantage of systems that incorporate module-level power electronics (MLPE) is that energy production can be monitored and tracked on a module-by-module basis (as shown in Figure 4-17).

As more and more utility customers are integrating battery banks into their systems to minimize demand charges or adjust load demand to time-of-day pricing, there is a need to monitor load demand as well as PV energy production. This is done with the use of current transformers, or CTs.

CTs measure current passively, without interrupting the circuit in any way. They are placed around the conductor and use the magnetic field to measure current flow.

They are then connected to the monitoring system through sensor wires. The monitoring system can be programmed to draw power from or send power to the battery bank, depending on instantaneous load demand.

System monitoring can be handled in house, or subcontracted to firms that specialize in this service.

A simple residential system may be configured to send the homeowner an e-mail if the MLPE fails to report or is performing outside the expected range of operation. It will also track and report daily, weekly, monthly and lifetime power and energy output from the panels.

A more complex monitoring system will, in addition to the above, also:
- assess the PV system's overall technical and financial performance,
- display data at the module, string and system levels, for a single system or for multiple PV arrays,
- monitor the PV system's production, as well as load consumption over multiple circuits and sites,

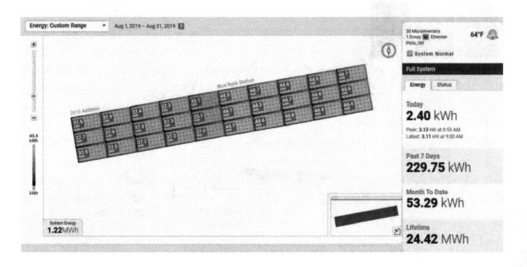

FIGURE 4-17: ENPHASE ENLIGHTEN PRODUCTION MONITORING SYSTEM

- provide prompt analysis and reporting tools based on real-time events,
- allow for easy and convenient management from a computer, tablet or phone,
- provide instant alerts regarding system issues (panel or inverter performance drops),
- integrate real-time weather data to predict system performance,
- allow access to real-time and historical system data with the ability to compare across sites,
- provide comprehensive billing analysis,
- dispatch repair crews in the event of a system malfunction.

Integrating Generators

GENERATOR

Many commercial businesses have **generators** in place that provide emergency power when the grid goes down. Increasingly, residential customers are installing them as well in areas where the grid is unreliable.

It is possible to connect a PV inverter to an electrical system that incorporates a generator if the output from the generator is stable and of high quality. The inverter will monitor the generator's output voltage, frequency and waveform, just as it does with power from the grid. If the AC waveform from the generator is grid quality, the inverter will attempt to synchronize with the generator.

If the AC input to the inverter does not dip, sag or surge when the PV system comes on line, then the inverter will remain online. But if the generator's output falls out of normal operating ranges, the inverter will shut off.

But assume the inverter remains operational. If more power is available from the PV system than is required to service the building's loads, then it will seek to go somewhere (normally onto the grid when the grid is connected).

FIGURE 4-18:

CONNECTING A GRID-TIED PV SYSTEM WITH A GENERATOR

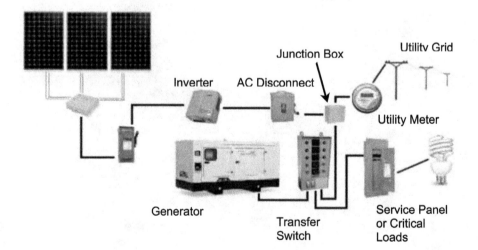

Since the grid is down (which has caused the generator to kick on), the excess power from the array, with no place to go, will cause a rise in the system voltage. This will in turn cause the inverter to shut down, as the system is now out of operational limits. So unless the generated power from the array is always less than the load demands of the business or home, a PV system connected in this fashion has no chance of working properly.

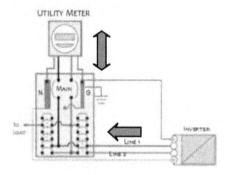

FIGURE 4-19: GRID-TIED SOLAR ARRAY INVERTER LOAD-SIDE CONNECTED TO THE MAIN SERVICE PANEL

That is the best case scenario. Worst case, the inverter may damage the generator by feeding power into the unit, or the generator may damage the inverter by backfeeding power into that device.

Normally the best method of connection when a generator is present is to connect the grid-tied PV system ahead of the generator transfer switch and the subpanel feeding the critical loads. Make the connection between the meter and the generator's transfer switch as illustrated in Figure 4-18.

A typical load-side connected grid-tied PV system is connected to a breaker within the existing service panel, as shown in Figure 4-19. The inverter is designed in such a way that it cannot be backfed by the utility.

If a generator is installed as shown in Figure 4-20, by incorporating a transfer switch between the meter and the main disconnect, the generator as well as the array can work together in powering loads. However there is a possibility the generator will backfeed power to the PV system when the system is isolated from the grid.

Alternatively, if the array is producing more power than the loads can handle, the system may attempt to backfeed the generator. Either situation may result in damaged equipment.

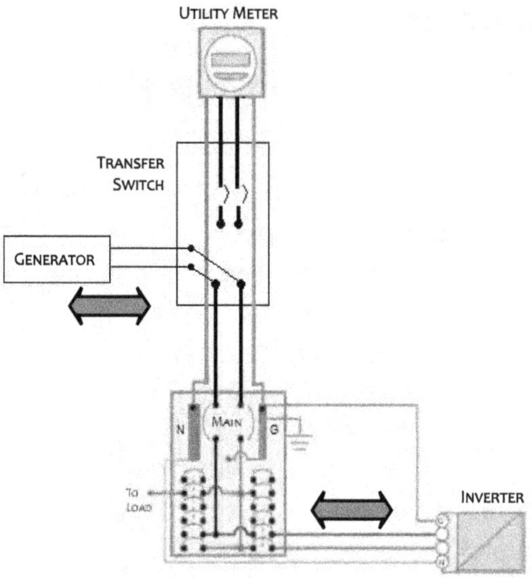

FIGURE 4-20: GENERATOR HOOKED UP TO A TRANSFER SWITCH. NOTE THAT WHEN CONNECTED IN THIS FASHION, THE PV ARRAY AND THE GENERATOR CAN BACKFEED.

By moving the PV connection to the supply side of the transfer switch, as illustrated in Figure 4-21, the PV array and inverter are physically isolated from the generator when it is in operation.

A fused disconnect should be located between the inverter and the supply side connection in the transfer

FIGURE 4-21:
GENERATOR AND PV
ARRAY CONNECTED
WITHIN TRANSFER
SWITCH SO THEY ARE
ISOLATED FROM EACH
OTHER

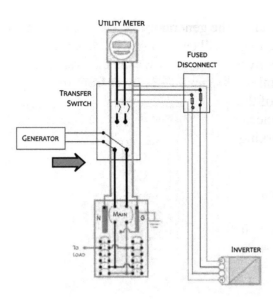

switch. The rating on the fuse will be the same amperage as the load side connected breaker.

When connected in this manner, when the grid goes down, the PV system goes down as well. The transfer switch disconnects the building from the grid, and in this case, from the PV system. The generator will service all the loads while the grid is down.

A standby generator may be the best alternative at sites that regularly experience multi-day power outages, as generators generally offer more available energy than a typical battery bank. Generators also tend to be less expensive than a comparable solar battery storage system.

However, for short duration outages, load shifting and peak shaving, an integrated battery storage system is a better choice. Plus, a battery can operate in tandem with a solar array when the grid is down - something a generator cannot do.

Many inverter/chargers now incorporate generator connection options. However generator controls (for loads and/or charging batteries) are controlled by battery voltage - so batteries are still required in these systems.

Microgrids

MICROGRID

Another system configuration that will transform the way energy is distributed is the **microgrid**.

A microgrid normally refers to small power systems that use local generation resources to meet local electricity needs. This definition could apply to any PV system that services a home or business, but in microgrids the concept is expanded over a wider area, such as a campus, military outpost, industrial center or even a community or village.

In practice, microgrids are typically developed and owned by a single entity, such as a university. But they may have multiple owners installing and controlling various pieces of the system.

Microgrids can and often do interact with the larger grid - or they may operate as their own separate mini-utility (a remote off-grid microgrid). The later is common when installed on islands or remote villages that have no access to the grid.

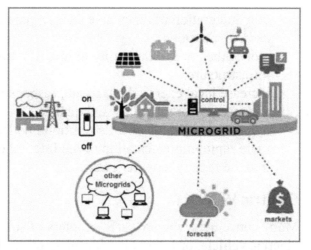

FIGURE 4-22: GRID CONNECTED MICROGRID

(*SOURCE: BERKELEY LABS, USDOE*)

If the microgrid interacts with the grid (as illustrated in Figure 4-22), its purpose will likely be similar to that of a PV system installed in a home or business; that is to provide power to the campus (or industrial park, or sub-division, etc.) while the grid is operational as well as supply emergency backup power when the grid goes down.

The microgrid is the logical extension of an electrical system that is transitioning from large centralized power sources to smaller distributed energy sources.

The electrical grid can be described in three large subsets. First is power generation. Then the transmission system, high-voltage lines that take power from the centralized power stations to the distribution system. And finally the lower-voltage distribution system that distributes bulk power to individual customers.

In a microgrid the power generation is localized, so the transmission system is unnecessary. Without any large infrastructure to maintain or repair, a microgrid is effectively hardened against widespread disruptions or natural disasters.

The **point of common coupling (PCC)** is where a microgrid connects to the main grid. In connected mode, the two systems operate in parallel, with the PCC maintaining equal voltage signals in both.

POINT OF COMMON COUPLING (PCC)

Like a grid-coupled PV system installed on a single building, the microgrid can import and export electricity from the parent grid in response to price signals or load demand. When the grid goes down, the microgrid can operate independently, drawing on local generation and storage capacity.

Benefits of microgrids include:
- resilience, as microgrids can temporarily disconnect from the central grid. Each microgrid can continue supplying power from their own generation sources or battery storage meeting local energy demand during widespread outages.
- local control over access to energy sources,

- easy integration of renewable energy generation sources - reducing global carbon emissions,
- reduce the need of the utility to invest in transmission and distribution infrastructure,
- increase local energy demand and response efficiency,
- enhance power reliability and quality,
- reduce transmission and distribution line losses,
- more rapid implementation of the Internet of Things (IoT) technologies into the facility's operations.

Electric Vehicles

ELECTRIC VEHICLE (EV)

Many consumers who are early adopters of solar energy are also drawn to the **electric vehicle**, or EV market for many of the same reasons. This technology, like solar, promises a low carbon alternative at an increasingly affordable price.

Purchases of EVs doubled in 2020, however total EVs on the road still represent a small portion, only 2.8% of all the vehicles registered. This is poised to change, however.

Nearly every major auto manufacturer has announced plans to transition their passenger car line to electric. Projections show that by 2025, sales of EVs will likely climb to 10% of all vehicles sold in the US with prices at or below the cost of internal combustion vehicles. By 2040 it is estimated EVs will account for more than a third of all vehicles purchased worldwide.

As the vehicle fleet transitions from oil to electric, increased electrical demand (projected in Figure 4-23) will place even more strain on an already stressed electric grid.

FIGURE 4-23: ANNUAL GLOBAL ELECTRICITY DEMAND FROM ELECTRIC VEHICLES (TWH)

(SOURCE: BLOOMBERG NEWS ENERGY FINANCE)

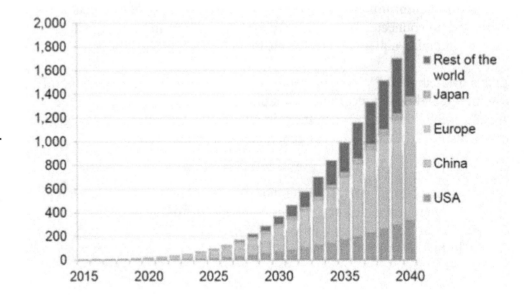

The average EV uses about 30 kWh of charge to travel approximately 100 miles. And according to government statistics, the average American drives about 30 miles per day. So it is fair to assume charging an EV will add about 10 kWh to the facility's daily load demand (per vehicle). This increased load demand should be factored in when designing a PV system.

EV Charging Stations

Recharging electric vehicles (EVs) is accomplished by connecting to **electric vehicle supply equipment (EVSE)**. From the perspective of the PV installer/designer, these charging stations often simply represent one more load in the system.

ELECTRIC VEHICLE
SUPPLY EQUIPMENT
(EVSE)

These charging stations can take a number of forms.

Level 1, 120-Volt Charging

This option is the simplest form of charging and requires nothing but an ordinary 120 Vac outlet on a 20 amp circuit. These units, similar to that pictured in Figure 4-24, are supplied by the vehicle's manufacturer. **Level 1 charging** stations normally draw about 1.4 kW when charging.

LEVEL 1 CHARGING

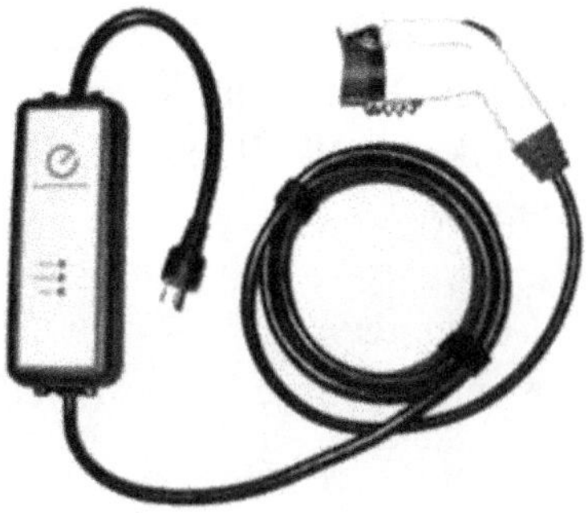

These systems are typically located in homes or employee parking lots and take 6-10 hours to fully charge a vehicle.

FIGURE 4-24: LEVEL 1 EV CHARGING CONNECTOR

Advantages
- low installation cost,
- low impact on utility peak demand charges.

Disadvantages
- charging is slow - around 3-5 miles (5-8 km) of range added per hour of charging.

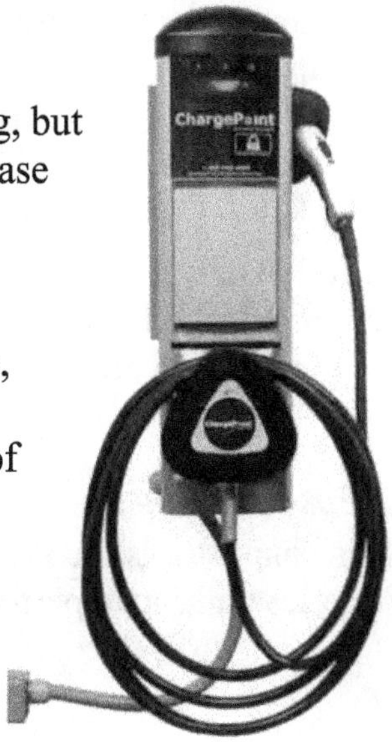

Level 2, 208/240-Volt Charging

Level 2 charging is much faster than Level 1 charging, but requires a 208 Vac three-phase or 240 Vac single-phase power connection.

FIGURE 4-25: LEVEL 2 EV CHARGING STATION

Level 2 charging stations, such as Figure 4-25 can theoretically provide up to 80 amps of current to EVs, although most operate only at about 30 amps. The rating of the unit will determine the ampacity rating of the circuit to which it is connected.

LEVEL 2 CHARGING

These systems are typically located in homes, shopping centers, or commuter parking lots and take 1-3 hours to fully charge a vehicle.

Advantages:
- charge time is significantly faster than Level 1. EVs will get between 10-20 miles (16-32 km) of range per hour of charge,
- more energy efficient than Level 1.

Disadvantages:
- installation costs are much higher than Level 1. This may potentially impact utility peak demand charges by creating a significant spike in demand.

DC Fast-Charging

DC FAST-CHARGING

FIGURE 4-26: DC FAST-CHARGING EV CHARGING STATION

DC fast-charging (sometimes called Level 3) equipment delivers high power directly into an EV's battery system, bypassing the need for a rectifier (that converts AC power from the grid to DC power that can be used in batteries). Charging speeds can be very fast, normally about 80% charge within 30 minutes.

These systems, as shown in Figure 4-26, are typically located in designated charging facilities and take about 30 minutes to fully charge a vehicle.

Advantages:
- charge time is dramatically reduced.

Disadvantages:
- much higher equipment and installation costs, ranging from $20,000-$100,000.
- potential for higher demand charges.
- competing standards are confusing to EV buyers and charging station operators.
- cold weather may require increased charging time.

Level 1 & 2 EV Charging Station Connector Types

Unfortunately, not all EVs use the same plug type while charging. Tesla and auto makers in Japan and Germany each use different plugs and communication protocols to link batteries to chargers, as illustrated in Figure 4-27.

SAE J1772 (Type 1)

This connector is the industry standard for all electric vehicles from North America and Japan performing Level 1 or Level 2 charging (home use).

Mennekes (Type 2)

The Mennekes Type 2 charger is the standard within Europe and most of the world outside North America and China. It is also used for Level 1 and Level 2 charging of Tesla models.

GB-T

The Level 1 and Level 2 charger is the standard for vehicles manufactured in China. After 2019, Tesla vehicles sold in China also are compatible with this charging standard.

Level 3 Fast Charge Connectors

Level 3 charging stations provide fast charging using DC current. Not all EVs are equipped to accept this form of charging.

CHAdeMO

This is the first of fast charging connectors originally implemented to be the industry standard. It was developed through the collaboration of five different Japanese automakers. As a result, the **CHAdeMO** (an abbreviation of CHArge de Move) connector remains the standard in Japan and on EVs from Japanese manufacturers. This includes automakers such as Toyota, Mitsubishi, Subaru, and Nissan.

CHADEMO

Combined Charging System (CCS)

Shortly after the CHAdeMO was introduced, a second Level 3 connector called the **Combined Charging System (CCS)** was developed. The CCS connectors differ from CHAdeMO in that they allow for AC/DC charging on the same port. CHAdeMO-equipped EVs require an additional J1772 connector cord to achieve Level 1 or 2 charging. This connector is the preferred mode of Level 3 charging for European and American vehicles, including BMW, Ford, Jaguar, GM, Volkswagen, and Tesla.

COMBINED CHARGING SYSTEM (CCS)

Tesla SC (SuperCharger)

This proprietary connector exists on all Tesla models in North America, although Tesla does offer CHAdeMO and CCS adapters for certain markets.

J1772 (Type 1)

Level: 1 and 2

Compatibility: 100% of electric cars from North America & Japan

Tesla: With adapter

Mennekes (Type 2)

Level: 1 and 2

Compatibility: electric cars from Europe

Tesla: Yes

GB-T

Level: 1 and 2

Compatibility: electric cars from China

Tesla: after 2019

CSS

Level: 1, 2 and 3

Compatibility: selected European & American cars

Tesla: Yes

CHAdeMO

Level: 3

Compatibility: selected Japanese cars

Tesla: with adapter

Tesla SC

Level: 3

Compatibility: only Tesla

FIGURE 4-27: CONNECTOR CONFIGURATIONS FOR VARIOUS EV CHARGING

| SMART CHARGING (V1G) | **Smart charging** is where the rate and/or time at which a vehicle is charged can be controlled while the vehicle is plugged in and involves the one way flow of energy from the charger to the car. This is referred to as uni-directional or V1G. |

Smart charging is where the rate and/or time at which a vehicle is charged can be controlled while the vehicle is plugged in and involves the one way flow of energy from the charger to the car. This is referred to as uni-directional or V1G.

The rate or time of the charging can be modified based on user settings to charge when electricity is cheapest, cleanest or in response to signals from the utility.

Vehicle to Grid (V2G)

Vehicle-to-grid (V2G) is a charging system in which plug-in electric vehicles can not only draw power from the utility, but can also export power from the vehicle to the grid. The vehicle can either return electricity to the grid (selling power during periods of peak load demand) or throttle their charging rate during periods of high energy cost (as is also possible using V1G).

Different terms are used to describe the various options where systems can draw energy from EV batteries.

Often referred to as V2X (to describe the concept in total) examples include:
- V2G: Vehicle-to-grid
- **V2H: Vehicle-to-Home**
- **V2B: Vehicle-to-Building / Business.**
- V2V: Vehicle-to-Vehicle
- V2X: Vehicle-to-everything

Vehicle-to-Home (V2H) or Vehicle-to Building (V2B) taps into the battery bank in the electric (EV) or **plug-in hybrid (PHV)** vehicles, using them as a replacement for a stationary energy storage system for a grid interactive system.

The fleet of electric vehicles can serve as a distributed storage system, since most vehicles are parked (and therefore could be connected to the grid) for about 23 hours each day.

V2G storage capabilities can also enable EVs to store and discharge power from solar arrays, serving as the battery backup for the home or business. Not only can this storage resource allow utilities to respond to fluctuations in load demand, the charging and discharging of EV batteries can assist in frequency regulation.

The Rocky Mountain Institute (RMI) has estimated that electrifying all of the light duty vehicles on US roads today would increase annual electricity demand by about 25%. This figure does not take into account all the medium and heavy-duty transportation needs, such as freight and public transit.

The rapid addition of such a significant load demand and changing load demand profiles present significant challenges to utilities. One projection by the consulting firm Wood Mackenzie, for example, predicted that just a quarter of a percent of Texas' cars charging simultaneously could crash the grid.

While the electrification of transportation will dramatically increase load demand on the grid, it also represents a tremendous potential storage resource.

It is estimated that by 2040 there will be around 200 million EVs in use worldwide, representing approximately 7 TWh of storage capacity.

Globally, loads draw about 15 TW of power at any one moment - so the combined storage capacity of EVs could, in theory, provide backup to approximately half the current loads (at least for a brief period of time).

V2X requires four things to function properly:
- a V2G enabled vehicle,
- a bi-directional charger,
- a communication system or 'protocol', such that the grid can communicate to the EV and vice versa, and
- a control system.

Challenges Facing V2G
While the advantages of tapping into the emerging EV storage resource are profound, so to are the challenges the industry faces if this is to become a reality.

Challenges include:

- Warranty issues. A significant barrier to V2G is the lack of **original equipment manufacturer (OEM)** support. Not all EVs and PHVs are compatible with V2G. The auto and utility industries have not agreed on standards. As of 2020, only two vehicles, the Nissan Leaf and Mitsubishi Outlander were equipped with V2G capability. In September 2020, Tesla unveiled a new EV battery design that allows for adaptation to the V2G technology. However, the V2G-compatible batteries are not anticipated to be in production until 2023.

  ORIGINAL EQUIPMENT
  MANUFACTURER
  (OEM)

- Standardization. To export the energy, the EV battery and the charger must communicate with each other, as well as with the grid. This is done using standardized communication protocols. At present there are at least four communication standards and protocols used widely in the EV market for DC charging. These are ChaDeMo (Japanese), CCS (EU and US), GB/T (Chinese) and Tesla (worldwide) Of these, only the ChaDeMo protocol currently supports V2X. The CCS protocol is planned to support V2H from 2020 and V2G from 2025, with testing ongoing on a draft form of the protocol.

- Lack of harmonization within the electric utility industry. EVs are mobile while utilities are not. Utilities and wholesale power markets must define what services they want, simplify rules for participation, and provide adequate compensation.

- Lack of EV owner interest. Most EV owners will likely not educate themselves as to the value of V2G or will be unwilling to risk their expensive EV by connecting it to the grid.

- Expensive charging stations. Early V2G-capable chargers are significantly more expensive than standard units. For example, the Wallbox residential V2G-capable L2 unit retails for around $4,000, compared to a V1G-capable EnelX Juicebox, which sells for approximately $650.

- AC or DC? Batteries store and export DC power. The grid and typical loads generate or use AC power. So power must be converted to DC when charging an EV and inverted to AC when exporting power from the EV. This can either be done in the charging station or within the vehicle itself. Currently different vehicles handle this process in different ways. Without a standard process, an effective V2G system will be difficult to achieve.

- Range Anxiety. EV owners are concerned that the use of the vehicle's storage capacity may drain the battery of the vehicle to a point where its range may be limited when needed. With this in mind, these systems typically limit discharge so the battery will always be charged to 70-90% of its capacity.

- Impact on battery life. The impact of V2X on EV batteries is a concern for vehicle owners. Many studies have been conducted on this issue, and most studies show that with proper controls, the life of the battery will not be significantly impacted by V2X.

Chapter 4 Review Questions

1) The situation where a distributed energy system is exporting energy to the grid when the grid is "down" or not functioning is known as:
   a) net metering
   b) decoupling
   c) phase unbalance
   d) islanding

2) Rapid shutdown provisions require that:
   a) all PV systems be equipped with MLPE devices on each panel
   b) all PV inverters must stop generating power once they sense that the grid is "down"
   c) all conductors leading from the array must have zero voltage present within 30 seconds of the main disconnect shut down
   d) no conductor within the array boundary can have a voltage greater than 80 Vdc once rapid shutdown has been initiated

3) A PV system that incorporates batteries and is designed to run critical loads only when the power from the grid is interrupted is called a:
   a) DC coupled system
   b) grid coupled system
   c) stand alone system
   d) critical load system

4) The transfer switch that automatically disconnects the PV system from the grid in the event of a power outage is often referred to as a:
   a) rapid shutdown initiator
   b) autotransformer
   c) current transformer
   d) DC/AC coupler

5) Which of the following is **NOT** a situation where incorporating an AC-coupled or DC-coupled system may be the appropriate solution?
   a) time of use shifting
   b) peak demand reduction
   c) where net metering is not allowed
   d) to improve the efficiency of the system

6) When batteries are incorporated into a system to store energy during periods when power from the grid is less expensive, to then be used when power from the grid is relatively more expensive is known as:
   a) peak shaving
   b) self-consumption
   c) load shifting
   d) time-of-use pricing

7) The device used to monitor the amount of energy flowing through a conductor is referred to as:
   a) current transformer (CT)
   b) module-level power electronics (MLPE)
   c) voltage regulator (VR)
   d) maximum power point tracking systems (MPPT)

8) A customer wishes to install a battery backup system that will provide 6 hours of backup power to critical loads should the grid goes down. A load assessment has been conducted and it has been found that the critical loads draw 3.5 kWh per hour when operating. The following also apply:
   - the total system derate is 87%
   - the array receives 3.78 hours of insolation each day
   - the monthly load demand is 1,525 kWh
   - the nominal voltage of the battery bank to be configured is 48 Vdc
   - the site has a power factor of .96
   - the depth of discharge of the battery bank will be set to 90%
   - the array is 35 kW in size
   - the inverter used is 98% efficient
   - The lowest temperature ever experienced on site is -35°C

   To what size (in amp-hours) should the battery bank be configured?
   a) 385.87 Ah
   b) 437.5 Ah
   c) 496 Ah
   d) 502.87 Ah

9) Lead acid deep cycle batteries should be charged at a rate no faster than _____ to avoid damaging them and shortening their functional life.
   a) C1
   b) C5
   c) C10
   d) C20

10) When designing an AC or DC coupled system, rapid shutdown provisions require:
   a) that a rapid shutdown initiator be installed within 1 foot of the array boundary
   b) that no more than 30 volts be present on the battery output circuit within 30 seconds of disconnecting the system from the grid
   c) that a second rapid shutdown initiator be installed that shuts down the battery bank
   d) rapid shutdown does not apply when the system is operating as a stand alone system.

11) Which of the following is **NOT** a form of load management?
   a) critical load panels
   b) frequency-based decentralized controllers
   c) ripple control
   d) plug and process loads

12) Which of the following is **NOT** an advantage of incorporating microinverters into a large array?
   a) no risk of arc faults
   b) no risk of ground faults
   c) automatic compliance with rapid shutdown requirements
   d) automatic phase imbalance correction within 3-phase systems

13) A subarray that has two output conductors, one positive and one negative is referred to as a:
   a) monopole subarray
   b) bipolar subarray
   c) DC coupled subarray
   d) branch circuit subarray

14) Which of the following is **NOT** an advantage of designing a system with multiple inverters rather than one single larger inverter?
   a) no single point of failure
   b) component performance monitoring is less difficult
   c) each subarray can have unique panels (not all panels need to be uniform)
   d) AC wiring of the system is less complex

15) A PV system that combines the lower voltages of multiple subarrays to provide a higher total system output voltage is known as a:
   a) monopole subarray
   b) bipolar subarray
   c) DC coupled subarray
   d) branch circuit subarray

16) Which of the following is **NOT** a typical function of a commercial-scale remote monitoring system?
   a) monitor the system's technical and financial performance
   b) provide real time data about individual components performance
   c) allow for remote rapid shutdown and anti-islanding control
   d) dispatch repair crews in the event of a system malfunction

17) In order to avoid the risk of backfeeding a generator connected to a PV array, the designer of the system should:
   a) select a generator that incorporates a diode to prevent backfeeding
   b) connect the PV system on the supply side of the transfer switch
   c) connect the generator to a separate breaker on the service panel
   d) incorporate a fused disconnect between the inverter and the generator

18) A microgrid connects to the main grid at the:
    a) point of common coupling
    b) distribution transformer
    c) distribution sub-station
    d) transmission sub-station

19) Which of the following is **NOT** a common Level 3 charging station connector configuration?
    a) SAE J1772
    b) CHAdeMO
    c) combined charging system (CCS)
    d) Tesla SuperCharger

20) The smart charging of electric vehicles is sometimes referred to as:
    a) V2X
    b) V1G
    c) V2G
    d) V2B

21) Which of the following is **NOT** a major challenge that must be overcome if V2G is to gain widespread adoption?
    a) lack of industry standardization
    b) the technology is not yet ready to handle bi-directional charging
    c) EV manufacturer's warranties may not support bi-directional charging
    d) lack of EV owner interest in and/or understanding of V2G technology

- Identify the issues to address during a site survey.
- Understand how to conduct a remote site survey.
- Define the advantages and disadvantages of various types of roof mounted systems.
- Examine the impact of the structure's design and condition.
- Understand loading and setback restrictions.
- Determine inter-row shading and ground cover ratios.
- Calculate the amount of space required for the array.
- Identify concerns when constructing a ground mounted system.
- Explore the unique issues involved with tracking systems.
- Calculate the total solar resource fraction of the site.
- Determine the location of the balance of systems.
- Evaluate factors effecting load side and supply side connections
- Understand requirements for battery storage.
- Explore the use of drones in solar.

Chapter 5

Conducting a Site Survey

Now it is time to take a look at the specific site to see if it is appropriate for a photovoltaic system, and if so, determine what system is best for this particular application and location. In other words, time to conduct a **site survey**.

SITE SURVEY

Site Assessment Checklist

Most installer/designers develop a checklist of information about the client and the site that will be crucial in designing a PV system for that location.

Much of this information may be gathered remotely, but many critical items can only be assessed by physically inspecting the site.

Document all aspects of the site with photos for later reference.

Common details gathered during a site survey include:
- contact name and physical location of the project,
- percentage of load to be offset by the PV array,
- electric utility servicing the property (if grid-tied),
- permits required and the authority having jurisdiction (AHJ),
- any deed restrictions, city ordinances, utility restrictions, historical designations or other items that may affect the installation of a PV system on the property,
- historic or environmental concerns,
- desired mounting option (roof, ground, BIPV, etc),

- will battery backup be incorporated into the system?
- location of the point of connection to the grid (usually the electric meter),
- location of the inverter(s),
- location of the balance of systems (BOS), for example the disconnects, conduit raceways, etc,
- shading issues,
- preliminary hazard assessment,
- esthetic issues to address,
- location of the service panel(s), size of service available (100A, 200A, etc.), and suitability of existing panel to receive input from a solar array,
- distance between the array and the service panel (or point of connection).

For a roof mounted system, additional information will be required such as:
- pitch (angle) and orientation (azimuth) of the roof,
- available space on the roof,
- roof obstructions (dormers, air conditioning units, etc.),
- access issues to the roof,
- roof type (shingle, metal, built up, flat, etc.),
- age and condition of the roof,
- rafter size, type and spacing,
- height of roof.

For ground mounted systems, a site assessment will observe:
- space available,
- soil type and condition,
- slope of the desired location for the array,
- drainage issues,
- is a fence required?

Specific attention should be paid to the existing electrical service panel. Items to note include:
- Manufacturer,
- busbar rating,
- amp service from the utility (main breaker rating),
- available space in the unit to add breakers,
- type of service and voltage (for example, 3-phase 208 V or single-phase 240 V),
- existence of a sub-panel and distance from the main panel if applicable,
- existing grounding type and location.

Issues to Address

A complete site assessment involves more than simply determining the physical layout of the system. There are a number of additional concerns which will require a bit of research.

These issues involve:
- ownership of the property and system,
- local rules and regulations,
- insurance concerns,
- utility connection process and restrictions.

Ownership Issues

Who owns the building and under what terms is often a large factor in whether it is suitable for solar.

Own versus Rent

The majority of businesses lease the property where they are located rather than own. In the US, 36% rent rather than own their homes.

Most commercial leases range from 3-5 years in duration, while residential leases are generally year-to-year. Clearly, with such limited agreements, renters are hesitant to invest in a system that will take 7-10 years to pay for itself.

In a rental situation, the benefits of solar may accrue to both the landlord and the tenant, but how they each benefit will be effected by the structure of the lease.

Benefits to landlords may include:
- reduced exposure to rising energy prices,
- enhancing the marketability of the building (can be marketed as a "green lease"),
- lowers occupancy costs which may result in the ability to charge higher rent,
- improves tenant retention due to lower operating expenses.

Benefits to tenants may include:
- lower electricity costs,
- predictable electricity costs for budgeting purposes,
- supporting corporate or personal sustainability goals,
- demonstrating environmental responsibility to employees and/or the community.

While the benefits may be clear, there are also significant barriers when seeking to install solar on a leased property. These include:

- Multiple parties are involved in the decision making process, often with very different motivations.

- Leases often require the tenant pay all utilities, so the building owner may see little benefit in sharing in the cost of a solar installation.

- The tenant (if paying for the system) may require a very short payback period on the investment, as their lease may not extend beyond five years.

- Most commercial property owners are limited liability companies (LLC). If the system is to be financed, there may be significant concerns that the property will continue to make payments if they lose their tenant(s).

- Many LLCs that own and manage commercial and multi-family properties are set up in such a way as to have limited tax liability. So the federal investment tax credit on solar may have no benefit.

Third party PV system ownership is a very common way to install solar on leased buildings. In third party ownership, a solar developer owns the system and then sells the power to either the landlord, the tenant, or the utility (depending on how the lease agreement is structured).

Having a third party involved can eliminate the short term system payback requirement and introduces an owner that can monetize the tax benefits of system ownership.

Title Concerns

In real estate, a clear title on a property is important to any potential sale or transfer. The addition of solar on the property may have implications in this regard.

FIXTURE

If the solar array system is considered personal property, then it adds no value to the property itself. But if it is considered a **fixture**, it may affect the property value. This distinction should be spelled out clearly in any agreement between the building owner, the tenant and/or solar leasing company.

If a building owner leases a PV system, the leasing contract often states that any property transfers are contingent on the new buyer being eligible to continue with the leased equipment. If the buyer is not approved, the owner of the building must buy the panels from the leasing company.

Guaranteeing access to sunlight is fast becoming an important part of property ownership. The most practical solution to the problem is the negotiation of solar easements between property owners.

Under such an agreement, the property owner who has installed a solar array receives assurances from the neighboring property owner that the sunlight which travels over the neighbor's property would always be available. The neighbor, and all subsequent owners, would be restricted in building or planting trees which could block the sunlight.

Some states have legally permitted the creation of solar easements. In such cases, title insurance is an important tool for establishing and enforcing continued access to the available solar resource.

Legal Issues

Local private and government rules and regulations (with regards to planning, zoning, and development) can have a very significant impact on solar energy installations. They often discourage solar energy projects by increasing the time and expense required for solar installations.

Local Rules and Regulations

Zoning ordinances often specify what type of development is permitted by-right within particular zoning categories. The local AHJ may have adopted rules that include small rooftop and ground-mounted solar installations as by-right development in all major zoning districts.

If so, this streamlines the process for permitting solar PV systems. If this is not the case, then a zoning review may be required before the project can proceed.

Local government, office parks or home owners associations may also place restrictions on PV systems that address:

- Aesthetics. For example, many zoning codes require screening for rooftop mechanical equipment. Some communities may require flush-mounted systems where modules must be mounted parallel to the plane of the roof.

- Height. Height restrictions may block the construction of some solar PV installations if the building is already at the maximum allowed height.

- Shading. There may be strong regulations in place supported by tree preservationists and urban foresters that limit a property owner's right to remove or trim trees that may impact a solar array.

- Ground mounted systems. Some communities choose to restrict ground-mounted solar in residential and commercial zoned districts. Even where permitted, ground mounted installations may present additional considerations and regulations such as grading, set back requirements, and storm water management. Many communities limit the percentage of the lot that may be covered by buildings or impervious surfaces. Generally, ground-mounted PV arrays are considered impervious surfaces.

Historic Districts

More than 2,400 local jurisdictions have historic preservation ordinances that require a special review of projects proposed within historic districts.

If the zoning code does not address solar installations within historic districts, it is safe to assume that solar is not allowed.

Insurance issues

As permanent attachment, rooftop solar arrays are typically considered part of the building (a fixture). As such, they are normally covered by property insurance against losses due to wind, hail, lightning, vandalism, broken tree limbs, fire, etc. This assumes they are owned by the building owner. Leased panels must be insured by the provider.

Systems that are not located on the insured building, such as covered parking or ground mounted arrays, may be considered out buildings or personal property, and should be specifically listed on the policy to ensure full coverage.

Some commercial policies are reluctant to insure solar arrays for a number of reasons. They present a risk that's relatively new in the realm of insurance. There is limited data to the true risk involved so insurance companies may simply wish to avoid the unknown.

Also, solar panels generate electricity. There is an added risk (in addition to simple replacement costs) of fire and/or personal injury.

Ground mounted systems further add the risk of vandalism and/or theft.

There are a number of insurance products that may or may not be associated with a solar project. These include:

GENERAL LIABILITY
INSURANCE

- **General Liability Insurance.** General liability provides coverage for the death or injury to persons or damage to property owned by third parties. Rooftop installations typically require additional liability insurance given the risks involved in working from height the higher likelihood of damage from high winds.

PROPERTY RISK
INSURANCE

- **Property Risk Insurance.** This type of insurance covers the policy holder against losses due to theft, vandalism and natural disaster (such as weather events).

ENVIRONMENTAL
RISK INSURANCE

- **Environmental Risk Insurance.** More common in larger developments, Environmental damage coverage protects system owners from costs associated with environmental damage done by their development or preexisting issues that become apparent due to the development of the site. These costs may include cleanup, restoration, as well as injuries (illnesses) that result from the pollution.

BUSINESS
INTERRUPTION
INSURANCE

- **Business Interruption Insurance.** Business interruption insurance is often required to protect the cash flow during the development of the project, or for the commercial enterprise that relies on the array for electricity.

Utility Issues

The utility will require that certain conditions be met before the interconnection process may begin. These may include:

- Does the applicant have control of the site? If the applicant is the site owner, then this is not an issue. But third-party developers must have secured all required leases before the process can begin.

- What size system will be installed (kW) and how much variability exists around that amount? Utilities may have different application processes for different sized systems, and may also restrict the production to a percentage of site consumption.

- Where is the expected **point of interconnection (POI)** or point of common coupling (PCC)?

- Is it anticipated that the system will export power from the site (as in a power purchase agreement) or will the power be used on site only?

- What type of inverter will be used? The inverter will need to comply with UL 1741 or UL 1741-SA depending on the requirements of the utility.

- The utility may wish to see a one-line drawing of the system even before beginning the formal application process.

- The utility may also require the installer be licensed or certified.

- General liability insurance may be required to protect the property owner and the grid.

- There will generally be an application fee, often based on the size of the proposed system.

Application process

If the system is to be connected to the grid, an interconnection application must be submitted to the local utility. This application should be one of the first steps in the development process, to ensure the system is approved and does not sit idle while waiting for the utility to approve it.

The application process varies widely from state to state and utility to utility.

There is generally a simplified screening process in place, but if the project falls outside this process and requires supplemental review, the applicant might be required to pay for the cost of that review.

In areas where there are already a significant number of solar installations, the application process may require an engineering review to determine if the distribution system requires upgrades (such as larger wire or upgraded transformers).

The cost of these upgrades may be passed on to the PV system developer. Power pole transformers cost anywhere from $3,000 to $7,000 each, depending on how much electricity they're designed to handle.

> POINT OF
> INTERCONNECTION
> (POI)

Load/Power Factor Review

Under certain circumstances, adding a PV array to a facility may result in a lower power factor as measured by the utility. Utilities often require large commercial or industrial customers not fall below a pre-determined power factor or they will be assessed under a different (and more expensive) rate schedule.

Most larger inverters are programmable, allowing the installer to minimize the effect of the system on the power factor of the facility. If this is not possible, the installer may need to add power-factor-correcting capacitors to the facility.

Remote Site Assessment

REMOTE SITE ASSESSMENT

Most designers begin the process by first conducting a **remote site assessment**. While not a substitute for a comprehensive on-site assessment, it can provide a rough estimate of costs and issues to inspect closely when on site.

LIDAR

These online systems utilize Google Earth or **lidar** (light detection and ranging) data that creates a three-dimensional image of the property (as illustrated in Figure 5-1), allowing the designer to determine not only orientation, but the angle of the roof and height and shading effect from nearby trees and other obstructions.

Lidar is a remote sensing method that uses light in the form of a pulsed laser to measure variable distances on the Earth's surface. This light pulse data can generate precise, three-dimensional information about the shape and surface characteristics of the site.

FIGURE 5-1: REMOTE ASSESSMENT IMAGE CREATED USING LIDAR IMAGERY

NREL has estimated that remote assessment solar design software can save about $0.17/W per 5-kW system (or about $850 per install).

One concern with this process is that the lidar data may be out of date, making the assessment inaccurate and unreliable.

There are a number of systems available on the market - and each functions in slightly different ways. However the process for conducting a remote site assessment is fairly uniform.

After entering an address of the location in question, the system will bring up an image of the property (generally from Google Earth's database). The designer can use a tool to define the area where the array will likely be placed (either on the roof or on the ground).

Potential shading issues may be clear from the image or some systems incorporate a 3-D feature that allows the designer to see shading in three dimensions.

Once the array boundaries have been defined, system information such as the panel selected, the orientation and angle of the array, the height of the building, and setback limits can be entered. The system will then populate the defined area with panels (as illustrated in Figure 5-2) and estimate energy output for the array.

The designer can modify the system, changing orientation, altitude, setbacks, row spacing, ground cover ratio, or even change the selected panel if desired. Obstructions such as air conditioning units, access doorways, vent pipes or trees can be identified and some systems will even plot the shading from those objects and restrict panels from being placed within the shadow.

Nearly all remote assessment systems integrate data from PV Watts and generate an estimate of annual production based on the information entered and the data from PV Watts.

Some more advanced systems will allow designers to integrate inverters into the system as well as other balance of system equipment such as racking and disconnects. They can then generate a one-line drawing and/or CAD drawing of the system as well as an initial cost estimate.

FIGURE 5-2:
COMMERCIAL ROOFTOP SYSTEM DESIGNED USING REMOTE SITE ASSESSMENT TOOL

(FROM HELIOSCOPE)

Determine Available Sunlight (PVWatts)

The amount of sunlight striking any square meter of land at a specific location will vary from moment to moment.

SOLAR CONSTANT

At the outside edge of the earth's atmosphere the amount of energy in the sun's rays is on average (varies due to earth's elliptical orbit and is known as the **solar constant**) is about 1366 W/m². As sunlight passes through clouds, it is scattered by the atmosphere, or deflected back into space. The energy contained in it decreases. By the time it hits the earth's surface it usually will measure less than 1000 W/m². On a clear day it can measure more.

SOLAR IRRADIANCE

STANDARD TEST CONDITIONS

Solar irradiance, on a clear day, at sea level, when the temperature is 25ºC (77ºF) - is 1000 watts per square meter. These conditions (in the solar world) are referred to as **standard test conditions**. But the universe rarely provides such an ideal situation.

PLANE OF ARRAY

DIRECT NORMAL IRRADIANCE

DIFFUSE HORIZONTAL IRRADIANCE

REFLECTED IRRADIANCE

The **plane of array (POA)** is a term often used to quantify the total irradiance that falls on a given solar array. This term includes:
- **direct normal irradiance** - the sunlight that directly strikes the solar panel,
- **diffuse horizontal irradiance** - the indirect irradiance that strikes the panel that is the result of scattering within the atmosphere,
- **reflected irradiance** - the light energy hitting the panel that is reflected by nearby surface (often referred to as albedo).

PEAK SUN HOURS

So the accumulated total sunlight striking a square meter of earth over a 24-hour period, divided by 1000 watts (the ideal energy received in an hour) will provide the number of **peak sun hours** for a specific location.

Expressed mathematically, it is:

Peak Sun Hours = Total Daily Energy from the Sun (watts) / 1000 (watts)/hr

For example, if the total amount of energy from the sun hitting a square meter area (angled directly at the sun) in Nebraska during the month of October is measured, the answer for an average day will be about 4,760 watts. This would then be expressed as 4.76 hours of "ideal" sunlight received each day for that month.

Peak Sun Hours = 4,760 watts / 1000 watts/hr = 4.76 hrs

INSOLATION

The terms "peak sun hours", "irradiance" and **"insolation"** are sometimes used interchangeably.

Insolation is short for **in**coming **sol**ar radi**ation**.

The amount of energy hitting a solar panel will depend on its angle in relation to the horizon (**altitude**) and the direction it faces (**azimuth**). The angle is measured against a theoretically "flat" earth - so a panel lying on the ground would have an altitude of 0 degrees and a panel that is placed on a vertical wall would have an altitude of 90 degrees.

The azimuth is measured with solar north considered 0 degrees, so solar south would be at 180 degrees (east at 90 degrees and west at 270 degrees).

ALTITUDE

AZIMUTH

Nearly every remote site assessment system incorporates data from **PVWatts**. The PVWatts Calculator was developed by NREL, a national laboratory of the U.S. Department of Energy) and provides free of charge access to estimates of the energy production and cost of energy of grid-connected photovoltaic (PV) energy systems throughout the world.

PVWATTS

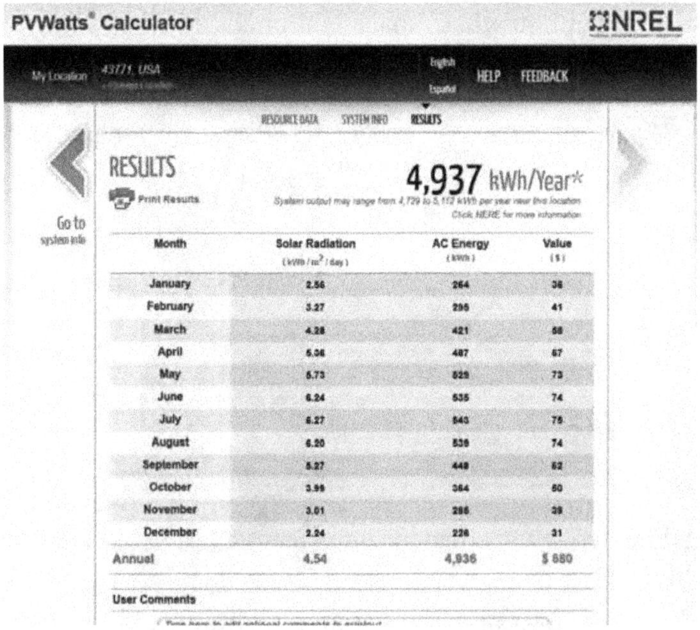

FIGURE 5-3: MONTHLY INSOLATION ESTIMATES FROM PVWATTS

The system asks for information such as the address of the site, the angle and azimuth of the array, system size, module type (standard, premium or thin-film), mounting type (fixed, roof mount, tracking), system efficiency (derate), inverter/load ratio, ground cover ratio and cost of electricity at the site.

Once the data is entered, the system will project the hours of insolation as well as the value of the energy produced for that site, as shown in Figure 5-3.

On Site Assessment

While much can be accomplished remotely, many issues can only be effectively evaluated by a physical **on site assessment** or site survey of the location where the system is to be placed.

ON SITE ASSESSMENT

Locating the System on the Site

The home or business owner may already have firm ideas regarding where the array should be located. This may or may not be the ideal spot for the array.

The greatest space requirements will be for the solar panel array itself. During the site inspection, it is important to determine where the array should be placed, as well as where all the remaining balance of system (BOS) should be located.

Mounting Options

There are several mounting options available when placing a PV array, with advantages and disadvantages for each option.

Roof Mounted Systems

Many PV systems are mounted on top of the building's roof. This is perhaps the best option where space is limited (no room for a ground-based system) or security is an issue (gets the array away from possible damage or theft).

FIGURE 5-4: EXAMPLE OF A PROPERLY DESIGNED ROOF-MOUNTED PV ARRAY

ROOFTOP ARRAY

FLUSH-TO-ROOF

For aesthetic purposes, it is best to mount the **rooftop array** parallel to the roof surface (**flush-to-roof**), centered and squared with the edges of the roof and the roof lines (as demonstrated in Figure 5-4).

Several concerns should be addressed when considering placement of an array on a rooftop. These include:

- Is the roof facing the right direction (south)?

- Is there enough available space on the roof to hold all the panels required?

- Is the angle of the roof appropriate for the desired pitch of the panels? If the pitch is too great (60 degrees, for example) it may give the array a winter bias when a summer bias is desired.

- Is the condition of the roof suitable to support the weight and stress of a PV system? Check the roof for wear and damage. A structural engineer may need to be called in to assess the building if it appears that it may not support the added weight or construction activity.

DEAD LOAD

LIVE LOAD

- The weight of a system is not just the weight of the panels and racking system themselves (referred to as **dead load**). Typically the dead load of a roof-mounted system (racks and panels) is about 3-5 pounds per square foot. Refer to the standard *ASCE 7 - Minimum Design Loads for Buildings and Other Structures* for additional guidance. The **live load** of the system may also include the weight of accumulated snow, as well as

FIGURE 5-5: PV
BALLASTED MOUNT
RACKING SYSTEM

(FROM IRON RIDGE)

the weight from the **lift force** and **drag force** of wind as it passes over the panels (acting a bit like the wing of an airplane).

LIFT FORCE

DRAG FORCE

WIND LOADING

- Wind forces might add as much as 50 pounds per square foot of **wind loading** force on the structure. Make sure the mounting hardware, screws, panels and roof structure can resist the forces that the system will impose on the building. This may be especially important in areas periodically exposed to very high winds.

- Determine the age of the existing roof. If the shingles or other roofing materials will need to be replaced in a few years, the PV system will need to be removed to accomplish this. It may be best to mount the system elsewhere, or wait until a new roof has been installed before installing a rooftop PV system.

- It is important to select a mounting system that allows at least three to six inches of air gap between the bottom of the panel and the surface of the roof. This allows for the **passive cooling** of the panels, and avoids any condensation, corrosion, or accumulation of debris (such as leaves).

PASSIVE COOLING

- Roof penetrations are also a problem. Most commercial mounting systems try to minimize the number of penetrations, to guard against leaking – but anytime a roof is penetrated, problems are bound to happen. On flat roofs (very common in commercial structures), penetration of the roof can be avoided by installing a **ballast mount system** such as the example shown in Figure 5-5. These systems rely on weights to hold them in place, rather than lag screws.

BALLASTED SYSTEM

Measuring the Angle of the Roof

When installing a system on a typical residential home, the existing angle and orientation of the roof will nearly always determine the altitude and azimuth of the array.

FIGURE 5-6:
DETERMINING THE PITCH
ANGLE OF A ROOF USING
A PHONE

In the past, fairly complicated calculations were required to determine the angle of the roof. Today, most smart phones can be outfitted with a free app

TABLE 5-1: ARRAY ANGLES THAT CORRESPOND TO COMMON RISE/RUN PITCH OF BUILDINGS

Array Angle	Roof Pitch	Array Angle	Roof Pitch
4.8°	1 rise / 12 run	30.3°	7 rise / 12 run
9.5°	2 rise / 12 run	33.7°	8 rise / 12 run
14°	3 rise / 12 run	36.9°	9 rise / 12 run
18.4°	4 rise / 12 run	39.8°	10 rise / 12 run
22.6°	5 rise / 12 run	42.5°	11 rise / 12 run
26.6°	6 rise / 12 run	45°	12 rise / 12 run

that gives the precise angle when placed against the roof decking, as demonstrated in Figure 5-6.

RISE AND RUN

The pitch of a roof (in construction terms) is generally referred to as a ratio between the **rise and run.**

For instance, if the pitch rises 4 inches vertically (the rise) for every 12 inches of horizontal distance (the run), the roof is said to have a 4:12 pitch. If it rises 12 inches vertically for every 12 inches horizontally, it has a 12:12 pitch.

Table 5-1 provides a handy conversion between this form of measurement and degrees of pitch.

Rafter Design

Many design tools and/or mounting systems require that the type of rafter, as well as its spacing be noted. This is because most pitched roof-mounted systems are designed to attach to the support rafter, in a manner similar to that shown in Figure 5-7.

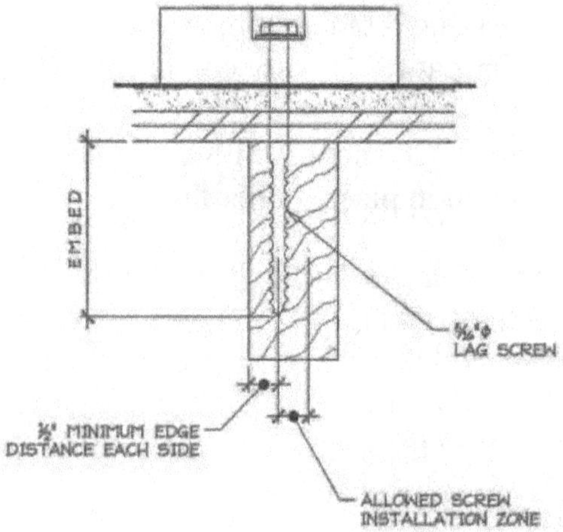

FIGURE 5-7: PV MOUNTING RACK FOOTER PROPERLY SECURED TO SUPPORT RAFTER

(FROM CALIFORNIA SOLAR PERMITTING GUIDEBOOK)

The lag bolts will normally be attached to the horizontal span of the rafter. But these rafters can be configured in a number of ways. It is important to understand the terminology used in describing the various styles of roof structures.

Typical pitched residential roof rafter systems include:

- manufactured wood roof truss,
- struts to wall below,
- simple attic,
- cathedral ceiling.

It is also important to note the spacing of the rafters (how far apart they are from each other) as well as the size of the wood used.

Normally in modern (post 1970) residential construction, the rafters will be spaced either 16 inches, 24 inches, or 36 inches on center (measured from the center of one rafter to the center of the next rafter).

The wood used will likely be a 2 x 4 (1.5 inches x 3.5 inches), 2 x 6 (1.5 inches x 5.5 inches) or a 2 x 8 (1.5 inches x 7.25 inches).

Affect of Orientation on MPPT

All panels in the array should, if possible, face the same direction. This will balance the output from the system. If this is not possible, balanced strings should be installed with independent **maximum power point tracking (MPPT)** (for example, one string of 12 panels facing west and one string of 12 panels facing east, independently controlled at the inverter). If there is only a single MPPT, then the output from the strings should be balanced (in this example, 2 strings, each with 6 panels facing east and 6 panels facing west).

> MAXIMUM POWER POINT TRACKING (MPPT)

Flat Roof Design

No two roofs are the same and requirements vary from state to state. It is common that authorities having jurisdiction set a minimum requirement for roofs to support a concentrated weight of 300 lbs.

Concentrated weight means that this load is placed directly on a single area on the roof. It is common, for example, that a commercial flat roof should be able to support a 300 lb HVAC unit that may only occupy one square meter (10 square feet) of roof space.

> CONCENTRATED WEIGHT

While this weight capacity is in most cases more than enough to handle the addition of a solar array, it should be noted that flat roofs are prone to snow build-up and water ponding. This is because a flat roof does not have a slope that takes advantage of gravity to allow snow or water to shed off down naturally. This can cause problems with wire management and placement of electrical connections.

Pre-Engineered Building

Often referred to as a **Butler style** building, this type of pre-engineered metal building are commonly used for light industrial or agricultural purposes, as shown in Figure 5-8. They are characterized by pre-engineered metal walls and/or wood pole barn construction.

Because metal buildings are designed for such tight weight tolerances, it is

FIGURE 5-8: EXAMPLE OF PRE-FABRICATED METAL OR BUTLER STYLE BUILDING

> BUTLER STYLE

necessary to be cautious when adding an array to this type of structure.

The International Existing Building Code (IEBC) allows for a 5% increase in loads to existing buildings. Because metal building roofs are constructed with lightweight materials, installing solar panels may exceed this limit.

Before beginning a project on a pre-fabricated building, it is necessary to have accurate information about the existing structure. The most economical way to get that information is from the original design drawings. If the original drawings are not available, then an assessment from a structural engineer may be required.

There may also be existing issues that will affect the building's load capacity. There may be missing parts and pieces, for instance sag angles or flange braces, and the overall structure may be weakened due to rust or poor maintenance. It may be necessary to reinforce/retrofit the secondary framing (purlins) or primary framing (moment frames or other structural members).

Age and Condition of Roof
According to the National Association of Home Builders (NAHB), asphalt shingle roofs last about 20 years. The life expectancy of a solar array is 25 years or longer.

Solar panels may actually extend the life of the roof by protecting it from exposure to the elements. Being protected from ultraviolet light, rain, hail and other forces that contribute to wear means the roof should last longer than it would otherwise.

One study found that, under solar panels, the temperature of a building's ceiling stayed five degrees cooler than the ceiling of a building without solar panels.

If the roof is more than five years old, the installer should consider having a professional evaluation done to determine whether it should be replaced prior to installing solar panels.

Roof Covering
Racking systems have been developed for nearly every conceivable type of roof covering available on the market.

Common sloped roof coverings include:
- shingles (asphalt, metal, composite),
- rolled asphalt,
- masonry tiles,
- Slate,
- wooden shakes,
- metal (including raised seam).

Wood and slate roofs are far from ideal candidates for solar. These roofing materials are brittle, so solar panel installers will likely cause damage to the roof during installation. Another concern with installing solar on a wooden shingle roof is that it can present a fire hazard.

Common flat roof coverings include:

- Built-Up Roofing (BUR) Membrane - essentially a tar-and-gravel roof, built with multiple layers (piles).

- Metal Roofing - comes in a variety of styles and materials

- Modified Bitumen Roofing - reinforced roof fabrics that are applied to act as "carriers" for bitumen, which is later cut and installed in layers similar to BUR membranes.

- Thermoset (EPDM) Roof Membrane - a type of synthetic rubber roofing

- Thermoplastic (PVC & TPO) Roof Membrane - lightweight, highly reflective, and provide excellent weathering. It is also resistant to UV light, punctures or tears, bacterial growth, and most chemicals.

- Garden "Green" Roofing System - a layer of vegetation planted over a waterproofing system that is installed on top of a flat or slightly–sloped roof..

Roof Warrantees

A new roof is a substantial investment. As a consequence, many manufacturers of roofing products provide warrantees on the product as well as the initial installation of the roofing system.

These warrantees generally include:

- A manufacturer's warranty that covers the materials against manufacturing defects.

- A workmanship warranty from the contractor that covers the initial installation.

- An extended manufacturer's warranty that covers contractor workmanship along with expanded coverage for the products. This extended coverage may apply to:

  ○ Coverage for all roof system components: Excluding flashing, wood decking and fasteners

  ○ Lengthy, non-prorated, or continuous coverage for defective materials: Typically includes labor costs for repairs or replacements and is extendable for up to 50 years

  ○ Workmanship coverage against installation errors of the roof system.

FIGURE 5-9:
RESIDENTIAL ROOFTOP
SYSTEM DESIGNED TO
MEET THE SETBACK
REQUIREMENTS IN THE
INTERNATIONAL FIRE
CODE

3 feet at ridge

3 feet on all sides

16 inches at eave

In most cases, if the solar panels and the racking system are installed by a qualified solar company according to the manufacturer's specifications, a solar energy system should not void the roof warranty.

However, if the solar company does not adhere to the manufacturer's specifications—whether due to lack of training or lack of care—the roof warranty may very well be voided. It is always best to check with the warranty guarantors prior to being work on a roof that is under warranty.

Setbacks

INTERNATIONAL FIRE CODE (IFC)

In 2012 the **International Fire Code (IFC)** set some very specific requirements when placing solar panels on the roof of residential and/or commercial buildings. These rules do not apply to non-habitable detached buildings such as carports, garages, or barns.

In order to allow access to the roof to firefighters, and space to cut ventilation holes to allow smoke to escape a burning building, the array must be set back from the structural edge (not including awnings) at least three feet on each side of the array and three feet from the ridge on residential buildings, as illustrated in Figure 5-9. The IFC does not specify the setback at the eave, but good practices dictate at least 16 inches to avoid excessive wind loading.

FIGURE 5-10:
COMMERCIAL ROOFTOP
SYSTEM DESIGNED TO
MEET THE SETBACK
REQUIREMENTS IN THE
INTERNATIONAL FIRE
CODE

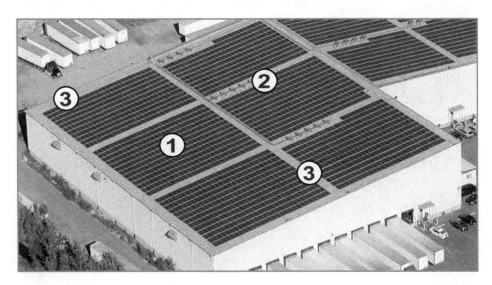

If less than 33 percent of the roof face is covered with solar, then the IFC allows for an 18 inch setback on both sides of the top ridge. If the building is equipped with a sprinkler system, then an 18 inch setback is allowed on both sides of the top ridge for systems where the array covers 66 percent or less of the roof's surface.

Flat roof systems on commercial buildings can be quite large, as demonstrated in Figure 5-10. They must be designed in a way that allows access to the entire roof by firefighters in an emergency.

The 2021 International Fire Code (IFC) requires:

- a minimum 6-foot-wide clear perimeter around the edges of commercial roofs larger than 250 by 250 feet. However, if either axis of the roof is 250 feet or less, the perimeter pathway can be reduced to a minimum of 4 feet. Indicated by (3) in Figure 5-10.

- a 4-foot clear area around the access hatch, (2)

- there must be at least one 4-foot wide clear pathway between the access hatch to the roof and the perimeter pathway, (2)

- no section of the array can be larger than 150 feet x 150 feet, with 4-foot pathways between the sections, (1)

Designers must allow for smoke ventilation areas between the array sections. This can be accomplished in any of three ways. These include:

- pathways that are at least 8 feet wide,

- in buildings where gravity operated dropout smoke vents (devices designed to automatically vent smoke in the event of a fire) are installed. Pathways between the array sections can be no less than 4 feet wide and border all skylights and/or smoke/heat vents, or pathways that are 4 feet wide with 4-by-8-foot "venting cutouts" located every 20 feet on alternating sides of the pathway.

Loading Issues

When placing an array on top of a roof, it is important that the structure can support both the dead weight (the physical weight of the panels and the racking system), as well as the live weight (which includes snow loads, wind loads, and in some cases, seismic loads).

Dead Loads

Most roofs built or renovated since 1970 have had to comply with building codes that are more than adequate to support the dead load weight of a solar array.

Local building codes will provide guidance as to the amount of weight allowed on roofs within that jurisdiction. In most locations the local

INTERNATIONAL BUILDING CODE (IBC)

authorities will follow the recommendations found within the **International Building Code (IBC).**

Usually PV arrays will only add about three to four pounds per square foot of dead weight load to the structure (less than the weight of a second layer of shingles). As long as the system is below five pounds per square foot, the system should be well below any weight restrictions that may apply.

Live Loads

Any load on the roof that is not constant, is considered a live load. Live loads include the added weight (both pressing down and pulling up) from wind, the weight of snow, and even the weight of someone walking on the roof.

- Wind Loads: The amount of wind present will vary from place to place. Check with the local building department to determine the wind load calculations they recommend. Remember that wind not only presses down on the structure, but also pulls up (like the wing of an airplane). So mounting hardware, such as lag screws must be sized in such a way as to keep the array in place under all conditions that may occur on the site.

- Snow Loads: In most cases the amount of snow that will accumulate on the rooftop should have been calculated in the original building design. Depending on how the array is mounted, the array may affect where the snow accumulates (in drifts). So some additional calculations may be necessary. A structural engineer may be required if snow loading appears to be an issue.

- Seismic Loads: Racking systems that are physically attached to the roof (with mounting brackets or lag screws) generally do not require additional seismic load consideration. Ballasted systems may require additional seismic load support. Again, check with the local building department for seismic requirements for specific jurisdictions.

When dealing with structural issues, most PV designers and installers are not qualified to determine if a building is sound. When in doubt, a qualified structural engineer should be consulted.

Wind /Snow/Seismic Load Calculations

Wind flowing over a roof-mounted solar array applies forces to the panels, fasteners, the racking system and the roof. On ground-mounted arrays, the force of the wind will eventually be transmitted through the structure to the ground. There are also lift forces that can be significant.

All systems have limits on how much wind force they can withstand, so it is critical that wind loads on PV arrays be understood.

The **American Society of Civil Engineers' (ASCE)** *Minimum Design Loads for Buildings and Other Structures* ASCE 7 standard provides guidance to the PV industry in calculating wind and snow loading limitations.

ASCE

The wind load for a project depends on the height of the building, the size of its roof, its surroundings and the layout of the solar array. Portions of the array located near the edges or corners of a rooftop are normally more affected by the stresses placed on them by the wind.

For smaller residential systems flush-mounted on a sloped roof, it is generally considered that the array and mounting system will not add significantly to the live and dead load of the structure. If the building official requires documentation to this effect, most racking system manufacturers can provide engineering studies conducted on their products. Manufacturers of racking system typically request the postal code of the location where the array will be installed, and factor in wind, snow and seismic loads when designing the system for that site.

For older structures, and large commercial installations, a structural engineer should conduct a roof assessment to evaluate the roof's structural integrity, and determine that the design of the PV system meets the snow, seismic and/or wind loads specified by local building codes.

Flat Roof Systems
It is quite common for commercial facilities, and even some residential dwellings that have flat roofs. It should be noted, however, that even roofs considered flat have a minimal slope to them. Often they have a rise of 0.25 inch over a 12-inch run - referred to as a 1/4:12 pitch.

There are three main options employed by flat roofed racking systems to secure them to the roof.

These include:
- attached,
- ballasted,
- hybrid - a combination of ballasted and attached.

Flat roof systems that attach to the structure entail making penetrations into the roof itself. Many designers seek to avoid this, especially on flat roofs as they are prone to leak even under the best of circumstances.

Attachments may include standoffs welded or screwed in place, curbs integrated into the roofing or steel grids suspended above the roof surface. In some cases the racking system can be attached directly to the roof deck, or they may be attached to the supporting rafters.

One advantage of attached racking systems is that the amount of dead load weight added to the roof with a ballasted system can be avoided. Additionally, most ballasted systems are limited to a maximum 20° pitch to avoid wind uplift. Attached systems can be used when a greater pitch is required.

Ballasted systems are quite commonly used to place larger arrays on flat roofs. These systems rely on gravity and friction to hold the array in place. Typically the weight of concrete blocks (ballast) is used to secure the system in place.

Advantages of ballasted systems:
- no roof penetrations,
- often does not void the roof's warranty,
- faster install, decreased labor costs,
- rarely visible from the ground (low tilt angle).

Disadvantages of ballasted systems:
- adds a great deal of dead weight to the roof (structure may not support it). These systems generally add more than 5 lbs. per square foot of dead weight (as compared to less than 3 lbs. per square foot with attached systems),
- may have wind and seismic load limitations,
- limited to low tilt angle (generally 20 degrees or less).

East/West Mounting Systems

Occasionally the southern exposure on a commercial structure might be blocked or shaded (such as a tall building located just south of the array). Or the available space on the roof might be limited and the designer needs to cover as much of it as possible with panels.

FIGURE 5-11: EAST/WEST FLAT ROOF MOUNTING SYSTEM

(FROM KINETIC SOLAR RACKING AND MOUNTING)

EAST/WEST FLAT ROOF MOUNTING

East/west flat roof mounting systems (shown in Figure 5-11) are designed to address these problems, but are also gaining in popularity for a number of additional reasons, even when shading is not an issue.

Advantages of these systems include:
- can fit more modules on a roof (avoids inter-row shading),
- more consistent energy production throughout the day.

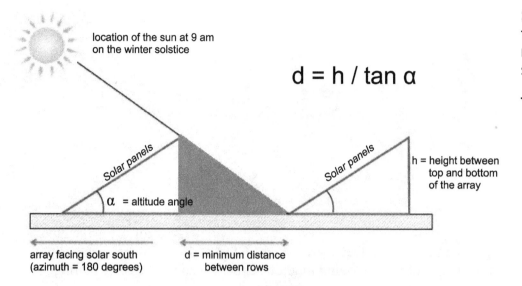

FIGURE 5-12: EQUATION TO CALCULATE INTER ROW SPACING IN A SOLAR ARRAY

$$d = h / \tan \alpha$$

location of the sun at 9 am on the winter solstice

Solar panels

Solar panels

α = altitude angle

h = height between top and bottom of the array

array facing solar south (azimuth = 180 degrees)

d = minimum distance between rows

Disadvantages include:
- problems with wire management can occur with these systems, as the low profile may result in wires becoming submerged in standing water.

Inter-Row Shading

Often larger arrays will be oriented in rows. It is important to ensure that one row does not cast a shadow upon the row behind it (a situation known as **inter-row shading**).

INTER-ROW SHADING

A good rule to follow is to allow a distance of three times the height of the top of the array between the rows (at 40° latitude). Less offset is required closer to the equator (twice height at 30°), and more offset is required in locations closer to the poles (4 times height at 45°).

For more exact calculations, The formula for calculating minimum inter-row shading (or shading from any nearby structure that may block the sun) is:

$$d = h / \tan \alpha$$

Where,
- "d" is the minimum distance between rows,
- "h" is the height differential between the top of one row and the bottom of the row to the north and,
- "α" is the altitude angle of the sun at that location at 9 am on the winter solstice (the moment when the sun will be at its lowest point relative to the horizon) as indicated in Figure 5-12.

A **sun chart** like that shown in Figure 5-13 is necessary to determine the altitude for a specific location. There are a number of online sources to create these charts by simply entering a zip code or latitude and longitude coordinates.

SUN CHART

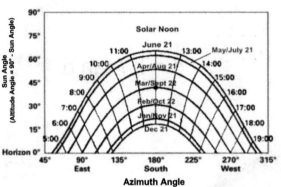

Seattle, WA: Latitude 48°; Longitude - 122°

For example, if the top of the northern row is 6 feet above the bottom of the southern row, and the angle of the sun is set at about 15 degrees, then:

minimum distance (d) = 6 feet (h) / .268 (tangent of 15°) = 22.39 feet

If the designer had used the "rule of thumb" method (placing the rows 18 feet apart, 3 times 6 feet at 40° latitude), then a slight amount of inter-row shading might be experienced (in the early morning and late afternoon around the winter solstice).

Reducing the altitude angle of the panels (thereby reducing the height difference between the top of one row and the bottom of the adjacent row), will allow rows of panels to be placed closer together without the risk of inter-row shading. In the above example, if the height difference were reduced to 3 feet, then:

minimum distance (d) = 3 feet (h) / .268 (tangent of 15°) = 11.2 feet

GROUND COVER RATIO (GCR)

This allows more panels to be placed in a limited area, or increases the **ground cover ratio (GCR)**. The GCR is simply the size of the actual solar panels divided by the area the array occupies. Panels that lie flat in relation to the horizon have a GCR of 1.0 - meaning that if viewed from directly above, 100% of the area to be used in the array is covered with solar panels.

A GCR of .50 means that, when viewed from above, only half of the area occupied by the array is covered by panels (spaced to avoid inter-row shading and to provide access pathways).

A higher ground cover ratio might prove significant, especially on a commercial flat roof with a limited area available for panels. For example, take two extreme examples of the same building.

For example, assume an array mounted on a flat roof such as the one depicted in Figure 5-14. The total area inhabited by the array is 13 feet x 16 feet = 208 sq ft. The panels themselves, however, only take up 144 sq. ft. (2 ft x 3 ft x 24 panels). The ground cover ratio in this case would be .69 (144 sq ft / 208 sq ft).

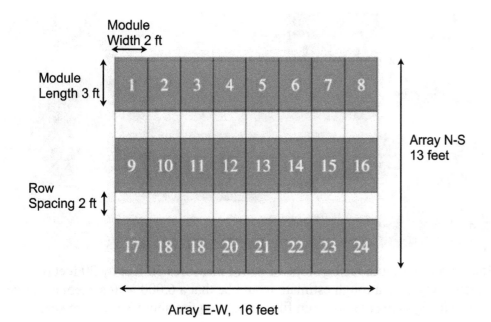

Module
Width 2 ft

Module
Length 3 ft

Row
Spacing 2 ft

| 1 | 2 | 3 | 4 | 5 | 6 | 7 | 8 |

| 9 | 10 | 11 | 12 | 13 | 14 | 15 | 16 |

| 17 | 18 | 18 | 20 | 21 | 22 | 23 | 24 |

Array N-S
13 feet

Array E-W, 16 feet

A quick check of PV Watts shows that at a 40 degree angle (Columbus, OH, 10% system loss, 7.2 kW system), the system will produce 9,364 kWh per year.

Assume that by reducing the angle to 5 degrees, the inter-row spacing could be reduced to 6 inches (rather than 2 feet). The array area now only occupies 160 sq ft (10 feet x 16 feet). The panel size has not changed, so the new GCR is calculated as 144 sq ft/160 sq ft = .90. But because the angle is no longer ideal for maximum power generation, the annual output at a 5 degree angle will be only 8,696 kWh.

This example demonstrates that while the annual energy production has declined by 7% (9,364 kWh - 8,696 kWh)/9,364 kWh), the size of the area required for the array has been reduced by 23% ((208 sq ft- 160 sq ft) / 208 sq ft).

As the price of panels and mounting systems decline, the ability to squeeze more and more panels into the available and limited space, even if the design does not maximize the generating capacity of each individual panel, becomes an increasingly attractive option in many situations.

Estimating Maximum Array Size for Space Available

During the initial site evaluation, the designer will often be asked to estimate just how many panels can fit on any given roof. The answer will in large measure depend on how unobstructed (with dormers, vent pipes, chimneys, access hatches, skylights, etc.) the surface is.

Assuming a flat or pitched roof with no obstructions, a good rough rule of thumb for systems that use crystalline panels is about 10 watts per one square

FIGURE 5-15: A SMALL GROUND-MOUNTED ARRAY

foot. So if the south facing slope of a roof measures 30 feet by 20 feet (600 square feet), then a rough estimate would be that a 6,000 watt system could be installed. Systems that use thin film panels require about 30% more space.

For larger ground mounted systems, a rough rule of thumb is 4 acres for every 1 MW of fix-mounted crystalline panels.

Ground Mounted Systems

At many sites, the only suitable location for the solar array is on the rooftop. However if the site allows, **ground mounted systems** offer a number of advantages, as well as some challenges.

GROUND MOUNTED

Advantages of ground mounted systems include:
- can be oriented as needed, rather than based on the orientation of the building,
- avoids putting penetrations into the roof, which always have the potential result in leaks or may void roof warranties,
- are easier to access for maintenance (such as snow removal),
- operate in a cooler environment, rather than on a hot roof,
- no need to haul all the materials up onto a roof,
- avoids any additional stress to the building due to wind or snow loads.

Some disadvantages associated with ground mounted systems:
- zoning and land use restrictions,
- uneven terrain (hills, slopes and valleys),
- soil type,
- nearby ground cover (fire regulations require that brush be cleared within 10 feet of the perimeter of ground mounted systems),
- water and drainage issues,
- foundation requirements,
- security (fences, for example, for safety reasons or to prevent damage and/or vandalism),

- vehicle access.

Foundation work will be required for ground mounted systems such as the system shown in Figure 5-15, as well as determining if any buried utilities will be affected during construction.

There are two major design components when installing a ground mounted system. The first is structural, ensuring that the mounting system can withstand the forces that will be exerted upon it over the life of the system. And these forces can be substantial.

For example, in the Boston area, winds can approach speeds of 120 miles per hour and static snow loads are roughly 60 pounds per square foot. Depending on rack design, these loads can translate to as much as 5 tons of force per foundation.

The second design component that must be evaluated is **geotechnical**. This involves the evaluation of soil conditions so that they can be incorporated into the structural design of the mounting system.

> GEOTECHNICAL

Data that must be gathered regarding the site includes: soil composition, bearing capacity, groundwater level and surface water runoff.

Brownfield/Greyfield Development

Legislative priorities as well as a desire to turn under utilized land to productive use has led to increased attention as to where larger solar arrays may be sited.

The Environmental Protection Agency (EPA) defines a **brownfield** site "*as any land in the United States that is abandoned, idled or underused because redevelopment and/or expansion is complicated by environmental contamination that is either real or perceived.*"

> BROWNFIELD

They estimate that there are 450,000 brownfields in the US, covering over 15 million acres.

It is estimated that there are more than 10,000 closed and capped landfills under public and private ownership in the US. These have few complementary uses and little or no long-term income potential for owners. Landfills are one example of sites that offer elevated, unshaded sites for PV systems. Development of these sites create a new source of lease revenue for landfill owners and property-tax revenue for municipalities.

A color code is often used when describing potential sites. A **greenfield** is is a site in undeveloped, natural condition or one that is in agricultural use. Use of this type of site often meets resistance from advocates who contend that

> GREENFIELD

there are better uses for such unspoiled locations - such as keeping it agricultural.

GREYFIELD

A **greyfield** is similar to a brownfield but without the environmental concern. Typical greyfield sites are commercial properties, previously used as parking lot, shopping centers and shopping malls, hotels or office buildings or multiple family residential buildings.

BLACKFIELD

A **blackfield** is a site where the soil is so contaminated that private development cannot take place without governmental assistance and oversite.

BRIGHTFIELD

Placing a solar array on otherwise contaminated land (such as an abandoned strip mine or a closed landfill) results in what is often referred to as a **brightfield**,

There are a number of advantages in developing solar facilities on brownfield/greyfield sites.

These include:
- financial incentives are often in place to encourage this type of development.
- development on these sites can sometimes benefit from streamlined permitting and zoning.
- they are usually located in close proximity to power lines and public roads, which can save significantly on the construction costs.
- puts otherwise blighted properties into productive use.

While these contaminated sites offer unique opportunities for solar development, there are also issues that must be addressed that do not typically occur with greenfield or rooftop development.

These include:
- they generally require additional permits and approvals from federal, state and local agencies. For example, brownfields may be superfund sites, which requires permits and oversite from the U.S. EPA.
- these sites have been classified as polluted for a reason. The full extent of the pollution may not be at first apparent. Workers on the site may be exposed to hazardous conditions, and toxins may be released during development which must be addressed and remedied. Additional personal protective equipment, dust control, pollution monitoring, contaminant handling, segregation and disposal measures may be necessary for worker safety and environmental protection.
- development timelines will likely be extended due to the added review requirements, adding cost to the project.

- landfills are typically capped with liners and soils that cannot be disturbed with a pile-driven racking system. They require the use of a ballasted system, where the solar panels are held in place by concrete blocks.

Ground Mounted Design Options

As the PV industry has grown and matured, so too have the number of options for placing solar arrays on sites other than the "traditional" rooftop.

FIGURE 5-16: POLE-MOUNTED PV ARRAY

These ground mounted options include:
- multi pier ground mounted racking systems,
- single **pole mounted** systems (as shown in Figure 5-16),
- ground mounted ballasted systems,
- tracking systems, which can be single axis or dual axis,
- solar carports and canopies,
- floating solar arrays such as the one shown in Figure 5-17. Known as **floatovoltaics**, these systems are often placed on reservoirs and water treatment facilities.

POLE MOUNTED

FLOATOVOLTAICS

Restrictions on Ground Mounted Systems

Those wishing to install a ground mounted system may face some permitting restrictions that are not applicable for rooftop arrays.

FIGURE 5-17: FLOATOVOLTAIC PV ARRAY

These may include:

- Location. Ground mounted systems shall might be restricted to rear or side of the building, or in a place where they cannot be seen from the road.

- Ground cover limitation. Permits may restrict the percent of the lot covered by the array, or permitted only on lots of a certain size.

- Setback requirements. It is common that a minimum setback from buildings and property lines is required for all ground mounted arrays.

- Height restrictions. Ordinances generally set a height restriction, setting a maximum height of the array.

- Screening. Appropriate landscaping and/or fencing may be required for safety and screening purposes.

- Undergrowth. The AHJ may require that gravel or well maintained crops (such as mown grass) be present under the array. The International Fire Code requires a 10-foot clear brush-free perimeter be maintained around all ground mounted solar arrays.

- Glare. Ground mounted solar energy systems should be installed so as to prevent any negative impact of glare or reflection on any neighboring property or right-of-way.

- Slope. The array may be restricted from being placed on any grade with a slope greater than 20 degrees.

Site Preparation

A great deal of work must be done to prepare the site for a ground mounted system.

Assess the Site

Identify the property lines. There may be required setbacks from the edge of the property. The area where an array can legally be placed should have been defined early in the planning process, but confirm this before beginning the installation. Existing drawings should be available from the property owner, the surveyor, or the local building department.

EASEMENT

Check also if any **easements** exist on the site that may impact the placement of the system. An easement is a legal arrangement that gives another the right to cross or otherwise use someone else's land for a specified purpose.

Call and have all underground utilities identified and marked.

Another issue that may arise is storm water runoff. Many sites have been engineered to manage the flow and accumulation of surface water, so ensure the system will not disrupt the civil engineering already incorporated into the site.

For smaller installations, access to the site might not pose a large obstacle, although getting cement to the site might present a challenge. But larger installations usually involve large pieces of construction equipment.

Pathways, room to operate, loading and unloading areas all should be available. Consider as well that during construction the equipment will disrupt the site. Mud can be a serious problem, bogging down equipment and generally making a mess of things. It may be that temporary (or permanent) access pathways will need to be created.

Fencing

During construction and after, security should be a concern. Ground mounted systems by their very nature are more accessible than rooftop systems. This makes them a target for thieves, vandals, or even children at play.

A fence around the system is not only a good idea, but often required by code in many jurisdictions. Codes require that there must be a clear 10-foot pathway around the perimeter of the array, so any fence should be outside this area.

Grounding of the perimeter fence should be done at least once, within 50 feet of the point where power from the array leaves the site to connect with the grid. These conductors may be overhead or buried.

Bonding and grounding of the fence should be accomplished in the following manner:

- Drive an 8-foot grounding electrode at the point of grounding inside the perimeter of the fence.

- Bond the rod to a fence post using a conductor sized appropriately for the system, but not smaller than a #8 AWG copper conductor.

- Any barbed wire or wire mesh that is part of the fence itself should be bonded to the fence post near the ground rod, using the same sized copper bonding jumper as determined above.

- The gates in the fence shall be bonded to the fence post using the same size copper bonding jumper as described above, and that fence post bonded and grounded to another grounding electrode. If the gate is located within 50 feet of the conductors leaving the array, then the grounding electrode at the gate can serve as the sole ground. If not, then multiple ground rods will be required. If a gate in the perimeter fence is positioned underneath the power lines, then fence posts on both sides of the gate must be bonded and grounded as described.

Conductor Accessibility

The NEC requires that all conductors and connections be secured away from the reach of those not trained or qualified to work on the system (such as the neighbor's children, for example).

Article 690.31(A) states that circuits operating at 30 volts or more located in a "readily accessible location" must be protected. While most conductors in a PV installation are within conduit, the PV source circuit typically is composed of loose (accessible) conductors running from the panel to the combiner box.

Rooftop installations are generally interpreted as not readily accessible, so this provision typically applies to ground mounted systems.

The conductors can be protected by:
- containing the PV source circuit in a raceway,
- building a fence around the array (no longer accessible),
- locating the conductors at least 8 feet above the ground surface.

FIGURE 5-18:
HORIZONTAL AXIS
TRACKING SYSTEM

The 2017 code added a fourth option, stating that conductors connected with MC connectors (such as the standard MC4 connector) are also considered inaccessible, since separating them requires a tool.

However a number of inspectors are reluctant to accept standard terminations as being inaccessible. So specific ground mounted installations may have to protect PV source circuit wiring.

Tracking Systems

SUN TRACKING
SYSTEM

DUAL-AXIS TRACKING
SYSTEM

SINGLE-AXIS
TRACKING SYSTEM

HORIZONTAL AXIS
TRACKING SYSTEM

There are devices, or **sun tracking systems**, that will automatically adjust the angle of the solar array to face the sun as it tracks in the sky. If the system adjusts for both altitude and azimuth, it is referred to as a **dual-axis tracking system**. If it only adjusts for one of these dimensions, it is a **single-axis tracking system**.

The most common single-axis tracking systems move groups of panels by changing their orientation from east to west throughout the day. These are referred to as **horizontal axis tracking systems**. The panels are typically mounted on a pivot rail that is oriented in a north-south direction, as shown in Figure 5-18. The panels pivot from facing east in the morning to facing west in the evening, lying flat at solar noon.

SELF-SHADING

POWER DENSITY

VERTICAL-AXIS
TRACKING SYSTEM

Horizontal tracking systems not only increase the insolation striking the array (by as much as 30%), but can be packed closely together without increasing the chance of **self-shading** (the shadow from one panel falling on another panel). This allows for more panels, and therefore more power (higher **power density**) in a smaller amount of space.

For latitudes above 45°, **vertical axis tracking** systems may be an option.

These panels are oriented vertically to the ground, and pivot from east to west as the sun tracks in the sky. Due to the vertical nature of the system, however, the units must be spaced a fair distance apart to avoid self-shading.

Tilted single axis tracking systems, such as the one shown in Figure 5-19, are set at a fixed angle that is optimal to the specific location. They then track east to west during the day, following the angle of incidence with the sun.

Because of their relatively high profile, tilted and vertical axis tracking systems are subject to increased wind loading (additional stress placed on the system as wind passes over it). Studies have shown that tilted single axis tracking systems can harvest 6-7% more power than horizontal single axis systems - rates that are nearly as efficient as dual axis tracking systems.

The movement of the tracking system can be achieved through the use of motors, known as **active tracking**, or by the heating and cooling of refrigerant-like liquid/gas elements, known as **passive tracking**.

Passive solar trackers have no electrical motor turning the solar array. They use the heat of the sun to change the balance of the tracker, causing canisters filled with a low boiling point gas fluid to move to the west side of the array, making it heavier throughout the day, turning the array to the west. During the night, the system cools down and the array turns back to the east.

If the array is attached to a racking system that cannot be adjusted, this would be considered a **fixed-mount** system. Typically with such a system, the array is only directly facing the sun twice each year.

Recent studies have shown that for smaller PV systems (less than 10 kW), the average installed cost of systems with tracking was 19% higher than fixed-mount systems. Costs increased for larger systems by about 15% when tracking systems were incorporated.

However, manufacturers of tracking systems claim that they will increase power output over a fixed-mount array by as much as 30-40%. So despite the maintenance concerns, tracking systems may be a practical consideration in some instances.

But for the present, fixed-mount systems comprise the vast majority of installed systems. If a location received the exact same amount of sunlight each month of the year (which never happens in reality), then the angle of a fixed array should be set at the site's latitude.

At the spring and the autumn equinoxes, the rays of the sun will then point directly (at a 90° angle) at the array.

$$\text{array angle = latitude}$$

For example, if an array were to be placed in Washington, DC (latitude 39° N), the optimum year-round angle would be 39° .

If local conditions are such that there is a great deal of sunlight during the summer months, and a relatively small amount of sunlight during the winter months (as is often typical in mid-latitude regions), then the array might be oriented with a lower angle (pointing more directly overhead). This altitude adjustment is referred to as a **summer bias**.

To find the ideal summer bias, take the latitude and subtract 15°.

$$\text{summer bias = latitude - 15}°$$

An array in Washington DC with a summer bias would be at a 24° angle.

To adjust this same array for a **winter bias**, add 15° to the altitude of the year-round position of the array. In this example, an angle biased towards generating more power in the winter months would be 39° + 15° = 54° .

Calculating the ideal angle for a fixed-mount array at a specific location may not be as simple as selecting the year-round, summer or winter bias settings.

The monthly variation of solar insolation can make for some fairly complicated calculations. By running various altitude angle settings through PVWatts, it is possible to determine the optimum angle for a site, given the variations of available sunlight from month-to-month.

Some smaller systems have pre-drilled holes in the mounting brackets that allow the home owner to make periodic adjustments manually. This fairly low-tech feature can greatly increase the efficiency of the system – allowing for maximum production during the winter as well as during the summer. Racks of this type are referred to as an **adjustable frame** mounting system.

SUMMER BIAS

WINTER BIAS

ADJUSTABLE FRAME

FIGURE 5-20: ADJUSTING THE PIER HEIGHT ON SOLAR TRACKING SYSTEM TO ADJUST FOR LAND CONTOUR

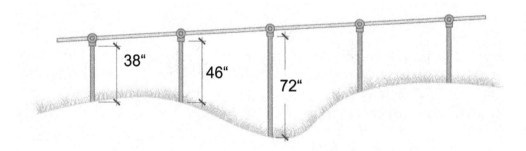

38"   46"   72"

Uneven Terrain Issues

While a solar tracking system may increase output from a solar array by as much as 25%, these systems have traditionally been designed to work only on flat or relatively flat surfaces.

Often the cost of grading the site can run more than 5% of the total development budget, plus cause a number of disruptive effects such as wind-blown dust, rainwater erosion and other environmental problems that result from the grading process.

Also, flat accessible land is often at a premium and could be better used for other purposes - such as agricultural.

When faced with uneven terrain, the developer can either level the array by varying the height of the piers (poles), as shown in Figure 5-20.

Issues may arise when doing so, however. If a post is too tall, wind and snow loads may require stronger foundations as well as more robust poles. This will add significantly to the cost of the system.

If the posts is too short, the panel may touch the ground when tracking, there may be insufficient clearance to mount gear boxes, electrical equipment and wire harnesses to the posts - or drifting snow may become a problem.

Another option is to allow the system to articulate, or follow the contour of the land, as illustrated in Figure 5-21.

These systems can present problems as well.

Articulation also allows the same size posts to be used throughout the site, which reduces the total cost of the tracker. On flat land the weight of the array bears down vertically on the posts. However, on sloped terrain, the weight of the system wants to slide down the hill, which creates a **slope load** force on the post.

SLOPE LOAD

In recent years a number of **all-terrain tracker systems (ATTs)** have come on the market that are designed to address these challenges and allow for systems to be placed on rolling terrain.

Advantages and Disadvantages of Tracking Systems:
Solar tracking systems offer a number of advantages and disadvantages over fixed mount solar arrays.

Advantages include:
- tracking systems generate 10 to 25% more electricity than fixed mount systems of the same size in the same location,
- the increased production allows for smaller arrays to generate a specific output, optimizing land use,
- they can be used to generate a greater amount of electricity during peak load demand times of the day.

Disadvantages include:

- tracking systems are more expensive than their stationary counterparts, adding $0.08 – $0.10/W to the cost of the project.

- there is more maintenance required than a traditional fixed rack. These are mechanical systems which will periodically need to be serviced or repaired.

- tracking systems are a more complex system than fixed racking, requiring more site preparation. This includes additional grading of the site, more trenching and wiring to service the mechanical portion of the system.

- solar trackers are generally designed for climates with little to no snow load, making them a potential problem in colder climates.

- fixed systems can generally be placed on slopes up to 20% the E/W direction, while tracking systems are typically restricted to slopes less than 10% in the N/S direction.

Soil Investigation

The soil at a site will vary not only across the site (horizontally) but also as vertically. From a mounting systems point of view, the soil must be able to resist and support the forces and loads placed upon it by the array.

Developers typically drill a number of core samples at the site as part of the **geotechnical survey** to determine the various soil types that exist at different layers deposited at the site. Another technique is to dig a 10-foot deep trench that gives a better picture of what lies beneath the surface. This allows engineers to identify and document soil boundaries, determine the seasonal high-groundwater level, the percentage and size of rock fragments, unsuitable soil horizons, depth to bedrock, etc.

GEOTECHNICAL
SURVEY

Typically **soil corrosivity** and **resistivity testing** will also be conducted. Highly corrosive soil may require thicker pilings, resistive coatings, or other techniques that may increase the longevity of the foundation. Soil with high moisture content, high electrical conductivity, high acidity, and high dissolved salts will be the most corrosive to metals placed within it.

Distance between at least 3 times the depth

SOIL CORROSIVITY TEST

RESISTIVITY TEST

Soil resistivity testing is required to ensure the array is properly grounded. The lower the resistance of the soil, the better. Soil composition, moisture content, and temperature all impact the soil resistivity.

Generally, dry rocky soil will have much greater resistivity than moist farmland or clay type soils.

To measure soil resistivity, site developers typically perform a **Wenner 4-Point Test**, as illustrated in Figure 5-22.

WENNER 4-POINT TEST

Four earth ground stakes are driven into the soil in a straight line, equal distances from one another. The distance between the stakes should be at least three times that of the stake depth. For example, if the depth of each ground stake is three feet (.91 meters), make sure the distance between each stake is greater than nine feet (2.73 meters).

A testing meter is then used to generate a known current through the two outer ground stakes and the drop in voltage potential is measured between the two inner ground stakes. Using Ohm's Law (V=IR), the test meter then calculates the soil resistance.

Soil load testing can be accomplished with the use of heavy equipment, hydraulic jacks or chain hoists to apply horizontal and vertical foundation test loads.

SOIL LOAD TEST

Axial compression tests apply the downward forces that might be experienced on the site. **Horizontal load tests** can determine how much a foundation deflects laterally when subjected to expected design loads.

AXIAL COMPRESSION TEST

HORIZONTAL LOAD TEST

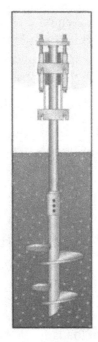

AXIAL TENSION TEST

An **axial tension test** can determine how well a foundation resists uplift forces and estimates the pullout load.

When conducted in combination, these tests measure the soil bearing capacity for the specific loads and foundation type anticipated for the site.

The designer should also factor in the impacts of snow and even maintenance. For example, the system may need to be raised a few feet to allow for the accumulation of snow in the winter and to allow access to mowing equipment in the summer.

Foundation Types:

PIER

There are a number of options when selecting the **piers**, or support poles (piles) used in ground mounted PV systems.

These include:
- driven pile,
- earth screw,
- helical anchor,
- Ballast,
- drilled and grouted piles.

DRIVEN PILE

Driven pile piers normally offer good lateral and vertical support in soils that are firm and well compacted (silt and clay). Where they are practical, they typically offer the most economical option. Driven piles, however, are not usually suitable if the site has soil that consists of coarse gravel or rock. Also, equipment access limitations typically limit driven pile foundations to slopes less than 15°.

FIGURE 5-23: HELICAL ANCHOR SUPPORT FOR GROUND MOUNTED PV SYSTEM

EARTH SCREW

Earth screw piers are normally suitable within a wider range of soil and site conditions. When pilot holes are pre-drilled, they can be installed in rocky soils and even bedrock. Earth screws are typically a bit more expensive than driven pile, but offer good pullout resistance and can be installed on slopes up to 30°.

HELICAL ANCHOR

A **helical anchor** consist of a helical bearing plate attached near the bottom of a narrow shaft, as illustrated in Figure 5-23. They are normally a more expensive option than either driven piles or earth screws.

Helical anchors are often used in sites with soft soil, such as clean sand. The bearing plate provides good pullout resistance, however the narrow shaft does not provide much lateral bearing capacity.

If the site is environmentally sensitive, helical piles may prove to be the preferred solution. They do not require excavation or soil removal and installation creates a minimal vibration disturbance. They also avoid drill cuttings (soil raised to the surface as the result of drilling a hole). This prevents soil mixing and maintains the natural landscape.

Ballasted systems, either precast or pour-in-place concrete foundations, may be the best option where drilling into the soil is either undesirable or impractical.

Ballasted systems, for example, are often used in brownfields or landfills where disturbing the soil may cause damage to the environment. Even abandoned parking lots can be suitable locations for ballasted systems and do not require damaging the surface of the lot.

A ballasted system can be more easily moved if necessary. However, ballasted ground mounts can not be placed on a site with more than a 5° slope, and are often quite expensive when compared with alternative mounting options.

Drilled and grouted concrete piers have traditionally been the "go to" foundation of choice for small to medium sized projects. They involve drilling a hole to below frost level, placing a metal post into that hole, and then filling it with concrete.

> DRILLED & GROUTED

Advantages of concrete piers are that minimal equipment is required for installation, and they can be relatively shallow compared to driven steel piles. The disadvantages are that they use concrete (not an environmentally preferred option), are labor intensive and take days to cure.

Why Foundations Fail
Experience demonstrates that foundations for ground mounted PV systems generally do not fail because the system exceeded design loads. Foundations fail due to a loss of soil-bearing capacity caused by high groundwater levels, soil erosion or **soil liquefaction**. Soil liquefaction occurs when saturated or partially saturated soil is subjected to a sudden change in stress (like an earthquake) and loses strength and stiffness, causing it to behave like a liquid

> SOIL LIQUEFACTION

They also fail from frost heaving or because of expansive clay soils. Or construction activities for the array installation itself may destabilize the soil or impair drainage at the site.

Building Integrated Photovoltaics (BIPV)

Architects and designers are increasingly integrating photovoltaics into the design of the building or structure itself. More times than not, these **building integrated photovoltaic (BIPV)** systems utilize thin film panels, that can be

> BUILDING INTEGRATED (BIPV)

modified (such as in the case of solar awnings as illustrated in Figure 5-24) to become part of the building itself.

Figure 5-24: Building integrated PV system

While BIPV systems hold a great deal of promise as the industry matures, to date they have typically not achieved commercial success due to three factors:

- they are typically more expensive than ordinary solar installations, even when taking into account the avoided materials (shingles, etc),
- they are never as reliable as ordinary solar installations, and
- they often cannot meet rapidly evolving safety requirements (such as arc-fault, rapid shutdown, fire clearances, etc.).

Another growing application is the use of PV panels to provide shaded parking such as is illustrated in Figure 5-25. This will become even more widespread as the fleet of electric vehicles (EVs) expands – providing not only a covered parking area, but easy access to solar-powered EV recharging stations.

Shading Issues

A shadow cast upon just a portion of a solar panel can reduce the output from that panel by as much as 50%. And if a panel is affected, then the output of the entire string will also be reduced.

So it is important to ensure that the array is placed so as to avoid the shade of nearby trees, buildings, telephone poles, or any other obstruction that may potentially block the sun. PV arrays should be placed so that there is no shading for a minimum of six hours during the middle of the day. This period of unobstructed sunlight is often referred to as the **solar window**.

SOLAR WINDOW

Figure 5-25: Solar panels utilized to provide covered parking

(Photo from Ecogeek.org)

It is also important to remember that shadows cast by nearby objects will change over the course of the day and over the course of a year. Aside from the ever-changing angle of the sun in relation to the location of the array, plants tend to grow and bare branches will be covered with leaves in the spring.

Solar Pathfinder

To avoid the complexity of calculating the angles of all nearby potential obstructions, most PV installers use a tool such as a **Solar Pathfinder®** pictured in Figure 5-26. This relatively inexpensive tool (starting at around $300 dollars) combines a sun chart for the location's latitude with a reflective dome that provides a visual representation of nearby potential sources of shade.

FIGURE 5-26: SOLAR PATHFINDER WITH STAND AND CARRYING CASE

(PHOTO FROM SOLAR PATHFINDER)

SOLAR PATHFINDER

The unit should be placed level to the ground (there is a level bubble to assist with that task). Orient it towards true south (a compass is also integrated into the unit to assist with this).

The clear plastic dome will then act as a lens, bending the reflected image of all nearby objects degrees and imposing them over the sun chart inserted below the lens. In this way, the unit projects an image of shading issues for that location throughout the year.

More expensive models incorporate GPS devices, true south locators, and cameras to capture the image for later analysis.

FIGURE 5-27: SUNEYE 210 SHADE TOOL

The sun chart incorporates small white numbers inside the half-hour divisions. These are values that have been calculated to account for the relative energy in each half-hour. Hours near solar noon have a higher relative energy than those nearer to dawn or dusk. All numbers added horizontally will add up to 100 (or 100%). The sum of all the numbers that are unshaded will provide an approximate percentage of time during that month that the site will be free from shading.

For example, if the numbers in the unshaded region for a given month add up to 72, then 72% of the available energy in the sun during that month will not be impacted by nearby obstructions. If shading is from deciduous trees, assign only half the value as shaded during months when leaves will be off the trees.

Tools other than the Solar Pathfinders, such as the SunEye® by Solmetric, such as shown in Figure 5-27, as well as a number of apps for smart phones are also available to assist with shading analysis.

Total Solar Resource Factor (TSRF)

For any given site, based on its location on the earth and weather conditions, there is a certain anticipated amount of power available, known as that location's **total solar resource**.

TOTAL SOLAR
RESOURCE

However, the actual orientation and angle of an array rarely matches the ideal for a given location. The slope and orientation of the roof will often dictate how a system is installed. And shading might also contribute to limiting the amount of energy the array can gather.

So once the orientation (azimuth) and the angle (altitude) of the array have been determined, and an analysis of shading issues at the site has been completed, the resulting energy that can actually be produced by the system can be determined.

It is not the total energy available for sunlight at the site, but rather the amount the array can gather given the actual orientation and accounting for any shading. This may be expressed as a percentage (actual/ideal), often called the **total solar resource fraction (TSRF)**.

TOTAL SOLAR
RESOURCE FRACTION

Tools such as PV Watts will calculate the energy available based on the angle and orientation. The actual energy the system can gather based on the angle and orientation (actual/ideal) is known as the **tilt and orientation factor (TOF).**

TILT AND
ORIENTATION FACTOR

Tools such as the Solar Pathfinder or the SunEye can assist in calculating how much will be lost due to shading. The amount lost due to shading is known as the **shading factor (SF)**, or shade impact factor. Combined, the TOF and the SF are used to determine the TSRF.

SHADING FACTOR

Some grants and incentive programs that assist in the funding of solar projects may require a minimum TSRF in order for a project to qualify. The state of Oregon's residential energy tax credit program, for example, requires systems have a 75% TSRF or better to qualify.

Other Issues Impacting the Location of the Array:

Assuming the perfect location for the array has been found, sketch out the system (with locations and measurements) for future reference. That task completed, there are still a few other issues to consider during the site inspection. These include:

- Aesthetics. How will the array look when integrated onto the site? Are there ways to design the system to assist with it fitting into the character of the property and/or neighborhood?

- Legal Issues. Some sub-divisions or municipalities have restrictions regarding the placement of solar arrays. Check to make sure there are no ordinances or other legal restrictions that limit or prohibit the placement of a solar array in the location selected.

- Insurance Issues. Is adequate insurance in place to protect all parties during the installation, and is insurance in place to provide for the added value of the property after the installation is complete?

- **Future proof.** It is hoped that this system will provide power to the homeowner for 20 or 30 years. Check for trees or bushes that might grow and cause a problem in the future. Try to take these into account if possible. Also ask about any future building plans that might impact the array.

FUTURE PROOF

- Conduct a site **hazard assessment**. During installation, panels and ladders, trucks and people will be loaded and unloaded. Determine if there are any hazards (low electric lines, nearby swimming pool, vicious dogs, whatever) that may impact construction.

HAZARD ASSESSMENT

- Determine staging/lifting/access areas. Make sure there is room to bring the materials to where they need to be. And determine how panels will be raised up on the roof (should that be their destination).

- Determine where the cables will run. Calculate their distances, and see if there are any obstacles (driveways, other utilities, gardens, etc) that must be taken into account.

- Find out if there are any other unusual conditions that come into play at this location (such as excessive wind, snow, earthquakes, flooding, etc) that will affect the design of the system.

- Confirm the electrical utility/authority that has jurisdiction at this location. Make sure what you are planning does not violate any of their local rules.

Determine the Location of the Inverter

Several factors come into play when determining the location of an inverter within a PV system.

microinverters connect directly to the panels, so they will be installed either directly on the frame of the panel, or on the rail system immediately under the panel. But locating a string inverter may not always be as straight forward.

Indoor or Outdoor

Most string inverters are contained within NEMA 3R or NEMA 4X containers, allowing them to be mounted in outdoor conditions. However, when mounted outdoors, care should be taken to minimize the unit's exposure to the elements: such as rain, snow or direct sunlight.

Inverters do produce heat when operating, so if mounted indoors, they should be mounted in a well-ventilated area.

When mounted outdoors, inverters should be accessible but should not be placed in a location that may present a hazard to vehicle or pedestrian traffic. Care should also be taken to guard the unit against theft and/or vandalism (fenced enclosure, for example).

Mounting Restrictions

In order to restrict moisture from finding its way inside the unit, most manufacturers restrict the angle at which the inverter may be safely mounted. Generally this will be at about a 15 degree incline. Most inverters are designed to mount vertically on a wall.

The National Electrical Code defines workspace clearance requirements for PV systems up to 1000 Vdc in NEC Section 110.26. Requirements for 1500 Vdc systems can be found in NEC Section 110.30.

The NEC requires that the clear work space of at least 3 feet in front of the inverter at a width not less than that of the unit (or 30 inches, whichever is greater). The height of the workspace should be 6.5 feet or the height of the unit (whichever is greater).

The clearances required in the inverter's manual may exceed the NEC requirements. For example, the NEC may allow inverters to be mounted on a wall with no space between them (provided the enclosure door opens 90 degrees). However the manual may require clearances around the inverter of 4 to 18 inches for airflow and cooling purposes. Failure to follow the manufacturer's installation guidelines may void the warrantee of the unit.

Determine the Location of the Balance of Systems (BOS)

The balance of systems (BOS) may include the battery bank, charge controller, disconnects, racks, wire, conduit, meters and/or remote sensing equipment. Basically everything except the solar panels and the inverter(s).

Often these are sub-categorized into two groups, the electrical BOS and the structural BOS. The electrical BOS includes components such as charge controllers, cables, monitoring electronics, meters, etc. The structural BOS includes the racks, other support structures, conduit, shelving, mounting brackets, etc.

These items should be located as close as possible to the array (to minimize cabling runs) but also meet the following criteria:

- Electronics should be located in a protected, water proof and weather protected location.

- They should NOT be located in direct sunlight (to avoid heat and UV issues).

- They should be insulated against extreme temperatures (many of the electronic components will list the range of ambient temperatures they are designed to operate within). Some of these components may be rated only for indoor installation (check the manufacturer's specifications).

- Battery banks should be housed in a well-ventilated locations (batteries give off hydrogen gas when charging), and temperature controlled environment (extreme heat and cold will also impact the functioning of the batteries).

- The batteries should also be protected from any combustible sources. They should NOT be co-located where open flames are present (from a gas furnace, for example).

- The BOS should be protected from children, pets, rodents, vandals and any potential physical hazard (such as flying debris from lawn mowers).

- There may be **clearance** requirements for the equipment (above, below, beside - and working clearances in front of the units). These are typically 36 inches deep x 30 inches wide x 6 feet 6 inches high.

  CLEARANCE

- Consider **height requirements,** the NEC requires that disconnects (the center of the grip of the handle or the circuit breaker) not be located more than 2 meters (6 feet 7 inches) above the floor or working platform. Outdoor disconnects and equipment should be located high enough off the ground to ensure they are not impacted by drifting snow.

  HEIGHT REQUIREMENTS

- AC and DC disconnects must be located near any installed string inverter. It may also be necessary to install additional disconnects, such as an AC disconnect located within 10 feet of the utilities service connection.

Locate the **service entrance** used by the existing utility provider (it is likely required that a system disconnect be placed at this location). The utility meter is usually located near the existing service entrance.

SERVICE ENTRANCE

It may be practical to locate inverters and other electronic components of the BOS (such as charge controllers) near the existing service panel or breaker box (typically indoors). Ensure there is ample room for the equipment and that the area is protected from excessive heat and moisture.

Find and Evaluate Existing Electrical Equipment

When doing a site evaluation, it will be necessary to locate existing electrical equipment, such as the service meter, the main distribution panel, any sub panels, grounding electrode, any generators, or other electrical equipment that will impact the PV installation.

For larger commercial systems, also locate and obtain the ratings of the utility transformer, service disconnecting means, service entrance conductors, supply breaker ratings, and even load breaker ratings.

How a PV system is interconnected to the grid is primarily dictated by the system size (based on AC output current), the requirements of the local utility company, and possibly rebate and incentive program requirements.

Service Panel

ELECTRICAL SERVICE PANEL

Locate the building's main **electrical service panel**, similar to an example illustrate in Figure 5-28, and any subpanels that may be present.

FIGURE 5-28: SINGLE PHASE SERVICE PANEL

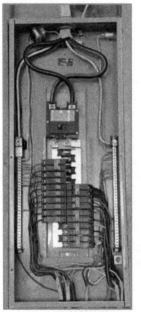

Document the make and model, and verify the busbar rating. Remember that different manufacturers require different breakers (this is not a one-size-fits-all industry). Also verify the level of service entering the building from the utility. These amp ratings will be important in determining if a load side connection is possible.

Also determine if there is enough space in the service panel for another two-pole breaker required for the PV system interconnection. If the service panel is inadequate for the connection, it may be necessary to upgrade the panel or find another location at which to connect the PV system.

Service Voltage

Primary distribution lines (on the grid side of the transformer) typically have voltages ranging from 2,300 to 39,000 volts. At the **distribution transformer**, these voltages are stepped down to meet the requirements of the home or business served (these are referred to as secondary lines or voltage).

DISTRIBUTION TRANSFORMER

Most residential buildings will receive 240 Vac single-phase/slit phase service (120 Vac/ 240 Vac) from the utility. The amount of current provided by the utility will vary depending on the needs of and contract with the home owner. The most common current provided are 100 amps, 200 amp, and in some cases 400 amp service.

Many small commercial buildings may also receive single phase voltages. But more typically, the site will receive three-phase service. Smaller commercial systems may receive 208 Vac/120 Vac three-phase service, and larger systems may receive 480 Vac / 277 Vac service.

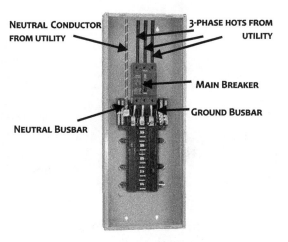

FIGURE 5-29:
THREE-PHASE ELECTRIC SERVICE PANEL

The type of service provided to the facility will generally be noted on the electric meter servicing the property. But it should also be readily apparent when looking at the service panel, as the unit will be serviced by three hot lines feeding the main breaker, as shown in Figure 5-29.

Most inverter manufacturers offer units that will work with either 240 single-phase or 208 three-phase power. Often these systems will even recognize the connected service automatically (no programming required).

A few inverter manufacturers have even begun to offer inverters that can directly connect to the grid at 480 Vac. Often these units are used in community solar projects, agricultural aggregate metering and other large distributed generation projects.

Step-Up and Step-Down Transformers
In most cases, however, a facility that receives three-phase 480 V/ 277 V service will require the installation of a **step-up transformer**, such as the unit pictured in Figure 5-30, to convert the three-phase 208 Vac output of the inverter to be compatible with the three-phase 480 Vac service from the grid. In this application, the transformer works as an alternating current (AC) voltage-to-voltage converter.

> STEP-UP TRANSFORMER

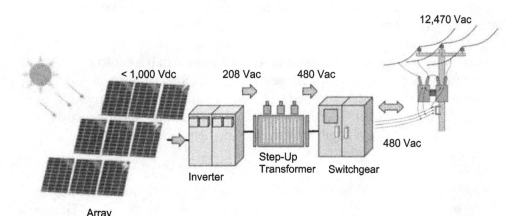

FIGURE 5-30:
208 VAC TO 480 VAC STEP-UP TRANSFORMER

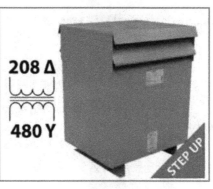

The capacity of the transformer (specified in kVA or MVA) will depend on the projected maximum power exported from the solar array.

The transformer is placed in the system between the inverter (outputting in this example at 208 Vac) and the grid connection (providing service at 480 Vac) as shown in Figure 5-31.

If the system is connected directly to the distribution grid (as is the case in a feed in tariff situation), then the step up transformer would have to be selected to match the distribution network voltage (typically between 4,000 - 35,000 volts).

STEP-DOWN
TRANSFORMER

A **step-down transformer** may already be present in the building to service loads that operate at 480 Vac, 277 Vac, 208 Vac and 120 Vac respectively. For example, the main service coming into the building is 480/277 volt 3-phase 4-wire Wye configuration. Some of this power may be used to feed the 277 volt fluorescent office lighting and parking lot lighting and 480 volts output used to service factory equipment and the rooftop air conditioning system.

A portion of the incoming power can be stepped down in the building through a 3-phase step down transformer. The resulting 3-phase 208 V / 120 V output is fed through a distribution panel, servicing the various lower voltage loads.

Multiple Meters Servicing the Site

Many businesses have multiple utility meters that serve a building or group of buildings on the site. This presents a challenge when designing a PV system for the business.

Many state's net metering rules treat each utility meter as a separate customer, even though they may be servicing the same business.

For example, a large recreational facility wishes to install solar to provide power for their business. They are served by three meters, each installed over the years as the business expanded. There is a building in the complex that houses an indoor soccer field that has a south facing roof which would be ideal location to place a large array that would serve the needs of the entire complex.

An easy solution would be for the utility company to combine the billing on all the meters, treating it as one system (from a billing perspective). However

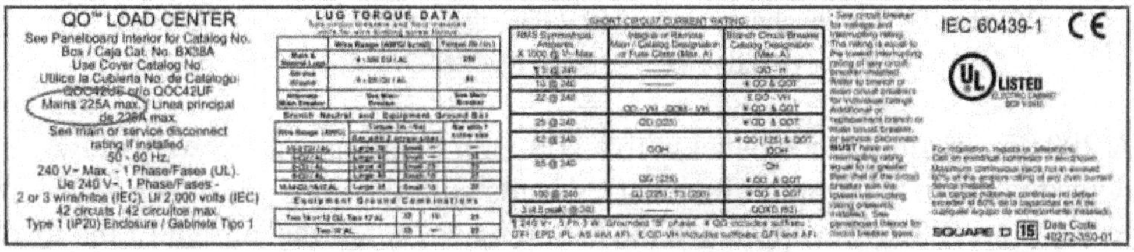

FIGURE 5-32: SERVICE PANEL SPECIFICATION LABEL WITH AMPACITY LIMITS INDICATED

in many cases this practice, known as totalizing metering, additive billing, plural meter billing, conjunctional metering, or **aggregated billing** is prohibited by law.

AGGREGATED BILLING

If conjunctional metering is not possible, there are essentially two ways we deal with this situation.

- Design and size three solar arrays to approximate the energy use on each meter and connect the systems accordingly. This will very likely result in an increased cost of installation, as additional trenching and longer cable runs may be necessary to connect each array or section of a large array to the individually serviced electrical systems.

- Combine all of a facility's meters into a single meter. The up front cost of doing so may be substantial, but may be less than designing and installing three separate arrays.

A third option has recently come on the market, which is a behind-the-meter system that allocates an array's production to multiple meters (at an apartment complex, for example). Systems such as this, however, are still under development and not yet widely available.

Load Side Connection

Many residential and small commercial systems are net-metered, and are connected to the building through a **load side connection** (typically a back-fed circuit breaker in an AC service panel) of existing service equipment.

LOAD SIDE CONNECTION

While this is the easiest method of connecting a PV system to the grid, larger systems will run up against a sizing limitation set by the NEC. The NEC requires that the sum of all input breakers amperage may not exceed 120% of the panel's **busbar** rating. The busbar rating is usually noted on the manufacturer's label on the panel door, as illustrated in Figure 5-32.

BUSBAR

A common residential panel (100 amp rating) will only allow a maximum PV input breaker of 20 A. Since the NEC requires there be a 25% safety margin when sizing wires, 125% of the inverter's output current cannot exceed 20 A (in this example). Assuming the inverter's output is 240 Vac, then the maximum array size in this situation would be:

20 A (allowable 120% of busbar rating) x 240 V (inverter output) / 125 % (NEC safety margin)
= 3,840 W (maximum inverter output)

A 200-amp rated service panel with a 200-amp main disconnect will allow twice the inverter output (which corresponds with the array size) of 7,680 watts. The 120% rule applies to the breaker size, not to the current of the load feeding that breaker.

Supply Side Connection

A larger service panel could be installed, but that option may be expensive and disruptive. More commonly, larger systems, and systems that receive feed-in-tariff payments, are interconnected directly to the utility on the utility side of a building's main service disconnect (the supply side). This is referred to as a **supply side connection** or sometimes as a **line side connection.**

SUPPLY SIDE CONNECTION

LINE SIDE CONNECTION

In cases where a supply side connection is required, the output from the PV array interconnects to the grid at a point between the existing electric meter and the main disconnect.

A supply side connection requires coordination with the utility company, as the service to the building may need to be "shut off" on the utility's side of the system before the connection can be made. In many cases the utility also requires that their electricians be involved in any supply side connection.

There is the additional complexity of just who owns the wire where the connection is to be made.

When making a supply side connection, this connection must be made on the customer's side of the **service point**, this is the **demarcation point** between the utility and the customer. On the utility's side of the demarcation point, they are responsible for the equipment and wires. On the customer's side, the building owner is responsible.

SERVICE POINT

DEMARCATION POINT

It is often assumed that the service point is at the meter. But in some cases, the service point is at the power pole or the underground distribution transformer.

FIGURE 5-33: EXAMPLE OF COMMERCIAL SWITCHGEAR UNIT

Switchgear

In a residential setting, the electrical system will likely be controlled through a service panel and a disconnect or two. But in a large commercial or industrial system, the electrical controls will likely be a bit more complex and housed in a **switchgear** assembly, as shown in Figure 5-33.

SWITCHGEAR

Switchgear is a term that describes a unit that contains a wide variety of switching devices that are designed to control, protect, and isolate power systems. They may also incorporate devices that regulate and meter the power system.

Switchgear typically include the following:
- switches,
- fuses,
- isolators,
- relays,
- circuit breakers,
- lightning arresters,
- potential and current transformers,
- indicating devices.

There are three different classes of switchgear systems: low-voltage, medium-voltage, and high-voltage. High-voltage switchgears are those that control 75 kV of power or more. Medium-voltage switchgear are used in systems from 1 kV up to 75 kV. Low-voltage switchgear are designed to regulate systems of up to 1 kV.

The term **switchboard** is sometimes used synonymously with switchgear. However, these two devices have different functions. Switchgear is designed to connect and isolate load equipment to and from power sources, while switchboards are used to direct the flow of electricity within a power distribution system.

SWITCHBOARD

Conduit Pathways and Existing Grounds

During the site inspection, it is important to get a general idea of where the conduits and/or cable trays, as well as the grounding conductors will be placed.

When planning for conduit pathways, consider:
- equipment placement,
- hazards or obstacles,
- local regulations,
- climate,
- aesthetics.

GROUNDING ELECTRODE CONDUCTOR (GEC)

GROUNDING ELECTRODE

GROUND ROD

Locating and identifying the grounding components during the site survey is also important. The location of the existing **grounding electrode conductor (GEC)** and **grounding electrode** (often a **ground rod**) will be critical in determining the path of the PV system grounding conductor(s) to interconnect the two systems.

Location of Disconnects

The National Electrical Code provides a fair amount of detail and guidance into the placement of disconnects within a PV system. These disconnects are designed to separate various portions of a circuit or equipment from other portions of the circuit or equipment within the same system. They also provide means of disconnecting one system from another system.

For example: the solar array must have a disconnect to isolate it from the inverter; the inverter must be isolated from the battery bank; any generator must have a disconnect to isolate it from the loads and the grid; and the entire system must have the ability to disconnect from the grid.

READILY ACCESSIBLE The NEC states that these disconnects must be installed in a **"readily accessible** location." (NEC 690.13(A)) So what exactly does this mean? Further guidance can be found in Article 100 where it is defined as:

"Accessible, Readily. Capable of being reached quickly for operation, renewal or inspection without requiring those to whom ready access is requisite to take actions such as to use tools (other than keys), to climb over or under, to remove obstacles or to resort to portable ladders and so forth."

The disconnects must be incorporated into the device they are meant to isolate (such as an inverter) or within 3 m (10 ft) of the equipment. Where the disconnect is readily accessible to unqualified persons and operating above 30 V, any door or cover on the enclosure must be locked or require a tool to open it (NEC 690.15).

In a rooftop residential system, it is often impractical (and inaccessible) to place a DC disconnect at or near the array. So a single DC disconnect would be installed at or near the inverter. But for larger rooftop systems and ground mounted systems, an additional DC disconnect is typically placed near the array to isolate the array from the rest of the system.

Only a single disconnect is required if the inverter is located within 10 ft of the main building load center and a backfed breaker in that load center is used as the PV system disconnect.

But generally the local utility requires an outside disconnect be installed within 10 feet of the service entrance location (normally the electric meter). This external disconnect also serves as the rapid shutdown initiator, turning off the power flow from the array at its source (the array itself) when the disconnect is placed in the open position (turned off).

Installations that incorporate multiple arrays at a single site, or multiple power sources such as a wind turbine, battery bank backup or generators, must group these disconnects in a common location. There must be no more than six switches required to turn off all power sources, and the switches located in a common enclosure or group of separate enclosures mounted near each other.

Battery Bank Location

Care should be taken in determining the placement of energy storage systems (ESS) within a facility. This is not something that can be treated as an afterthought, but should be considered during the initial site inspection if batteries are to be incorporated into the system.

Batteries pose a considerable safety concern, and their safe storage and maintenance is addressed in rules developed by OSHA (Occupational Safety and Health Administration).

Traditionally, the most common type of battery used in photovoltaic systems are **lead-acid batteries**. These normally come in two broad categories, vented and **recombinant valve regulated lead-acid (VRLA)** - or more commonly referred to as **flooded** and **sealed**.

In flooded cell batteries the **electrolyte** is in liquid form, while in VRLA batteries it is suspended in a gel or **absorbent glass mats (AGM)**. The electrolyte is a mixture of 35% sulfuric acid and 65% de-ionized water. Lead acid batteries often release hydrogen gas, which can be explosive when confined and exposed to an ignition source. Flooded batteries release hydrogen continuously during charging while VRLA batteries release hydrogen only when overheated and/or overcharged. A flooded battery will emit approximately 60 times more hydrogen than a similar sealed battery. There are a number of safety and health hazards associated with batteries.

| LEAD-ACID BATTERY |
| VRLA |
| FLOODED |
| SEALED |
| ELECTROLYTE |
| ABSORBENT GLASS MAT (AGM) |

These include:
- electrical hazards,
- fire and explosion hazards,
- chemical hazards,
- other related hazards.

Care must be taken to protect those working on the battery system as well as those who may be in or occupying the facility where it is located.

Typical safety concerns imposed by batteries include:

- Electrical shock from touching the exposed terminals of the batteries or conductors attached to them.
- Short circuits that can cause a sudden release of the stored energy of the battery, resulting in an arc or explosion.

- Overcharging, which can result in damage to the battery, leaking of acid, or in severe cases, explosion due to the excessive release of hydrogen gas.
- Injury from lifting or moving the heavy batteries in an improper way.
- Burns from exposure to spilled sulfuric acid.

For economic reasons and efficiency, the battery bank should be located as close as possible to the other electronic components of the system, such as the inverter and charge controller. This may be complicated, however by a number of safety requirements that will impact where and how the system will be stored on the site.

NFPA 855

NFPA 855

NFPA 855 (Standard for the Installation of Energy Storage Systems) is a new National Fire Protection Association Standard developed to define the design, construction, installation, commissioning, operation, maintenance, and decommissioning of stationary energy storage systems.

The organization adopted NFPA 855 in 2019. It set out to standardize and codify installations of lithium-ion batteries, as well as other new technologies. The standards also include lead-acid and nickel-cadmium (Ni-CD) batteries.

This standard restricts the placement of ESS at a site. For example, within residential homes (1-2 family dwellings), the standard states that *"ESS shall not be installed in a living area of dwelling units or in sleeping units other than within utility closets and storage and utility spaces."*

NFPA 855 further outlines that storage systems in a residential setting can only be installed in:

- attached garages separated from the dwelling unit (maximum size allowed in this location is 80 kWh)

- detached garages or other non-occupied buildings (maximum 80 kWh)

- outdoors either attached to the exterior wall or mounted on the ground, located at least 3 feet from any doors or windows (maximum 80 kWh)

FIGURE 5-34: SECURE WELL LIT, WELL VENTILATED BATTERY STORAGE ROOM.

- or in an enclosed utility closet or room or storage room (maximum size allowed within the building is 40 kWh).

Interestingly the NFPA 855 does allow the home owner to use an electric vehicle parked outside or in the garage as a battery backup system for the home - but only on a temporary basis. It states that the use of an EV for battery backup should not exceed 30 days.

Factors to consider when designing a battery enclosure include:

- Batteries must be stored in an enclosure or room that provides for a one-hour or longer fire protection separation from the occupied portions of the building.

- These rooms or enclosures must be well vented to the outside to prevent hydrogen gas from accumulating and/or escaping into the occupied portions of the building. Two air changes per hour minimum is recommended.

- The floor of the room or enclosure must be acid resistant and designed to prevent the accumulation of acid.

- Facilities for the drenching of the eyes and body shall be provided within 25 feet of the work area for emergency use.

- Precautions should be taken to keep the stored batteries away from open flames (not stored near furnaces, for example).

NEMA Rating	Description
Type 1	Indoor. Protects against dust, light, and indirect splashing but is not dust-tight.
Type 2	Indoor. Drip-tight. Similar to Type 1 but with addition of drip shields; used where condensation may be severe.
Type 3, 3X*	Indoor/outdoor. Weather-resistant. Protects against falling dirt and windblown dust, against weather hazards such as rain, sleet and snow, and is undamaged by the formation of ice.
Type 4, 4X	Indoor/outdoor. Watertight.
Type 5	Indoor. Dust tight, drip and splash protection.
Type 6	Indoor/outdoor. Submersible.
Type 7	Indoor. For use in areas with specific hazardous conditions.
Type 8	Indoor/outdoor. For use in areas with specific hazardous conditions.
Type 9	Indoor/outdoor. For use in areas with specific hazardous conditions.
Type 10	Meets the requirements of the Mine Safety and Health Administration
Type 11	General-purpose. Protects against the corrosive effects of liquids and gases. Meets drip and corrosion-resistance tests.
Type 12	Indoor. Provides some protection against dust, falling dirt, and dripping non-corrosive liquids
Type 13	Similar to 12 but also meets oil exclusion tests.
	*X indicates additional corrosion protection; commonly used near salt water.

TABLE 5-2: NEMA ENCLOSURE RATING SYSTEM

FIGURE 5-35: VENTED
BATTERY STORAGE UNIT
FOR SMALLER PV SYSTEM

(FROM THE GREEN POWER
COMPANY)

- There should be enough space available to safely work on the battery bank system, including required clearances and pathways, as demonstrated in Figure 5-34.

- The storage area should be secured from access by untrained persons and well marked with the appropriate signs.

- Doors must open outwards.

- The room must be accessible to first responders. For example, local code may require that stationary storage battery systems shall not be located in areas where the floor is located more than 75 ft above the lowest level of fire department vehicle access, or where the floor level is more than 30 ft below the finished floor of the lowest level of exit.

For smaller battery banks, many vendors offer secure and vented cabinets designed to store and protect the system, as illustrated in Figure 5-35.

These enclosures typically offer features such as:
- venting (as hydrogen gas is lighter than air, venting should be at or near the top of the enclosure),
- cable management,
- access restriction (locks),
- spill containment,
- protection from environment (moisture, heat, dropped tools, etc).

NEMA

Cabinets and enclosures are rated by the **National Electrical Manufacturers Association (NEMA)**. They are rated based on certain performance criteria, as outlined in Table 5-2.

Solar installers are particularly concerned with three ratings for enclosures used in PV systems.

- *NEMA Type 1* – These enclosures are for indoor use only and provide a limited degree of protection against access to hazardous parts, as well as to equipment inside (against falling objects, dirt, etc).

- *NEMA Type 3R* – These enclosures are for indoor or outdoor use. They provide a limited degree of protection against access to hazardous parts, as well as to equipment inside (against falling objects, dirt, etc). But they also provide a degree of protection with respect to harmful effects on the equipment from water (rain, sleet, snow); and that will be undamaged by the external formation of ice on the enclosure.

- *NEMA Type 12* – These enclosures are for indoor use only but provide protection against water, unlike NEMA Type 1 enclosures.

Stationary storage battery systems located outdoors must generally be separated by a minimum 5 ft from the following:

- lot lines,
- public ways,
- buildings,
- stored combustible materials,
- hazardous materials,
- high-piled stock,
- other exposure hazards.

Additional Design Criteria when Installing Battery Systems

- Live parts of battery systems for dwellings must be guarded to prevent accidental contact by people or objects.

- Flexible battery cables are listed RHW or THW, 2/0 minimum for battery cell connections. NOTE: welding cables, marine, locomotive (DLO), and automotive cables do not meet the current Electrical Code requirements.

- Flexible battery cables do not leave the battery enclosure. Flexible, fine strand cables are only to be used with terminals, lugs, devices, and connectors that are listed and marked for such use.

- High interrupt, listed, DC-rated fuses or circuit breakers must be used in battery circuits. The **ampere interrupting capacity (AIC)** must be at least 20,000 amps.

AMPERE INTERRUPTING CAPACITY (AIC)

- Cables longer than five feet (5 feet) to inverters, DC load centers, and/or charge controllers must be in conduit.

- Conduits that enter the battery enclosure should be located below the tops of the batteries. This is to avoid accidental ventilation of gases into electrical equipment where sparks may occur.

- A DC disconnect should be provided for all ungrounded conductors at the battery bank.

- If the DC disconnect at the batteries is not within sight of the inverter/charge controller, then an additional disconnect is required at the connected equipment.

- When the disconnect for the battery bank is not within sight of the PV system AC and DC disconnecting means, all of the disconnects must be labeled to refer to the locations of all of the other disconnects in the system.

- Energy storage systems shall be listed to UL 1989 or 9540 as applicable.

Use of Drones

DRONE

For solar projects, one of the most common use of **drones** is in the initial survey and system design. A drone can be used to evaluate the site (rooftop or ground mounted) without requiring the surveyor to physically climb onto the roof or walk the property.

UNMANNED AIRCRAFT SYSTEM (UAS)

While commonly referred to as drones, the more correct terminology is to refer to these vehicles as **unmanned aircraft systems (UAS)**. For drones that weigh less than 55 lbs., the FAA classifies them as small Unmanned Aircraft Systems (sUAS).

Systems are available that allow the collection of accurate measurements of the installation site as well as photograph the structure. This process not only saves time, but is safer and often provides more accurate data.

Drones can also be used at other stages of the installation process. For example, during installation, drone footage can assist installers detect safety hazards (such as ice on roof surfaces), monitor worker progress without having to climb up on the building, and provide installation aerial imaging and terrain mapping status updates.

Large scale solar projects are often spread out over very large areas in often harsh environments. Checking each panel for defects can take hours. With

FIGURE 5-36: DRONE CLEANING A SOLAR PANEL

(FROM AIROBOTICS)

drones, pilots can cover the entire area quickly. The drone can be outfitted with thermal imaging sensors that can be used to check panels for damage or anomalies.

Drones can also be equipped to provide periodic maintenance, such as the cleaning of remote panels, as illustrated in Figure 5-36.

Issues when using Drones

There are concerns that must be addressed when using or operating a drone.

Commercial Use

The Federal Aviation Administration (FAA) has established certain rules for small, unmanned aircraft that apply to commercial and recreational use. But many of these regulations remain unclear. Adding to the confusion is that state and local laws often conflict with or contradict the federal regulations.

REMOTE PILOT CERTIFICATE

An FAA license, or **remote pilot certificate**, is required to fly a drone commercially. The FAA determines whether the drone flight is commercial or recreational based on the intent of the flight at the moment of drone take-off. Clearly a site evaluation of a solar installation would be considered a commercial activity. If the FAA becomes aware of unlicensed drone activities, the operator could be fined up to $32,666 per violation.

All commercial drones must be registered with the FAA. Each registered drone is given a unique number that starts with an "N" or "FA." This registration number must be placed on a drone in either a visible place or in the battery compartment, so long as no tools are required to open it.

Safe Operation

Safety is a concern when operating drones. To avoid mid-air collisions, drones should be programmed with "sense and avoid" capabilities that match those of manned aircraft. This means that drones must be able to detect a potential collision and maneuver to safety. When these systems fail, falling drones can pose a serious risk to people and/or property.

Fines may also be imposed for flying a drone in an unsafe manner. Penalties may also include revocation or suspension of a remote pilot's certificate or denial for one year of an application for a remote pilot's certificate.

Examples of unsafe operations may include night flying, flying out of the line-of-sight of the operator, or flying over people.

Flights are allowed only in unrestricted airspace up to 400 feet altitude with a maximum drone speed of 100 mph.

Avoiding **restricted airspace** and giving right-of-way to manned aircraft is among the many other requirements. Restricted airspace is an area of airspace typically used by the military in which the local controlling authorities have determined that air traffic must be restricted or prohibited for safety or security concerns.

RESTRICTED AIRSPACE

Privacy Concerns

One of the most common concerns from the public about the use of drones is one of privacy. Drones can collect data and images not only of the site being surveyed, but nearby properties as well. Neighboring property owners should be informed in writing that a drone is being used and permission obtained in certain situations.

Site Hazard Assessment

OSHA (the Occupational Safety and Health Administration) requires that site managers perform a safety assessment on every project. Installing a PV system can be risky. There are inherent risks associated with lifting and placing solar panels onto rooftops. Installers also work with electrical systems that present a risk from shocks or arcs.

Installers often work under extreme weather conditions, facing injury from either extreme heat or cold.

During the site inspection, it should be determined:
- What type of ladders or scaffolding will be needed?
- Is fall protection required, and where will it be secured?
- What barriers will be required and where will they be placed (around skylights, access hatches, roof edges, etc.)?
- Where will materials be staged during the installation?
- Where will vehicles and equipment be parked on the site?
- Is any cleanup required prior to construction to ensure a safe and uncluttered work environment?
- Is the building structure adequate for the installation and personnel?
- Is there adequate access to the site during the installation?
- Are there any hazards imposed from traffic (both people and vehicles) during installation?
- Are there any potential slip and fall hazards present?
- Are there any dangerous substances stored on the site?
- and many other site-specific concerns.

Chapter 5 Review Questions

1. When conducting an initial site assessment, which of the following are issues that are typically **NOT** investigated during this process?
   a) ownership of the property and system
   b) return on investment calculations
   c) utility connection process and restrictions
   d) orientation of the array

2) Which of the following is **NOT** an insurance product that often must be purchased during the construction of a large array?
   a) errors and omissions insurance
   b) general liability insurance
   c) business interruption insurance
   d) property risk insurance

3) Which of the following is **NOT** a common concern that must be addressed with the utility prior to interconnection?
   a) the angle and orientation of the array
   b) the inverter's rating and certification or listing
   c) the size of the array
   d) location of the point of common coupling

4) A common concern with lidar imaging is:
   a) that systems which employ it are expensive and difficult to use
   b) the perspectives are in two dimensions, making shading issues difficult to identify
   c) the satellites used in the system are often not available in remote locations
   d) the data used in these systems are often out-of-date and unreliable

5) The sum of direct normal irradiance, reflected irradiance and diffuse horizontal irradiance is known as the:
   a) albedo
   b) peak sun hours
   c) insolation
   d) plane of array

6) Which of the following tools would be useful in determining if a specific site has enough sunlight available to support a PV system?
   a) PV Watts
   b) a solar window
   c) a declination chart
   d) a plane of array

7) When determining whether or not a PV array can be placed on a rooftop, which of the following is **NOT** generally a concern?
    a) dead load
    b) live load
    c) critical load
    d) system load

8) In most jurisdictions, flat roofs must be built to support a minimum:
    a) 300 lbs concentrated weight
    b) 17 kW solar array
    c) a 6 rise/12 run pitch
    d) 6:1 live load/ dead load ratio

9) On a flat commercial roof, the International Fire Code (IFC) requires all of the following **EXCEPT**:
    a) a three-foot (3-ft.) setback of the array from the ridge and on both sides of the roof line
    b) a four-foot (4-ft.) clear area around all access hatchways
    c) no section of the array can be larger than 150 feet by 150 feet
    d) a six-foot (6 ft) setback around the perimeter of the roof For buildings larger that 250 ft x 250 ft

10) When placing an array on a roof, which of the following should be considered?
    a) the live weight
    b) the dead weight
    c) condition of the rafters
    d) all of the above

11) The wind load placed on an array is dependent upon all the following conditions **EXCEPT**:
    a) the height of the building
    b) the azimuth of the array
    c) the size of the roof area
    d) the topology of the land around the building

12) An advantage of a ballasted rooftop system is:
    a) no seismic and wind load limitations
    b) low tilt angle (generally less than 20 degrees)
    c) adds very little dead weight load to the roof structure
    d) very few roof penetrations required

13) In calculating the minimum distance between rows in a solar array (d) to avoid inter-row shading, where:

h =   the height differential between the top of one row and the bottom of the row behind it

α =   is the altitude angle of the sun at that location at 9 am on the winter solstice

A =   the azimuth of the array

I =   hours of insolation at the site

Then the distance between rows is calculated using the following equation:
a) $d = A \times I / \alpha$
b) $d = h / \text{tangent } \alpha$
c) $d = \text{cosine } \alpha / h$
d) $d = I / \text{cosine } \alpha$

14) The size of the actual solar array panels divided by the total size of the area the array covers is known as the:
a)   plane of array
b)   total resource fraction
c)   ground cover ratio
d)   IFC setback factor

15) There are 68 panels in an array. Each panel measures 3 ft x 5 ft (15 square feet) when viewed from directly overhead. The perimeter of the array boundary measures 100 ft x 20 ft. What is the ground cover ratio of this array?
a)   7.5%
b)   0.51
c)   1,020
d)   2,000

16) A client wishes you to give a "ballpark" estimate on the size of the array that might be placed on the south-facing portion of her sloped roof. It appears to be oriented at about 25 degrees. When measured, the south-facing portion of the roof surface is 40 feet by 25 feet. The total area of the roof is 40 feet by 50 feet. There is a chimney (3 ft x 4 ft) at the ridge at one end of the roof. There are no other obstructions.

What would be a realistic estimate of the size of the array that could be installed assuming crystalline panels are used?
a)   19.5 kW
b)   9.6 kW
c)   6.8 kW
d)   not enough information is provided to give an informed guess

17) A site where the soil is so contaminated that private development cannot take place without governmental assistance and oversite is known as a:
    a) greenfield
    b) greyfield
    c) blackfield
    d) brightfield

18) Which of the following is typically **NOT** normally a requirement or restriction placed on a large ground mounted solar array by AHJs?
    a) setback requirements from existing buildings and property lines
    b) screening put in place to limit the visibility of the array
    c) restrictions on the amount of glare from the array that might impact neighbors or passing traffic
    d) limiting the hours during the day when the array may be in operation

19) Which of the following is **NOT** an advantage of a ground-mounted PV system over a roof-mounted PV system?
    a) can be oriented as required rather than determined by the building's orientation
    b) no fire codes apply to ground mounted systems
    c) panels operate in a cooler environment
    d) avoids placing added stresses upon the building's structural supports

20) A conductor is **NOT** considered inaccessible if:
    a) a fence with a locked gate is constructed around the array
    b) it is terminated with an MC4 connector
    c) a warning sign is placed within 3 feet (one meter) of the conductor
    d) it is located at least 8 feet above the ground surface

21) One disadvantage of an east/west ballasted flat roof mounting system is:
    a) increased ground cover ratio (GCR)
    b) more space required to avoid inter-row shading
    c) low profile minimizes cable management options
    d) none of the above

22) Two ground-mounted sub-arrays of twelve (12) 300-watt panels (three rows, four columns each are constructed and oriented at an azimuth of 180 degrees and an altitude of 45 degrees. One sub-array is placed 20 feet due north of the other.

    Which of the following situations will likely experience the **GREATEST** amount of inter-row shading throughout the year?
    a) oriented landscape and located at 50 degrees north latitude
    b) oriented portrait and located at 50 degrees north latitude
    c) oriented landscape and located at 35 degrees north latitude
    d) oriented portrait and located at 35 degrees north latitude

23) A horizontal axis tracking system:
   a) adjusts the altitude angle (solar elevation) each day as the sun tracks from its apex at dawn and dusk to its zenith at solar noon
   b) adjusts its azimuth orientation from east to west as the sun tacks from dawn to dusk
   c) adjusts the altitude angle (solar elevation) throughout the year as the solar elevation of the sun varies seasonally
   d) adjusts its azimuth orientation throughout the year as the solar elevation of the sun varies seasonally

24) Which of the following is **NOT** an advantage of a sun tracking system?
   a) increased energy production per square meter
   b) panels can be placed closer together with less risk of self-shading
   c) can be used to maximize production during peak load demand
   d) are less expensive to install over the active life of the system

25) Evaluating the soil conditions prior to designing and installing a ground-mounted system is referred to as a:
   a) geotechnical survey
   b) geothermal evaluation
   c) geological assessment
   d) geohydrolic identification

26) Which of the following is **NOT** a common foundation type used in ground-mounted PV systems?
   a) driven pile
   b) earth screw
   c) helical anchor
   d) tiled and grouted pier

27) A site assessment has been conducted on a residential system. PV Watts reports that at a 29 degree altitude at 180 degree azimuth, the site will receive optimal sunlight (total solar resource), with insolation of 4.65 hours. However, at the actual angle and pitch of the roof, the calculated insolation for this site is 3.95 hours. An evaluation at the site finds that about 13% of the total available sunlight that could possibly strike the array is lost due to shading.

   What is the total solar resource fraction (TSRF) of this site?
   a) 87%
   b) 85%
   c) 74%
   d) 72%

28) The service voltage a building receives from the utility is generally determined at the:
   a) inverter
   b) distribution transformer
   c) sub-station
   d) service panel

29) A large office building is provided 480/277 Vac power from the grid. The facility needs to power a 208 Vac air handling unit. To do so, a _____ must be installed on site.
   a) distribution transformer
   b) step-up transformer
   c) step-down transformer
   d) pad mount transformer

30) A customer has a 400 amp service panel with 400 amp service from the utility. What is the largest single-phase 240 Vac output inverter that can be load side connected to this service panel?
   a) 12.29 kW
   b) 15.36 kW
   c) 19.2 kW
   d) the inverter must be supply side connected as the service panel has reached its maximum rated capacity

31) A supply side connection is made:
   a) between the demarcation point (usually the utility meter) and the main disconnect
   b) at the distribution transformer
   c) at a point on the service panel busbar as far away from the main connection point as possible
   d) on the utility side of the meter

32) Disconnects within a PV system must meet all the following conditions **EXCEPT**:
   a) be rated for DC voltage
   b) be installed in a readily accessible location
   c) must be lockable or require a special tool to open
   d) must be clearly marked

33) The code/standard that sets out the design, construction , installation, commissioning, operation, maintenance and decommissioning of stationary energy storage systems is:
   a) UL 1741-SA
   b) NEC Article 690
   c) NFPA 855
   d) IEEE 1547

34) Current codes/standards require that ESS sized between 40 kWh - 80 kWh in residential settings be installed:
   a) in a lockable well-ventilated enclosed utility closet or storage room with a door that opens outward
   b) outdoors only, secured to the exterior wall of all structures including the residence, attached and detached garages or storage buildings, and mounted at least 3 feet away from all doors and windows
   c) within a NEMA 3X-rated well-ventilated enclosure when placed within the living area of a building
   d) within attached and/or detached garages, as well as mounted to the outside of the structure

35) Which NEMA enclosure rating indicates indoor/outdoor weather resistance?
   a) Type 1
   b) Type 2
   c) Type 3
   d) Type 5

36) When using a drone to assist a designer/installer paid to evaluate a rooftop during a site evaluation:
   a) no license or permit is required if the drone weighs less than 55 lbs
   b) the operator must hold a remote pilot certificate or face a fine up to $32,666 per violation
   c) a permit must be obtained from the local AHJ and signed release forms must be completed (if possible) from all neighboring properties
   d) all drones (recreational and commercial) must be registered with the FAA and the registration number posted prominently on the side of the unmanned aircraft

Chapter 6

Codes, Standards & Listings

A host of laws, ordinances, codes, standards, product listings and industry certifications are designed to facilitate the safe design, installation and operation of PV systems.

While all these rules and regulations must be complied with, they are different in nature from each other.

A **code** is a set of rules that a group of people (hopefully industry experts) recommend for others to follow. It is not a law, but can be adopted into law by a local authority having jurisdiction (AHJ).

> CODE

Building codes set minimum standards for structures and buildings to protect public health, safety, and welfare.

A **standard** tends be a more detailed in nature, outlining industry best practices that if followed, should result in meeting the code. In other words, the code states what to do and the standard states how to do it.

> STANDARD

There are quite a number of different types of standards. These include:

- *Industry Standards:* These outline industry best practices for processes, products, services, practices and integration.

- *National Standards*: Standards that are enforced or offered as a reference by a nation.
- *International Standards:* Standards that are adopted by many nations.
- *Quality Standards:* A broad category of standards for ensuring that processes, products and services conform to pre-determined specifications.
- *Professional Standards:* Standards that can be used to guide a profession such as project management standards that outline processes, practices and a common vocabulary. In many cases, a professional can be certified against a standard based on their career and satisfactory completion of training and/or testing.
- and many more...

PRODUCT LISTING

A **product listing** or product certification indicates that a product has been independently tested and found to comply with a specific product quality standard. Both the standard and the testing organization are often referenced when indicating compliance. For example, UL/ANSI 1703 that indicates the solar panel has been tested by Underwriters Laboratories (UL) and found to be in compliance the the American National Standards Institute (ANSI) 1703 standard.

CERTIFICATION

A professional **certification** is issued when an organization (usually a non-profit trade association) determines that an individual or a company has complied with the requirements as set out in a professional standard.

National Electrical Code

NATIONAL ELECTRICAL CODE (NEC)

NATIONAL FIRE PROTECTION ASSOCIATION

In the USA, the **National Electrical Code (NFPA 70 or NEC)** is published every three years by the **National Fire Protection Association** and seeks to create a safe standard for the installation of electrical wiring and equipment.

The NEC (Figure 6-1) is not a federal law, but must be adopted by local or state governing bodies to have the effect of law.

In the United States authorities having jurisdictions (AHJ) over the development and enforcement of building codes are: states, counties, and municipalities. Most AHJs adopt codes that contain only a few modifications to nationally developed model codes.

FIGURE 6-1:
NATIONAL ELECTRICAL CODE (NFPA 70)

WWW.NFPA.ORG

NFPA 70
National Electrical Code
2020
nec

Often these bodies are slow to adopt the most recent version of the code (most recent update released in 2020), so note that older versions of the code may be the required guide in many parts of the country (as indicated in Figure 6-2).

And not every state or local jurisdiction formally adopts codes that may apply to a specific industry or trade (such as the NEC). State-wide adoption generally sets a minimum standard. Local cities or counties can adopt more stringent requirements or adopt standards for which no state code exists.

FIGURE 6-2:
STATE-BY-STATE ADOPTION OF NEC AS OF JULY 2021

When a roof is repaired or major components within an existing system are replaced, local authorities may require that an installed system be upgraded to comply with the currently adopted NEC for that location. Check with local building authorities if there is any question as to which NEC version applies.

In addition to the United States, the NEC has been adopted within Mexico, Costa Rica, Venezuela, Colombia and a number of other nations around the world.

Sections in NEC that Apply to Solar PV

PV systems are electrical in nature, so much of the code is important in designing and installing a complete system, **Article 690** of the code specifically addresses photovoltaics. Article 705 addresses the specific requirements of interconnected systems, and Article 250 focuses on bonding and grounding of electrical systems.

ARTICLE 690

Other sections of specific interest to PV installers include:
- Article 480 - Battery Storage Systems
- Article 706 - Energy Storage Systems >1 kWh
- Article 691 - Large Scale Photovoltaic Electric Power Production Facility
- Article 710 - Stand Alone Systems
- Article 712 - DC Microgrids

Additional Codes

In addition to the NEC, the **International Residential Code (IRC)** includes standards that apply to solar PV systems.

INTERNATIONAL RESIDENTIAL CODE

INTERNATIONAL FIRE CODE (IFC)

The **International Fire Code (IFC)** outlines solar guidelines relating to fire access and fire safety. Like NFPA 70, this code is updated every three years. The most

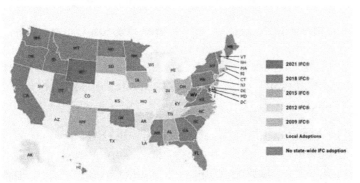

FIGURE 6-3:
STATE-BY-STATE ADOPTION OF IFC AS OF JANUARY 2022

recent edition was published in 2021. And as is the case with the NEC, not every state has adopted the IFC, and those that have may not have adopted the most recent edition (as shown in Figure 6-3).

While many jurisdictions have adopted the IFC, some states have adopted the **NFPA 1, Fire Code**, which addresses many of the same issues.

NFPA 1 FIRE CODE

Part of the codes' objective is to ensure that firefighters can respond effectively and safely to a fire. PV systems are a concern for firefighters because, during a fire, roof-mounted PV systems can impede access to the roof or become a potential shock hazard. Where PV systems are installed on the ground, vegetation and near-by structures could provide a means of spreading fire, and the PV panels could become a shock hazard for anyone with access to the array.

A specific web-based search tool (I-Codes) has been published by the International Code Council that allows users to determine if local AJHs have adopted the IFC. The NFPA has a similar tool (Codefinder) for those jurisdictions that have adopted the NFPA 1 code.

NFPA 855 (Standard for the Installation of Energy Storage Systems) is a new National Fire Protection Association Standard developed to define the design, construction, installation, commissioning, operation, maintenance, and decommissioning of stationary energy storage systems.

The 2021 versions of IFC, IRC, and NFPA 1 based their ESS fire code requirements on the NFPA 855 standard. So if a local jurisdiction has adopted any of these as codes, the NFPA 855 is in effect.

The International Residential Code and the International Building Code require rack-mounted rooftop PV systems to be installed according to the manufacturer's instructions, the National Electrical Code, and Underwriters Laboratories product safety standards.

As of 2021, the International Residential Code (IRC) is in use or adopted in 49 states, the District of Columbia, Guam, Puerto Rico and the U.S. Virgin Islands. The International Fire Code (IFC) is in use or adopted in 41 states, the District of Columbia, NYC, Guam and Puerto Rico. As of January 2020, the NFPA 1: Fire Code has been adopted and is enforceable in 19 states.

INTERNATIONAL ENERGY CONSERVATION CODE

The **International Energy Conservation Code (IECC)** contains specifications for onsite renewable energy generation in commercial systems. It is a model code adopted by many states and municipal governments for the establishment of minimum design and construction requirements for energy efficiency.

INTERNATIONAL MECHANICAL CODE

The **International Mechanical Code (IMC)** regulates the design and installation of mechanical systems, appliances, appliance venting, duct and ventilation systems, combustion air provisions, and solar systems. The provisions focused on solar within the document govern the design, materials, construction and quality of roof assemblies and rooftop structures.

The **Canadian Electrical Code (CEC)** published by the CSA (Canadian Standards Association) is used in Canada.

The **IEC 60364** published by the International Electrotechnical Commission (IEC) is used as a basis for electrical codes in many European countries.

The British Standard, **BS 7671** is the set of regulations for electrical wiring used within the United Kingdom.

Australian/New Zealand Standard, **AS/NZS 3000:2007 Wiring Rules** is used in Australia and New Zealand.

CANADIAN
ELECTRICAL CODE

IEC 60364

BS 7671

AS/NZS 3000: 2007
WIRING RULES

Canadian Electrical Code

Like the NEC, the CEC is updated every three years (2018, 2021, 2024, etc). While the two codes are largely similar, there are differences that must be addressed when installing a system. Varying wire gauge designations, differences in clearances and ampacity limitations are examples of requirements that must be checked and complied with.

In 2012 the CEC added *Section 64: Renewable Energy Systems* to the code to more fully address the rapidly evolving technologies. However, solar electric systems remained in Section 50. In the 2018 revision, solar technologies were moved to Section 64.

This section includes:
- 64-002 - Special terminology
- 64-058 - Overcurrent protection
- 64-060 - Disconnecting means
- 64-062 - Wiring methods
- 64-066 - Ungrounded renewable energy power systems
- 64-070 - Equipment bonding
- 64-110 - Unbalanced interconnections (inverters)
- 64-112 - Utility-interactive point of connection (inverters)
- 64-202 - Voltage of solar photovoltaic systems
- 64-210 - Wiring methods
- 64-212 - Insulated conductor marking or colour coding
- 64-214 - Overcurrent protection for apparatus and conductors
- 64-216 - Photovoltaic DC arc-fault protection
- 64-218 - Rapid shutdown
- 64-220 - Attachment plugs and similar wiring devices
- 64-222 - Photovoltaic module bonding

Standards

In addition to codes, there are also a number of national and/or international standards that provide guidance on how to install PV systems to industry best practices.

IEC 60364

INTERNATIONAL
ELECTROTECHNICAL
COMMISSION (IEC)

The **International Electrotechnical Commission (IEC)** produces standards, including the *IEC 60364: Electrical Installations for Buildings*, for use in its 82 member countries. The IEC is world-wide in scope, influencing the way work takes place throughout all continents, but its influence is most felt in Europe.

IEC 60364

Unlike the NEC, the **IEC 60364** is not intended to be used directly by designers, installers or enforcement/inspection officials. It is intended to be used only as a guide to those developing national wiring rules.

The portion of the standard that applies to the design of photovoltaics is IEC 60364-7-712 (2017).

IEC 62446-1:2016 defines the documentation required following the installation of a grid connected PV system. It also describes the commissioning tests, inspection criteria and documentation expected to verify the safe installation and correct operation of the system. It is for use by system designers and installers of grid connected solar PV systems as a template to provide effective documentation to a customer.

IEC 60904-2:2015 gives requirements for the classification, selection, packaging, marking, calibration and care of photovoltaic reference devices. This standard covers photovoltaic reference devices used to determine the electrical performance of photovoltaic cells, modules and arrays under natural and simulated sunlight. It does not cover photovoltaic reference devices for use under concentrated sunlight.

CENELEC

The **Central European Normalization Electrotechnique (CENELEC)** is the European committee for electrotechnical standardization. Designated as a European Standards Organization by the European Commission, CENELEC is a non-profit technical organization that publishes the European standard for Electrical installations and protection, referred to as HD 60364.

BS 7671

BS 7671

British standard *BS 7671 "Requirements for Electrical Installations* is the national standard in the United Kingdom for electrical installation and the safety of electrical wiring in domestic, commercial, industrial, and other buildings. This standard is essentially the UK version of the HD 60364. Requirements that are UK specific and not derived from HD 60364 can be identified by the number 200, 201, 202 etc. For example, Regulation 412.1.201:

The current version is BS 7671:2018 (the 18th Edition) issued in 2018 and came into effect from 1 January 2019.

The part of the standard that addresses PV specifically is *Section 712, Solar photovoltaic (PV) power supply systems*.

IEEE 1547

The **IEEE Standard 1547** was created to establish a technical standard for interconnecting distributed energy systems (referred to in the standard as **distributed energy resources (DER)**) with electrical power systems (EPSs) - in other words, the grid. As technology became more sophisticated and more and more systems were connected to it, issues arose that needed to be addressed.

IEEE 1547

DISTRIBUTED ENERGY RESOURCE (DER)

The latest revision, IEEE 1547-2018, changed the testing standards for distributed energy systems to create harmonized interconnection requirements and offer flexibility in performance requirements.

In the past, inverters were required to disconnect from the grid when power quality issues arose. Changes in IEEE 1547-2018 now require smart inverters to sense grid conditions and respond accordingly.

These standards are of significant importance to utility grid operators as well as equipment manufacturers in order to ensure compliance.

ANSI/UL 3741 Hazard Control Standard

First published in December 2020, **ANSI/CAN/UL 3741:** Standard for Safety for Photovoltaic Hazard Control, is intended to set guidelines for the installation of PV arrays subject to rapid-shutdown requirements. This standard is designed to keep firefighters out of hazardous electrical current paths when responding to emergency situations in homes and buildings with PV systems.

ANSI/UL 3741

Product Specific Standards

There are a number of standards directed at the manufacture of specific solar products. Installers should take care to ensure that all the products installed in a system meet these industry standards.

UL 1703 - Solar Panels

The **ANSI/UL 1703** standard covers flat-plate photovoltaic modules and panels intended for installation on or integral with buildings, or to be freestanding (that is, not attached to buildings). These requirements cover modules and panels intended for use in systems with a maximum system voltage of 1500 V or less.

ANSI/UL 1703

The solar panel market is global in nature. So in 2017, Underwriters Labs (UL) harmonized its PV module safety standard to the IEC 61730 international standard for modules.

UL 1741-SA - Inverters, Controllers, Converters

ANSI/UL 1741-SA

ANSI/UL 1741 is a product safety standard that establishes manufacturing and testing requirements for inverters, converters, controllers and interconnection system equipment for use within distributed energy systems.

CALIFORNIA RULE 21

In 2017 California became the first US state to require the use of advanced, or "smart inverters" in solar projects. This requirement reflected changes made to **California Rule 21** that required inverters have certain capabilities to help ensure proper operation of the electric grid as more and more renewables are connected. The goal of these changes is to make PV systems and the grid more resilient during both normal and abnormal operating conditions.

UL, in 2016, revised the 1741 standard, issuing UL 1741-SA (SA standing for supplemental addendum).

Tests performed under UL 1741-SA include:
- enhanced anti-island testing to ensure PV systems disconnect when required,
- voltage and frequency ride through and ramp rate control testing ensure PV systems act in a predictable fashion as the grid experiences fluctuations,
- must trip test,
- ramp rate (normal & soft-start),
- specified power factor.

While not every jurisdiction requires that newly installed equipment meet the newer UL 1741-SA standard (some still require only compliance with UL 1741), all major inverter manufacturers design and test their new inverters to the UL 1741-SA standard.

UL 1973 - Stationary Batteries

UL 1973

UL 1973 is a safety standard for stationary batteries for energy storage systems that is not specific to any one battery technology or chemistry, and can apply to Li-ion battery ESSs, as well as ESSs using other battery chemistry. The standard includes construction requirements, safety performance tests, and production tests.

UL 2703 - Racking Systems

UL 2703

This standard covers rack mounting systems and clamping devices for flat-plate photovoltaic modules and panels that comply with UL 1703. It does not cover tracking systems for PV.

UL 9540 - Energy Storage Systems

UL 9540

An energy storage system (ESS) certified to **UL 9540** is comprised of a UL 1973 certified stationary battery that is then evaluated for use with a power conversion system, such as a UL 1741 certified inverter (integrated together as a complete system).

FIGURE 6-4:
UL SERVICE MARKS

(IMAGE FROM UNDERWRITERS
LABORATORIES)

Approved and Tested Products

The use of equipment that has been tested and approved for its specific application is required by most codes and standards (such as the NEC).

Manufacturers submit their products to facilities (referred to as a **national recognized testing laboratory**, or NRTL) that test them under laboratory conditions to ensure that they conform with the appropriate industry standard.

NATIONAL
RECOGNIZED TESTING
LABORATORY (NRTL)

Approved equipment is identified with a listing label indicating that it conforms with a specific standard.

UL Marks

Underwriters Labs (UL) is likely the most recognizable of the NRTLs within North America. They offer a number of service marks for products (illustrated in Figure 6-4) that have been tested and/or evaluated within their facilities.

A **UL Listing Mark**, indicates that the product has been tested and found to be in compliance with a specific standard. This mark is generally accepted by the code bodies as evidence that the product has been approved as conforming with the standard's requirements.

UL LISTING MARK

The **UL Classification Mark** indicates that the product has only been tested under limited circumstances.

UL CLASSIFICATION
MARK

The UL marks generally indicate if they have been tested for the United States, Canada or both - as indicated with the letter "C" for Canada and the letters "US" for the United States.

Electrical Testing Labs/Intertek (ETL)

Electrical Testing Labs/Intertek (ETL) is another widely recognized NRTL that tests products for conformance with various standards.

FIGURE 6-5: ELECTRICAL
TESTING LABS/INTERTEK
LISTING MARK

There is essentially no difference in the testing process or acceptance of the designations issued by UL or ETL (Figure 6-5).

ELECTRICAL TESTING
LABS/INTERTEK (ETL)

FIGURE 6-6: CANADIAN STANDARDS ASSOCIATION LISTING MARK

> CANADIAN STANDARDS ASSOCIATION

Canadian Standards Association (CSA)

In addition to writing codes and standards, CSA also provides NRTL services, testing and listing products that conform to applicable industry standards. Their marks are recognized throughout North America and are considered interchangeable with UL and ETL.

A CSA mark that contains the indicator "US or "NRTL" demonstrates that the product is certified for the US market (Figure 6-6).

FIGURE 6-7: CE LISTING MARK

> CE MARK

CE Mark

The **CE Mark** (an abbreviation of "Conformité Européenne" - French for "European Conformity") indicates that the product conforms with health, safety, and environmental protection standards for products sold within the European Economic Area. The marking (Figure 6-7) is also found on products sold outside the EEA that have been manufactured to EEA standards.

Unlike the UL, ETA or CSA marks, this designation is not subject to an independent third-party evaluation. The manufacturer of the product self-assesses whether the product meets the requirements outlined by the European Economic Area. As a result, it does not (in and of itself) meet the code requirements as an approved product with relation to a specific standard.

Safety Regulations

Most nations have, over the years, developed a "safety bill of rights," that seeks to assure the safe and healthful conditions for working men and women. These are largely created to minimize the risk of injury and death caused by accidents on the job.

Occupational Safety and Health Administration (OSHA)

FIGURE 6-8: OCCUPATIONAL SAFETY AND HEALTH ADMINISTRATION (OSHA)

> OCCUPATIONAL SAFETY AND HEALTH ADMINISTRATION

The **Occupational Safety and Health Administration (OSHA)** was established in the United States in 1971 as a result of the Occupational Safety and Health Act of 1970. It's mission was to ensure safe and healthful working conditions for working men and women by setting and enforcing standards and by providing training, outreach, education and assistance.

While no accurate statistics were maintained prior to 1970, it is estimated that in 1970 around 14,000 workers were killed on the job. That number fell to approximately 4,340 in 2009. Over that period of time, U.S. employment nearly doubled.

OSHA (Figure 6-8) officials are empowered to conduct site inspections (without notice) and issue fines or citations when violations are found.

OSHA requires that all employers to:
- follow all relevant OSHA safety and health standards,
- find and correct safety and health hazards,
- inform employees about chemical hazards through training, labels, alarms, color-coded systems, chemical information sheets and other methods,
- notify OSHA within 8 hours of a workplace fatality or within 24 hours of any work-related inpatient hospitalization, amputation or loss of an eye,
- provide required personal protective equipment at no cost to workers,
- keep accurate records of work-related injuries and illnesses,
- post OSHA citations, injury and illness data and OSHA information in the workplace where workers will see them,
- and not retaliate against any worker for insisting upon enforcing their safety rights under the law.

A number of organizations offer training in workplace safety practices. The OSHA Outreach Training Program provides workers with basic and advanced training about common safety and health hazards on the job. Students receive an OSHA 10-hour (commonly referred to as an **OSHA 10 certification**) or 30-hour course completion card (**OSHA 30 certification**) at the end of the training.

OSHA 10
CERTIFICATION

OSHA 30
CERTIFICATION

Canadian Centre for Occupational Health and Safety (CCOHS)

The **Centre for Occupational Health and Safety** is the Canadian equivalent of OSHA. The CCOHS was created in 1978 by an Act of Parliament - Canadian Centre for Occupational Health and Safety Act. The act in part stated that all Canadians had "…a fundamental right to a healthy and safe working environment.".

CENTRE FOR
OCCUPATIONAL
HEALTH AND SAFETY

European Agency for Safety and Health at Work (EU-OSHA)

The **European Agency for Safety and Health at Work (EU-OSHA)** was founded in 1994, with a goal to collect, analyze, and distribute information to those involved in occupational safety and health.

EUROPEAN AGENCY
FOR SAFETY AND
HEALTH AT WORK

The main difference between the US and the EU agencies is that the US OSHA has the power to create laws and levy fines to companies throughout the United States. In the EU, each individual country is responsible for conducting workplace inspections, establishing work safety laws, and enforcing the regulations.

Licensing and Certification

State and local jurisdictions typically establish standards for electrical work and the qualifications required of contractors and individuals to perform electrical work.

The National Electrical Code defines a **qualified person** as *"one who has skills and knowledge related to the construction and operation of the electrical equipment and installations and has received safety training to recognize and avoid the hazards involved."*

What determines if one is "qualified" varies from state-to-state and by local jurisdiction rules and requirements. Licenses and certification are the credentialing tools that AHJs use to help ensure that solar installers possess the competence and expertise to install PV systems safely and according to codes and standards.

Some states require that PV installers hold a state-issued license while others do not. Some states have developed specific solar PV installation licensing schemes, while others require that solar installers hold a general electrician license as a minimum credential to perform or oversee electrical work on PV installations.

What qualifies as "electrical work" also varies from state to state. Some states require a licensed electrician must pull the permit and make the final connection to the grid. Other states require that a master electrician be on site during the entire installation.

In addition to licensure, some solar incentive programs require that solar installers hold a third-party certification in order for the system to be eligible for the incentive.

It is important to understand the specific licensing and/or certification requirements of the AHJ where work is being performed.

PV Installer Certification Programs

As any industry matures, standards and industry best-practices begin to emerge, elevating the quality of work and products within that industry. Certification programs emerge so consumers will have an unbiased way to assess the qualifications of people they may wish to employ. It has been no different in the evolving industry of photovoltaics.

Since the year 2000, three distinct PV third-party certification programs have emerged within the United States. These are offered by: **NABCEP** (North American Board of Certified Electrical Practitioners), ETA-I (Electronic Technicians Association International), and UL (Underwriter's Laboratory).

North American Board of Certified Energy Practitioners (NABCEP)

NABCEP was founded in 2000 as the nation's first non-profit organization to offer credentials to professionals working in the renewable energy industry (specifically solar and wind power). Over the past decade, NABCEP (Figure 6-9) has become a widely recognized certification program within the photovoltaic industry.

Raising Standards. Promoting Confidence.

FIGURE 6-9: NORTH AMERICAN BOARD OF CERTIFIED ENERGY PRACTITIONERS

WWW.NABCEP.ORG

The NABCEP Solar PV Professional Installation certification is designed for individuals already working within the PV industry.

Candidates must:
- have experience in the PV field acting as the person responsible for installing PV systems. Depending on the category selected, all candidates for the Solar PV Installation Professional exam must provide documentation for three (3) or five (5) installations where they have acted in the role of contractor, lead installer, foreman, supervisor, or journeyman,
- a minimum of 58 hours of advanced PV training and,
- an OSHA 10-hour construction industry card or equivalent.

NABCEP does offer an entry-level examination, however this exam does not lead to any certification offered by the organization.

NABCEP also offers a PV Technical Sales Certification designed for persons employed in the PV industry as a sales person, application engineer, financial or performance analyst, or site assessor.

Candidates must have PV sales experience, as well as an OSHA 10-hour construction industry card or equivalent.

Areas of focus within this program include:
- qualifying the customer,
- site analysis,
- conceptual design,
- financial costs and incentives,
- financial benefit analysis and financing,
- non-financial benefit analysis,
- performance analysis,
- preparing proposals.

Electronics Technicians Association International (ETA-I)

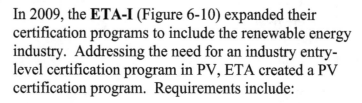

The Electronics Technicians Association International (ETA-I) was founded in 1978 and has certified over 150,000 individuals around the world in over 80 technical programs.

In 2009, the **ETA-I** (Figure 6-10) expanded their certification programs to include the renewable energy industry. Addressing the need for an industry entry-level certification program in PV, ETA created a PV certification program. Requirements include:

PV Level I

Attend an ETA-approved school (40-hours) and pass the ETA Level One written exam and hands-on assessment OR
- OJT (on-the-job training) with an ETA-approved employer for a minimum of 12 months and pass the Level One written exam.

The ETA certification is valid for a period of four years. It may be renewed under the following conditions:
- working in the industry that pertains to the certification,
- completion by a supervisor of the Employer Verification Form, and
- provide proof of 24 hours of continuing education.

If these conditions have not been met, the individual must retest to renew their certification.

Candidates who have not been working in the industry that pertains to the certification are required to attend an ETA-approved hands-on refresher course and show proof of 24 hours continuing education or retest to renew their certification.

PV Level II

In 2019 ETA instituted a Level II PV certification program designed for those who have:
- been working in the industry and document (signed off by customers and/or supervisors) on-the-job installation experience checklist.
- a minimum of 60 hours of PV training and,
- an OSHA 10-hour construction industry card or equivalent.
- obtain Customer Service Specialist certification.

Underwriter's Laboratories

In 2010 UL also entered the field of PV certification, offering its own version of a photovoltaic certification program. In order to participate in the UL (Figure 6-11) program, applicants must:

- be a licensed electrician or a final year apprentice in the NJATC PV training program,
- complete the hands-on, classroom-based PV training program with either UL Knowledge Services or the National Joint Apprenticeship and, Training Committee (NJATC),
- apply for and pass the UL certification examination.

FIGURE 6-11:
UNDERWRITERS
LABORATORIES LOGO

WWW.UL.ORG

Chapter 6 Review Questions

1) A document that has been adopted into law with the purpose of setting minimum standards designed to protect the health, safety and welfare of those who come in contact with a building or system is known as a:
   a) code
   b) standard
   c) listing
   d) certification

2) Before being adopted into law and referred to as the National Electrical Code (NEC), the document is referred to as:
   a) IEEE 1547
   b) NFPA 1
   c) IEC 60364
   d) NFPA 70

3) Which NEC article does **NOT** generally apply to the design and installation of PV systems?
   a) Article 480
   b) Article 690
   c) Article 706
   d) Article 770

4) The code/standard that addresses setback requirements on commercial roof mounted PV systems is:
   a) NEC Article 690
   b) NEC Article 770
   c) IFC
   d) NFPA 855

5) The code/standard that applies to the manufacture of flat-plate photovoltaic panels is:
   a) IEEE 1547
   b) UL 1703
   c) ANSI/UL 3741
   d) UL 1741-SA

6) The code/standard that applies to the manufacture of smart inverters is:
   a) UL 1973
   b) UL 1703
   c) ANSI/UL 3741
   d) UL 1741-SA

7) The code/standard that applies to the manufacture of energy storage systems (ESS) is:
   a) UL 1973
   b) UL 1703
   c) UL 3741
   d) UL 9540

8) A designation from a national recognized testing laboratory (NRTL) that indicates a product has only been tested under certain limited circumstances is referred to as a:
   a) listing mark
   b) conditional mark
   c) classification mark
   d) certification mark

9) Which of the following is a common service mark issued from a national recognized testing laboratory?
   a) UL listed
   b) ETA classified
   c) CE
   d) OSHA approved

10) In the USA, which agency is tasked with ensuring the safe and healthful working conditions at places of employment?
    a) UL
    b) ETL/Intertek
    c) USDA
    d) OSHA

11) The NEC defines a _____ as *"one who has skills and knowledge related to the construction and operation of the electrical equipment and installations and has received safety training to recognize and avoid the hazards involved."*
    a) licensed electrician
    b) certified professional
    c) site supervisor
    d) qualified person

12) Which of the following organizations does **NOT** offer a professional certification program that is recognized within the PV industry?
    a) ETL/Intertek
    b) ETA-I
    c) UL
    d) NABCEP

Chapter 7

Selecting the Components

Chapter Objectives:

- Identify the various types of solar cells and modules.
- Understand standard test conditions and the various measured ratings of PV panels.
- Explore options and issues surround module level power electronics.
- Determine selection criteria for combiner boxes and DC disconnects.
- Examine the selection criteria for inverters incorporated into the system.
- Define California Rule 21 and its impact on smart inverters.
- Understand DC-to-AC ratio and what is meant by clipping.
- Design systems that incorporate storage systems.
- Understand the NEC's definition of the PV disconnect.
- Understand the various components involved in adding a generator to the system.

Before a complete photovoltaic system can be designed and installed, it is important to understand how all of the system components function and how they interact with each other.

This chapter will define each system component, beginning at the solar panel and work down through the system to the load (the device that actually uses the power, such as a light or a computer). Bear in mind that not every component is used in every system.

Solar Panels

Solar panels can be constructed in various ways (**monocrystalline, polycrystalline, thin film**) but most are simply solar cells connected together.

Cell Types

Far and away the two most common types of solar cells used in residential and commercial installations are monocrystalline (Mono-SI) and polycrystalline (Poly-SI). Both are made primarily of silicon.

While the longevity of both silicon cells is considered equal, monocrystalline cells tend to be a bit more efficient and cost a bit more than polycrystalline cells.

As the price difference between monocrystalline and polycrystalline cells narrow, the market share captured by monocrystalline technology has become dominant in recent years.

SOLAR PANEL

MONOCRYSTALLINE

POLYCRYSTALLINE

THIN FILM

TABLE 7-1: MARKET SHARE AND EFFICIENCY BY CELL TYPE

Cell Type	*Market Share	**Best Efficiency
monocrystalline (Mono-SI)	80 %	26.7 %
polycrystalline (Poly-SI)	15 %	24.4 %
amorphous silicon (a-Si)	0.1 %	10.9 %
cadmium telluride (CdTe)	4 %	21.0 %
copper indium gallium selenide (CIGS)	0.9 %	23.4 %

* Worldwide production in 2020 (Frounhofer ISE)   ** Tested under laboratory conditions in a module

Thin-film panels are increasingly used in utility-scale systems and can be constructed from a variety of materials, with the main options being amorphous silicon (a-Si), cadmium telluride (CdTe), and copper indium gallium selenide (CIS/CIGS).

In 2020, monocrystalline cells accounted for 80% of global PV cell sales (up from 66% in 2019 according to research by the Fraunhofer Institute), polycrystalline cells held a 15% share (down from 29% in 2019), and thin-film accounted for only 5% of global sales.

CADMIUM TELLURIDE

Cadmium telluride (CdTe) thin-film solar cells are the most common type of thin-film solar cell. They are more economical compared to the standard silicon thin-film cells. While low-cost and stable, there is a concern that the trace amounts of cadmium in the cells presents a hazardous waste concern.

AMORPHOUS SILICON

Amorphous silicon (a-Si) thin-film cells are the earliest and most mature type of thin-film technology. These solar cells are produced by using noncrystalline silicon. Amorphous silicon is less expensive to manufacture compared to crystalline silicon. This type of silicon is also popular due to its abundance, non toxicity, and cost-effectiveness however it is inefficient compared to other technologies.

COPPER INDIUM GALLIUM SELENIDE

Copper Indium Gallium Selenide (CIGS) cells are more efficient than a-Si cells. However, these cells are less efficient and more costly compared with CdTe solar cells. Another issue is that indium is a relatively rare metal mostly supplied from China. However, CIGS cells are relatively non-toxic, whereas the cadmium used in CdTe cells is highly toxic.

Market share and efficiencies of each type cell are detailed in Table 7-1.

N-Type versus P-Type Cells

DOPED

Crystalline silicon (c-Si) cells are **doped** with various chemicals to encourage power production. The main difference between a p-type and an n-type solar cells is the number of electrons they contain as a result of this doping.

A solar cell is divided into two bands, the **valence band** and the **conduction band**. The energy contained in sunlight (photons) "knocks" an electron across the **bandgap** between these layers, creating a current of electricity. The band that gives up an electron, creating an electron hole, is the valence band. The band that receives the electron is the conduction band.

In a **p-type cell,** the base layer is usually doped with boron, which has one less electron than silicon. As a result, the base layer is positively charged in relation to the upper layer of the cell. When exposed to sunlight, electrons move from the upper negatively charged layer (the valence band) to the positively charged lower layer (the conduction band).

In an **n-type cell** the base layer is doped with phosphorus, which has one more electron than silicon, resulting in a base layer that is negatively charged in relation to the upper layer of the cell. When exposed to sunlight, electrons move from the lower negatively charged layer (the valence band) to the positively charged upper layer (the conduction band).

The first solar cells were developed by Bell Labs and primarily used in the space program. The p-type cell was found to be more resistant to space radiation and degradation. So since NASA was using the p-type cell, this technology became dominant as the industry grew and matured.

In recent years, n-type cells have become increasingly popular. Since n-type cells use phosphorus instead of boron, they are immune to boron-oxygen defects, which cause decreased efficiency and purity within the cell. N-type cells have also proved to be more efficient and are not affected by **light-induced degradation (LID)**.

Light-Induced Degradation (LID)

LID refers to a degradation of performance and quality due to direct sunlight exposure during the initial hours of panel setup.

LID is caused when trace amounts of oxygen that have been locked in the molten silicon as the crystals are grown combine with boron. When first exposed to sunlight, this oxygen-boron compound can trap electron-hole pairs which otherwise would have taken part in the current generation process of the panel.

This loss of production is more pronounced in monocrystalline solar cells as compared to polycrystalline cells.

According to NREL, LID can reduce the efficiency of p-type silicon solar cells by about 2%, which adds up to a significant drop in power output over the 30- to 40-year lifespan of the panel.

VALENCE BAND

CONDUCTION BAND

BANDGAP

P-TYPE CELL

N-TYPE CELL

LIGHT-INDUCED DEGRADATION (LID)

Solar Cell Size

SOLAR MODULE

The first consumer-available **solar modules** (the terms solar panel and solar module are typically used as interchangeable in the industry) were released in 1983 and had a rated power of 48 watts. They consisted of 36 cells with the dimensions 100 x 100 mm each. This cell size was available on the market until about 1996.

Then in 1996 a module rated at 120 watts was produced with cells measuring 125 x 125 mm and was considered the standard size for many years.

M2 WAFER

In 2012, the M0 wafer with dimensions of 156 mm x 156 mm was introduced, followed quickly by the **M2 wafer** (156.75 mm) which eventually become the dominant size. As a result of these dimensions, the average module size was 1640 or 1650 x 992 mm (length x width) for a 60-cell solid cell module.

In recent years the trend has been for manufactures to increase the size of wafers used to create solar modules. In 2016 the M4 wafer (161.75 mm) was introduced, then the M6 water (166 mm), followed by the M10 wafer (182 mm) and the **G12/M12 wafer** (210 mm).

G12/M12 WAFER

Energy Payback

One question that often arises when discussing solar installations is, how much energy does it take to produce a solar panel? In other words, is solar really a green alternative when producing energy?

ENERGY PAYBACK

These questions concern the **energy payback** of the module - or, how long will it take the module to produce as much energy as it took to create it?

According to NREL, as of 2022, the average energy payback of a silicon panel is between 2.5 to 3 years. Creating silicon wafers is a fairly energy intensive process requiring the melting and refining of silicon crystals.

Thin film technologies are much less energy intense, with an energy payback of between 0.8 - 0.9 years. Perovskite panels use even less energy during production, with an energy payback of between 0.18 - 0.35 years.

Module Size

SERIES

Crystalline solar panels (monocrystalline and polycrystalline) are comprised of a number of solar cells connected in **series**. When cells are connected in series, the voltage increases.

For many years the standard solar module consisted of 60 M2 wafer cells. As a result of the dimensions of these cells, the average module size was around 1650 mm (65 inches) x 992 mm (39 inches) for a 60-cell module. These modules generally weigh about 42 pounds.

Electrical Specifications		
Model	VBHN330SA16	VBHN325SA16
Rated Power (Pmax)[1]	330W	325W
Maximum Power Voltage (Vpm)	58.0V	57.6V
Maximum Power Current (Ipm)	5.70A	5.65A
Open Circuit Voltage (Voc)	69.7V	69.6V
Short Circuit Current (Isc)	6.07A	6.03A
Temperature Coefficient (Pmax)	-0. 30%/°C	-0. 30%/°C
Temperature Coefficient (Voc)	-0. 174V/°C	-0. 174V/°C
Temperature Coefficient (Isc)	1.82mA/°C	1.82mA/°C
NOCT	49.2°C	49.2°C
CEC PTS Rating	306.5W	301.7W
Cell Efficiency	22.09%	21.76%
Module Efficiency	19.7%	19.4%
Watts per Ft.[2]	18.3W	18.0W
Maximum System Voltage	600V	600V
Series Fuse Rating	15A	15A
Warranted Tolerance (-/+)	+10%/-0%*	+10%/-0%*

FIGURE 7-1: EXAMPLE OF SOLAR PANEL SPECIFICATION SHEET

(FROM PANASONIC)

The weight of the solar module is important as OSHA has imposed a 50-pound limit on items designed to be carried and installed by a single individual. Heavier than this 50-pound limit requires two people to install each module.

From 2009 to around 2018, the average module power output increased from 230 W to 315 W due to advances in the efficiency of the cells. The number of cells and their dimensions remained the same.

Around 2016, manufacturers began offering 72-cell (M2 wafers) that measured about 78 inches x 39 inches and weighed just under the 50 pound **OSHA lifting weight limit**. By adding 12 cells to the panel, the rated output of each panel increased to between 350 - 400 W. With installation time and manpower required to install each panel remaining the same, the increased output helped reduce the overall cost of the project (as measured per watt).

OSHA LIFTING WEIGHT LIMIT

With the introduction of the even larger 96-cell module, the 50-pound OSHA limit was shattered, requiring two people to safely install each module. This module was primarily targeted at the larger commercial and utility-scale systems, where installations are conducted in a more "assembly-line" manner with more installers available on the job site.

Today, standard cell and module size is largely a thing of the past. Manufacturers are increasingly opting for a variety of cell sizes and numbers, each claiming their selection provides benefits in various situations and conditions.

Module Ratings

There are a number of electrical specifications associated with each module, as indicated in Figure 7-1.

Testing a solar module by touching the leads of a multimeter to the connections at the back of the panel with no load attached will indicate the panel's **open circuit voltage (Voc).**

The **maximum power voltage (Vmp)** is the voltage the panel will produce **under load**. This measurement is sometimes referred to as the panel's **rated voltage**.

Standard test conditions (STC) assume that irradiance, the power in the sunlight hitting the panel, is 1000 W/m². It also assumes the temperature of the solar cell (usually measured at the back of the panel), is 25° C (77° F). It also assumes the panel is operating under 1.5 atmospheres (approximately sea level in the mid-latitudes).

There are a number of other specifications commonly associated with solar panels with which the designer/installer will need to be familiar. The **short circuit current (Isc)** is theoretically the highest current (amps) that the panel can generate under standard test conditions (although a panel can generate higher current if irradiance exceeds 1000 W/m² and higher voltage as temperatures fall below 25° C).

OPEN CIRCUIT VOLTAGE (VOC)

MAXIMUM POWER VOLTAGE (VMP)

UNDER LOAD

RATED VOLTAGE

STANDARD TEST CONDITIONS

SHORT CIRCUIT CURRENT (ISC)

FIGURE 7-2: TYPICAL IV CURVE FOR PV PANEL SHOWING MAXIMUM POWER POINT, VOC AND ISC

MAXIMUM POWER CURRENT (IMP)

RATED CURRENT

IV CURVE

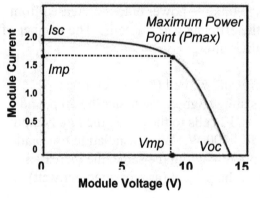

The maximum current a panel can generate while under load and tested at standard test conditions is known as its **maximum power current (Imp),** or also sometimes referred to as it **rated current**.

Panel manufacturers will also provide the **IV curve** for the panel which visually displays these ratings, as shown in Figure 7-2.

Module Efficiency

In recent years a number of manufacturers have started promoting high-efficiency panels. Average panel efficiency has increased from around 15%

to above 20% as manufacturers incorporate the latest solar cell technologies and innovations.

High efficiency is typically defined as a panel with a **conversion efficiency** (how well the panel takes the available energy of the sun and converts it into electricity) of 19% or higher.

Assuming the panel selected is of high quality, most designers are primarily concerned with the panel's cost per watt of generated power. If a high efficiency panel costs 30% more to produce 20% more power, it has little appeal. But in cases where roof space is limited, more efficient panels can be the solution to the problem.

The cell design plays a significant role in panel efficiency. Key features include the silicon type, busbar configuration, and passivation type (PERC).

IBC Cells

Panels that are constructed using **interdigitated back contact** (IBC) cells are currently the most efficient (20-22%) due to the high purity N-type silicon substrate and no losses from busbar shading.

IBC cells have a grid of dozens of conductors integrated into the rear side of the cell, as illustrated in Figure 7-3. Traditional cells use visible ribbon busbars and multiple fingers on the front side of the cell.

By moving the electrical connections to the back of the cell, this design avoids shading issues caused by the wiring. They also provide a cleaner appearance to the panel.

FIGURE 7-3: THE REAR SIDE OF AN IBC CELL SHOWING THE FINE METAL GRID CONDUCTORS

(FROM SUNPOWER)

While expensive, IBC cells are not only more efficient but also much stronger than conventional cells. The rear electrical layer reinforces the cell and helps prevent micro-cracking.

PERC Cells

PERC (Passivated Emitter and Rear Cell or Passivated Emitter and Rear Contact) solar cells is a relatively new innovation in solar cell technology that is gaining wide acceptance. It is estimated that by 2021 PERC cells will comprise over 40% of the total worldwide market share.

Most traditional crystalline solar cells contain at least three elements.
- **Absorber** – typically a semi-conductor such as silicon which absorbs incoming photons,

MEMBRANE

CONTACTS

- **Membrane** – usually a PN-junction which prevents the excited electron from recombining to its original layer, and
- **Contacts** – that collect the electrons and connect the cells together and to a load.

A PERC cell adds an additional layer (a dielectric passivation layer as shown in Figure 7-4) to the bottom of the cell that:
- makes the flow of electrons more steady and consistent, thereby producing more electric current,
- Increases the cell's ability to capture light – unabsorbed light is reflected back up to the solar cell for a second absorption attempt, producing additional energy,
- Reflecting specific solar wavelengths that normally generate heat - keeping the cell cooler and therefore more efficient.

PERC cells are approximately 6-12% more efficient than standard PV cells, without adding much additional cost.

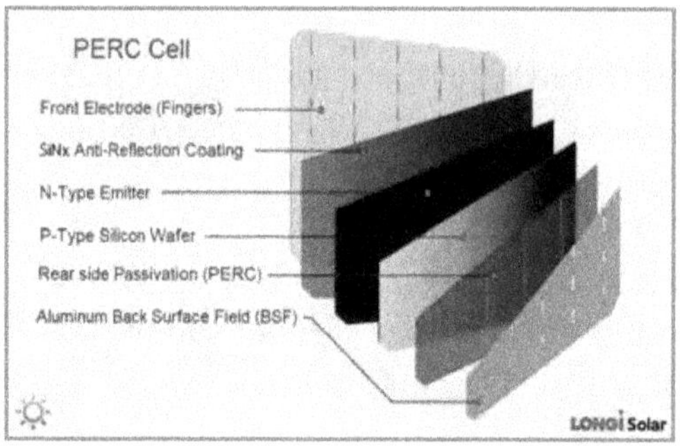

FIGURE 7-4: LAYERS WITHIN A PERC CELL

(FROM LONGI SOLAR)

PERC Cell

Front Electrode (Fingers)
SiNx Anti-Reflection Coating
N-Type Emitter
P-Type Silicon Wafer
Rear side Passivation (PERC)
Aluminum Back Surface Field (BSF)

LONGi Solar

HJT CELLS

HETEROJUNCTION

HJT Cells

Heterojunction (HJT) solar cells add additional ultra thin-film layers of amorphous silicon on either side of the traditional P-N junction, forming what is known as a **heterojunction**.

The additional silicon layers enhance the diode quality of the cell, reducing the recombination of electrons with electron holes, reducing loses and increasing cell efficiency.

Busbar Changes

Changes in the busbars of solar panels is also emerging as a way to increase a panel's efficiency. Busbars are the ribbon conductors on the surface of the cell. The busbars are connected to tiny **feeder conductors** (as shown in Figure 7-5), and together they transport current from the cell to the junction box.

FIGURE 7-5: BUSBAR AND FEEDER CONDUCTORS ON A SILICON SOLAR CELL

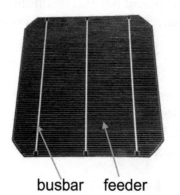

busbar   feeder

FEEDER CONDUCTORS

As PV cells have become more efficient they generate more current. As a result, most manufacturers have moved from 3 busbars to 5 or 6 busbars. Some have even begun incorporating up to 12 very thin round wires rather than flat busbars.

More busbars shade a greater portion of the surface of the cell, reducing conversion efficiency. However, multiple busbars provide lower resistance and a shorter path for the electrons to travel, resulting in higher performance.

Split Cell Panels

Split modules and **half cut cells** are another innovation in module production designed to improve efficiency. Panels are created by cells that are half the traditional size. Half-cell modules have solar cells that are cut in half, which improves the module's performance and durability. Traditional 60- and 72-cell panels will have 120 and 144 half-cut cells, respectively.

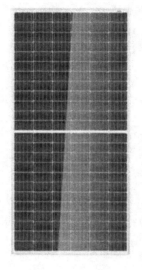

FIGURE 7-6: HALF CUT CELL OR SPLIT CELL MODULE

SPLIT MODULES

HALF CUT CELLS

The panel is configured into two distinct modules (each with the same voltage but half the current as a traditional module) as seen in Figure 7-6. These modules are combined in series within the junction box (doubling the voltage). located at the center back (rather than top) of the panel.

By reducing the current within the panel, there are lower resistive losses through the busbars allowing for smaller conductors and less loss due to shading. The lower current also translates to lower cell temperatures, which reduces the potential formation and severity of **hot spots** that can result from shading, dirt or cell damage.

HOT SPOTS

Shingled Cells

Shingled cells are constructed by overlapping thin film cell strips that can be assembled either horizontally or vertically across the panel.

SHINGLED CELLS

Shingled cell are made by laser cutting a normal full size cell in to 5 or 6 strips and layering them in a shingle configuration using rear side connection adhesive.

The overlap of each cell strip hides a single busbar that interconnects the cell strips. This design covers more of the panel surface area since it doesn't require front side busbar connections that partially shade the cell,

Temperature Coefficients

The **temperature coefficient** is the amount of power that is lost as the cell temperature increases, and/or the amount of power gained as cell temperature decreases.

TEMPERATURE COEFFICIENT

All solar cells and panels are rated using standard test conditions (STC - measured at 25°C). As the temperature changes, voltage is affected quite a lot while amps are affected as well, but to a lesser degree. Both will have an affect on the amount of power the panel produces.

Panel specifications generally provide three different temperature coefficients. The first two, **temperature coefficient of Pmax** and the **temperature coefficient of Voc** are essentially measuring the same thing, simply providing a percentage change that differs only because the calculations it is used for begin at a different voltage point.

For example, if calculating the maximum number of panels allowed in a string, the starting point is Voc (the maximum theoretical voltage the panel can produce under standard test conditions). To calculate how temperature affects this calculation, the system designer would use the temperature coefficient at Voc.

If calculating the minimum number of panels in a string, the designer would use the temperature coefficient at Pmax (in order to avoid over estimating the effect of temperature during normal operations).

A typical polycrystalline cell may experience temperature coefficients between 0.4 to 0.43 % /°C, meaning that the panel will produce up to 0.43 % more power for every °C the cell temperature falls below 25°C (standard test conditions). Conversely, the panel will produce a similar amount less power for each °C the cell temperature rises above 25°C.

About 90% of this effect is the result in changes in voltage, but about 10% is the result of changes in produced amps, as indicated by the third temperature coefficient normally provided on panel specs; the **temperature coefficient of Isc.**

Power Tolerance
No two solar panels will produce power in exactly the same amount - not even when they are the same model from the same manufacturer. A panel may be rated in watts (measured at STC), but the output is really stated to fall within a range around that number.

Power tolerance is a measure of how much electrical power a solar panel may produce above or below its rated capacity. For example, a power tolerance of -5%/+5% on a 100-watt panel would mean the panel could produce 95 W to 105 W under real-world conditions.

Additional specifications often reported by the manufacturer and considered when selecting solar panels include:
- rated power (measured in watts, found by multiplying Vmp x Imp),
- physical dimensions,
- weight of the unit (normally less than 50 pounds),
- type of cells in the module (monocrystalline, polycrystalline, etc),

TEMPERATURE COEFFICIENT OF PMAX

TEMPERATURE COEFFICIENT OF VOC

TEMPERATURE COEFFICIENT OF ISC

POWER TOLERANCE

- cell efficiency (how much of the sun's energy is actually converted into electricity by an individual cell),
- module efficiency (how much of the sun's energy is actually converted into electricity by the entire module),
- maximum operating temperature,
- and more.

Nominal Voltage Rating

Commonly a solar panel for a stand-alone PV system will be described as a 12-volt, or 24-volt panel. This designation refers to the panel's **nominal voltage**.

NOMINAL VOLTAGE

But such a reference does not mean that the panel always generates 12 or 24 volts of energy. As a cloud covers the sun, for example, voltage generated from any panel will drop. As full sunlight returns, the panel will generate more power. In fact a panel with a nominal rating of 12 volts will typically operate between 14 to 18 volts in full sunlight when the system is under load (powering something).

A traditional M2 cell produces about 0.5 Vdc. If 36 cells are connected together, the output of the panel will be about 18 volts (under standard test conditions). This is ideal for charging a 12-volt nominal battery, so a panel of this size is typically referred to as a 12-volt (nominal) panel. 72 cells connected together in series generates about 36 volts, and is normally considered a 24-volt (nominal) panel.

The nominal rating is a shorthand way of letting designers and installers of stand-alone PV systems know how to select the proper panel to go with the rest of the components. A nominal 12-volt panel will be compatible with a nominal 12-volt battery, and a nominal 12-volt charge controller, and so on.

Module Tier Rating System

There are literally hundreds of solar panel manufacturers producing product around the globe. With so many to choose from, it is often difficult to determine if a company is legitimate or not. With this in mind, Bloomberg New Energy Finance Corporation has rated solar panel manufacturers based on their financial stability.

Solar panels are divided into three broad categories; tier 1, tier 2 and tier 3.

Most large panel manufacturers are rated as **tier 1** (the highest rating). This rating, however, only reflects their financial status and not the quality of the panels produced.

TIER 1 RATING

A tier 1 designation is awarded to about 2% of the panel manufacturers. It indicates that they have:

- produced panels for more than 5 years,
- are either publicly traded on a major stock exchange or have a strong and stable balance sheet,
- have a fully automated production process with a high degree of vertical integration,
- and have invested significantly in marketing their brand.

TIER 2 RATING

A **tier 2** manufacturer is a somewhat younger company that does not generally have the same research & development as well as marketing budget of their larger competitors. They usually buy the wafers from a tier 1 manufacturer. Not all of the manufacturing processes are automated in a tier 2 company, which means there is a higher risk of faults during production.

TIER 3 RATING

A **tier 3** manufacturer is usually a very young company. They often employ many of the same manufacturing techniques of the tier 1 group. However, the cells may be soldered by hand which again means that there is a higher fault risk than with an automated process.

Typically tier 1 solar panels cost 10-30% more than tier 2 and tier 3 solar panels.

The tier designation was originally determined by Bloomberg New Energy Finance and was designed to describe the economic health of the manufacturing company - not the quality of the panel produced.

Bifacial Modules

BIFACIAL MODULE

Bifacial modules produce solar power from both sides of the panel. Both the front and back of the panel contain exposed solar cells, as shown in Figure 7-7.

FIGURE 7-7:
COMMERCIALLY
AVAILABLE BIFACIAL
SOLAR MODULES

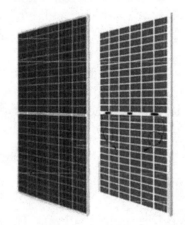

ALBEDO

When bifacial modules are installed on a highly reflective surface (like a white commercial roof or on the ground covered with snow or sand), bifacial module manufacturers claim up to a 30% increase in production from the extra power generated from the **albedo** energy (the light energy reflected up from the surface below the panel) collected by the cells located on the rear of the panel.

Several field studies have found, however, that actual increases in production are substantially less (3-10%).

MONOFACIAL

Bifacial panels typically cost 6-10% more than equivalent **monofacial** modules. But given that modules are only a fraction of the overall installed cost, a fairly modest increase in energy output may more than justify the additional cost of bifacial modules

Limits to Cell Efficiency

The maximum theoretical efficiency that a single-bandgap solar cell can achieve with non-concentrated sunlight is about 33.7%. This is known as the **Shockley-Queisser limit,** named for scientists William Shockley and Hans-Joachim Queisser who first calculated it in 1961.

SHOCKLEY-QUEISSER LIMIT

Current solar cell technology limits the absorption of the energy contained in sunlight in a number of ways.

All objects emit electromagnetic radiation through the **black-body radiation effect** (unless the object is at absolute zero). Approximately 7% of all the energy falling on the cell is lost to this effect.

BLACK-BODY RADIATION EFFECT

Another limitation is that within silicon, the conduction band is about 1.1 eV away (the bandgap) from the valence band. Only photons from the visible light portion of the **electromagnetic spectrum** will produce power under these conditions. Radio waves, microwaves, and most infrared photons do not have enough energy to move electrons across the band gap. About 19% of the potential energy contained in sunlight is less than 1.1 eV.

ELECTROMAGNETIC SPECTRUM

On the other end of the of the spectrum, blue light (ultra violet) has too much energy and is converted to heat, rather than electron flow. This accounts for another 33% loss of potential energy from sunlight.

Recombination issues as well as impedance matching result in additional losses. As a result, without fundamental changes to the architecture of solar cells, the efficiency is limited to about 33%.

Emerging Technologies

As is the way of things, there is a constant push to develop ever more efficient systems. It is no different with solar PV technology.

CONCENTRATOR PV MODULES

Concentrator Photovoltaic Modules (CPV)
Concentrator photovoltaic modules (CPV) shown in Figure 7-8 increase the efficiency of the module by concentrating additional sunlight (through the use of mirrors or multi-dimensional surfaces) onto the PV cell. These systems are generally more expensive than more typical **flat-plate modules**.

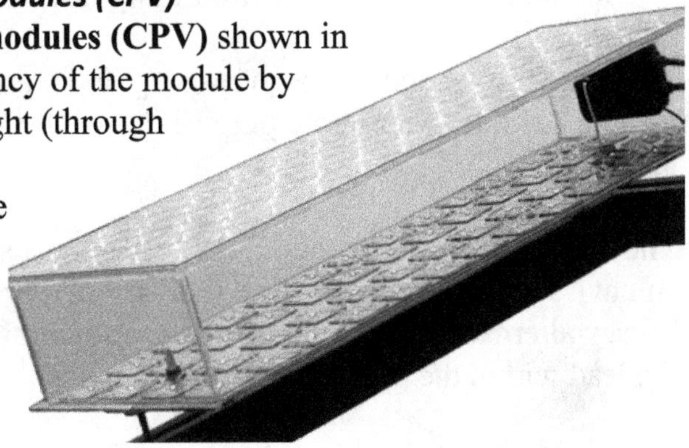

FIGURE 7-8:
CONCENTRATOR PV MODULE

(PHOTO FROM SOLAR ENERGY SYSTEMS, ISG)

FLAT-PLATE MODULE

Multi-Junction Photovoltaic Cells

Multi-junction photovoltaic cells employ multiple layers of thin films. Each layer can more efficiently absorb light within a very narrow band. In combination, these cells can more efficiently absorb light over a wider portion of the electromagnetic spectrum than a typical solar cell.

This technology is also often referred to as **tandem solar cells**.

According to the US Department of Energy, multi-junction solar cells with three junctions have theoretical efficiencies over 45 percent, while single-junction cells have obtained efficiencies of about 33.5 percent. Adding more junctions (potentially up to 5 or 6 junctions) could boost efficiency to over 70 percent.

Perovskite Solar Cell

Another promising emerging PV technology is the **perovskite** solar cell. This term refers to the type of material the cell is made from, as well as its special crystalline structure.

Experiments with this type of material began at Brown University in 2009, achieving rates of efficiency of less than five percent. By 2012, researchers discovered how to make a stable thin-film perovskite solar cells with conversion efficiencies over 10%. By 2021, conversion efficiency of perovskite solar cells skyrocketed, with laboratory results as high as 25.2%.

Researchers began combining perovskite solar cells with conventional silicon solar cells – recording efficiencies for these perovskite-on-silicon tandem cells at as much as 29.1%.

Experts hold out great hope for this technology because:
- the materials are much cheaper than traditional silicon,
- production processes are much less expensive,
- they capture energy at a slightly different bandwidth than silicon, so hold the promise of being used in tandem with silicon to expand efficiency,
- perovskite cells can be transparent or many colored, making them ideal for solar windows or other building integrated applications.

Although this technology is promising, there are still a number of issues that need to be addressed before perovskite will become a major player in the solar industry.

The cells contain trace amounts of lead. The use of toxic lead in perovskite is an environmental concern in an industry that presents itself as the "green" energy alternative. Ongoing efforts are attempting to find a replacement for the lead within the cells.

The long term stability of perovskite solar cells is another major problem not yet overcome. Perovskite solar cells are highly sensitive to moisture in ambient air as well as excessive heat (>90 ºC).

Heat and moisture can result in the decomposition of perovskite film, causing it to degrade and lose some of its photovoltaic properties.

It is thought that this technology is about 5-10 years from being practical in the field. Achieving this potential will require that manufacturers overcome barriers related to stability of the material and environmental concerns over lead content within the cells.

Solar Panel Connectors

Most solar panels on the market today are pre-wired, fitted with MC (multi-contact) connectors designed to fit easily together and provide a weatherproof connection.

Early versions of pre-wired solar panels used a connector known as the **MC3** (pictured in Figure 7-9).

MC3 CONNECTOR

First introduced in 1996, MC3 connectors were referred to as a "multi contact" unit with a 3mm² contact assembly pin. These types of connectors have been phased out in favor of the newer locking connectors and are no longer supported by the National Electrical Code (NEC).

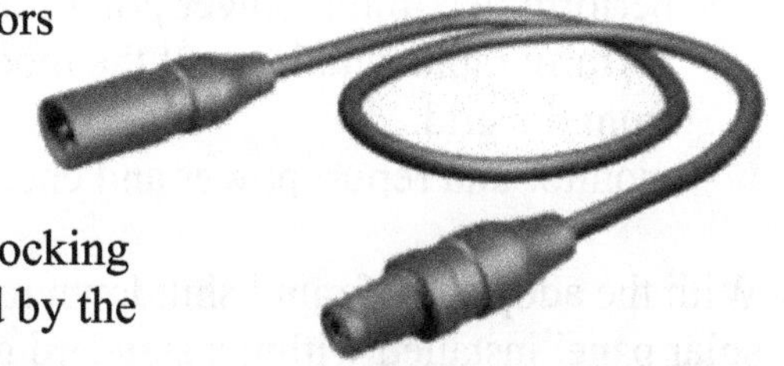

FIGURE 7-9: MC3 (ALSO REFERRED TO AS A SOLARLINE 1) CONNECTOR

The newer **MC4 connector** is self-locking to ensure a tight and lasting connection. The MC4 connector as shown in Figure 7-10 incorporates a flexible water tight seal and is supplied with "male" and "female" terminations to minimize the chance of incorrect connections.

MC4 CONNECTOR

The MC in MC4 stands for the manufacturer Multi-Contact (currently Stäubli Electrical Connectors) and the "4" for the 4mm diameter contact pin. It is actually a brand name that has come to be used to describe an entire category of connectors (similar to how the term Kleenex or Xerox have been used in their industries to describe tissues or duplicating).

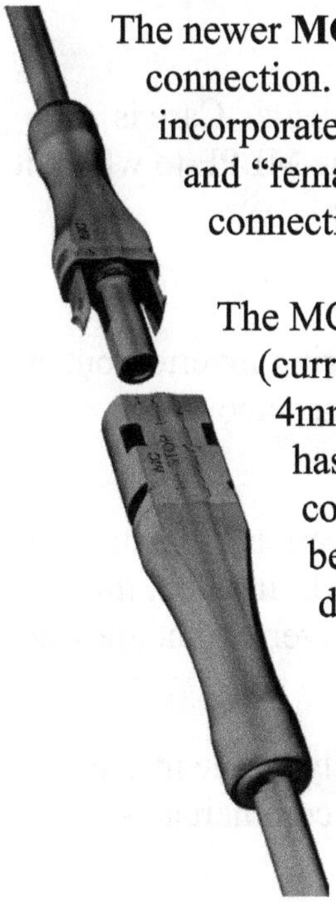

FIGURE 7-10: MC4 (ALSO SOMETIMES REFERRED TO AS A SOLARLINE 2) CONNECTOR

Similar (and compatible) products are available from other manufacturers, such as the H4 connector that is manufactured by Amphenol and the T4 connector from Canadian Solar.

When the male connector of one panel is inserted into the female connector of an adjacent panel, it makes a series connection - the output voltage increasing to the sum of the two panels, but the amps remain constant (output current of two panels equals the output current of each individual panel).

For a proper seal, these connectors require the use of a cable with the correct diameter for a tight fit. Normally MC4 connectors are double-insulated (wire insulation plus a black sheath) and **UV (ultra-violet light) resistant** (many cables deteriorate if used outdoors without protection from sunlight).

UV RESISTANT

Module-Level Power Electronics (MLPE)

Module-level power electronics (MLPE) is a term that refers to a category of electronic devices that are designed to attach directly to a a single solar panel or in some cases, a small group of panels.

Depending on the type of MLPE selected, these devices are designed to perform one or more of the following functions at the panel level:
- convert the DC output from the panel into AC power,
- optimize the the string voltage to match the design input voltage of the inverter,
- perform maximum power point tracking (MPPT) at the module level,
- perform rapid shutdown at the module when the system is disconnected from the grid,
- monitor and report power and energy production for each module.

With the adoption of rapid shutdown requirements in the 2017 NEC, every solar panel installed within a standard grid-tied system on an occupied building is required to incorporate a MLPE to curtail power output from the panel when the system is disconnected from the grid.

MLPEs generally have very specific power input requirements. Care is required to ensure the panel selected is compatible with the MLPE to which it will be attached.

Microinverters

MICROINVERTER

Microinverters provide all the functionality of a larger string inverter, but at the module level. They provide all of the functionality listed above for MLPEs.

In 1993, Mastervolt introduced the first grid-tied microinverter, the Sunmaster 130, designed to mount directly to the back of a solar panel. In 2000, the Sunmaster 130 was replaced by the Soladin 120, a microinverter that allowed panels to be connected directly into any wall socket.

In 2008, Enphase released the M175, the first commercially viable micro-inverter available to the general public for residential and commercial solar

PV applications. The recommended input power was 185 W and the maximum output power was 175 VA.

Enphase introduced the M190 and M210 in 2009. The Enphase M190 microinverters are electrically compatible with most 60 and 72 cell PV modules while the M210 microinverters are electrically compatible with most 72 and 84 cell PV modules. They were followed with products that could accept DC input up to 365 W and AC output up to 280 VA.

In 2017 microinverters became standardized to the new smart inverter standards as outlined in UL1741-SA, with the introduction of the IQ6 and IQ6+ units from Enphase.

In 2022 Enphase introduced the IQ8 series, which has the ability to work as an AC coupled inverter (providing power when the grid is down), with or without battery backup integration.

Enphase has become a dominant force within the inverter market, accounting for 48% of all inverters sold in the US as of November 2021.

Power Optimizers

Unlike a microinverter which operates independently converting the input power from the panel to AC output, the job of a **power optimizer** is to operate the module at a voltage that allows the panels in a string to match the DC bus voltage (usually 380 Vdc or 400 Vdc) required by a fixed-voltage string inverter.

> POWER OPTIMIZER

In addition to matching the string voltage to the inverter, power optimizers typically perform all the other functions of an MLPE with the exception of inverting the DC output of the panel into AC current.

SolarEdge is the dominant player in the power optimizer market, accounting for 40% of inverter sales in the US (November 2021).

Additional MLPEs

A number of manufacturers offer MLPEs that are compatible with a variety of string inverters. An example of these products can be seen in the Tigo line of MLPEs, illustrated in Figure 7-11.

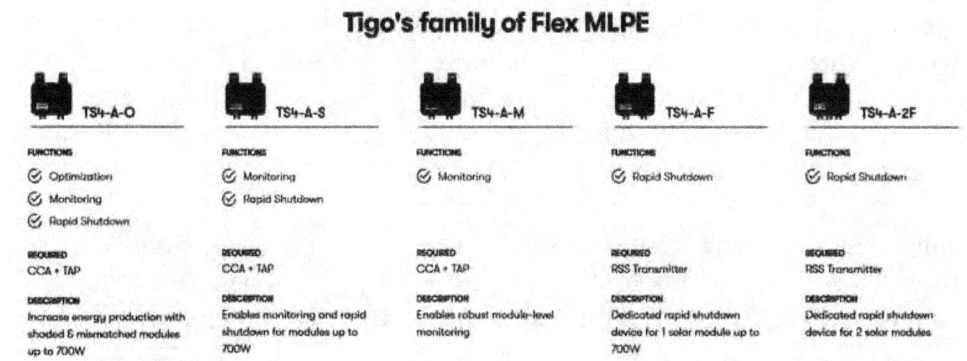

Tigo's family of Flex MLPE

	TS4-A-O	TS4-A-S	TS4-A-M	TS4-A-F	TS4-A-2F
FUNCTIONS	Optimization, Monitoring, Rapid Shutdown	Monitoring, Rapid Shutdown	Monitoring	Rapid Shutdown	Rapid Shutdown
REQUIRED	CCA + TAP	CCA + TAP	CCA + TAP	RSS Transmitter	RSS Transmitter
DESCRIPTION	Increase energy production with shaded & mismatched modules up to 700W	Enables monitoring and rapid shutdown for modules up to 700W	Enables robust module-level monitoring	Dedicated rapid shutdown device for 1 solar module up to 700W	Dedicated rapid shutdown device for 2 solar modules

FIGURE 7-11: TIGO FAMILY OF MLPE DEVICES

(FROM TIGO)

These devices can provide MPPT tracking and/or production monitoring and/or rapid shutdown initiation.

Panel Junction Boxes

JUNCTION BOX

On the back of each solar panel there is a small box where the cables connect to the panel itself. This is referred to as the **junction box,** as illustrated in Figure 7-12. At its core, it is simply a plastic box that protects the electrical connections and bypass diodes from the elements (heat, water, dust, etc).

FIGURE 7-12: JUNCTION BOX ON BACK OF SOLAR MODULE

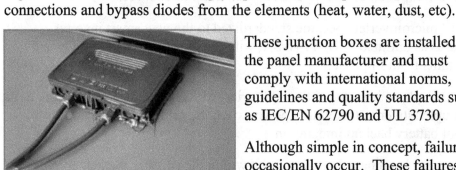

These junction boxes are installed by the panel manufacturer and must comply with international norms, guidelines and quality standards such as IEC/EN 62790 and UL 3730.

Although simple in concept, failures do occasionally occur. These failures most often include burnt bypass diodes, melting of plastic components, broken latches and the separation of external connectors. Since junction boxes function in high temperature environments, extreme heat can be the cause of some of these failures. Water seepage and the corrosion of connectors and wires may result if the integrity of the box is compromised.

The technology of junction boxes is evolving, becoming increasingly "smart". Companies such as Tigo are bringing out junction boxes with printed circuit boards that can be integrated into solar panels with monitoring, optimization and rapid shutdown capabilities. Other manufacturers are even adding inverter technology into junction boxes.

According to a study by the International Technology Roadmap for Photovoltaic Results, junction boxes with additional functions of microinverters, monitoring, rapid shutdown and/or power optimizers will likely gain a 20% market share by 2027.

Combiner Boxes

STRINGS

For larger PV installations, quite a number of solar panels will be connected together in an array. Those panels connected in series, are referred to as **strings** (when hooking panels together in series, the voltage increases, but the amps remain the same). Once the maximum voltage of the system is reached, additional strings must be added to provide enough power to service the home or business.

COMBINER BOX

Rather than run a wire from each string to the inverter (which might be some distance away), the wiring for these strings are typically connected together in a **combiner box**. Multiple wires enter the box from the strings, and are connected together in **parallel** within the box. When connected in parallel (negative to negative, positive to positive), the voltage remains the same but amps increase.

FIGURE 7-13: PRE-WIRED COMBINER BOX

(FROM ECO-WORTHY)

PARALLEL

Only one circuit (the conductors will need to be larger to handle the increased amps of the system) leaves the box (and the array) to connect to the rest of the system.

While these combiner boxes offer a weatherproof location to connect the strings together, they also provide **overcurrent protection** (fuses and/or breakers) for each string – protecting the modules, as well as the wiring system and equipment connected to it.

OVERCURRENT PROTECTION

Many combiner boxes are offered pre-wired as shown in Figure 7-13. Connections are made simply by snapping the MC4 connector into the proper connection point on the box.

Some units may also offer LED monitor indicators that demonstrate at a glance if there is a problem with one or more of the strings. Others incorporate **data monitoring**, such as is illustrated in Figure 7-14, and can accommodate large numbers of strings.

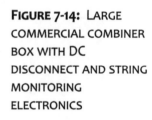

FIGURE 7-14: LARGE COMMERCIAL COMBINER BOX WITH DC DISCONNECT AND STRING MONITORING ELECTRONICS

DATA MONITORING

Individual string monitoring is often used in commercial PV systems to track the performance of each string of PV modules to ensure the system is working as it should. Combiner boxes with data monitoring capability are often referred to as "smart" or "intelligent" combiners.

This is especially helpful in trouble shooting as it reduces time (and therefore money) in correcting disruptions to the array's production.

The combiner box may also house a DC disconnect switch (to isolate the array from the rest of the PV system). If a disconnect is not incorporated into the combiner box, it is still good practice to locate one as close as practical to the array. The 2014 NEC requires that a means of disconnection be located within 6 feet of the array for roof mounted arrays.

For larger systems, care must be taken in selecting the appropriate combiner box for the system. Issues to address include:
- rapid shutdown compliance,
- negative grounding for transforrmerless inverters,
- voltage and current rating of the system,
- maximum number of PV source circuits,
- maximum number of PV output circuits,
- rating of the enclosure,
- remote monitoring capabilities,
- arc fault protection,
- lightning and/or surge protection.

Impact of Inverter Type on Combiner Box Selection

Before selecting the combiner box it will be necessary to know the type of inverter that is planned for the system. Microinverters, for example, generate AC current. So a combiner box rated for AC power will be necessary if it is to be incorporated into a microinverter system.

FIGURE 7-15: COMBINER BOX WIRING FOR SYSTEM WITH A STRING INVERTER WITH TRANSFORMER

(FROM SOLAR NOVUS TODAY)

In a system with a single traditional string inverter, the combiner box provides a fairly straightforward method for making parallel connections.

The positive wire from the string is connected to the overcurrent protection (circuit breaker) and these are connected together (as shown in Figure 7-15). The negative wire from the string is typically connected to a busbar.

In a system such as this, the wiring system will be grounded (connected to the grounding system) within the inverter through the negative, or grounded, conductor.

Combiner Boxes for Transformerless Inverters

TRANSFORMERLESS INVERTER

Increasingly, designers are incorporating **transformerless inverters** (often referred to as ungrounded) into their PV designs. Transformerless inverters have the advantage of being lighter in weight than inverters with transformers, generally have higher efficiency ratings, and are capable of dual MPPT inputs (depending on manufacturer).

When a transformerless, or ungrounded inverter is used, the negative wires from the array must be fused in a manner similar to the positive wires. Both the positive and the negative wires must also be connected to a disconnect of some sort.

While only one leg of the circuit (positive or negative) must be connected to an overcurrent device, it is common that both the positive and negative conductors are connected to circuit breakers as illustrated in Figure 7-16.

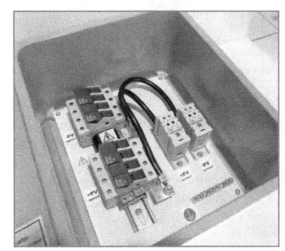

FIGURE 7-16: COMBINER BOX THAT ALLOWS FOR FUSING (BREAKERS) ON THE NEGATIVE AS WELL AS POSITIVE CONDUCTORS FROM THE ARRAY

Voltage & Current Rating
Commercial systems in the US can be wired to 1,000 volts. If the inverter is rated to 1,000 volts, the combiner box should be rated to this higher voltage as well.

The box should also be rated to handle at minimum the combined current rating of the circuit breakers. For example, if the design calls for five 20-amp breakers connected to the PV source circuits, the box should be rated to handle at least 100 amps.

Maximum Number of PV Source Circuits
Combiner boxes come with space for a maximum number of string connections. Ensure the number is sufficient for the system, as well as any future expansion that may be planned.

Maximum Number of PV Output Circuits
If the system incorporates more than one string inverter, it may be desirable to use a combiner box that allows multiple output circuits.

Junction Box Versus Combiner Box

At its core, a combiner box serves three basic functions. It allows for:

- a transition point, normally transitioning from exposed PV wire to a different wire type that will be contained within conduit,
- a protected environment to place overcurrent protection (fuses and breakers),
- as well as a parallel connection to reduce the number of conductors that feed the next piece of equipment in the system.

Increasingly inverters provide for multiple string connections, allowing for more granular MPPT control.

When all strings are combined in parallel, the maximum power point tracking is combined on all connected strings (in extreme cases, shading on one panel would then affect the output of the entire array). With multiple MPPT connections, shading on a panel in one string will not affect the output from the other strings.

While multiple strings running to the inverter will likely result in increased power output, it will also require more wire.

In cases of multiple strings connected to the inverter, a junction box rather than a combiner box is used. In almost every respect the junction box performs all the same functions, however no parallel connection is made.

The term can be a bit confusing as the connection box on the back of the solar panel is also referred to as a junction box.

Listings

All selected combiner/junction boxes should be UL 1741 listed. Every approved electrical enclosure also has a National Electrical Manufacturers Association (NEMA) rating. The ratings on PV combiners include NEMA 3 and 3R (rated for outdoor use in limited orientations), as well as NEMA 4 and 4X (boxes can be mounted in any orientation, from vertical to horizontal).

Terminal Temperature Limits

Unless otherwise stated, terminals for wire sizes less than #1 AWG are assumed to be 60°C (140°F). Wire sizes over #1 AWG are assumed to be rated for 75°C (167°F) unless otherwise indicated.

Arc Fault Protection

ARC FAULT

The NEC requires that PV systems be protected from **arc faults** within the inverter. When electrical systems arc, they generate a lot of electrical "noise." Arc fault sensors see this noise signature and shut down the portion of the system, suppressing the arc.

In large systems with perhaps hundreds of strings combined and attached to a single inverter, the noise from an arc in a single string may not be enough to be recognized by the inverter. A portion of the array may be arching, but the system does not recognize the problem.

Some larger combiner boxes incorporate arc fault protection at the string level. This not only isolates the problem, but allows the normally functioning part of the array to continue to produce power.

Lightning & Surge Protection

Lightning is the number one cause of catastrophic failures in solar electric systems and components. A properly designed and installed bonding and grounding system will help minimize damage (by providing a clear pathway to ground), but is not a guarantee against damage.

An average lightning strike measures about 30,000 amps, however NASA has recorded strikes during the Apollo launches as high as 100,000 amps. Fuses and breakers will not help in the event of a lightning strike. They are simply not designed for this purpose.

A **surge protection** device such as the unit shown in Figure 7-17 is designed to "clamp down" on extreme surges (as high as 115,000 amps) to a current and voltage that the system can withstand.

SURGE PROTECTION

Multiple units can be installed and should be located as close as possible to the source of the surge (the array or the grid connection, for example). Surge protection is commonly installed in combiner boxes (to protect the system from lightning that may strike the array) or in the main AC load panel (to protect from surges that may come in from the utility grid connection).

Incorporating Multiple Combiner Boxes

In larger systems, a number of combiner boxes may be incorporated into the design, each combining strings from a portion of the array, known as a **sub-array**.

SUBARRAY

When three or more source circuit combiners are used, the NEC requires that the feeder circuits between each combiner box and the inverter must be fused (protected). This is typically accomplished by incorporating another DC combiner box located near the inverter, normally called a **recombiner box**, or a subarray combiner, as shown in Figure 7-18.

RECOMBINER BOX

When the recombiner is incorporated into the inverter (two or more strings connected directly to the inverter), it is often referred to as the **input combiner**.

FIGURE 7-18: RECOMBINER BOX

(FROM AMTEC INDUSTRIES)

DC Disconnects

It is not only a good idea, but required that DC system power sources (such as a solar array or a battery bank) have the ability to be isolated from the rest of the system. This is accomplished through the use of a **DC disconnect**.

INPUT COMBINER

DC DISCONNECT

At a minimum, these disconnects should be located between the array and the inverter (or charge controller, when one is present) and between the battery bank and the inverter.

It is also required that a DC disconnect be located within 3 meters (10 feet) of the equipment it is protecting (NEC 690.15 (A)). In most cases within grid tied systems, this equipment would be the inverter. In the case of a stand alone or DC coupled system, the first electronic equipment connected to the array would likely be the charge controller.

Make sure that the disconnect is indeed rated for DC power (such as the unit shown in Figure 7-19), since DC-rated units work differently than the more familiar AC disconnect (switches, fuse boxes and circuit breakers must also be rated for DC).

FIGURE 7-19: A TYPICAL LABELED DC DISCONNECT

The NEC requires that a disconnect be provided in a readily accessible location (a location that does not require the use of a ladder, for example) near the point where the wires from a PV system enter the building.

The NEC also requires that disconnects for the PV array, battery circuits, and AC circuits used in the system be grouped together and located near the inverter. This is to allow people who are perhaps unfamiliar with the installation (such as utility workers, emergency responders, etc.) to easily locate the method to shut down or disconnect the system. Local utilities may have other requirements that must be accommodated.

No more than six separate disconnects can be installed in a single PV system. This may seem limiting, especially for installations that use multiple inverters. But NEC Article 100 defines PV systems as "all of the components required to convert sunlight to electrical energy." Therefore, in a system with multiple inverters, each inverter would be considered a separate system and each could have up to six disconnects on the DC side of the system.

When selecting a DC disconnect, a number of factors should be considered.

These include:

- Ensure that it is rated for DC power. DC power, by its very nature is more difficult to interrupt than AC. The wave form of AC power crosses zero volts twice in each cycle. DC power must be forced to zero voltage. However, when a DC circuit is opened, the current does not stop immediately, but continues to flow over the open gap between the switch contacts via a low energy arc. A DC switch is designed to suppress this arc as quickly as possible.

- Make sure that the unit is rated to handle the maximum voltage of the system. The NEC limits the voltage of 1-2 dwelling residential systems to 600 Vdc. The voltage used in larger residential buildings and commercial systems has higher limits. Increasingly, systems of this type are designed up to 1,500 Vdc. The local authority having jurisdiction may allow or restrict this higher voltage.

- Make sure the current rating of the disconnect is adequate to handle the maximum current the system may produce, including the safety factors designed into the wiring system. In high temperature environments, it may also be necessary to factor in a temperature factor. Disconnects are available in a number of current ratings, but the most common are 30 amp, 60 amp, 100 amp and 200 amp.

- Fused or non-fused. The primary purpose of a disconnect is to interrupt the flow of electricity through a circuit. Most do this simply by physically breaking the contact of the positive conductor. Some units also incorporate overcurrent protection (fuses or circuit beakers) into the switch. This provides the added benefit of protecting against circuit overloads and short-circuiting.

- Ensure that the disconnect has the minimum appropriate number of **poles** (switched termination points). If two conductors are to be switched (as in a transformerless system), then two poles are required. If three conductors are to be switched, a three-pole unit such as the unit shown in Figure 5-17 is required.

POLES

- Indoor or Outdoor Rating. Indoor and outdoor ratings are fairly self-explanatory, but if the unit is going to be installed outside where it will be exposed to rain, wind and temperature variations, it should be rated for outdoor use. If the unit is located outside, it should also be shielded from direct sunlight (not on the south wall) and mounted a minimum of 36 inches above the ground.

Line Side/ Load Side Connections

When making connections to a disconnect, it is important to keep in mind that there is a **line side** connection point (the termination that is connected to the power source) and the **load side** connection point (the termination that is connected to the load) - as illustrated in Figure 7-20.

LINE SIDE

LOAD SIDE

The concept is that when the circuit is opened (turned off) at the disconnect, only the connection lug of the line side will remain energized. The rest of the unit will be safe to touch, especially critical when removing fuses (they should not be energized when removed).

Since there are two power sources in a PV system (the grid and the PV array). it can be confusing as to which is the line side and which is the load side.

FIGURE 7-20:
DISCONNECT WITH LINE SIDE CONNECTION AND LOAD SIDE CONNECTION INDICATED

An easy rule of thumb is to consider the inverter as the load. When placing a disconnect between the array and the inverter, the array is the line (energized) and it feeds the inverter (the load).

But when placing a disconnect between the inverter and the main service panel, the grid is considered the line (the power source) and the inverter is considered the load. The reason the inverter is not also a power source is because once the circuit is opened, the anti islanding feature will shut down power output from the inverter. The grid, however, will still remain "hot".

Selecting Inverters

INVERTER

INVERSION

The role of an **inverter**, is to convert the DC current from a solar array or battery bank into AC current (that can then be used by conventional AC appliances and fixtures). This is done through a process known as **inversion**.

In the early days of solar electricity, inverters were often not incorporated into the system. Without the inverter's power conversion, the entire system needed to be wired to handle the DC current, and DC fixtures and appliances had to be purchased and installed. This added greatly to the cost of a PV system, and often made the installation in an existing structure (already wired for AC) impractical.

Today, nearly all residential and commercial PV systems incorporate an inverter, so that conventional AC wiring and loads (appliances, lighting, etc) can be serviced by the system. This makes converting an existing home or business to run off a PV system much easier, since the existing wiring and appliances do not need to be replaced or modified.

It also provides a maximum degree in flexibility, allowing the system owner to use either grid-supplied power (AC power), or power from the solar array (DC converted to AC).

Grid-Tied Inverters

GRID-TIED INVERTER

Grid-tied inverters are used in systems that are connected to the utility grid.

Since these units export power that is not used to service loads back onto the grid, the output signals (voltage and frequency) must match the power coming from the utility company on a continuous basis, even as that power signal fluctuates.

They also include **anti-islanding** features, which automatically shut down the PV system whenever they detect that there is no power on the grid. This is a safety issue – protecting utility workers who may be repairing the lines. The utility worker may assume there is no electricity flowing (as the power grid is down), however the PV system could still be pumping electricity onto supposedly "dead" lines... and the result could be fatal.

ANTI-ISLANDING

A basic grid-tied inverter generally does not incorporate any battery backup. While this is the least expensive option, it does have the disadvantage that when the grid goes down, the home or business will be without power.

When selecting a grid-tied inverter, consider:

- The maximum DC voltage the unit can receive from the solar array. In the U.S., this voltage is limited by the NEC and should never exceed 600 Vdc for one or two-family residential systems. It is increasingly common, however for commercial systems to be configured to 1,000 Vdc or even 1,500 Vdc.

- The minimum DC voltage the unit can receive from the solar array and still produce power. If the inverter shuts down due to low voltage, it must go through a start-up procedure before going back on-line, further reducing the efficiency of the system.

- The **maximum power point transfer** (MPPT or MPP) voltage range. This is the voltage range where the inverter operates most efficiently. The normal operating voltage of the array should fall within this voltage range.

MAXIMUM POWER POINT TRANSFER

- AC output voltage. Output voltages from grid-tied inverters in the U.S. are typically 240 Vac single phase for residential systems. Many commercial buildings operate with three-phase electrical systems. The selected inverter must match the service provided by the utility.

- The power rating, or the watts the inverter can generate. For grid-tied inverters, this power rating should be related to the amount of power the array is designed to generate. It is not based on the load the home is expected to draw (as is the case with a stand-alone inverter).

- The output frequency (measured in hertz). In the U.S. this should be 60 Hz.

- Conformity with the local utility provider. These units are designed to match the utility power exactly, so discuss the inverter selection with the local utility provider to assure compatibility. The inverter must be marked with a UL1741 or UL1741 SA listing, stating it has been approved as a **utility inter-tie device**.

- The conversion efficiency of the unit.

- Communications and diagnostics. Most inverters now come with fairly sophisticated communications and diagnostic capabilities. These allow installers and clients to track the performance of the array as well as troubleshoot problems.

- How many strings can be connected directly to the inverter.

Multiple String Inverters

Some inverters have the ability to connect two or more strings directly to the inverter.

This presents a number of advantages, as outlined in Table 7-2, however it does require that multiple conductors be run from the array to the inverters, rather than combined in a combiner box. This may require additional disconnects as well as require conduit fill calculations.

Grounded or Ungrounded Inverters

Historically it has been common for the conducting wires to be attached to the DC grounding system at one point, typically within the inverter (as shown in Figure 7-21). In the United States, this connection has usually been made through the negative (grounded) conductor. In a grounded system, the negative wire is connected to the grounding system at only one point, often through the **ground fault protection device (GFPD)**.

A DC ground fault can occur when current flows through the equipment grounding conductor (EGC). This typically occurs due to damaged conductor insulation, improper installation, pinched wires, or water, which can create an electrical connection between the conductor designed to carry current and the EGC. The ground fault protection device senses the current within the grounding system and shuts down the system until the fault is corrected.

Grounded systems incorporate a transformer within the inverter, which creates a physical separation between the DC side of the system and the AC side of the system. The two sides of the system are physically **isolated** from each other.

UTILITY INTER-TIE DEVICE

GROUND FAULT PROTECTION DEVICE (GFPD)

ISOLATED

TABLE 7-2
ADVANTAGES OF MULTI-STRING INVERTERS OVER SINGLE STRING INVERTERS

	Single String	Multiple Strings
Allow connecting strings with different solar azimuth angles	No	Yes
Allow connecting strings with different solar tilt angles	No	Yes
Allow connecting different string lengths	No	Yes
Allow connecting strings of dissimilar modules	No	Yes
Provide better monitoring/troubleshooting	No	Yes

Since the systems are isolated, the NEC treats them as two separate electrical systems, each requiring its own path to ground.

As a result, there is a DC ground connected to the inverter, and the AC output from the inverter continues on and is eventually connected to an AC ground.

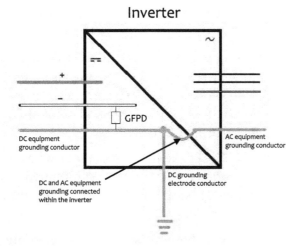

FIGURE 7-21:
ELECTRICAL DIAGRAM OF A GROUNDED INVERTER

Since a ground is directly connected to the inverter (the DC ground), these inverters are often referred to as **grounded inverters**. This is a bit misleading, however, as all inverters are connected to the grounding system in one form or another.

GROUNDED INVERTER

More and more frequently installers are opting to use transformerless inverters (sometimes referred to as ungrounded inverters), for use within ungrounded systems. This type of PV system is already the norm in most parts of the world today.

There is no transformer in these units, the electrical connection between the DC and the AC side of the system are directly connected. Since they are not isolated, there is no need for two separate grounding systems. So these transformers are often referred to as **ungrounded inverters**, as there is no DC ground required from the inverter.

UNGROUNDED INVERTER

Advantages of ungrounded systems may include:
- enhanced ability to detect ground faults,
- they are generally about 2% more efficient in converting DC to AC current than comparable transformer-based inverters,
- increased safety, as the shock potential is between the positive and negative conductors and not between the current carrying conductors and ground,
- transformerless inverters typically weigh less, are more compact, and more efficient than traditional inverters,
- the more efficient inverters generate less heat, making active cooling components (fans) unnecessary.

Three-Phase Power
In the US, most smaller (residential) grid-tied PV systems will produce 120/240 Vac single-phase power. But a number of commercial systems will be connected to three-phase service from the grid. The inverter should match the power supplied by the utility.

Some typical three-phase options include:

- 120/208/240 Vac three-phase in a Delta configuration. This configuration is often found to power loads in older commercial and industrial facilities. It is popular because traditional 120 Vac and 240 Vac loads can be supported. However, it has largely been replaced by Wye configured three-phase systems because it is difficult to properly balance.

- 208Y/120 Vac three-phase four wire configurations are commonly used in commercial buildings with limited electrical loads. 120 Vac is available between each line and the ground, while 208 Vac is available between any two lines.

- 480 Vac three-phase Delta is commonly used in commercial and industrial buildings with large motor loads. Only 480 Vac power is available through this service.

- 480Y/277 Vac is used to supply commercial and industrial buildings with larger motor demands. Between any two lines there's 480 Vac, and between any line and the neutral there's 277 Vac. The 277 Vac is often used for ballasted lighting.

Large Commercial String Inverters

String inverters for larger systems offer a number of features that may not be available in smaller residential units. These features include:

- Reverse polarity protection on DC inputs
- **Multiple MPPT tracking zones** - allows several sub-arrays of varying sizes to be connected and function independently.

MULTIPLE MPPT
TRACKING ZONES

- Adjustable reactive power features
- Adjustable power factor (PF) features
- Remote power curtailment (shut down the system remotely)

Bimodal Inverters

Bimodal inverters (sometimes called **hybrid inverters** or battery-based inverters - although this term can also refer to stand-alone inverters) are also available. These combine the functionality of stand-alone and grid-tied inverters. These are used in systems that require a dependable back up to the grid.

BIMODAL INVERTER

HYBRID INVERTER

Bimodal inverters function like a grid-tied inverter, until the electrical grid goes down. In a grid-tied system, the homeowner would simply be without power while the grid is down. A bimodal inverter senses that the grid is down, then physically disconnects from the grid. It then redirects power from the battery bank to critical loads, acting like a stand-alone system.

The inverter continues to monitor the grid. Once power is restored, it switches back to grid-tied mode.

Bimodal inverters are generally designed into DC-coupled systems at the start of the design process. In AC-coupled systems, the **battery-based inverter** is often added into an existing grid-tied system.

BATTERY-BASED INVERTER

When selecting and sizing an inverter for a DC-coupled or AC-coupled system:

- The continuous power output should be sized at about 120% of the anticipated load demands. This will allow the inverter to function at its optimal efficiency.

- If the hybrid inverter is connected directly to the array, it should be sized to handle the output of the array in a manner similar to sizing a grid-tied inverter.

- If the battery-based inverter is connected to an existing grid-tied inverter, then it should be sized at 125% of the output capacity of the grid-tied inverter to safely handle the pass-through current coming from the existing inverter when it is operating at its maximum capacity.

- If the battery-based inverter is connected to a charge controller, then it should be sized to handle the maximum output rating of the controller.

- The hybrid inverter should be compatible with the battery type (lead-acid, lithium ion, etc) as well as the battery bank's nominal voltage.

- A battery bank connected without a charge controller must be of sufficient capacity to avoid overcharging by the array.

"Smart" Inverters

In late 2017, California became the first U.S. state to require the use of advanced, or **smart inverters** in solar arrays. The changes outlining their use through updates to California Rule 21, seek to lessen the impact of distributed energy systems on the grid as more and more are integrated into the utility's distribution system. It is expected that these requirements will soon be implemented across the nation.

SMART INVERTER

Grid-tied PV arrays not only draw power from the grid, but they also feed excess power onto the grid. Up until now, PV systems have been required to disconnect from the grid when voltages or frequencies on the grid fall outside normal operating ranges. But if a large amount of these systems shut down, and then all try to reconnect at the same time, the grid will become stressed.

Smart inverters allow PV systems to remain connected to the grid under a wider range of voltage and frequency levels. Once smart inverters are widely deployed and connected to the grid, they have the potential to not only avoid stress, but can actually be used to improve the stability of the power on the grid. For example, dynamic volt/VAR operations (also called **dynamic reactive power compensation**) within the smart inverters can allow PV systems to assist in counteracting voltage deviations on the grid.

DYNAMIC REACTIVE POWER COMPENSATION

Where smart inverters are required, units installed must comply with UL1741-SA (as opposed to the previous listing of UL1741). Most manufacturers of inverters have compliant products available for the market.

This does mean, however, that many older models of inverters may not still be suitable for current installations in many parts of the country.

Functions within compliant smart inverters include:

- **voltage and frequency ride-through** (able to accept a wider range of deviation from the grid),

- **soft start reconnection**, by requiring PV systems to ramp up during reconnection or to reconnect randomly within a time window, the grid should avoid sharp transitions and as a result power quality problems of voltage spikes, harmonics, and oscillations including the possibility that the disruptions caused by the reconnection of large numbers of PV systems actually causes another power outage,

- **fixed power factor** - this allows the inverter to maintain a fixed power factor, adjusting the amount of real and reactive power output in response to changing conditions,

- new **ramp rate** requirements, designed to help avoid sharp transitions and the as a result, power quality problems of voltage spikes or dips, harmonics, and oscillations on the grid,

- updated anti-islanding provisions.

Potential Induced Degradation (PID)

Potential induced degradation (PID) is a phenomena that impacts the ions of a solar cell and results in the degradation of the output of that cell.

PID can significantly reduce the power output of a module within the first year of operation, with power losses as high as 70% in the first 18 months of operation.

PID occurs where there is a high negative potential relative to earth. It is

FIGURE 7-22:
COMMERCIAL ANTI PID DEVICE

(FROM AMBOYA)

aggravated in systems that experience high heat, high humidity, and high voltage. PID does not occur in grounded systems (where the negative pole of the inverter is grounded) or in systems less than or equal to 600 Vdc.

Anti-PID devices, such as the unit illustrated in Figure 7-22, can be connected to solar PV systems that renews PID affected solar modules during the night. The anti-PID device applies voltage to the module at night and reverses the power degradation.

These devices, however, may adversely affect the inverter. Care should be taken to ensure any anti-PID device installed is compatible with the installed inverter.

Matching Inverter Output with Panel Output

Inverters come in a variety of sizes based on the maximum output they are capable of producing (measured in watts or volt-amps). Typical sizes for residential systems include 3,800 watts, 5,000 watts, 6,000 watts, 7,600 watts, and more. Many models are compatible with both single and three-phase power systems. Newer models are also compliant with smart inverter requirements (UL1741-SA).

Commercial string inverters may range in size from 20 kW to 500 kW. They are typically three-phase units, either 120/208 V or 277/480 V.

It might seem logical that the array output must match the inverter's output. This is not, in fact, the case. The two are related, but do not have to be equal to each other.

To better understand this concept, it might be easier to visualize a single microinverter connected to a single panel (but the same holds true for an array connected to a string inverter).

The Enphase IQ8+ microinverter, for example, can be connected to panels that range in size from 235 - 440 Wdc. The larger the panel, the greater the power production. However, the output from the inverter will be limited to 300 VA, even if the input is greater than 300 W.

If a 360 Wdc panel were connected to an IQ8+ microinverter, the **DC-to-AC ratio** of the system would be 1.2 (360 Wdc/300 VA). This ratio is also referred to as the **inverter load ratio (ILR)**.

DC-TO-AC RATIO

INVERTER LOAD RATIO (ILR)

When the DC power feeding an inverter is more than the inverter power output, the resulting power is **clipped** and lost.

CLIPPED

This situation can exist for string inverters as well as microinverters. A 5,000 VA string inverter supplied by a 6,000 Wdc array would also have a 1.2 inverter load ratio (6,000 Wdc/5,000 VA).

While this might seem wasteful, many will argue that supplying an inverter with panels rated at a higher output is actually more cost efficient, especially as the cost of panels has declined rapidly in comparison to the cost of inverters.

FIGURE 7-23:

COMPARING 360 W
PANEL TO 300 W PANEL
PRODUCTION ON LESS
THAN IDEAL DAY WHEN
CONNECTED TO IQ8+
MICRO INVERTER

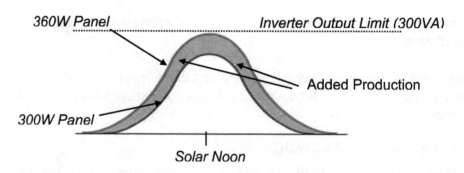

It is rare that a panel generates at its rated output level as measured at STC. Cool days with full sunlight do not happen frequently in most parts of the country. So comparing the two production curves on days when the conditions are less than ideal (as illustrated in Figure 7-23), a greater amount of power is produced on a significant majority of days.

And even on days when conditions are ideal (as shown in Figure 7-24), the increased amount of power generated in the "shoulders" of the curve exceeds the amount of power lost due to clipping.

While it is common for systems to be designed with a 1.2 DC-to-AC ratio, the economics of the industry are increasingly pushing design to higher ratios, as much as a 1.6 ratio. There is a limit to how much power can be fed into any specific inverter, however. This will be indicated by the maximum DC input specification of the inverter.

Input Specifications

The NEC limits residential PV array voltages to a maximum of 600 Vdc. Systems installed on multi-family units and commercial properties can be installed at a higher voltage (such as 1,000 Vdc as illustrated in Figure 7-25).

Inverters will also specify a minimum voltage and will not operate if the array is producing below that minimum. In the above example (CPS SCA25KTL-DO/US-208), the **startup voltage** is 300 Vdc, but once started, the operating range is between 200 - 950 Vdc.

STARTUP VOLTAGE

MPPT INPUT
VOLTAGE RANGE

This inverter operates best (the **MPPT input voltage range**) between 480-850 Vdc. If the DC voltage of a system is designed to operate at 700 Vdc

FIGURE 7-24:

COMPARING 360 W
PANEL TO 300 W PANEL
PRODUCTION ON IDEAL
DAY (25° C, 1000 W/M²)
WHEN CONNECTED TO
IQ8+ MICRO INVERTER

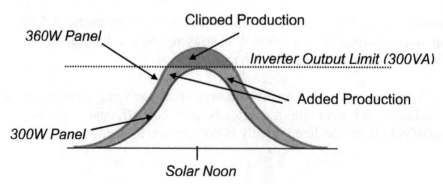

CPS

Model Name	CPS SCA25KTL-DO/US-208
DC Input	
Max. PV Power	45kW (17kW per MPPT)
Max. DC Input Voltage	1000Vdc
Operating DC Input Voltage Range	200-950Vdc
Start-up DC Input Voltage / Power	330V / 80W
Number of MPP Trackers	3
MPPT Voltage Range @ PF>0.99	480-850Vdc
Max. PV Short-Circuit Current (Isc x 1.25)	135A (45A per MPPT)
Number of DC Inputs	6 inputs, 2 per MPPT
DC Disconnection Type	Load-rated DC switch
DC Surge Protection	Type II MOV, 2800V_C, 20kA I_{TM} (8/20µS)
AC Output	
Rated AC Output Power @ PF>0.99	25kW
Max. AC Apparent Power (Selectable)	25kVA
Rated Output Voltage	208Vac
Output Voltage Range[1]	183 - 228Vac
Grid Connection Type	3Φ / PE / N (Neutral optional)
Max. AC Output Current @208Vac	69.5A
Rated Output Frequency	60Hz
Output Frequency Range[1]	57 - 63Hz
Power Factor	>0.99 (±0.8 adjustable)
Current THD @ Rated Load	<3%
Max. Fault Current Contribution (1 Cycle RMS)	64.1A (0.92 PU)
Max. OCPD Rating	125A
AC Disconnection Type	Load-break rated AC switch
AC Surge Protection	Type II MOV, 1240V_C, 15kA I_{TM} (8/20µS)

FIGURE 7-25: CPS SCA25KTL-DO/US-208 INVERTER SPECS

(FROM CHINT POWER SYSTEMS AMERICA)

under normal operating conditions, it would fall well within this operating range.

The inverter will also specify a **maximum operating input current** (135 amps for the CPS SCA25KTL-DO/US-208 model). Make sure the wiring system and overcurrent protection (fuses and circuit breakers) conform to this limitation.

> MAXIMUM OPERATING INPUT CURRENT

Another factor in selecting an inverter is to make sure it can handle the number of strings designed into the system. If the design calls for two strings connected directly to the inverter, but the inverter has only one point of connection (noted in the specification) – then this inverter will not work unless the design is altered to incorporate a combiner box.

The spec sheet on this inverter indicates it can handle up to 6 strings. One advantage of running multiple strings to the inverter is so each string can be optimized through MPPT. Note that this inverter only has 3 MPP trackers, so three sets of two strings are combined within the unit.

Other input limitations that can be gleaned from this spec sheet are:
- maximum power input: in this case it is 45 kW of DC power from the array. If the inverter were connected to a 45 kW array, with 25 kVA of AC output, the inverter-load ration of that configuration would be, 45,000 W/ 25,000 VA = 1.8,
- maximum DC voltage: this inverter has maximum of 1,000 Vdc,
- disconnect: a DC disconnect is integrated into this unit,
- surge protection: this unit also incorporates surge protection.

Output Specifications

A grid-tied inverter must be capable of matching the power signal of the grid to which it is attached. Otherwise power sent from the PV system to the grid will create harmonic distortions within the system.

In the United States, most homes and small commercial buildings with less than 400 amps of service will receive power in the form of single-phase, 240 Vac, at a nominal frequency of 60 Hz. In Europe it will operate at 230 Vac, with a nominal frequency of 50 Hz. Larger commercial systems may require three-phase power, most commonly 120/208 V or 277/480 V.

When selecting an inverter, ensure that it has obtained the UL 1741-SA listing (IEC 61727 in Europe), which indicates it has been approved as a utility inter-tie device. Talk with the local utility prior to selecting the inverter, since they may have specific conformance requirements with which the inverter must comply as part of their interconnection agreement.

The inverter output specifications will list a number of limitations that will be critical in the design of the system. These include:
- rated power output: in the example shown in Figure 7-25, the maximum output of this inverter is 25 kVA.
- rated output voltage: this inverter will produce 208 Vac three-phase power,
- maximum output current: the inverter output circuit wiring of this system must be designed to handle at least 69.5 A (times the 1.25 safety margin required by the NEC),
- frequency: this unit outputs at 60 Hz,
- disconnect: there is an integrated AC disconnect within this unit as well.

Other Specifications

Additional information will also be provided in the specification documentation. This includes:

> PEAK EFFICIENCY

> CEC EFFICIENCY

- efficiency: This is a percent measure of the conversion of DC electricity from the solar array to AC electricity to service the loads. Efficiency is generally provided in two units of measure. **Peak efficiency** is the efficiency of the inverter when it is performing at its best. However efficiency varies as conditions change. So manufacturers also provide a weighted **CEC (California Energy Commission) efficiency** rating that provides a better idea about the inverter's operating efficiency over the course of the day.

- enclosure type: the NEMA rating of the cabinet to indicate under which environmental conditions it may be mounted.

- installation orientation: at what angle can the unit be mounted to avoid water infiltration (for example, 15 to 90 degrees from horizontal)

- certifications: what certifications the unit has been tested to (for example, UL1741-SA Ed. 2, UL1699B, UL1998, CSA-C22.2 NO.107.1-01, IEEE1547)

- warranty: terms and time period

- dimensions, weight and more.

Inverter Power Factor Adjustment

The power output from a generating device, such as an inverter or a generator or even the grid itself, is normally expressed as kVA (kilo-volt-amperes).

kVA is the amount of power that is available for use, referred to as apparent power. This is the amount of power supplied by the inverter or the grid, measured in volt-amperes (VA).

kW is the amount of power that is actually used by the loads, referred to as real power measured in watts (W). In a 100% efficient resistive system, these two would be equal, or kVA = kW. The difference between the power that is used by the loads (W) and the power that is required to run the load (VA) is the power factor. The power that is required to run the load but is not actually consumed by the load is call the reactive power (VAR).

For example, if a building requires 100 kVA to power the loads, but the loads only use 90 kW of actual power to run, then that building would be operating at a power factor of 90 kW / 100 kVA = 0.90. In this case the grid would be supplying power to this building at a power factor of 0.90.

Adding a solar array to a site can have a significant impact on the power factor of that location. Especially for commercial sites (although this is increasingly happening with residential customers as well), utilities place limitations on the customer's power factor, imposing fees and penalties if it falls below a pre-determined level.

Take for example a site that has a load demand of 100 kW and a power factor of .95 (which would be well within the guidelines of the utility). In order to supply the 100 kW of real (or active) power, the utility would need to supply the facility with about 105 kVA of apparent power.

Now assume the factory installs a 60 kW solar array. If the array supplies only real power, then all of the reactive power needed would still need to come from the utility. But the utility is now only providing about 42 KVA rather than 105 kVA (the balance coming from the array). This would cause the power factor of the site to fall to around .77, well below the guidelines of the utility.

In order to avoid this situation, most commercial string inverters are equipped with the ability to program a power factor into the unit so as not to affect the power factor from power supplied by the grid.

Sizing an AC Coupled Inverter

When selecting an inverter for a DC-coupled system, the process is similar to one used when selecting a string inverter - the difference being that batteries will be added into the system.

But when configuring an AC-coupled system, an additional inverter is added into an existing system (as shown in Figure 7-26), and care must be taken to ensure that is is the right size and has the proper features.

Not all battery-based or hybrid inverters are compatible with the existing PV array inverter. So make sure the two inverters are compatible.

When selecting an inverter for an AC-coupled system, the following must be considered:
- battery-based inverter power output - continuous and surge rating (kVA),
- grid-tied to battery-based inverter charge rating (A),
- battery compatibility - the system voltage and battery type must be compatible with the battery-based inverter,
- battery bank maximum charge rating (A). The manner in which many AC coupled system charge battery banks is quite aggressive. AC coupling requires a robust battery bank to avoid overcharging,
- battery compatibility - system voltage and battery type

Battery-Based Inverter Power Output Rating

The output rating (in kVA) must also be enough to power the critical load maximum power draw (including continuous loads as well as surge demand). Size this in a manner similar to how a stand alone inverter would be sized based on the critical load demand, rather than the entire home's load demand.

Due to temperature derating in hot environments, the inverter should be at least 1.2 times larger than the highest continuous demand from dedicated or essential loads.

Size of the Battery-Based Inverter

When the grid is operating and the batteries are fully charged, all power from the grid-tied inverter flows through the battery-based inverter on its way to service the loads in the main service panel.

The output of your grid-tied inverter must be less than the output of the battery-based inverter. Excessive amps flowing into the unit could destroy the battery-based inverter. It is generally recommended that grid-tied inverter rating be 20% less than the battery-based inverter rating.

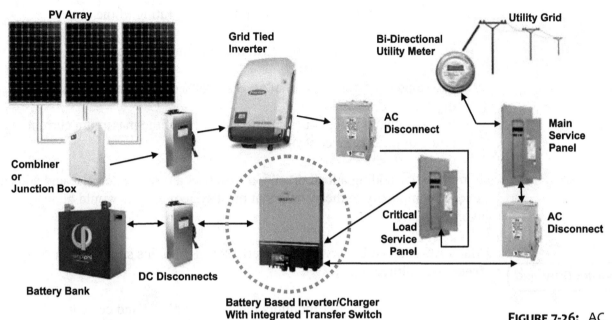

PV Array

Grid Tied
Inverter

Bi-Directional
Utility Meter

Utility Grid

AC
Disconnect

Main
Service
Panel

Combiner
or
Junction Box

Critical
Load
Service
Panel

AC
Disconnect

Battery Bank

DC Disconnects

Battery Based Inverter/Charger
With integrated Transfer Switch

FIGURE 7-26: AC
COUPLED SYSTEM
REQUIRES ADDITIONAL
INVERTER

In order to avoid a situation where the power flowing from the grid-tied inverter overwhelms the circuits and wiring within the battery-based inverter, it should have a capacity of at least 125% of the existing grid-tied inverter. For example, a system with an existing 4 kW grid-tied inverter will require a 5 kW battery-based inverter (4 kW x 125% = 5 kW).

Load Dumps and Dithering

The battery-based inverter also behaves as a charger, taking power from the grid-tied inverter and/or the grid and converting the AC current to DC to charge the battery bank.

When the grid is operational, the battery-based inverter will use AC power (from the array or grid) to keep the batteries fully charged in float mode. If there is more power being generated by the array than is needed by the loads and/or the battery, it flows to the grid. The grid serves as an unlimited **load dump**.

> LOAD DUMP

But once the grid is lost, all the power generated from the PV array (through the grid-tied inverter) is available to charge the battery bank and/or service the critical loads.

If there is too much power available from the array (the batteries are full and the critical loads have been satisfied), one of two things must happen. The excess power must either be diverted to a load dump (such as a hot water heater or a bank of resisters), or the power output from the grid-tied inverter must be reduced or shut off.

According to NEC 706.23(B)(2), load dumps, or **diversion loads** must:

> DIVERSION LOAD

- have a current rating not less than the current rating of the charge controller,
- have a voltage rating greater than the maximum voltage output of the battery bank (ESS),
- have a power rating (watts) of at least 150% of the charging source (in most cases the PV array,
- be connected with conductors rated at 150% of the maximum current rating of the charge controller.

In most cases, adding a load diversion system is a costly enterprise and adds a level of complexity to the system that most system owners would hope to avoid.

Many AC coupled battery-based inverters deal with this situation through **frequency dithering**.

FREQUENCY DITHERING

The battery-based inverter monitors the battery voltage and current continuously. As the battery bank charges and its voltage or current approaches it's capacity, the battery-based inverter increases its AC frequency.

In response, the grid-tied inverter will reduce its power output. If the frequency continues to increase, the grid-tied inverter will eventually shut down completely (when the frequency exceeds its operating limits).

As the battery bank charge level drops, the battery-based inverter will lower the frequency of the AC output. Once it falls within the operating limits of the grid-tied inverter once again, that inverter will restart and the process will begin again.

Ensure the Battery-based Inverter Compatible with Battery Bank
Just as every battery-based inverter is not compatible with every grid-tied inverter, they are also not compatible with every battery bank configuration.

All battery-based inverters are designed to be used with a specific nominal DC battery bank voltage. Ensure the voltage of the battery bank is compatible with the selected inverter.

Also, some battery-based inverters will not work with lithium ion batteries - while other systems will only work with lithium ion batteries. Often the frequency feathering technique may not be compatible with the electronic charging incorporated in lithium ion battery systems.

Battery Bank Sizing
When sizing the battery bank that will be connected to the battery-based inverter, it is important to ensure that the batteries do not discharge too quickly or charge too quickly.

In order to ensure the batteries do not discharge too quickly, calculate the number of batteries (or strings) in the following manner:

# of batteries > (maximum battery based inverter output (kVA) / inverter efficiency) / battery maximum discharge rate (kW)

The logic of this equation is that the maximum inverter output is the maximum power draw that can be servicing the loads at any point in time. But how much power will be pulled from the battery bank will actually be more than that - due to the inefficiency of the inverter in converting DC power to AC power.

There is also a limit to how quickly this power can be drawn from the battery (generally around C/2 rate of discharge). This **maximum continuous discharge rate** is generally calculated by multiplying the maximum battery discharge current by the battery's nominal voltage.

> MAXIMUM
> CONTINUOUS
> DISCHARGE RATE

So the battery bank must be big enough to allow for all the power required to be drawn from the battery bank at a slow enough rate as not to damage the batteries (and void the warranty).

So for example, assume the battery based inverter has a maximum output of 8 kVA and is 95.5% efficient. Also assume that the battery selected has a maximum continuous discharge rate of 1.92 kWdc (at C/2). Then:

# of batteries > [8.0 kVA (maximum inverter output) / 0.955 (inverter efficiency)] / 1.92 kW (battery maximum discharge rate) = 4.363 batteries

So this system would require a minimum of 5 batteries to avoid discharging at too fast a rate.

There is also a limit as to how quickly a battery should be charged. This **maximum continuous charge rate** is calculated by multiplying the maximum battery charge current by the battery's nominal voltage.

> MAXIMUM
> CONTINUOUS CHARGE
> RATE

In an AC Coupled system, significantly limiting the solar array's charging power can be difficult. Therefore, most battery-based inverter manufacturers will recommend that the battery bank be sized larger relative to the grid-tied inverter output. They do this by imposing a derate factor into the calculation. This derate factor should be provided by the manufacturer.

The formula for calculating the battery bank size to avoid charging at too fast a rate is:

# of batteries > maximum grid-tied inverter output (kVA) / derate factor x battery maximum charge rate (kW)

For example, assume the maximum output from the connected grid-tied inverter is 6 kVA. The battery based inverter manufacturer recommends a derate factor of 80% (0.80) and the maximum charge rate for the batteries selected is 1.92 kWdc (at C/2). So:

# of batteries > 6.0 kVA (maximum grid-tied inverter output) /
0.80 derate factor x 1.92 kW battery maximum charge rate = 3.9 batteries

This system would require a minimum of 4 batteries to avoid charging too quickly, but a minimum of 5 batteries to avoid discharging too quickly. So the system should be designed to incorporate a minimum of 5 batteries (or strings of batteries depending on their voltage) connected in parallel.

Incorporating a Generator in an AC Coupled System

If a generator is incorporated into an AC-Coupled system, when running, the generator will provide AC power to the battery based inverter, and through it, also to the grid-tied inverter (in AC coupled systems, sometimes referred to as the **PV inverter**, as it is connected to the PV array).

PV INVERTER

If the generator is of sufficient quality, the PV inverter will detect the AC signal and mistake it for the grid, and begin to produce energy from the array.

Most grid-tied inverters should not be used with a generator. Most generators will vary their output frequency and voltage as load change. An inverter trying to tie into that may not be able to follow the changing phase and might create current surges between the generator and the inverter - damaging the inverter as well as the generator.

Some better quality generators may have a much more stable output, but back feed from the inverter could damage the generator. For this reason, traditional grid-tied systems that incorporate a generator backup generally are designed in such a way as to shut down the inverter when the generator is running (powering all loads from the generator only).

Some battery based inverters (as illustrated in Figure 7-27) are designed to incorporate a backup generator. The manufacturer will provide guidance as to what size and type of generator is compatible with the inverter.

Most of these systems signal the generator to start when the battery bank discharges to a set point. Once the generator output is stable, the inverter switches the load to the generator and draws some power to charge the batteries.

The inverter is not actually running when the generator is in operation. All loads as well as the battery charging is handled by power output from the generator. Once the batteries have reached a suitable state of charge, the

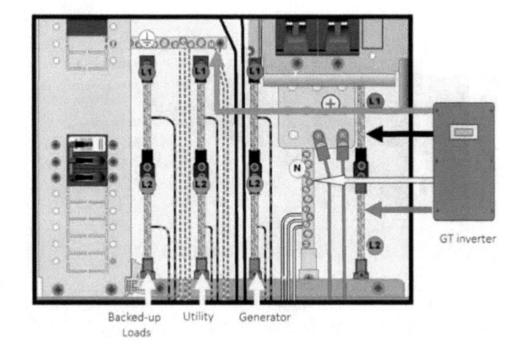

FIGURE 7-27: DIAGRAM
OF CONNECTIONS WITHIN
AN OUTBACK RADIAN
INVERTER CONNECTING
TO AN EXISTING GRID
TIED INVERTER

(FROM OUTBACK POWER
TECHNOLOGIES)

inverter turns off the generator and once again handles the powering of the critical loads.

Selecting Components for Microinverter/Optimizer Systems

Microinverter systems have become increasingly popular in recent years, even for larger commercial systems. With longer warranties than traditional string inverters (25 years versus 12 years), decreasing costs of the units, and the rapid shutdown requirements that mandate MPLEs installed with string inverters - the economics of installing even large microinverter systems as compared to string inverter systems continues to shift.

While the concept of microinverters has been around since the 1990s, until recently they had been viewed as a high-cost alternative that were primarily used when shading was an issue. Those economic calculations have changed significantly, and today microinverters comprise a significant and growing portion of residential systems installed, as indicated in Figure 7-28.

While microinverters (primarily from Enphase) and power optimizer systems (primarily from SolarEdge) play a significant part in small to mid-sized systems, the dominant portion of solar energy comes from larger commercial and utility-scale system installations.

In 2020, single phase systems accounted for only 10% of all solar resources installed (according to IHS Markit). Three-phase systems over 500 kW in size accounted for 34% of all production capacity installed that year, while three-phase systems less than 500 kW in size accounted for 56% of installed capacity.

FIGURE 7-28: LIGHT COMMERCIAL AND RESIDENTIAL INVERTER US MARKET SHARE BY BRAND, 2017-2021

(FROM ENERGYSAGE)

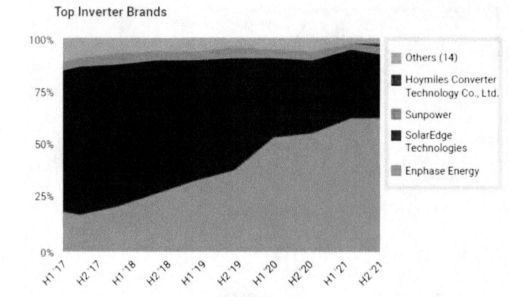

Top Inverter Brands

Others (14)

Hoymiles Converter Technology Co., Ltd.

Sunpower

SolarEdge Technologies

Enphase Energy

Microinverters

Microinverters convert the DC output of the panel to grid-compatible AC current at the panel. So there is no DC wiring, disconnects of overcurrent protection required. All components within the system must be rated for AC current.

FIGURE 7-29: ENPHASE IQ 8+ MICROINVERTER

(FROM ENPHASE)

Not every microinverter is compatible with every solar panel.

For example, the Enphase IQ 8 unit i(pictured in Figure 7-29) s compatible with 60-cell/120 half-cell and 72-cell/144 half-cell PV modules that are rated between 235 W - 440 W and do not generate more than 60 Vdc.

Many microinverters also require proprietary cable (Figure 7-30) that allow for easy AC parallel connections at each microinverter.

FIGURE 7-30: ENPHASE PROPRIETARY TRUNK CABLE

(FROM ENPHASE)

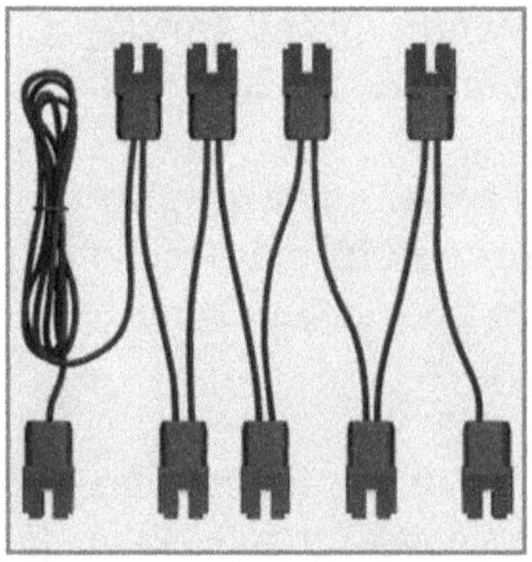

As these are pre-configured assemblies, there is no option in selecting the appropriate wire gauge. Connection limitations are imposed so as not to exceed the ampacity rating of the cable.

Power Optimizers

A hybrid inverter system also exists that lies somewhere between traditional string inverters and microinverters. These **DC-to-DC converters** (generally referred to as power optimizers) attach to each solar panel (like a microinverter). Like a

DC-TO-DC CONVERTER

microinverter, the power optimizer incorporates MPPT functions as well as anti-islanding functions.

Unlike a microinverter, however, the device does not convert the DC voltage from the panel to AC, but rather the optimizers perform a DC-DC voltage conversion, to keep the output of the array at a fixed DC voltage (such as 350 Vdc).

The array is then connected to a string inverter, as shown in Figure 7-31, that operates at a set voltage (rather than a range) and does not need to incorporate MPPT or anti-islanding functionality.

The leading manufacturer of power optimizers is Solar Edge. Their system works with a fixed voltage inverter that communicates with power optimizers that are connected to the panels (generally one to four panels for each optimizer). The current is set by the fixed voltage inverter at a level that maintains a constant voltage as the total output from the array varies with conditions. Each optimizer adjusts it own voltage accordingly.

For example, assume that ten 300 W panels with 300 W power optimizers (one per panel) are connected together in series, then connected to the fixed voltage inverter. Assuming ideal operating conditions, this string will generate 3,000 watts of power (300 W x 10 panels). The inverter can only accept a fixed voltage of 350 Vdc. 3,000 W / 350 Vdc = 8.57 amps. So a signal is relayed to all the optimizers, which transmit the 300 W of each panel at 8.57 amps and 35 volts (300 W / 8.57 amps). In this way the combined voltage output of the string will be 350 Vdc when it arrives at the inverter.

If conditions were less than ideal, say for example the string was only generating 2,000 W of power. The inverter still needs to receive the power at a fixed voltage of 350 Vdc. So in this scenario, a signal will be sent from the inverter to the optimizers that the power should be configured at 5.71 amps (2,000 W / 350 Vdc). Even though each panel is (on average) now producing

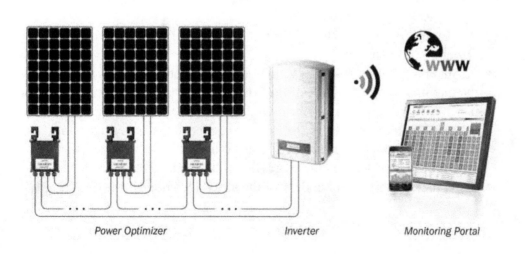

Power Optimizer   Inverter   Monitoring Portal

FIGURE 7-31: POWER OPTIMIZER SYSTEM

(FROM AURORA ENERGY)

CHAPTER 7: SELECTING THE COMPONENTS   PAGE 281

only 200 W of power, the voltage from the entire string will remain constant at 350 Vdc (2,000 W / 5.71 amps).

It is rare, however, that each panel in a string will generate exactly the same amount of power. So the communication between the inverter and the power optimizers is on the individual panel level. For example, if one panel was shaded and only producing 80 W, while one panel was partially shaded, producing 120 W, and the remaining 8 panels were producing 250 W - the inverter would receive a total of 2,200 W (8 panels x 250 W + 80 W + 120 W).

To maintain the 350 Vdc fixed voltage the inverter requires, a signal would be sent to all the optimizers to produce at a current of 6.285 amps (2,200 W / 350 Vdc). So the optimizer of each of the eight panels producing 250 W each would be transmitting power at 6.285 amps x 39.77 Vdc (250 W / 6.285 amps), the shaded panel optimizer would produce at 6.285 amps x 12.73 V (80 W / 6.285 amps) and the optimizer on the partially shaded panel would produce at 6.285 amps x 19.09 Vdc (120 W / 6.285 amps). The total voltage from the string will still be 350 Vdc (39.77 Vdc x 8 panels + 12.73 Vdc + 19.09 Vdc).

From the installer's point of view, it is only necessary to understand how many optimizers can be connected in series within each string. This information will be available in the manufacturer's instructions.

For larger installations, it is common practice to hook two or more solar panels to a single power optimizer unit. This can greatly reduce the cost of the installation while only marginally affecting the independent maximum power point functions (two panels will be affected by shading, rather than only one). Units are available that can handle the combined voltage of two panels up to 600 W, 700 W, 730 W, and 800 W.

When connecting multiple panels to a single power optimizer, care should be taken to ensure that:
  - all connected panels are identical,
  - the combined power rating of the panel (in watts) does not exceed the rating of the optimizer,
  - the maximum input voltage (Voc) at lowest temperature does not exceed the maximum input voltage of the power optimizer; if connecting multiple modules in series, the cumulative voltage should be used,
  - the maximum input current (Isc) does not exceed the maximum input current of the power optimizer. If connecting multiple modules in parallel, the cumulative amperage should be used.
  - the voltage within the boundary of the array does not exceed 80 Vdc.

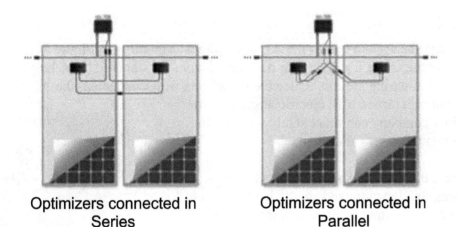

Optimizers connected in
Series

Optimizers connected in
Parallel

Multiple panels can be connected to the optimizer using either a series or parallel connection, as shown in Figure 7-32. When connected together in series,the voltages generated by the panels will be combined, so the optimizer must be rated to this higher voltage.

Special branch cable is available to connect 2, 3 or 4 panels to a single power optimizer in parallel. When connections are made in parallel, the current will accumulate. Make sure the branch cable is large enough to handle this accumulated current.

String Optimizers

Large commercial or utility-scale systems rarely incorporate optimizers on each panel. Designers can, however, incorporate **string optimizers** into the system to obtain some of the advantages that optimizers provide.

STRING OPTIMIZERS

The optimizer is located on each string between the panels and the combiner box, as indicated in Figure 7-33.

String optimizers allow for:
- larger strings,
- smaller combiner boxes with fewer disconnects and breakers,
- smaller conductors since current is managed and limited,
- MPPT control at the string level,
- less expensive fixed-voltage string inverters.

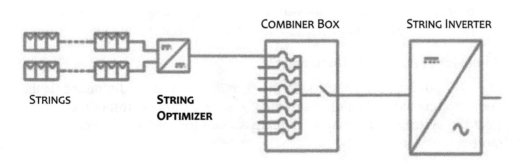

STRINGS   **STRING OPTIMIZER**   COMBINER BOX   STRING INVERTER

FIGURE 7-33: A LARGE SYSTEM WITH STRING OPTIMIZER

AC Disconnect

AC DISCONNECT

Next in the system comes the **AC disconnect** as pictured in Figure 7-34. This allows the entire PV system to be isolated from the standard household electrical wiring system. Once the PV system is disconnected (the AC disconnect turned off), electricians and/or the utility company can more safely work on the remaining electrical system.

FIGURE 7-34: FUSED AC DISCONNECT

These disconnects should be located in an accessible location, and should be compatible with the energy output (volts and amps) of the inverter(s).

Issues to consider when selecting an AC disconnect include:

- Ampacity rating of the AC output from the inverter(s).

- Voltage rating of the AC output from the inverter(s).

- Power phase - single phase or three phase.

- Poles. Typically disconnects will have either 1, 2 or 3 poles. For 120 Vac single phase, only one pole is required, to interrupt the line (hot) conductor. For 240 Vac service, two poles will be required to interrupt line 1 (black) and line 2 (red). For three-phase service, three poles will be required. The disconnect must simultaneously open all ungrounded conductors.

- If placed outdoors, ensure the unit is rated for outdoor use (NEMA 3R or better)

- Fused (contains overcurrent protection) or unfused.

- AC and DC disconnects must be located at the inverter (within 10 feet). Many inverter systems incorporate these disconnects within their wire management assembly.

- An AC disconnect must also be located within 10 feet of the service connection point (generally the electric meter in residential settings). They must be visible, externally operable, and lockable. They must also be installed so that the center of the operating handle, at it's highest position, is not more than 6 to 7 feet above the floor or working platform.

Where is the PV System Disconnect?

PV SYSTEM DISCONNECT

The NEC 2017, Section 690.13 clarifies that the **PV system disconnect** is the disconnecting means that separates the PV system from the rest of the electrical systems. This may seem pretty straightforward, but it gets a bit more complex in practice.

The growing number of PV system options often incorporate multiple power sources (batteries, generators, wind turbines, etc.) into the system. The 2017 NEC seeks to clarify where exactly the PV portion of the system is "turned off."

Essentially, if there is an additional power source upstream of the disconnect, then it is not the PV System Disconnect.

For example, in a grid-tied system with a string inverter and no additional power sources, the PV system disconnect is the AC disconnect, as indicated in Figure 7-35.

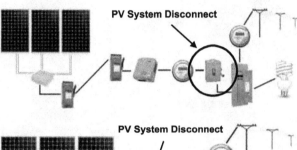

FIGURE 7-35: PV SYSTEM DISCONNECT FOR GRID-TIED SYSTEM WITH STRING INVERTER

In systems that incorporate AC modules (such as microinverters), the PV system disconnect is located as indicated in Figure 7-36.

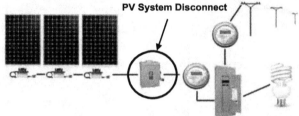

FIGURE 7-36: PV SYSTEM DISCONNECT FOR AC MODULE SYSTEMS

The PV system disconnect for a stand alone system (Figure 7-37) is not at the AC disconnect, as in the previous examples, but at the DC disconnect located near the charge controller, before the battery bank enters the system as an additional power source.

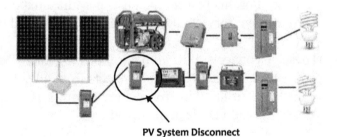

FIGURE 7-37: PV SYSTEM DISCONNECT FOR STAND ALONE SYSTEMS

The PV system disconnect for an AC-coupled multimode system will remain where it had been prior to the battery backup system being added to the system, as depicted in Figure 7-38.

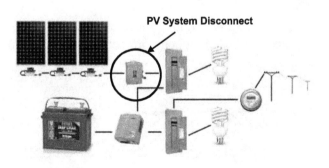

FIGURE 7-38: PV SYSTEM DISCONNECT FOR AC-COUPLED MULTIMODE PV SYSTEMS CONNECTED TO THE GRID

Multiple Inverter Systems

In large systems, multiple inverters may interconnect to a single **point of connection (POC)**, such as an **AC aggregation panel** (Figure 7-39). Make

POINT OF CONNECTION (POC)

AC AGGREGATION PANEL

sure the current rating of POC exceeds the sum of all the output current from the inverters feeding it.

FIGURE 7-39: FUSED AC AGGREGATION PANEL DESIGNED TO ACCOMMODATE INPUT FROM 4 STRING INVERTERS

(FROM SOLAR BOS)

 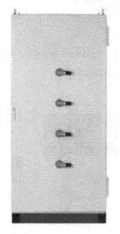

For example, if the system has four inverters, each producing 35 amps, then the inverter aggregation panel (illustrated in Figure 7-40) must be rated for at least 140 amps (4 x 35 A).

Six Handle Rule

The design of large PV systems can become quite complex, especially when incorporating multiple systems into a facility that may house multiple tenants (like an apartment building). There can be a number of power sources (generators, PV systems, the utility) all operating independently or in tandem with each other. Each of these power sources is considered a separate **service**.

In an emergency situation, when first responders arrive on the scene, it is important that they be able to disconnect all power sources in a timely manner. For this reason, the NEC permits a maximum of six disconnects for any electrical service (the **six handle rule**), found in NEC Article 230.71.

SERVICE

SIX HANDLE RULE

These disconnects must all be grouped together. Not just the disconnects from one service, but the disconnects from all services feeding power to the site. This is usually interpreted to be within 10 feet of each other, easily accessible and visible at one location.

If, for some reason, the disconnects cannot be grouped together, directories or a plaque must be in place indicating where all the disconnects are located.

The use of an AC aggregation panel can eliminate the potential of violating the six handle rule when connecting a large number (more than six) inverters

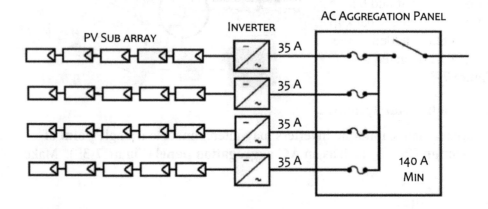

FIGURE 7-40: DIAGRAM OF AGGREGATION PANEL SERVING FOUR 35 A INVERTERS

to a facility. While a PV system is generally considered to be a separate service, many inspectors have interpreted the code differently, adding all disconnects from all service present when enforcing the six handle rule.

System Monitors

Most inverter systems now come with some sort of production monitoring system, either incorporated in a menu on the unit or, more commonly, accessible through a phone or computer.

There are also a number of third-party monitoring systems available that can be added to existing systems or incorporated into new installs if the designer determines they offer better features then the standard monitoring offered by the inverter manufacturer.

Increasingly these systems also monitor power consumption, either on a system level or by individual circuits or loads. The monitoring is performed through a current transformer (CT) such as illustrated in Figure 7-41 that is installed around a hot conductor and measures the amount of amps traveling through that conductor.

FIGURE 7-41: CURRENT TRANSFORMER (CT)

Whole system CTs are installed around the hots that feed the site, generally in the service panel between the electric meter and the main disconnect breaker.

Individual circuits are monitored by installing CTs on the hot lead leaving an individual circuit breaker.

CTs are limited by the the amount of amps they are capable of monitoring as well as the size of wire they can physically fit around.

These CTs are then connected through sensor wire to a data collection unit or **gateway**, which is then in turn connected either to a WiFi connection to the Internet or through mobile telephone service.

GATEWAY

Components in Adding a Generator

Often a home or business owner will wish to incorporate a generator to service all or selected critical loads when the grid goes down.

When a generator is added to a PV system, several things must generally happen for the system to work effectively.

First, the system must be disconnected from the grid to avoid islanding, or sending power onto the lines where a repair worker may be injured by the unexpected current.

Second, the solar PV system should be isolated from the generator to avoid power feeding from the generator to the inverter, or from the inverter to the generator. These functions are normally handled through an **automatic transfer switch (ATS)**.

AUTOMATIC
TRANSFER SWITCH

Also, the generator will need to be "told" to begin operation when the grid signal is lost or when the state-of-charge of the battery bank is low. This is made possible by incorporating an **autostart** unit into the system.

AUTOSTART

Generator Sizing

The generator used as backup will likely be installed in such a way that it is powering all the loads when operating. So it must be sized accordingly, large enough to continuously service all critical loads.

If the unit is also configured to recharge the battery bank at the same time (as in a stand-alone system), it is a good idea to size the generator at twice the capacity of the inverter. For example, if the system operates with a 5 kW inverter, install a 10 kW or larger generator.

It's a good idea to install a larger generator than required, especially at higher elevations where the generator is going to lose some of its power. Engines can lose around 3% of their power for every 1,000 feet above sea level. They also should be derated by an additional 1% for every 10 °F when operating in temperatures above 100 °F.

DUTY CYCLE

The capacity of a generator is dependent upon its **duty cycle** (the amount of time it is running versus the amount of time it is not running). Generators are generally classified into three duty cycle categories (Figure 7-42):

STANDBY POWER
RATING

- **Standby Power Rating**. Standby power rated generators are the most commonly rated generator classification. Their primary application is to supply emergency power for a limited duration during a power outage. These generators should not be run when connected to the grid (backfeeding). They should be sized at 125% of the maximum anticipated load.

PRIME POWER
RATING

- **Prime Power Rating.** The prime power rating is the maximum power available for an unlimited number of hours per year in a variable load setting. It is not advisable that the variable load exceed 70% average of the prime power rating during any operational period of 250 hours. If the engine is running at 100% prime power, yearly hours should not exceed 500.

CONTINUOUS POWER
RATING

- **Continuous Power Rating.** Continuous power rating is used in applications where supplying power is at a constant 100% load for an unlimited number of hours each year.

2-WIRE START

Off-grid generators paired with solar PV systems need **2-wire start capability** to allow the automatic generator start (AGS) function to work.

Model	Standby Rating		Prime Rating		Continuous Rating	
	60 Hz kW (kVA)	50 Hz kW (kVA)	60 Hz kW (kVA)	50 Hz kW (kVA)	60 Hz kW (kVA)	50 Hz kW (kVA)
DQKB	1750 (2188)	1500 (1875)	1600 (2000)	1350 (1688)	1450 (1813)	1200 (1500)
DQKC	2000 (2500)	1650 (2063)	1825 (2281)	1500 (1875)	1600 (2000)	1200 (1500)
DQKD	Not Rated	1800 (2250)	Not Rated	1600 (2000)	Not Rated	1320 (1650)
DQKH	2250 (2813)	2000 (2500)	Not Rated	Not Rated	Not Rated	Not Rated

FIGURE 7-42:
GENERATOR
SPECIFICATIONS FOR A
SELECTION OF CUMMINS
MODELS

When the batteries drop below a certain voltage, the AGS kicks in to turn on the generator and recharge the battery bank.

Most generators operate at one of two engine speeds: 1800 or 3600 RPM. The difference is based on engine design and the alternator being used. 1800 RPM generators are generally considered superior, as they are more fuel-efficient, however they are also generally more expensive. 3600 RPM generators tend to be less expensive but less efficient.

Automatic Transfer Switch

While it is possible to manually disconnect from the grid and then manually start a backup generator, such a process is cumbersome and prone to human error. Also, most jurisdictions would not permit such a setup.

As a result, when the power goes out, the load is generally transferred from utility power over to a backup power source using an automatic transfer switch.

It is imperative that this transfer is handled in a safe and reliable manner.

When selecting a transfer switch, examine the:
- transition mode,
- type of load it connects to,
- the continuous current rating,
- the voltage rating,
- system compatibility (with the generator and the inverter).

Transition Mode
Not all automatic transfer switches transition between power sources in the same manner.

- **Open transition** switching is sometimes referred to as "Break-Before-Make". This reflects the sequence of switching where the contacts for the original source (normally the grid) are opened before the contacts for the secondary source (the generator) are closed. This means there will be a short interruption of power as the generator is activated.

OPEN TRANSITION

- **Delayed transition** switching is primarily used where the loads supplied are primarily inductive or motor loads. The transition sequence is similar to open transition switching, however the power interruption is extended to allow residual voltages to decay and motors to slow.

DELAYED TRANSITION

- **Closed transition** switching is often called "Make-Before-Break." In this mode, the contacts for the backup source (the generator) are closed before the contacts for the original source (the grid) are opened. This results in momentary source paralleling that provides continuous power, avoiding momentary power interruption to sensitive loads. In order for this transition to work effectively, both power sources would need to be operational - so it could not be used in an unexpected grid outage.

Continuous Current Rating

The automatic transfer switch must be capable of supplying maximum current supplied it by any connected power source. Generally this will be the current rating of the main breaker of the service panel to which it is connected.

Voltage Rating

The voltage rating of the transfer switch must match the supply rating. In a single phase system, this will typically be 240 Vac. In a three-phase system, the voltage rating of the unit should match the voltage rating from the generator and the utility connection feeding the unit.

A transfer switch can be connected to two AC power sources that are not properly synchronized. It is therefore important that the unit can deal with resulting increased voltage.

Generator Autostart

Once the grid goes down, the automatic transfer switch is designed to isolate the system from the utility. But it is also necessary to start the generator. This is normally done in one of two ways.

An automatic transfer switch may incorporate a **mains detection**, designed to monitor the power supply from the utility. When it detect a mains failure, it disconnects from the grid and sends a signal to the generator to start. At this point, both the connection to the grid and the connection to the loads are in the open position.

Once the generator has started, it then sends an "available" signal back to the transfer switch. When the ATS receives this, it closes the connection to the loads. This would be an example of an open transition switch.

Automatic transfer switches without mains detection require that the mains detection be built into the generator or installed elsewhere in the system. When the generator detects a mains failure, it sends a signal to the ATS to disconnect from the utility. The generator will then start. The ATS then closes the connection to the loads.

Chapter 7 Review Questions

1) As of 2020, silicon-based solar panels accounted for about _____ of global sales.
   a) 10%
   b) 60%
   c) 75%
   d) 95%

2) The significant degradation of performance and power quality due to direct sunlight exposure of a solar panel during the initial hours of use is referred to as:
   a) doping
   b) light-induced degradation
   c) potential-induced degradation
   d) valence bonding

3) Until very recently, the dominant size of a solar cell was the:
   a) MC4 cell
   b) MC3 module
   c) M2 wafer
   d) MPPT doped

4) The highest voltage a panel can generate (under standard test conditions), with no load connected to it, is referred to as the panel's _____ .
   a) open-circuit voltage
   b) nominal voltage
   c) short-circuit voltage
   d) maximum power voltage

5) As the temperature of the PV array rises above 25 degrees C, the panel will:
   a) produce more power
   b) produce less power
   c) temperature does not affect the ability of a panel to produce power
   d) automatically disconnect at 35 degrees C

6) A type of solar cell that incorporates an additional layer to the bottom of the cell that increases the cell's ability to absorb light and is incorporated in about 40% of all panels sold worldwide is called a:
   a) PERC cell
   b) IBC cell
   c) HJT cell
   d) split cell

7) When a panel is listed as producing power within a range above or below its rated output under standard test conditions, this refers to the panel's:
   a) power factor
   b) nominal voltage rating
   c) temperature coefficient
   d) power tolerance

8) A tier 1 rated solar panel indicates:
   a) that the panel is of higher quality than a tier 2 or tier 3 panel
   b) that the panel is of lower quality than a tier 2 or tier 3 panel
   c) that the panel costs more than a tier 2 or tier 3 panel
   d) that the manufacturer of the panel is financially stable

9) Which type of solar module is designed to provide increased energy output due to albedo?
   a) PERC cell modules
   b) half cut cell modules
   c) bifacial modules
   d) concentrator modules

10) The theoretical maximum efficiency limit of a single-bandgap non-concentrated solar cell is referred to as the:
   a) Shockley-Queisser limit
   b) power tolerance
   c) maximum power point
   d) heterojunction limitation band

11) Today, most solar panels incorporate:
   a) MC1 connectors
   b) MC2 connectors
   c) MC3 connectors
   d) MC4 connectors

12) Which of the following is **NOT** a function that a MLPE (depending on the MLPE, it may perform one or more of these functions) is designed to perform?
   a) invert DC power to AC power
   b) power tolerance adjustment
   c) maximum power point tracking
   d) rapid shutdown at the module

13) A device often incorporated into a system where PV Source Circuits are connected in parallel is called a/an:
   a) combiner box
   b) charge controller
   c) overcurrent protection device
   d) array termination assembly

23) A factory has installed a 52 kW array. It takes 125 kVA to power the loads, but only 100 kW of real power is actually consumed by the machines (the loads). There is no battery backup or generator incorporated at this site. This facility has a/an:
   a) inverter load ratio of 0.52
   b) inverter load ratio of 0.416
   c) power factor of 1.25
   d) power factor of 0.8

24) When designing an AC couple system:
   a) only a single inverter is required, but its output must be capable of providing at least 1.2 times the total load demand
   b) the PV inverter must be 125% the size of the battery-based inverter
   c) the battery-based inverter must be 125% the size of the PV inverter
   d) the combined output of the two inverters must equal 1.2 time the total load demand

25) To avoid the cost and complexity of incorporating a load dump in the system, many AC coupled battery-based inverters utilize _____ to manage excess capacity.
   a) frequency dithering
   b) maximum power point tracking (MPPT)
   c) diversion loads
   d) solar panels will not generate power when there is no load present, so this is not a problem in an AC coupled system

26) To ensure the battery bank does not discharge too rapidly (damaging the batteries), design the battery bank using the following formula:
   A) # of batteries (or strings) = maximum grid-tied inverter output (kVA)/ derate factor x battery maximum charge rate (kW)
   b) # of batteries (or strings) = maximum battery-based inverter output (kVA)/ derate factor x battery maximum charge rate (kW)
   c) # of batteries (or strings) = maximum battery-based inverter output (kVA)/ inverter inefficiency / battery maximum discharge rate (kW)
   d) # of batteries (or strings) = maximum battery-based inverter input (kW)/ derate factor / battery maximum discharge rate (kW)

27) A string of 20 SolarEdge P370 power optimizers are used in an array. Each is connected to a 350 W panel. The power optimizers have the following characteristics:

Rated Input Power: 370 W
Maximum Input Voltage: 60 Vdc
Maximum Input Current: 13.75 A
Maximum Output Voltage: 60 Vdc
Maximum Output Current: 15 A

The string is connected to a SE7600H-US inverter with the following specs:
Rated Input Power: 11,800 W
Maximum Input Voltage: 480 Vdc
Nominal Input Voltage: 400 Vdc
Maximum Input Current: 20 A

Assuming the string is producing 5,000 W of power and all panels are behaving in an identical manner (no shading, etc), what is the output **CURRENT** of each panel under these conditions?
   a) 10.417 A
   b) 12.5 A
   c) 14.19 A
   d) 15 A

28) The number of power optimizers or microinverters that can be incorporated into a string/branch circuit is limited by:
   a) the size of the array
   b) the ampacity rating of the connecting conductors
   c) the voltage rating of the power optimizer or micro inverter
   d) the inverter load ratio (ILR)

29) The AC disconnect is **NOT** considered the main PV system disconnect (by the NEC) in which of the following configurations?
   a) grid-tied system
   b) stand-alone system
   c) AC-coupled system
   d) DC-coupled system

30) What is the maximum number of disconnects allowed by the NEC for any single electrical service?
   a) one
   b) two
   c) three
   d) six

Chapter 8

Sizing the Array

Once the load requirements have been determined, the site inspection is complete, and the budget is in place – it is time to begin designing the PV array.

But before the array can be configured, a number of critical decisions will need to be made. These include:

- What type of system will be installed (stand alone, grid tied, grid interactive)?
- If grid tied, what type of inverter system will be used (microinverters, power optimizers, string inverter)?
- Where will the system be mounted (roof mount, ground mount)?
- What brand and model solar panel has been selected?
- What brand and model inverter has been selected?

Armed with this information, the design of the array can begin.

Determining the Size of a Grid-Tied Array

The size of the array is expressed in terms of its total peak-watts of generating capacity.

In other words, how much power the array will generate per hour under ideal solar conditions (standard test conditions), when the sun's rays are assumed to be providing 1,000 watts per square meter at a temperature of 25°C.

The amount of power the home or business will need over the course of a month should have already been determined, either through a load analysis, or more commonly, by checking the customer's most recent utility bills. Once the total demand is known, the system owner will need to determine the percentage of the power they would like the array to offset.

Budget will have a major role in determining the size of the array. But if the budget will allow it, it is often best to oversize the array, making it bigger rather than smaller. Electrical use tends to increase over time. Or if money is tight, perhaps design the system so that it can easily be expanded in the future as more money becomes available.

When designing a grid-tied system, it is important to consider the rules and requirements of the utility provider. Many utilities place severe penalties on systems that produce more than they consume.

Most states have placed net metering requirements on investor-owned electric utilities. This typically means that the utility must pay retail for electricity generated by their customers through PV systems (in other words, the meter runs forward and backward with no regard for the price of the product). But if a customer generates more power than they consume (generally determined over the course of a year), they suddenly become a utility provider, like any other power company. The homeowner then falls outside the net metering law and the utility may determine they will only pay wholesale rates for the electricity generated.

Future-Proofing Designs

As the various sizes and ratings of the components in the system are calculated, bear in mind that situations change over time.

Will the home or business expand at some future date? Is there a reason to expect that additional electricity will be needed in the future (might they purchase an electric vehicle in a few years, for example)?

It is a lot easier to place larger wires and larger components today, rather than redesign and perhaps have to replace parts of the system at a later date.

It is, of course, a balancing act. Customers do not want to pay for things that will never be used. But if the system is expanded in the future, they will find it very cost effective to install larger than currently required wiring and overcurrent protection, which may cost a little more during the initial installation, but will save a lot of money in the future.

Grid-Tied Array Sizing Example

To understand the process better, imagine a large dairy farmer has asked for an estimate on how much it might cost to install solar to power their operation.

A remote site assessment determined that a large barn (Figure 8-1) would likely be the best location for the array, as it appears to have plenty of roof space and one plane of the roof faces directly south.

FIGURE 8-1: DAIRY BARN ROOF WHERE ARRAY WILL BE INSTALLED

The owner of the dairy farm has indicated that the grid has proven very reliable over the years and they have no interest in a battery backup system.

They provide a copy of their utility bill, and the use profile indicates that they use 16,185 kWh per month on average, as indicated in Figure 8-2.

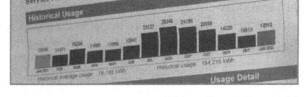

FIGURE 8-2: LOAD ANALYSIS CONDUCTED BY EXAMINING CURRENT ELECTRIC BILL

An onsite visit to the property confirmed that there were no shading issues. The slope of the roof was measured and found to be at a 20 degree angle. The orientation (azimuth) of the building was true south (180 degrees).

The roof in question measures 16 feet x 80 feet. Using a rough (very rough) rule of thumb of 10 watts per square foot, it can be assumed that the south-facing roof section could handle a 13 kW array (16 ft x 80 ft = 1,280 x 10 W = 12,800 kW).

The existing service from the grid is three-phase, 480/277 V. The system will be supply-side connected between the meter and an existing transformer, so the inverter output will need to match the 480/277 V signal from the grid.

Calculate the Array's Generating Capacity

Assume this site is located in northern Ohio.

A search of PV watts shows that, given the angle and orientation of the roof, the average annual insolation figures (hours of peak sunlight) for this location is about 4.6 hours per day.

The farm needs 16,185 kWh of power each month, and there are (on average) 30.5 days in a month. So the average daily load for this site is:

16,185 kWh (per month) / 30.5 days (per month) = 530 kWh (per day)

Each day (as determined from PV Watts), there are 4.6 hours of peak sunlight available at this site. So the next step is to determine how large the array must be, given the available insolation:

530 kWh / 4.6 hrs (insolation) = 115 kW

This calculation reveals that the array must be sized to 115 kW given the insolation available at the site, in order to offset the entire electric bill with power from the array.

Unfortunately, PV systems are not 100% efficient. A certain amount of energy is lost as the DC signal travels from the panels, through the wires and connections (voltage drop), charges batteries, and is converted to AC power within the inverter. In fact, up to 10% of the power can be lost as the DC energy is converted to AC by an inexpensive string inverter.

Shading, dust, aging mismatch and even air temperature (remember, panels are less efficient the higher the air temperature) will also effect how the system performs. Possible impacts on the efficiency of the system are highlighted in Figure 8-3.

DERATE FACTOR

So it is necessary to adjust for these inefficiencies by applying a **derate factor** to the size of the array.

Derate Factor Components

A number of factors combine to determine the derate factor used in sizing a PV system. Not all factors apply to every system.

These factors include:

MODULE NAMEPLATE DC RATING

- **Module nameplate DC rating** derate: This accounts for variations in the efficiency of PV panels that are inherent in the manufacturing process. Not all panels are identical. Typically the maker of the panel will indicate that each panel will operate at the rated levels, +/- 5% (or some other factor). Some panels will work better than the rating, some less well. When connected in a string, the string will operate at the lowest common level. So if multiple panels are combined and tracked as a string, then +/- 5% becomes minus 5%. When each panel is controlled independently, with a power optimizer, micro inverter, or MPPT device on a module level power electronic connected to each panel, then the nameplate rating should even out to zero, as some will perform better and some will perform slightly worse.

- Inverter and transformer derate: Some power is lost as the signal is converted from DC to AC within the inverter. This efficiency factor will be provided in the inverter specifications. If a transformer is included in the system (converting from 480 V to 208 V, for example), that will also introduce inefficiency into the system.

MODULE MISMATCH

- **Module mismatch** derate: Whenever two panels are not operating at exactly the same voltage-current, then neither will operate at peak efficiency when connected with the other panel. Again, this is only a

Component Derate Factors	Component Derate Values	Range of Acceptable Values
PV module nameplate DC rating	0.95	0.80 - 1.05
Inverter and Transformer	0.92	0.88 - 0.98
Mismatch	0.98	0.97 - 0.995
Diodes and connections	0.995	0.99 - 0.997
DC wiring	0.98	0.97 - 0.99
AC wiring	0.99	0.98 - 0.993
Soiling	0.95	0.30 - 0.995
System availability	0.98	0.00 - 0.995
Shading	1	0.00 - 1.00
Sun-tracking	1	0.95 - 1.00
Age	1	0.70 - 1.00
Overall DC to AC derate factor	0.769	

FIGURE 8-3: DERATE FACTORS FOR SOLAR ARRAY

(FROM NREL)

factor when the panels are connected together without an independent MLPE controlling each module.

- Diodes and Connections derate: Each diode and connection inserts a bit of resistance into the circuit. This results in a loss of voltage.

- DC Wiring derate: This accounts for the voltage drop experienced in the wiring system from the panels to the inverter. In a micro inverter system, there would be no DC wiring derate.

- AC Wiring derate: This accounts for the voltage drop experienced in the wiring system from the inverter to the load.

- **Soiling** derate: Any dirt, snow or film from pollution on the front surface of the panel will reduce its performance. This number can be significant in some dirty environments that receive infrequent rainfall. Rain will generally clean most panels, however a 2001 California study showed that nearly one inch of rain is required to effectively clean a panel (light showers may just move the dirt around). Another study showed that losses due to soiling range from 1.5% to 6.2% annually, depending on the installed environment.

SOILING

- **System availability** derate: This accounts for the amount of time over the year when the system might be down for maintenance or utility outages. While this might be useful in calculating annual power production, it is unlikely to be helpful during the commissioning of the system.

SYSTEM AVAILABILITY

- Shading derate: A well placed and oriented array should have no problem with shading. But if shading cannot be avoided, it should be accounted for when derating the system.

- Sun-Tracking derate: Systems that employ a mechanical single or dual-axis tracking system will find that they do not always maintain the optimum angle at all times. Inefficiencies in these systems are accounted for in this factor.

AGE DERATE

- **Age derate:** As panels age, they will experience a loss of performance (typically about .01% to .05% per year).

- Round-trip battery efficiency. For stand-alone systems, the round-trip battery efficiency must be added into the overall system derate factor. DC-coupled and AC-coupled systems that rely on batteries during infrequent power outages could safely ignore this derate factor as they will not (hopefully) operate off battery power for a long enough period of time to effect the efficiency of the system over the course of a year.

Every system is different, and over the years systems have become more efficient, so the derate factor changes over time. In evaluating this site, it is determined MLPE will be attached to each panel, eliminating module mismatch and module nameplate efficiency derating. There is also no shading at the site. This is a fairly dusty environment, so soiling will likely be an issue.

So the derate is calculated as:

Inverter (96%) x DC wiring (98%) x AC wiring (99%) x connections (99.5%) x soiling (95%) = 0.96 x 0.98 x 0.99 x 0.995 x 0.95 = 0.88 or 88% efficient.

So for purposes of this example, assume the system is 88% efficient (or a derate factor of 0.88).

Some grant programs that provide incentives that subsidize the cost of solar installations hold the customer and/or installer liable if the system produces less power than projected. In those cases it would be best to be very conservative when derating the system.

The 100% efficient array size previously determined will need to be adjusted for anticipated inefficiencies:

115 kW (array size) / 0.88 (derate factor) = 130.68 kW (adjusted array size)

So roughly speaking, this site will require a 130 kW array to meet the current electrical needs of the farm.

Determine the Number of Panels in the Array

Figuring out the number of required panels at this point is straightforward.

Simply take the total generating capacity required (in this case, 130,680 W) and divide it by the number of watts generated by each panel.

Assume that a Canadian Solar CS6X 320W solar panel has been selected (just to pick one at random), rated to generate 320 W per hour of peak sunlight. The rated generating capacity is obtained from the panel's specifications, shown in Figure 8-4.

130,680 W (required) / 320 W (peak generating capacity) = 408.375 panels

Since a partial panel cannot be installed, this result may be rounded up or down depending on other design factors (such as panel layout, available space, etc.)

ELECTRICAL DATA / STC*			
CS6X	310P	315P	320P
Nominal Max. Power (Pmax)	310 W	315 W	320 W
Opt. Operating Voltage (Vmp)	36.4 V	36.6 V	36.8 V
Opt. Operating Current (Imp)	8.52 A	8.61 A	8.69 A
Open Circuit Voltage (Voc)	44.9 V	45.1 V	45.3 V
Short Circuit Current (Isc)	9.08 A	9.18 A	9.26 A
Module Efficiency	16.16 %	16.42 %	16.68 %
Operating Temperature	-40°C ~ +85°C		
Max. System Voltage	1000 V (IEC) or 1000 V (UL)		
Module Fire Performance	TYPE 1 (UL 1703) or CLASS C (IEC 61730)		
Max. Series Fuse Rating	15 A		
Application Classification	Class A		
Power Tolerance	0 ~ + 5 W		

* Under Standard Test Conditions (STC) of irradiance of 1000 W/m², spectrum AM 1.5 and cell temperature of 25°C.

ELECTRICAL DATA / NOCT*			
CS6X	310P	315P	320P
Nominal Max. Power (Pmax)	225 W	228 W	232 W
Opt. Operating Voltage (Vmp)	33.2 V	33.4 V	33.6 V
Opt. Operating Current (Imp)	6.77 A	6.84 A	6.91 A
Open Circuit Voltage (Voc)	41.3 V	41.5 V	41.6 V
Short Circuit Current (Isc)	7.36 A	7.44 A	7.50 A

* Under Nominal Operating Cell Temperature (NOCT), irradiance of 800 W/m², spectrum AM 1.5, ambient temperature 20°C, wind speed 1 m/s.

FIGURE 8-4: PANEL SPECIFICATIONS FOR THE CANADIAN SOLAR CS6X SOLAR MODULE

If the system is using microinverters or power optimizers, then calculations are complete. This system would use about 408 panels with a similar number of microinverters or power optimizers (assuming one optimizer per panel).

But if a string inverter is to be used, then it will be necessary to calculate the maximum and the minimum number of panels that can be connected in series to the selected inverter.

Determine the Maximum Number of Panels in each String
At this point it will be necessary to select an inverter(s) for the system. The string connections must be compatible with the input specifications of the unit selected.

Several factors will go into the selection of the inverter. First, the output signal must match that of the point where the array is connected to the power system. It has been determined that in this example, the output of the inverter must be three-phase 480 V / 277 V WYE.

The size of the array is 130 kW. So the inverter must handle that amount of power output. If an inverter/load ratio of 1.2 has been determined as optimum, the the inverter will need to be 130 kW / 1.2 = 108 kW or so in size.

There are a number of options at this point, but for the sake of illustration, assume the installer has a preference for SMA inverters and has found a good

Technical data*	Sunny Tripower CORE1 33-US	Sunny Tripower CORE1 50-US	Sunny Tripower CORE1 62-US
Input (DC)			
Maximum array power	50000 Wp STC	75000 Wp STC	93750 Wp STC
Maximum system voltage		1000 V	
Rated MPP voltage range	330 V...800 V	500 V...800 V	550 V...800 V
MPPT operating voltage range		150 V...1000 V	
Minimum DC voltage / start voltage		150 V / 188 V	
MPP trackers / strings per MPP input		6 / 2	
Maximum operating input current / per MPP tracker		120 A / 20 A	
Maximum short circuit current per MPPT / per string input		30 A / 30 A	
Output (AC)			
AC nominal power	33300 W	50000 W	62500 W
Maximum apparent power	33300 VA	50000 VA	66000 VA
Output phases / line connections		3 / 3-(N)-PE	
Nominal AC voltage		480 V / 277 V WYE	
AC voltage range		244 V...305 V	
Maximum output current	40 A	64 A	79.5 A
Rated grid frequency		60 Hz	
Grid frequency / range		50 Hz, 60 Hz / -6 Hz...+6Hz	
Power factor at rated power / adjustable displacement		1 / 0.0 leading ...0.0 lagging	
Harmonics THD		<3 %	
Efficiency			
CEC efficiency (preliminary)	97.5%	98%	98%

deal on the SMA SUNNY TRIPOWER CORE1 62-US model. Since this model has a nominal AC output of 62.5 kW, two units will need to be installed and connected to the array.

Looking at the inverter specs, as illustrated in Figure 8-5, the unit has a maximum input voltage of 1,000 Vdc. The minimum start-up voltage of the unit is 188 Vdc.
It is important when designing the system that the combined string voltage does not exceed the capacity of the inverter under any conditions that may be experienced on the site. Where voltage is concerned, the colder the temperature, the higher the voltage. So the maximum string voltage will be calculated for the coldest day ever experienced on the site.

It is also important that on the warmest day the site may experience, that the voltage reach at least the startup voltage of the inverter - otherwise no power will be generated.

The design of the grid-tied system should incorporate voltages high enough to avoid voltage drop issues (which will also save some money on the cost of wiring, as smaller wire can be used with higher voltages), but must also remain within the upper and lower voltage limits of the inverter.

In this example, restrict the design of the voltage from the array to the absolute maximum allowed (1,000 Vdc). However, in reality any voltage within the operating range of the inverter will work(188 - 1,000 Vdc).

With this in mind, it is necessary to determine the absolute maximum voltage the array might ever generate under any environmental conditions to which it is exposed.

Under standard test conditions, the absolute maximum voltage a single solar panel can generate is known as its open circuit voltage (Voc). The Voc of the Canadian Solar CS6X 320W solar panel is 45.3 Vdc.

This voltage is generated under standard test conditions (which assume the operating temperature is 25° C). The panel will generate less voltage as the temperature increases.

Conversely, a solar panel will generate MORE voltage as the temperature DECREASES. So the colder the air temperature becomes, the more power the panel will generate.

TEMPERATURE CHARACTERISTICS	
Specification	Data
Temperature Coefficient (Pmax)	-0.41 % / °C
Temperature Coefficient (Voc)	-0.31 % / °C
Temperature Coefficient (Isc)	0.053 % / °C
Nominal Operating Cell Temperature	45±2 °C

FIGURE 8-6: TEMPERATURE CHARACTERISTICS FOR CANADIAN SOLAR CS6X MODULE

A quick look on the Internet shows that the coldest temperature ever recorded for this location is -30° C (-22° F).

In looking at the panel temperature characteristic specifications (Figure 8-6), note that the **temperature differential factor** (often referred to as the **temperature coefficient**), when measured against Voc, for this panel is -0.31%/°C. This means that for every degree Celsius the cell temperature rises over 25°C, the panel will produce 0.31 % less voltage (when measured against its Voc). Conversely, for every degree Celsius DECREASE in temperature, the panel will produce that much MORE voltage than indicated by the Voc.

TEMPERATURE DIFFERENTIAL FACTOR

TEMPERATURE COEFFICIENT

There is a potential that the ambient temperature at this location might drop to -30° C (it has happened at least one time in the past). STC tests at 25°C. So there is a potential of 55°C (25°C - -30° C) difference, or Δ **delta**, between the operating temperature on the coldest day experienced and the temperature at which the module was tested.

Δ DELTA

Δ 55°C (the difference between standard test conditions and the possible lowest temperature) x 0.31% / °C the temperature coefficient (Voc) for this panel) = 17.05%

So on the coldest day ever experienced, this panel may produce 17.05% MORE voltage than rated under STC. The Voc must be adjusted for possible colder temperatures (in this case, 45.3 Voc x 1.1705 (100% + 17.05%) = 53.02 Vdc)

It is theoretically possible for the panel to generate up to 53.02 Vdc should there be perfect sunlight on the coldest day ever recorded for this location. With this possibility in mind, use 53.02 Vdc as the "worst case" output voltage number from the panel.

To determine the maximum number of panels in each string, divide 1,000 Vdc (the maximum voltage determined the array should generate) by the maximum voltage output possible from a single panel (in this case, 53.02 Vdc on the coldest day ever recorded).

1,000 Vdc / 53.02 Vdc = 18.86 panels

This means that the maximum number of panels that can be designed into a string (and still remain below 1,000 volts on the coldest of days at this site) is 18.86 panels. Since a portion of a panel cannot be installed, this number must be rounded DOWN - in order to ensure the voltage output remains below 1,000 volts. So the strings of this array can be no larger than 18 panels.

TABLE 8-1: AMBIENT AIR TEMPERATURE CORRECTION FACTORS

(FROM NEC TABLE 690.7(A))

Ambient Temperature (°C)	Temperature Correction Factor
24 to 20°C	1.02
19 to 15°C	1.04
14 to 10°C	1.06
9 to 5°C	1.08
4 to 0°C	1.1
-1 to -5°C	1.12
-6 to -10°C	1.14
-11 to -15°C	1.16
-16 to -20°C	1.18
-21 to -25°C	1.2
-26 to -30°C	1.21
-31 to -35°C	1.23
-36 to -40°C	1.25

There is an alternative way of determining the maximum panels allowed in each string. By using temperature correction factors found in the NEC Table 690.7(A) (reproduced in Table 8-1), it is possible to arrive at a similar, although less precise result.

For example, if the coldest temperature ever recorded for a site was -30° C, then multiply the Voc by the correction factor found in the appropriate row in the table (1.21 in this example).

45.3 Voc x 1.21 = 54.81 Vdc
1,000 Vdc / 54.81 Vdc = 18.24 panels, rounded down to 18 panels

However, the NEC code states that if the temperature coefficient of the panel is available, it must be used to determine the maximum length of the string, rather than Table 690.7(A) as it is always a bit more precise. In the age of Internet access to the panel specifications of nearly every solar panel ever manufactured, it is hard to envision a situation where the temperature coefficient is not available.

Determine the Minimum Number of Panels in Each String
The maximum number of panels that can be in each string has been determined, but the inverter also is rated to require a minimum voltage in order for it to function.

Assume this minimum is 188 Vdc input (this rating is obtained from the inverter specifications). There must be at least that amount of voltage reaching the inverter from the array in order for the system to generate usable power.

In this calculation, refer to the Vmp rating (the voltage the panel generates at its maximum power point) rather than the Voc. This is because minimum voltage should be based on normal operating conditions, rather than under open circuit conditions that will skew the voltage higher than normal.

Just as a solar panel will generate more voltage as the temperature drops, it will generate less voltage as the temperature increases. So now it is necessary to find the hottest temperature this site will experience, and adjust accordingly.

The highest temperature ever experienced at this location has been researched and found to be 41° C (106° F). However, working on a roof can be much hotter than the ambient air temperature.

So it is recommended by **ASHRAE (American Society of Heating, Refrigerating and Air-Conditioning Engineers)** that the ambient air temperature be adjusted as follows:

- 35° C for arrays mounted less than 6 inches above the deck of the roof.
- 30° C for arrays mounted more than 6 inches above the deck of the roof.
- 25° C for arrays mounted on poles.

ASHRAE

Assuming this array is mounted on a racking system that is 6 inches or less above the roof deck, add 35° C to 41° C and find the array might potentially experience operating (cell) temperatures as high as 76° C. Standard test conditions measure at 25° C, so the difference or delta between the two is 51° C.

The temperature coefficient at Vmp (note that there is a different coefficient used, since it is necessary to now test for normal operations rather than "worst case") is -0.41 % / °C. Often this coefficient will be noted in the panel specifications as the temperature coefficient at the maximum power point or Pmax. So in this case, the panel will produce 0.41% LESS voltage for each degree the temperature increases over 25° C (the standard test condition).

Δ51°C (the difference between standard test conditions and the possible highest temperature) x -0.41%/°C (the temperature coefficient at Pmax for this panel) = -20.91%

So 20.91% of the voltage output will need to be deducted from the Vmp (100% - 20.91% = 79.09%) of the panel to adjust for possible higher temperatures.

36.8 Vmp x 79.09% = 36.8 Vmp x .7909 = 29.1 Vdc

In order to determine the minimum number of panels required in each string, take the minimum operating voltage of the inverter (in this example 188 Vdc) and divide it by the minimum voltage a single panel might generate on the hottest day experienced at this location (29.1 Vdc).

188 Vdc / 29.1 Vdc = 6.46 panels

In this case, since the result is the minimum number of panels required – round UP. So the string must be at least seven (7) panels in order to safely generate the minimum power required by the inverter on the hottest day of the year.

These calculations show the strings can range from 7 to 18 panels in length in order to stay within the minimum voltage requirement and the maximum voltage restriction.

Determine how Many Strings are Required

It has already been determined that 408 panels are required for this array to produce 100% of the power used at the site. If the maximum number of panels in each string is 18, then the minimum number of strings for this system would be:

408 panels / 18 panels per string maximum = 22.67 minimum # strings

A quick check of the inverter specifications show that each inverter can handle up to 12 strings. The specs show that the unit has 6 MPPT trackers with up to 2 strings connected to each tracking device. So this inverter can connect 12 strings, but with only 6 MPPT devices, pairs of strings will be combined in the unit (this may impact the efficiency of the array if shading is an issue).

Since there are two inverters in the system, it can accommodate up to 24 strings (12 strings per inverter x 2 inverters).

If the system were designed to the maximum capacity of the inverters, then:

24 strings x 18 panels per string = 432 panels

Only 408 panels were required to meet 100% of current load demand, so this configuration may overproduce for the site (432 panels / 408 panels = 106% or so). Often state net metering guidelines limit production. In Ohio the limit is 120% of current use. So this system would likely still comply with net metering requirements.

MPPT VOLTAGE INPUT RANGE

This anticipated operating voltage falls well within the **MPPT voltage input range** (the range where the inverter operates at peak efficiency) of a typical grid-tied inverter.

On a day that matches STC conditions, 18 panels connected in series would produce at:

36.8 Vdc (Vmp) x 18 panels in a string = 662.4 Vdc

The MPPT voltage range for this inverter is between 150 Vdc - 1,000 Vdc.

Determining the Size of a Stand-Alone System Array

Since the amount of sunlight available varies throughout the year, as do load requirements, the design of a stand-alone array must take into account the

	Solar Insolation (hr/day)	Load Demand (kWh/month)	Design Ratio
January	2.88	851	295 kW
February	3.84	1152	300 kW
March	4.24	1103	260 kW
April	5.37	505	94 kW
May	5.8	481	83 kW
June	6.11	733	120 kW
July	6.14	652	106 kW
August	6.02	641	106 kW
September	5.53	499	90 kW
October	4.09	416	102 kW
November	3.31	816	247 kW
December	2.5	409	163 kW
Average	**4.65**	**688**	**148 kW**

TABLE 8-2: SAMPLE DESIGN RATIO CALCULATIONS FOR FARM LOCATED NEAR COLUMBUS, OH WITH ARRAY AT 28° ALTITUDE

"worst case" situation. For example, load demands might be highest during the winter, when solar insolation is at its minimum for this location.

When calculating the size of a grid-tied array, the designer incorporates monthly averages into the calculation.

688 kWh (average monthly load) / 30.5 days per month =
22.56 kWh per day/ 4.65 (average solar insolation) =
4.85 kW / .90 (system derate) = 5.39 kW

For a stand-alone system, the design must utilize the month with the highest **design ratio** (month's load/month's insolation), not the annual averages. In Table 8-2, this month would be February. This is referred to as the **critical design month**.

DESIGN RATIO

CRITICAL DESIGN MONTH

1152 kWh (critical monthly load) / 30.5 days per month =
37.77 kWh per day/ 3.84 (critical month solar insolation) =
9.83 kW / .75 (system derate) = 13.11 kW

Note that the array for the stand-alone system is significantly larger than a grid-tied system would be for the same property. This is due to the fact that the design ratio for the critical design month (in this case, February) is twice that of the annual average.

Also, an additional 15% inefficiency has been added to the system to account for the relatively low **roundtrip efficiency** of power flowing through a lead-acid battery.

ROUNDTRIP EFFICIENCY

The roundtrip efficiency of a battery is the difference between the amount of power that goes in (in charging) and the amount that leaves (available to

TABLE 8-3: SAMPLE
DESIGN RATIO
CALCULATIONS FOR
FARM LOCATED NEAR
COLUMBUS, OH WITH
ARRAY AT 58° ALTITUDE

	Solar Insolation (hr/day)	Load Demand (kWh/month)	Design Ratio
January	3.38	851	251 kW
February	4.25	1152	271 kW
March	4.11	1103	268 kW
April	4.74	505	106 kW
May	4.66	481	103 kW
June	4.74	733	120 kW
July	4.83	652	155 kW
August	5.13	641	125 kW
September	5.27	499	95 kW
October	4.36	416	95 kW
November	3.84	816	212 kW
December	2.97	409	138 kW
Average	**4.36**	**688**	**158 kW**

power the load). Lead acid batteries normally experience internal losses of between 10%-30%.

For example, 100 Wh of energy used to charge the battery bank may only result in 85 Wh of power leaving the battery bank.

Lithium-ion batteries generally perform better, with about a 90%-95% roundtrip efficiency.

As a result of round-trip efficiency, it is a good practice to increase the derate factor of a system that incorporates lead-acid batteries by at least 15%

Since stand-alone system sizes are based on the critical design month, rather than the annual average, it may be advantageous to set the altitude of the array to maximize power output during the critical design month, even if it lowers overall annual production, as demonstrated in Table 8-3.

If the angle of the array is shifted towards a winter bias, from 28° altitude to 58° altitude, the resulting array size needed to meet the critical design month's load requirements is smaller, even though the total annual production is less.

The new calculation would be:

1152 kWh (critical monthly load) / 30.5 days per month =
37.77 kWh per day/ 4.25 (critical month solar insolation) =
8.89 kW / .75 (system derate) = 11.85 kW

String Calculations for a Stand-Alone System:

Voltage increases as units are connected in series, so if the panel's nominal voltage is 24 Vdc, connecting two of these panels in series will result in a nominal 48 Vdc system. Three in series will result in a nominal 72 Vdc system, and so on.

Traditionally, charge controllers and inverters used in stand-alone systems operate with input at 48 nominal volts. So in such a system, two 24-volt panels would be connected in series (strings), then combined in a combiner box.

Stand-alone systems that incorporate an **MPPT charge controller** (buck-boost) will require string calculations similar to those conducted for grid-tied inverters, using the maximum input voltage of the charge controller as the upper limit of the voltage for each string. A **buck-boost charge controller** incorporates a DC-to-DC voltage converter,. Within the charge controller, high voltage from the array is converted to a voltage that matches the battery bank. No minimum voltage will need to be calculated, as the MPPT charge controller does not need a minimum voltage to function.

> MPPT CHARGE CONTROLLER

> BUCK-BOOST CHARGE CONTROLLER

String Calculations for a Micro Inverter System

Calculating the strings for a system that incorporates microinverters is about as straightforward as it gets. Once it has been determined how many panels are required to power the load, then one micro inverter attaches to each panel. All strings are strings of one.

There are microinverters on the market that allow more than one inverter per module (two and even four). So in these cases, once again, no string calculations are required (simply attach as indicated in the instructions).

Branch Circuit Calculations for a Micro Inverter System

microinverters are connected together in parallel using a proprietary cable obtained from the manufacturer. When connecting in parallel, the ampacity increases rather than the voltage. So the gauge of the wire used in the system will limit the number of microinverters that can be connected together in a **branch circuit.**

> BRANCH CIRCUIT

OUTPUT DATA (AC)	IQ 7 Microinverter		IQ 7+ Microinverter	
Peak output power	250 VA		295 VA	
Maximum continuous output power	240 VA		290 VA	
Nominal (L-L) voltage/range²	240 V / 211-264 V	208 V / 183-229 V	240 V / 211-264 V	208 V / 183-229 V
Maximum continuous output current	1.0 A (240 V)	1.15 A (208 V)	1.21 A (240 V)	1.39 A (208 V)
Nominal frequency	60 Hz		60 Hz	
Extended frequency range	47 - 68 Hz		47 - 68 Hz	
AC short circuit fault current over 3 cycles	5.8 Arms		5.8 Arms	
Maximum units per 20 A (L-L) branch circuit³	16 (240 VAC)	13 (208 VAC)	13 (240 VAC)	11 (208 VAC)
Overvoltage class AC port	III		III	
AC port backfeed current	18 mA		18 mA	
Power factor setting	1.0		1.0	
Power factor (adjustable)	0.85 leading ... 0.85 lagging		0.85 leading ... 0.85 lagging	

FIGURE 8-7: ENPHASE IQ 7 AND IQ 7+ MICROINVERTER OUTPUT SPECIFICATIONS

(FROM ENPHASE)

As indicated in Figure 8-7, the Enphase IQ 7 micro inverter will produce 1.0 amps (240 VA continuous output / 240 Vac) when operating in a single phase system. When installed in a three phase 208 Vac system, each unit will produce 1.15 A (240 VA / 208 Vac).

The proprietary trunk cable connecting these units together has an ampacity rating of 20 amps. Incorporating the 1.25 NEC safety margin, each circuit can carry a maximum of 16 amps (20 A / 1.25 = 16 A)

So no more than 16 Enphase IQ 7 units can be connected together in parallel in each branch circuit when producing 240 Vac single phase power. When operating in three-phase, no more than 13 IQ 7 microinverters can be connected in parallel (16 A / 1.15 A each = 13.9 rounded down to 13).

Different microinverters operate at different ampacity, and the proprietary cable may vary, so check the specification sheet for the inverter selected.

String Calculations for Power Optimizer Systems

A single power optimizer can be attached to a single panel or to multiple panels. It is common for installers to attach two panels in series, attached to a single optimizer (make sure the optimizer is rated for the combined power output of the two panels).

This practice can save a significant amount of time and money when installing large commercial systems. However the advantages of the optimizer (MPPT functions, monitoring, etc) will now be shared over two panels.

Special connectors are available to allow three and four panels to be connected in parallel and then connected to a single optimizer.

With the increasing availability and use of high voltage panels (such as 96-cell high-efficiency panels), special care must be taken to avoid violating the 80-volt within the array boundary rule imposed in the rapid shutdown provisions of the 2017 NEC.

If multiple panels are connected in series to a single MLPE (such as a power optimizer), the combined voltage may exceed the 80-volt limitation. For example, a Panasonic 325 W, 96 cell panel has a Voc rating of 69.6 Vdc.

FIGURE 8-8: DUAL INPUT POWER OPTIMIZER

(FROM SOLAR EDGE)

Connecting two together in series would clearly violate 80-volt limitation. Even though the output voltage from a power optimizer is only one volt when the system is shut down, the voltage from the

		General optimizers	Commercial optimizers
Single phase inverters	Minimum	8 (6 with P405/P505)	N/A
	Maximum	25	N/A
SE9KUS, SE14.4KUS, SE43.2KUS	Minimum	10 (8 with P405/P505)	8 optimizers, 16 modules
	Maximum	25	30 optimizers
SE10KUS, SE20KUS, SE33.3KUS, SE66.6KUS, SE100KUS	Minimum	18 (14 with P405/P505)	13 optimizers, 26 modules
	Maximum	501	30 optimizers

FIGURE 8-9: STRING LIMITATIONS FOR POWER OPTIMIZERS

(FROM SOLAR EDGE)

panels to the optimizer is within the array boundary (and greater than the imposed limit).

Even panels with a Voc rating less than 40 Vdc might violate this limitation when connected in series if temperatures fall below 25°C (standard test conditions).

Some MLPE manufacturers have addressed this issue by allowing two panels to be connected to the unit in parallel, keeping the voltage within limits. MLPEs such as the one illustrated in Figure 8-8 incorporate two sets of male and female connection points (**dual input**) for attached panels.

DUAL INPUT

String length calculations for power optimizers have typically been performed by the product manufacturer. On the specification sheet (Figure 8-9) provided with the fixed voltage inverter, it will state:
- minimum number of optimizers in a string,
- minimum number of modules in a string (if multiple panels are required for the particular optimizer),
- maximum number of optimizers in a string,
- maximum number of modules in a string (if multiple panels are required for the particular optimizer),
- maximum power output (watts) of each string.

For single-phase systems, the string sizes are generally between 8 (minimum) - 25 (maximum). For three-phase systems, the string sizes are generally between 16 (minimum) and 30 (maximum).

Note that a string with more than 30 optimizers does not meet the NEC rapid shutdown requirements for systems installed on buildings. Each power optimizer generates a 1 volt signal voltage when disconnected from the grid. More than 30 units connected in series would exceed the 30 Vdc rapid shutdown limitation.

Sizing an AC and DC Coupled Array

When used simply as an infrequent emergency power source when the grid goes down, the array size of an AC coupled or a DC coupled system can be calculated in the same manner as a simple grid-tied system.

However, increasingly these systems are used to allow for more self-consumption of array power, as the utility limits how much they pay for net metered power and/or institute time-of-day pricing that makes the use of stored power a more attractive option than grid-provided power.

If the battery bank is to be used frequently as a source of power for the loads, it would be a good idea to incorporate the battery bank's roundtrip efficiency into the derate factor when sizing the system. This will result in a larger array than if this inefficiency were ignored.

With AC-coupled systems there is also an added battery-based inverter incorporated into the system. Add the inefficiency of charging (converting the AC from the PV inverter into DC power to charge the batteries) as well as the inefficiency of converting the DC power from the batteries into AC power for the loads. Again, this will require a larger array due to the increased inefficiencies of these conversions.

Calculating Space Required for the Array

Just how many panels can fit on any given roof? The answer will in large measure depend on how unobstructed (with dormers, vent pipes, chimneys, access hatches, skylights) the surface is.

In today's PV design world, the most common way of determining how many panels will fit in a given location is to use an online design software tool such as PVSketch, as illustrated in Figure 8-10.

These tools generally integrate with Google Earth (for images of the site) and with PVWatts (for irradiance data). They also contain a vast database of

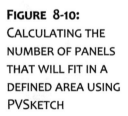

FIGURE 8-10:
CALCULATING THE NUMBER OF PANELS THAT WILL FIT IN A DEFINED AREA USING PVSKETCH

product specifications, such as panel physical size and output as well as inverter specifications.

The designer inputs the address of the site. An image of the property is presented. Once the array location is selected, the system allows the designer to map the exact location of the array and select a panel. The tool then populates the area designated for the array with panels, calculating how many will fit within the selected area.

While these tools are extremely helpful, there may be occasions when the designer needs to calculate array size manually.

Rooftop Systems

Assuming a flat or pitched roof with no obstructions, a good rough rule of thumb for systems that use crystalline panels is about 10 watts per square foot. So if the south facing slope of a roof measures 30 feet by 20 feet (600 square feet), a rough estimate would be that a 6,000 watt system could be installed within this space. Systems that use thin film panels require about 30% more space.

To get a closer estimate of the space required for a system, start with the fact that under standard test conditions, a panel's rating assumes the irradiance of the sun will be 1,000 W/m^2.

So the area required for any given array can be calculated as:

Total Area Required = Array Power Output / (1000 W/m^2 x Panel Efficiency)

For example, if the output required from the array has been determined to be 6.8 kW, and the panel selected has a conversion efficiency of 18%, then:

Total Area Required = 6,800 W / (1000 W/m^2 x 0.18) = 37.78 m^2

The array would require 37.78 m^2 (or about 407 sq ft). Space would also have to be allocated on the roof for required minimum setbacks as well as access paths on flat roofs.

But knowing the area required for the array may not indicate just how many panels will fit on a specific site.

To calculate this, it will be necessary to know:
- the size of the portion of the roof where the array will be sited,
- setback requirements for the location,
- the size of the panel selected. Do not forget to include the space required for mounting hardware (usually about ½ inch between panels). This can have a serious accumulated impact on larger arrays.

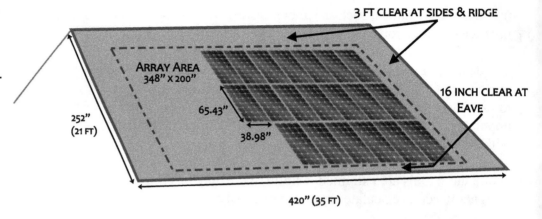

FIGURE 8-11: PLACING 20 PANELS ON A 35 FT X 21 FT ROOF AREA

- the number of panels in the array,
- the angle of the array for ground mounted or flat-roof systems (although the angle may already have been factored in calculating the array size while determining distances required to avoid inter-row shading),
- orientation of the panels, either portrait or landscape. This will largely be determined by the racking system selected.

For example, assume it was determined that a 5.8 kW system was required to meet a household's needs. A 290 W panel was selected (20 panels total, 5,800 W / 290 W = 20), and the array was configured into two strings of 10 panels. A review of the panel's specifications show that it measures 65.43 inches by 38.98 inches.

When doing the site visit, the south-facing portion of the roof was measured and found to be 21 feet x 35 feet, with no obstructions (pipes, vents, chimneys, etc).

To calculate the area available to mount an array, subtract the required clear perimeter aisles from the overall dimensions of the roof. The International Fire Code requires three feet (36 inches) of clear access area on the sides and ridge of the roof. Good wind loading design requires a minimum of 16 inches at the eave.

So in this example, a roof space measuring 21 feet (252 inches) by 35 feet (420 inches) can only accommodate an array measuring:

420 inches width - 72 inches (36 inches x 2 sides) = 348 inches width
252 inches height - 52 inches (36 inches + 16 inches) = 200 inches height

The selected panel is 65.43 inches in height and 38.98 inches in width. The orientation will be portrait, with ½ inch mounting connectors attached between each panel (adding to the width of the array).

So the maximum number of panels in each direction equals:

348" (array area width) / 38.98" (panel width) + .50" (connector) = 8.81 panels
200" (array area height) / 65.43" (panel height) = 3.06 panels

The logical choice might be to try to arrange the panels in two rows of 10 panels (as there are to be 20 in the array). However only eight (8) panels can fit horizontally. Fortunately three rows will fit (barely), so the array could be arranged as illustrated in Figure 8-11 in two rows of seven panels, and one row of six (20 in total).

Note that the physical layout does not have to match (nor rarely does it) the logical string calculations, in this case two strings of 10 panels.

Ballasted Systems
The first step in determining the size of a ballasted array that can be placed on a flat roof is to determine the size of the roof itself. The amount of open rooftop area with good sun exposure can be determined using satellite imagery or measured on site.

The array layout must also accommodate obstacles, the shadows cast by these obstacles, and required setbacks. These spaces are known as **exclusion areas**.

EXCLUSION AREAS

Ballasted systems do not generally lay flat parallel to the pitch of the roof, as do typical residential systems. The modules are installed with a tilt relative to the roof surface, and as a result, cast a shadow. Rows of panels must be set far enough apart to avoid inter-row shading.

Roof space is a valuable and limited resource. Commercial system owners often wish to maximize the production of power relative to the amount of space available, or **power density**, of the roof.

POWER DENSITY

A low tilt angle (10 degrees or below) or dual-tilt configurations (East-West facing - as shown in Figure 8-12) increase the power density of ballasted solar arrays. These configurations reduce the shadow cast by each solar module, allowing the rows of modules to be placed closely together.

FIGURE 8-12: EAST-WEST ORIENTED BALLASTED SOLAR ARRAY

(PHOTO FROM K12 SOLAR)

When designing for optimum array spacing, it is important to consider the minimum distance required for maintenance purposes. It is possible in some configurations to place panels so close together that there is no room to access panels for routine maintenance.

How much of the surface available (defined by the outside boundary of the array) is covered with panels producing power is known as the ground coverage ratio (GCR). If there are no gaps or walkways within the array boundary, then the array would have a ground coverage ratio of 1.0 (or 100%).

To calculate the array size that could be placed on a flat roof, first calculate the amount of useable space. This would include:

Total Roof Area - Exclusion Areas (pathways and obstructions) = Area Available for Array

Then take into account the ground cover ratio (how much of the available space is actually covered with panels).

Area Available for Array x Ground Cover Ratio = Area Covered by Panels

The power output under standard test conditions is 1000 W/m^2. But solar panels are not 100% efficient. To calculate actual power production (at STC):

Area Covered by Panels (m^2) x Panel Efficiency = Array Power Production (at STC)

So for example, assume a building has been measured and it is 120 ft x 160 ft (19,200 square feet). There are perimeter setback requirements (6 feet) and access pathway requirements imposed by the International Fire Code. After calculating these, it is found that they will occupy about 17% of the roof space.

19,200 sq ft x .17 (pathways) = 3,264 sq ft

An analysis of obstructions (vents, air conditioning units, access hatches, etc) find that they and their shadows take up an additional 22% of the roof space. So the total exclusion area of the roof space is:

19,200 sq ft x .22 (obstructions and shadows) = 4,224 sq ft

Added together, there is 7,488 sq ft of exclusion area on the roof (or 19,200 sq ft - 7,488 sq ft = 11,712 sq ft of useable space for the array).

Assume the racking design selected has a ground coverage ratio of 0.66. This accounts for the space between rows of panels to avoid inter-row shading. So the total available space that is actually producing power is:

11,712 sq ft x 0.66 (GCR) = 7,730 sq ft

At this point the array space will need to be converted to square meters, as the irradiance at STC is 1,000 W per square meter. 1 square foot = 0.092903 square meters, so:

7,730 sq ft x 0.092903 = 718 square meters

If the panel were 100% efficient, then the array would produce 1,000 W for every square meter. Assume the panel selected has an efficiency of 22%, then:

718 sq m x 1,000 W (STC) x 0.22 (efficiency) = 157,960 W or 158 kW

Ground Mounted Systems

While available rooftop real estate may limit the size of an array that can be placed at a specific location, developers of large ground mounted solar arrays continue to seek ways to get more production out of less land. A 2021 study by the US Department of Energy's Lawrence Berkeley National Laboratory found that utility-scale solar power facilities have increased the power density by 43-52% during the past decade.

This greater power density has resulted in increased electricity generation per acre of 25-33%. In 2011, the average power density of a fixed-tilt utility-scale solar array was about 0.23 MW of DC power per acre. In other words, it took a little more than 4 acres to place a 1 MW array.

By 2019 the average power density had increased to about 0.35 MW of DC power per acre. Now it takes a bit less than 3 acres to place a 1 MW array.

The study determined that the ground coverage ratios for fixed-tilt arrays typically range from 40 to 50%. Tracking systems have a lower GCR, in the 25-40% range.

Most tracking systems are East-West oriented. In theory they rise to a 90° angle with relation to the ground, facing East at sunrise. At solar noon they would lie at a 0° angle with relation to the ground (flat), and then at a 90° angle with relation to the ground, facing West at sunset.

However, if they truly worked in this manner, the first row of panels would block all the others at sunrise and sunset. And the panels would have to be spaced quite a distance apart to avoid shading early in the morning and late in the evening.

So most tracking systems incorporate **backtracking**, that flattens the angle of the panel in early morning and late afternoons to avoid inter-row shading. When a tracking system is backtracking, it is actually sacrificing its orientation toward the sun in order to prevent module shading. This practice generally produces more energy than a fixed tracking of the sun, keeping the panel at a 90° angle to the sun and thus incurring shade (and panel mismatch) losses.

BACKTRACKING

A tracking system with a GCR of 50% will end up backtracking for over a third of the operating hours of the array, representing about 25% of the array's energy yield.

The study shows that the power density for tracking systems has also risen in recent years, from 0.16 MW per acre in 2011 to about 0.24 MW per acre in 2019.

ENERGY DENSITY

While the power density is less for tracking systems (due to greater spacing requirements), the **energy density** (the amount of energy produced per acre) may be greater for tracking systems due to the fact that the tracking process increases energy production by facing the panels more directly at the sun for more of the day.

In 2019, the average energy density for US utility-scale fixed-tilt arrays was 447 MWh/year/acre while the average energy density for tracking systems was 394 MWh/year/acre.

Chapter 8 Review Questions

1) Placing larger than needed wire in a PV system so that the array might easily be expanded at some point is an example of:
   a) future proofing
   b) excess load capacity
   c) enhanced power factor
   d) time-of-use pricing

2) A couple in Des Moines, Iowa wish to have a grid-tied solar array installed on the roof of their home. The installer/designer conducts a site inspection and determines the following:

   - the azimuth of the building is 160 degrees
   - the angle of the roof is 22 degrees
   - there is a shading factor of 88% (12% loss due to shading)
   - there is a 2% loss due to voltage drop and connections and 3% for micro inverter inefficiency
   - PV Watts indicates and average annual insolation of 4.76 hours
   - a search of the Internet indicates the temperature extremes at this location are: 42ºC (108ºF) hottest ever and -32ºC (-25ºF) coldest ever
   - the average monthly electric consumption of the household is 700 kWh
   - the couple would like the array to offset 95% of their electric bill

   What size array would best meet the needs of this household?
   a) 4.58 kW
   b) 4.82 kW
   c) 5.52 kW
   d) 6.11 kW

3) Voltage drop, loss due to connections, inverter inefficiency, shading, and dust all combine in the calculation of a system's:
   a) power factor
   b) derate factor
   c) load factor
   d) variability factor

4) The change in the amount of volts or amps a panel will produce as the temperature of the cell increases or decreases above standard test conditions is known as the:
   a) derate factor
   b) power factor
   c) temperature coefficient
   d) ambient air variation

5) An auto dealer in Las Vegas has decided to install a 19 kW system (more or less) that utilizes Canadian Solar 275 W panels. It will also incorporate a 20 kW string inverter with a 200 - 600 Vdc input range and 240 Vac output. The temperature extremes at this location are: 47°C (117°F) hottest ever and -13°C (8°F) coldest ever. This will be a ballasted flat roof mounted system. The specifications for the panels are as follows:

Nominal Max Power (Pmax)	275 watts
Optimum Operating Voltage (Vmp)	31.3V
Optimum Operating Current (Imp)	8.80A
Open Circuit Voltage (Voc)	38.3V
Short Circuit Current (Isc)	9.31A
Module Efficiency	16.8%
Temperature Coefficient (Pmax)	-0.41 % / °C
Temperature Coefficient (Voc)	-0.31 % / °C

What is the maximum size to which each string can be configured?
a) 12 panels maximum
b) 13 panels maximum
c) 14 panels maximum
d) 15 panels maximum

6) What is the minimum number of panels to which each string can be configured in the above situation (question 5)?
a) 6 panels minimum
b) 7 panels minimum
c) 8 panels minimum
d) 9 panels minimum

7) For a ballasted PV array where the panels are located more than six (6) inches above the deck of the roof, ASHRAE recommends adding _____ to the hottest ambient air temperature when calculating minimum string sizes.
a) 20°C
b) 25°C
c) 30°C
d) 35°C

8) The voltage range where the inverter operates at peak efficiency is known as the:
a) MPPT voltage input range
b) temperature coefficient at Vmp
c) optimal power factor
d) Inverter voltage set point

9) When designing a stand-alone system, the array is usually sized to meet the needs of the month with the highest design ratio. This ratio is calculated as follows:
   a) month's average load / month's average insolation
   b) month's highest load / month's lowest load
   c) month with highest insolation / month with lowest insolation
   d) highest insolation of any month / highest load of any month

10) If only 90 % of the power entering a battery bank can be utilized by the load due to the battery's internal losses, this battery bank is said to have a:
    a) 90% roundtrip efficiency
    b) 90% power factor
    c) 10% power factor
    d) 10% load loss

11) A PV designer has been asked to design a flush-to-roof mounted stand-alone system for a hunting cabin near Charlotte, NC. The temperature extremes at this location are: 40°C (104°F) hottest ever and -25°C (-13°F) coldest ever. She has determined the array will be 4.2 kW with 2 days of autonomy. It will be a 48 Vdc system with a 48 Vdc charge controller, 48 Vdc battery bank and a 5 kW pure sine wave inverter. She has opted to use SolarWorld 350 W panels. The specifications for the panels are as follows:

Peak power (Pmax)	350W
Peak power voltage (Vmp)	38.4V
Peak power current (Imp)	9.17A
Open circuit voltage (Voc)	48.0V
Short circuit current (Isc)	9.82A
Nominal Voltage	24V
Module Efficiency	17.54%
Temperature Coefficient (Pmax)	-0.42 % / °C
Temperature Coefficient (Voc)	-0.29 % / °C

    What is the maximum size to which each string can be configured?
    a) 2 panels per string
    b) 4 panels per string
    c) 6 panels per string
    d) 8 panels per string

12) The typical derate factor of a grid-tied system includes all of the following **EXCEPT**:
    a) inverter efficiency
    b) impact from shading
    c) battery bank roundtrip efficiency
    d) voltage drop

13) The circuit connecting microinverters together is referred to as a:
   a) string
   b) feeder circuit
   c) PV source circuit
   d) branch circuit

14) Assuming a ground cover ratio of 1.0 (no rows or spaces between panels), the area required for a solar array can be calculated using which of the following formulas?
   a) total area required = array power output / 1000 W/m² (STC)
   b) total area required = 1000 W/m² (STC) / individual panel output (W)
   c) total area required = [1000 W/m² (STC) / individual panel output (W)] x hours of insolation
   d) total area required = array power output (W) / [1000 W/m² (STC) x panel efficiency]

15) A homeowner has a south-facing sloped roof with no obstructions. It measures 25 feet from eave to ridge by 40 feet. How many Hanwha 345 W panels (78.5 in × 39.4 in × 1.38 in or 1994 mm × 1000 mm × 35 mm) can be placed on the roof meeting all codes and wind load design criteria?
   a) 20 panels
   b) 24 panels
   c) 30 panels
   d) 36 panels

16) Maximizing the production of power from an array relative to the amount of space available is known as (the):
   a) power optimizing
   b) output maximization
   c) power coefficient
   d) power density

17) A tracking system that flattens the angle of the rows of panels in the early morning and late afternoon to avoid inter-row shading incorporates:
   a) backtracking
   b) power density maximization
   c) energy density maximization
   d) wind load minimization

Chapter 9

Wiring the System

Now that the equipment has been selected, the array sized and sited - it is necessary to connect everything together.

Wiring the System

Electrical wire (**conductors**) in the U.S. are measured using the **American Wire Gauge (AWG)**. Sizes used in PV systems typically range from 0000 AWG (the largest) to 40 AWG (smallest). Although for most PV applications, the minimum wire size should be no smaller than 12 AWG.

CONDUCTOR

AMERICAN WIRE GAUGE (AWG)

The larger the wire, the lower the resistance (resulting in less voltage drop). Thicker wire is also capable of carrying more current without fusing (becoming damaged).

Insulation

There are also different types of **insulation** cladding (covering) the metal conductors. The various forms of insulation serve various functions. The insulation covering the conductor can protect the cable from heat, moisture, ultraviolet light or chemicals. Some insulation materials are manufactured so as not to emit toxic gases when burned (important when installed indoors).

INSULATION

Some insulation styles commonly used in PV systems are highlighted in Table 9-1.

A wire with the designation of "-2" such as THW-2 generally means that this wire is permitted in environments experiencing continuous 90°C (194°F) operating temperatures.

Wires located in conduit should be assumed to be in a wet environment.

PV WIRE

USE - 2

Wires located on rooftops are in a high heat environment. Codes require that the wire connecting PV panels together must be either **PV Wire** or **USE-2**. Wires run inside a building must be rated for indoor use.

Color Coding of Wires

The color of the insulation on a conductor indicates its function or use.

COLOR CODING

Note that the **color coding** for AC and grounded DC applications, as indicted in Table 9-2, are similar, but not the same. The terminology used to describe the wires are also different between AC and DC systems.

The color code used may be slightly different for DC systems depending on whether the system is grounded through the negative wire, through the

TABLE 9-1: COMMON TYPES OF CONDUCTORS USED IN PV SYSTEMS

Type	Name	Max. Temp.	Environment	Insulation
THHN	Heat Resistant Thermoplastic	90 C (194 F)	Indoor Dry or Damp Locations	Flame Retardant, Heat Resistant Thermoplastic
THW	Moisture& Heat Resistant Thermoplastic	75-90 C (167-194 F)	Indoor Dry or Wet Locations	Flame Retardant, Moisture and Heat Resistant Thermoplastic
THWN	Moisture& Heat Resistant Thermoplastic	75 C (167 F)	Indoor Dry or Wet Locations	Flame retardant, moisture and heat resistant thermoplastic
TW	Moisture resistant thermoplastic	60 C (140 F)	Indoor Dry or Wet Locations	Flame Retardant, Moisture Resistant Thermoplastic
UF and USE	Underground Feeder & Underground Service Entrance	60-75 C (140-167 F)	Outdoor Service Entrance	Moisture and Heat Resistant
USE-2 and RHW-2*	Underground Service Entrance	90 C (194 F)	Outdoor Dry or Wet and Service Entrance	Moisture and Heat Resistant
PV Wire	Photovoltaic cable	90 C (194 F) wet, 150 C (302 F) dry	Dry or Wet and Service Entrance	Moisture and Heat Resistant

AC (Alternating Current)		DC (Direct Current)	
Color	Application	Color	Application
Black, Red or other	Ungrounded Hot	Black, Red or other	Positive
White or Gray	Grounded Conductor (Neutral)	White or Gray	Solidly Grounded Conductor (Negative)
		Black, Red or other	Functionally Grounded Conductor (Negative)
Green, Green with Yellow Stripes, or Bare	Equipment Grounding Conductor	Green, Green with Yellow Stripes, or Bare	Equipment Grounding Conductor

TABLE 9-2: INSULATION COLOR-CODING OF AC AND DC WIRES

positive wire (although most systems in the U.S. are grounded through the negative wire), or ungrounded.

Systems that incorporate a **solid ground** (which are rare in today's market) require white or gray insulation on the grounded conductor. **Functionally grounded** systems, which are the norm, are no longer permitted (new in the 2017 NEC) to use white or gray insulation for the grounded conductor (usually the negative).

SOLID GROUND

FUNCTIONAL GROUND

A solidly grounded system connects the grounded conductor directly to the grounding system. This is usually done within the inverter. No breakers, fuses, or any other means of disconnection is permitted anywhere along the solidly grounded conductor.

But in today's market, all inverters have some means of disconnect (arc fault protection or ground fault protection) incorporated into the inverter on the grounded conductor, designed to disconnect the system in case of a problem.

As a result of this reality, the NEC recently acknowledged that grounded conductors within today's PV systems are not solidly grounded, but rather functionally grounded. As a result, the color codes that have traditionally designated negative (grounded) and positive (ungrounded) conductors have changed as well.

The NEC does not specify what color (other than they cannot be white, gray or green) should be used for ungrounded conductors. But in practice, most installers select red for the positive leg of the DC circuit and black for the negative leg. Typical color coding conventions are detailed in Table 9-3.

Typical Color Coding (US)	
Application	**Color**
DC Wiring	Positive - red, Negative - black
120V AC Wiring (single phase)	Hot - black, Neutral - white
240V AC Wiring (single phase)	Line 1 - black, Line 2 - red, Neutral - white
120V, 208V, 240V Three Phase AC Wiring	Line 1 - black, Line 2 - red, Line 3 - blue, Neutral - white
277V, 480V Three Phase AC Wiring	Line 1 - brown, Line 2 - orange, Line 3 - yellow, Neutral - gray

Installers must be consistent with the color coding throughout the installation. These color codes are strictly enforced in the field.

Sizes #4 AWG or Larger

For wire sizes #4 AWG or larger, the NEC allows colored tape to be placed around the wire near each termination point.

If, for example, an installer wishes to run #2 AWG wire, but can only find it in black, it is okay to use the black wire for both the positive and the negative (grounded conductor), so long as the positive circuit is identified with red tape wrapped around the conductor near each termination (assuming black for negative and red for positive).

For wire sizes smaller than #4 AWG, the properly colored insulation must be used.

Stranded/Fine Stranded Conductors

SOLID CORE

STRANDED

Wire used in electrical installations is often defined as **solid core** or **stranded**. Solid wires consist of a single solid conductor, whereas stranded wire consists of several thinner wires twisted into a bundle.

Installers will often select one type over another for a number of reasons. Stranded wire is more flexible and easier to pull through conduit. Where solid wire may be easier to terminate in some connections.

But not all stranded cable is created equally. It comes in various classes, as indicated in Table 9-4.

A smaller (#14-2 AWG) Class B cable, the most common stranded class, consists of 7 small conductors woven in a bundle. Larger (#1-4/0 AWG) Class B cable have 19 conductors.

Stranded Wire Class Codes		
Class Code	#14-2 AWG	#1-4/0 AWG
B	7 Strands	19 Strands
C	19 Strands	37 Strands
D	37 Strands	61 Strands
G	49 Strands	133 Strands
H	133 Strands	2597 Strands

TABLE 9-4: NUMBER OF CONDUCTORS IN VARIOUS CLASSES OF STRANDED WIRE

Where a #10 AWG Class B conductor would have 7 strands, a more flexible #10 AWG Class H finely stranded wire would consist of 133 very small conductors.

Increasingly PV installers are choosing fine stranded wire due to its flexibility and ease of installation. **Fine stranded** wire is considered any cable with more strands than Class B and Class C. This may, however cause problems.

FINE STRANDED

Many connection terminals and lugs should not be used with fine-stranded cables. The terminal must be marked or labeled specifically for use with fine-stranded conductors. Few of the normal screw-type mechanical terminals commonly used in the PV industry are listed for use with fine stranded wires.

Several problems may occur when using fine strand wire in terminals not rated for their use. The tightening screw may break the fine wire strands, reducing the amount of copper available to meet the listed ampacity. Additionally, the initial torque setting may not hold as the fine strands continue to compress after the initial tightening. Even with subsequent retorquing, the connection may still loosen.

Resistance

As current flows through a conductor, the material that makes up the conductor will offer some **resistance** (blocking just a bit of the flow). Using the water analogy, as the water flows through a pipe, it will rub up against the sides of the pipe, the friction causing the flow to slow just a bit. The water will, over time, flow just a bit slower because of this friction (resistance).

RESISTANCE

Voltage Drop

In the world of electricity, this friction, or resistance, will result in a drop in voltage (logically referred to as **voltage drop**). Resistance is measured in **ohms**, designated with the symbol Ω. The relationship between volts, amps and ohms can be calculated through the equation known as **Ohm's Law**.

VOLTAGE DROP

OHMS Ω

OHM'S LAW

This equation states:

FIGURE 9-1: OHM'S LAW
TRIANGLE

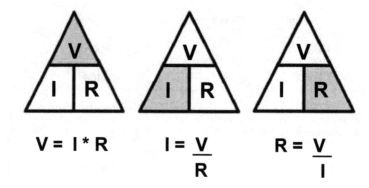

$$V = I * R \qquad I = \frac{V}{R} \qquad R = \frac{V}{I}$$

Volts = Current x Resistance (or, V = I x R)

OHM'S LAW
TRIANGLE

This equation is often depicted graphically using the **Ohm's Law Triangle**, a shorthand method (Figure 9-1) of visually seeing the resulting equation while solving for one of the variables.

Minimizing the Impact of Resistance on a PV System

Generally accepted practices in the PV industry seek to limit voltage drop within the wiring system to between 2% to 5%.

In order to reduce the impact of resistance (and the resulting voltage drop) on a PV system, the designer/installer can do a number of things:

- *Select the appropriate wire.* The material making up the wire will affect its resistance to the flow of electricity. Copper is an excellent conductor, and for this reason it is typically the standard material used in wires appropriate for PV systems.

TABLE 9-5: UNCOATED COPPER CONDUCTOR RESISTANCE CHARACTERISTICS MEASURED IN OHMS (Ω) PER 1,000 FEET MEASURED AT 75°C (167°F)

AWG	Solid Copper	Stranded Copper
18	7.77	7.95
16	4.89	4.99
14	3.07	3.14
12	1.93	1.98
10	1.21	1.24
8	0.764	0.778
6	—	0.491
4	—	0.308
3	—	0.245
2	—	0.194
1	—	0.154
0 (1/0)	—	0.122
00 (2/00)	—	0.0967
000 (3/00)	—	0.0766
0000 (4/00)	—	0.0608

- *Shorten the distance.* Resistance increases as the length of the wire increases. For example, a wire that has a resistance of 1.588 ohms at 1,000 feet of length, will have twice the resistance if the length of the run is increased to 2,000 feet (3.176 ohms). Reducing the length of the circuit will help in avoiding unwanted voltage drop.

- *Adjust the size of the wire.* The larger the wire, the less resistance this wire has to the energy flowing through it. Larger wires will create a system less prone to voltage drop. But larger wires cost more money. So a balance between price and performance must be reached when designing a PV system.

- Table 9-5 reflects the resistance characteristics of the various available copper wire sizes. In order to compare "apples to apples," the NEC in Chapter 9, Table 8, references the resistance of various wire sizes and types in terms of its resistance per 1000 feet or resistance per kilometer.

- *Increase the system voltage.* Even though the actual voltage drop does not change when changing the system voltage, the effective percentage of voltage lost decreases as the system voltage increases.

For example: the amount of voltage that may be lost in a cable run (voltage drop) may be calculated slightly modifying Ohm's Law (V = I x R).

When calculating resistance for a cable run within a PV system, the modified **voltage drop equation** is:

VOLTAGE DROP
EQUATION

$$V_d = I_{mp} \times R \times 2d$$

where... V_d = the voltage drop of the cable run
I_{mp} = the amps the string generates when operating at its maximum power point
R =   resistance from the NEC table for the selected wire (remember, this measurement is per 1000 feet)
$2d$ = twice the distance of the cable run (multiplied by 2 since there are two conductors in the cable to complete the circuit). This adjusts resistance for actual distance rather than the standard 1000 feet benchmark.

For example, if...

I_{mp} = 7.2 amps
R =   1.24 Ω / 1000 ft (10 AWG stranded copper)
d =   250 ft cable run

Then... V_d = 7.2 amps x (1.24 Ω / 1000 ft) x 2 (250 ft)
V_d = 7.2 amps x (1.24 Ω / 1000 ft) x 2 (250 ft)
V_d = 7.2 amps x 0.00124 Ω x 500 = 4.464 volts

Therefore, over a distance of 250 feet, using a #10 AWG stranded copper cable, transmitting 7.2 amps of current, there will be a loss of 4.464 volts.

If the system is operating at 12 volts and 4.464 volts are lost due to voltage drop, then 4.464/ 12 or 37.2% of the system voltage has been lost.

Clearly this is not an acceptable design. In fact, it is generally accepted that the voltage drop for the entire wiring system from array to load be limited to between 2% to 5%. To reduce the affect of voltage drop on the PV system, the designer could increase the voltage of the system.

If the nominal voltage of the system were raised to 200 volts, with the same voltage drop, then the loss due to voltage drop would be 4.464/200 or 2.23% of the available power. So while the amount of voltage drop due to resistance did not change, by increasing the voltage of the system, the percentage of the power lost was reduced from 37.2% to 2.23%.

Another factor that can affect resistance is the ambient air temperature. The hotter the cable gets, the more the resistance. Therefore protecting the cables from extreme heat will also help in system efficiency

Voltage Rise

When an inverter is connected to the grid, the combined resistance of the inverter output circuit as well as resistance on the grid can create a situation known as **voltage rise**. The net effect of this phenomenon is to increase the voltage of power leaving the inverter. If the voltage levels leaving the inverter increase beyond its normal operating range, it may result in **nuisance tripping** (the inverter turning off), even though the system has been properly designed.

Just as resistance can result in voltage leaving a source being reduced at its destination (voltage drop), it can also result in voltage at the source being increased to match the voltage at its destination (voltage rise).

All grid-tied inverters are designed to operate within an acceptable voltage output range. In a 240 V single-phase inverter, the range will likely be about 10% of the grid's nominal voltage. So the operating output voltage range would be between 216 Vac (240 V x .90) and 264 Vac (240 V x 1.10).

The utility service, on the other hand, is designed to operate within a 5% range of its nominal voltage. So the voltage on the grid may be as high as 252 Vac (240 V x 1.05). Additionally, the grid may have as much as 0.4 Ω of "natural" **impedance** (the effective resistance from the combined effects of resistance and reactance).

Ohm's Law states that V = I x R. So if the current remains steady (as it would from the inverter), and resistance increases, voltage will increase as well.

If the output from the inverter was 20 amps, and the impedance on the grid was at 0.4 Ω, then resistance from the grid would result in a voltage rise at the inverter of 8 Vac.

VOLTAGE RISE

NUISANCE TRIPPING

IMPEDANCE

The combined effect of resistance on the grid, higher voltages on the grid, and resistance in the inverter output circuit may result in voltages at the inverter rising to above the inverter's maximum operating limit.

For example, assume the maximum output voltage of an inverter is 264 Vac. Also assume the grid is operating at the high end of its allowable voltage limit (252 Vac), with 0.4 Ω of impedance (resulting in an 8 Vac increase at the inverter).

Even without factoring in any resistance from the inverter output circuit, the inverter will output at 260 Vac (252 V from the grid + 8 V voltage rise due to grid impedance). The inverter output circuit (under these conditions) cannot have more than 0.2 Ω of resistance (20 A x 0.2 Ω = 4 V) to keep below the inverter's 264 V maximum tolerance.

As with voltage drop, voltage rise issues can be addressed by reducing the length of the inverter output circuit or increasing the size of the conductors to reduce resistance on the circuit.

Ampacity Rating of Conductors

All other factors held equal, the **ampacity** rating of a conductor, or the amount of current a wire can carry without damage, will increase as the size of the wire increases. Ampacity limits are strictly enforced and are listed in the **NEC Table 310-15(B)16**, a portion of which is reproduced in Table 9-6.

Continuing the water analogy, this would seem to make sense. The bigger the pipe (or wire), the more water (electrical current) can flow through it.

> AMPACITY

> NEC TABLE 310-15(B)16

Temperature Ratings of Conductors

Note that different types of wire are rated for different temperatures. Conductors coated with insulations in column 1 (such as TW or UF) are rated for 60°C (140°F). Conductors in column 2 (RHW, THW, etc) are rated to operate in temperatures up to 75°C (167°F). Conductors in column 3 (PV, USE-2, THHN, etc) are rated to operate in temperatures up to 90°C (194°F).

Conductors must be sized by considering where they will terminate and how that termination is rated. If the termination within the equipment (or breaker) is rated for 75°C, the maximum temperature at that termination can be up to 75°C when the equipment is loaded to its full ampacity.

If a conductor rated for 60°C is used in this example, the additional heat at the connection above 60°C might result in insulation failure. If a conductor rated for 90°C was chosen, then it might carry excess heat to the point of termination, causing the termination to overheat or result in a premature opening of the overcurrent device.

As a result, the ampacity rating of the conductor should be selected based on the lowest heat rating of any termination or device to which that conductor is connected. A conductor with a higher heat rating can be used, but the ampacity must then be calculated based on the lower heat rating.

For example, the designer has determined that the ampacity requirements of a conductor is a maximum of 60 amps. This conductor terminates into an inverter with terminations rated to 60°C.

The design could specify the use of PV cable (rated at 90°C). However the ampacity for this cable must be taken from column 1 (60°C) of the table, rather than column 3 (90°C). So even though #6 AWG PV cable is capable of carrying 75 amps (well above the required 60 amps), the designer must specify #4 AWG PV cable (rated at 70 amps in column 1) due to the temperature rating of the termination.

The NEC gives specific direction when it comes to dealing with this issue. Article 110-14(c)(1)(a) states that for circuits rated at 100 amps or less, or circuits that use #14 AWG through #1 AWG conductors (which includes most PV circuits), the system must use:

- conductors rated at 60°C, or
- conductors with higher temperature ratings, provided the ampacity of such conductors is determined based on the 60°C ampacity of the conductor size used, or

TABLE 9-6: ALLOWABLE AMPACITIES FOR INSULATED CONDUCTORS

(FROM NEC TABLE 310-15(B)16)

Size AWG	60°C (140°F)	75°C (167°F)	90°C (194°F)	60°C (140°F)	75°C (167°F)	90°C (194°F)
	Types TW, UF	Types RHW, THHW, THW, THWN, USE	Types PV, THHN, THHW, USE-2	Types TW, UF	Types RHW, THHW, THW, THWN, USE	Types PV, THHN, THHW, USE-2
	COPPER			ALUMINUM		
18	–	–	14	–	–	–
16	–	–	18	–	–	–
14*	20	20	25	–	–	–
12*	25	25	30	20	20	25
10*	30	35	40	25	30	35
8	40	50	55	30	40	45
6	55	65	75	40	50	60
4	70	85	95	55	65	75
3	85	100	110	65	75	85
2	95	115	130	75	90	100
1	110	130	150	85	100	115
1/0	125	150	170	100	120	135
2/0	145	175	195	115	135	150
3/0	165	200	225	130	155	175
4/0	195	230	260	150	180	205

- conductors with higher temperature ratings if the equipment to which it is terminated is listed and identified for use with such conductors.

For circuits rated higher than 100 amps, or that use conductors larger than #1 AWG, similar rules apply. Article 110-14(c)(1)(b) states that these systems must use:
- conductors rated at 75°C, or
- conductors with higher temperature ratings, provided the ampacity of such conductors is determined based on the 75°C ampacity of the conductor size used, or
- conductors with higher temperature ratings if the equipment to which it is terminated is listed and identified for use with such conductors.

Effect of Temperature on Wire

Temperature effects the way wire conducts electricity. The higher the temperature, the greater the resistance and the less ability the wire has to conduct amps safely.

In order to give a point of reference, the NEC ampacity ratings found in the NEC are determined at an ambient air temperature of 30° C (86° F).

If the anticipated operating temperature of the wire is expected to be greater than 30° C (86° F), larger wire may be required. Correction factors to adjust for this increased temperature can be found in NEC Table 310-15(B)(2)(a), a portion of which is reproduced in Table 9-7.

The NEC has suggested that wires placed in conduits in exposed sunlight on or close to rooftops (less than 7/8th inch or 23 mm) will experience average temperatures 33° C (30° F) higher than the ambient air temperature.

TEMPERATURE CORRECTION FACTORS			
Temp (°C)	60°C	75°C	90°C
21-25	1.08	1.05	1.04
26-30	1	1	1
31-35	0.91	0.94	0.96
36-40	0.82	0.88	0.91
41-45	0.71	0.82	0.87
46-50	0.58	0.75	0.82
51-55	0.41	0.67	0.76
56-60	–	0.58	0.71
61-65	–	0.47	0.65
66-70	–	0.33	0.58
71-75	–	–	0.5

TABLE 9-7: AMPACITY TEMPERATURE CORRECTION FACTORS

(FROM NEC TABLE 310-15(B)(2)(A))

If the conduit or cable is not offset above the roof deck by an inch or more, 33° C should be added to the highest ambient air temperature when calculating the temperature correction factor.

Also, when many wires are placed into a **conduit** or **raceway**, the heat generated by the resistance within the conductors wires can increase the air temperature within the conduit.

CONDUIT

RACEWAY

TABLE 9-8: AMPACITY
ADJUSTMENT REQUIRED
WHEN PLACING MORE
THAN THREE
CONDUCTORS IN A
RACEWAY OR CONDUIT

(FROM NEC TABLE
310.15(B)(3)(A))

Number of wires in a single conduit or raceway	Percent of ampacity values found in NEC Table 310.15(B)(16) (inclusive of temp adjustment, if necessary)
4 to 6 wires	80%
7 to 9 wires	70%
10 to 20 wires	50%
21 to 30 wires	45%
31 to 40 wires	40%
41 or more wires	35%

When placing more than three current carrying conductors (excluding the ground) in a single conduit or raceway, adjustments must be made to the ampacity rating of the wire. In other words, the wire may be capable of conducting less current due to the build up of heat within the conduit.

NEC Table 310.15(B)(3)(a) outlines the adjustments required when placing multiple wires in a single raceway. As shown in Table 9-8, if 18 wires were placed in a single conduit or raceway, each wire would only be capable of transmitting half (50%) of the current they would be able to transmit if three or fewer wires had been placed in that same conduit.

Overcurrent Protection

The wiring and equipment that comprise a PV system are designed to only accept a certain amount of current. If current in excess of this maximum amount flows through the system, it could very likely damage or destroy the various components (and perhaps cause a fire).

FUSE

CIRCUIT BREAKER

OVERCURRENT
PROTECTION DEVICES
(OCPD)

For this reason, **fuses** and/or **circuit breakers** are incorporated into the system, designed to "blow" or trip off should excess current finds its way onto the circuit. Collectively these are known as **overcurrent protection devices (OCPD)**.

Often this overcurrent protection is incorporated into combiner boxes, disconnects, charge controllers and/or inverters. But regardless of where it is housed, overcurrent protection must be part of a well-designed system.

AMPERE INTERRUPT
RATING (AIR)

While short circuits in the PV output system will likely not be much more than the rated operating output current of the system, short circuits from batteries can be thousands of amps. The rating on breakers and fuses is known as its **ampere interrupt rating (AIR).** If current flowing through the OCPD exceeds the rating of the unit, it will open the circuit, preventing current flow that exceeds design parameters.

FIGURE 9-2: COMMON BACK-FED SINGLE-POLE, TWO-POLE AND THREE-POLE CIRCUIT BREAKERS

Available OCPD sizes were modified in the 2014 NEC and now include: 1, 3, 6, 10, 15, 20, 25, 30, 35, 40, 45, 50, 60, 70, 80, 90, 100, 110, 125, 150, 175, 200, 225, 250, 300, 350, 400, 450, 500, and 600 A ratings.

Fuses and breakers used in the DC circuits must be specifically rated for DC photovoltaic systems. Underwriters Labs (UL) has specific certifications for both fuses [UL 2579] and circuit breakers [UL 489B] specifically designed for use in DC PV systems.

Circuit breakers normally are available as single-pole, two-pole, or three-pole, as illustrated in Figure 9-2.

Back-Fed and Ground Fault Breakers

Any circuit breaker that does not specifically state on it that it can only be fed from the line or the load side is considered a **back-fed breaker**. This means that it will open (turn off) when current passing through it exceeds its rating - regardless of the direction from which the power originates.

Some breakers are designed to protect the circuit they are connected to should a ground fault occur. These are typically referred to as **Ground-Fault Protection of Equipment (GFPE) breakers**, or more commonly simply as GFPE breakers.

FIGURE 9-3: GROUND-FAULT CIRCUIT INTERRUPTER (GFCI) CIRCUIT BREAKER

BACK-FED BREAKER

GFPE BREAKER

GFCI BREAKER

Smaller GFPE breakers designed to protect a single load circuit can be easily identified by their white pigtail connection, as seen in Figure 9-3. These incorporate electronic ground-fault detection circuitry, or a trip solenoid, within the unit. These smaller breakers are called **ground-fault circuit interrupter (GFCI) circuit breakers**.

Most people are much more familiar with the receptacle type GFCI, such as shown in Figure 9-4, which protects a single outlet. GFCI breakers are

FIGURE 9-4: STANDARD
GFCI WALL OUTLET

designed to provide that same protection to the entire circuit.. GFCI work by sensing and comparing the amount of current flowing through the conductors. If there is a sudden imbalance (a ground fault) it then opens the circuit.

When a ground fault is detected, the breaker opens. But if it is back-fed, then the detection circuitry can be damaged. For this reason the terminals on these circuit breakers are identified with "line" and "load" markings.

FIGURE 9-5: LARGER
GFPE FAULT POWERED
CIRCUIT BREAKER THAT
MAY ALLOW FOR BACK-
FED CIRCUITS

Some larger GFPE breakers (Figure 9-5) have been designed to operate while back-fed. Unless marked as line and load, the breaker is assumed to be back-fed.

Continuous and Noncontinuous Loads

When it comes to sizing overcurrent protection, the NEC (Article 210.20(A)) makes a distinction as to where the load is **continuous** or **noncontinuous**. A continuous load is expected to run for three hour or more at its maximum ampacity rating.

CONTINUOUS LOAD

NONCONTINUOUS LOAD

A noncontinuous load (such as a clothes dryer, for example) will never be expected to operate at maximum ampacity for that period of time.

If the circuit contains a continuous load, then the breaker for that circuit must be rated at 125% of the expected maximum load. If the circuit only contains noncontinuous loads, then the breaker need only be rated for the maximum ampacity of the circuit (without the 25% additional capacity).

100% RATED BREAKER

80% RATED BREAKER

An exception to this requirement is if the breaker selected has been **rated for 100%.** If so rated, the extra capacity has already been factored into the ampacity rating (the continuous load rating) of the breaker. Less expensive, and more common **80% rated breakers** are rated for the noncontinuous loads, and the 125% factor must be applied if using with continuous loads.

Circuits in a PV System

In a simple grid-tied PV system, there are generally four distinct circuits within the system. Conductors connecting the solar modules to the combiner or junction box are collectively known as the **PV source circuit**, as illustrated in Figure 9-6. The circuit that connects the junction box to the DC disconnect is the **PV output circuit**.

PV SOURCE CIRCUIT

PV OUTPUT CIRCUIT

INVERTER INPUT
CIRCUIT

In a grid-tied system, the circuit from the DC disconnect to the inverter is the **inverter input circuit**. In a stand-alone system, the inverter input circuit connects the batteries to the inverter.

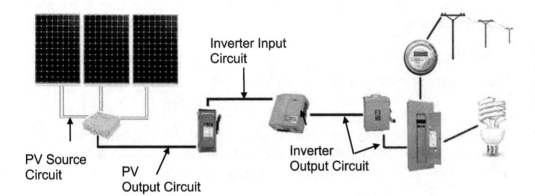

Inverter Input Circuit

PV Source Circuit

PV Output Circuit

Inverter Output Circuit

The AC portion of the system is referred to as the **inverter output circuit**.

In a stand-alone installation or an AC coupled or DC coupled system, the part of the system that connects the DC disconnect to the charge controller, and the charge controller to the batteries is known as the **battery input circuit**.

The size of the wire required is dependent upon the amount of current (not voltage) that flows through it. Larger current requires larger wire. NEC 706.32 states that conductors used within batter enclosures must be size 2/0 AWG or larger and rated as moisture resistant.

Since watts = volts x amps, if the voltage increases, the amps (current) required decreases to provide the same amount of power (watts). As a general rule, higher voltage systems require smaller wire (lower amps) within the system.

Kirchhoff's current law says that the total current going into a circuit must equal the total current going out. If it were not so, electrons would accumulate.

When a solar panel is disconnected from a load, it does not produce power. When generating power, there must be both voltage and current. With the load disconnected there is voltage (i.e. potential) but no current. Since the electrons liberated by the incoming light energy have nowhere to go, an equilibrium is developed in the system (no power in, no power out).

So where does the energy go when there is no load to service? It becomes heat energy in the panel which is ultimately radiated or conducted away. If two identical panels are placed side-by-side; one connected to a load and the other one not, the disconnected panel would be hotter than the connected one.

But a system that is connected to the grid (when it is operational) always has a load to service. The loads of the home or business will be serviced first by the

INVERTER OUTPUT CIRCUIT

BATTERY INPUT CIRCUIT

KIRCHHOFF'S CURRENT LAW

power from the array entering the system, but any excess will flow to the grid as predicted by Kirchhoff's Laws.

Wiring the PV Source Circuit

The PV source circuit connects the panels to the combiner box, or junction box.

Today most panels come "hard wired" with **pigtail** cables (already attached within the junction box), terminated with MC4 connectors (one male and one female). Series connections between panels are made by simply clicking these connectors together.

The strings are then connected to a junction box or combiner box (an electrical enclosure where overcurrent protection is provided for the string). Select a junction/combiner box that is compatible with the array as designed (number of strings, amp and voltage rating, etc.) Generally the combiner box is located close to the array, but in nearly all cases, extension cables will be required to connect the combiner to the end of the pigtails attached to the panel at the end of each string.

The NEC allows PV source circuit cables to be installed without the use of conduit or raceways. However these conductors "shall be supported and secured by staples, cable ties, straps, hangers, or similar fittings designed and installed so as not to damage the cable, at intervals not exceeding 1.4 m (4.6 feet) and within 300 mm (12 inches) of every outlet box, junction box, cabinet, or fitting." (NEC 334.30)

FIGURE 9-7: DIRECT METHOD OF WIRING A PV ARRAY

(FROM S-5! METAL ROOF ATTACHMENTS)

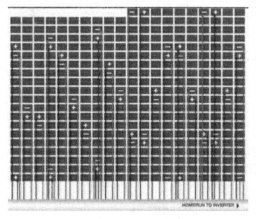

For smaller systems, it is common to install the PV source circuit wire using the **direct method**. This wiring layout simply connects the ends of each string to the junction/combiner box using a **home run** wiring method (illustrated in Figure 9-7), running a single wire **jumper** from the string to junction/combiner box.

These jumpers are typically individually measured and terminated on site to meet the specifications of each unique run.

This method has the advantage of simplicity and can be designed on site, but it:
- uses a great deal of wire,
- is labor intensive,
- does not scale well as the array size increases.

For larger arrays, the **trunk method** of PV source circuit design (shown in Figure 9-8) has its advantages. In this method, the ends of the strings are clustered around a central point or channel.

The ends of each string connect to trunk wiring that is run in conduits or raceways that are then home run to the junction/combiner box.

TRUNK METHOD

In this method, the trunk cables and the raceway need to be laid out and in place before the panels are installed.

While this method of cable design requires more advanced planning and perhaps the addition of a cable tray or conduit, it also:
- uses less wire,
- is more logically organized in larger systems,
- simplifies the layout process, and
- is less labor intensive on the site.

It is generally impractical to enclose all of the PV source circuit in conduit or within raceways, but all other PV circuits should be installed in conduit or enclosed raceways.

Ampacity Calculations of the Source Circuit

When connections are made in series, voltage is affected, but amps remain the same. When connections are made in parallel, amps increase but voltage remains constant.

By definition, a string coming from the array begins from one or more solar panels connected in series. Since amps are not affected by series connections, the amp rating of each string will be the same as the amp rating of a single panel within that string.

When determining the amp rating of a panel for wire sizing, use the "worst case" situation, which will be the Isc (amps short circuit), which assumes an irradiance of 1000 W/m^2 under standard test conditions.

However, conditions at the array might actually exceed irradiance assumed under STC. In fact, measured irradiance can be as high as 1,200 W/m^2 in some instances. Since amps generated by a panel are affected primarily by irradiance, the ampacity rating of the conductor used must be increased to account for the variability of the power contained within sunlight.

The **solar ampacity adjustment** for each string is calculated by multiplying the Isc by a factor of 1.25.

In all cases when calculating the ampacity of wire, the NEC requires that a safety margin of 20% be added to the anticipated maximum current estimates (this is accomplished by multiplying the anticipated current by a factor of 1.25. This standard **ampacity safety factor** is then calculated in addition to the adjustment for solar variation.

If the Isc of a string (found on a single panel within that string) is 9.43 amps, then the wire must be sized to handle a current of:

9.43 A (Isc) x 1.25 (solar variability) x 1.25 (safety margin) = 14.73 amps

Checking the NEC table, knowing that all panels use either PV or USE-2 wire, a minimum wire size of 16 AWG (rated for 18 amps) is required for this circuit. However today's panels typically are shipped with 12 AWG cable attached, so use 12 AWG at a minimum for this circuit.

Special NEC note: For PV systems operating at 50 volts or less (typically stand-alone systems), conductors may not be sized smaller than 12 AWG.

Sizing Overcurrent Protection
The sizing for overcurrent protection devices such as fuses or circuit breakers located in the combiner box is accomplished in a similar manner as determining the amp rating for the wires. However, for fuses and breakers, the amp rating is based on the Imp (normal operating ampacity) rather than the Isc (worst case ampacity).

So the overcurrent protection in the combiner box would be based on Imp (normal current under STC) x 1.25 (solar ampacity adjustment) x 1.25 (ampacity safety factor).

The NEC now requires that PV source circuits be protected by an OCPD within the combiner box for each string.

If the Imp of a string is 8.71 amps, then the wire must be sized to handle a current of:

8.71 A (Imp) x 1.25 (solar variability) x 1.25 (safety margin) = 13.6 amps

Always round up to the next available size when selecting a fuse or circuit breaker, but make sure that in rounding it up, the breaker does not exceed the ampacity limits of the wire to which it is connected..

In this example, a 15 amp DC breaker or fuse would be selected (rounding up from 13.6 amps). The wire selected (12 AWG PV wire) has an ampacity rating of 30 amps. So the breaker will work since it will trip long before the wire has reached its ampacity limit.

But what if a #8 AWG USE-2 wire had been selected for a circuit carrying 52.06 amps (after adjustments)? This size wire has an ampacity rating of 55 amps. But the next available breaker on the market (rounding up) is rated at 60 amps. If a 60 amp breaker is attached to a 55 amp rated wire, the effect is the same as if there were no breaker at all (for the wire would exceed its ability to carry current before the breaker trips). This is clearly not acceptable.

There are two options to solve this problem. One would be to install a 50 amp breaker (which might then trip under normal operating conditions), or a better solution would be to install larger 6 AWG wire (with an ampacity rating of 75 amps).

Like wire, overcurrent protection device ratings are determined under standard test conditions. Prolonged exposure to ambient temperatures greater than 25 °C may affect its ability to handle current, causing the element within the fuse to melt under loads lower than the system was designed to handle.

Care should be taken to locate overcurrent protection in shaded areas, away from direct sunlight. Check the manufacturer's specifications on how to derate the system when placing these devices in a high-temperature environment.

Special NEC Note: When using smaller wire sizes, the NEC sets limits on the size of fuses or breakers that can be used with these wires. For #14 AWG wire, the fuse must be 15 A or less. For #12 AWG wire, the fuse must be 20 A or less. For #10 AWG wire, the fuse or breaker must be 30 A or less.

Since the overcurrent device in the combiner box selected is only rated to a maximum of 20 amps, it is probably safer to use wire at least 12 AWG in size (larger wire can nearly always be substituted, but not smaller).

Adjusting for Temperature
Ampacity ratings for conductors assume a temperature of 30° C (86° F). In extremely hot locations, an adjustment must be made.

In smaller systems, cables in a PV source circuit are loose (not generally contained within a conduit or raceway) located under the panels, shaded from extreme heat. It is assumed that they are cooled by moving air, so typically no temperature adjustment is needed.

But in some installations (especially larger commercial systems on flat roofs), portions of the PV source circuit may be in conduit exposed to sunlight. Bundled cables are to be treated as if they are in conduit, as the conductors in the center are not exposed to cooling air and their ampacity rating will be affected by the increased temperatures.

Assuming the cables will be placed on the deck of the roof, then 33° C must be added to the temperature adjustment. It has already been determined that the hottest day on the site could reach 41° C, so:

$$41° C + 33° C = 74° C$$

Looking at for The temperature correction value (found in NEC Table 310-15(B)(2)(A)) for ambient air temperature that falls within the range of 71-75° C is .50. The ampacity rating of the cable must be multiplied by a factor of .50 or essentially cut in half due to high temperatures.

Stated another way, the maximum current of the cable must be derated for the capacity inefficiencies caused by excessive heat by this factor. This is accomplished by dividing it by the correction factor.

$$14.73 \text{ amps} / .50 \text{ (derate factor)} = 29.46 \text{ amps}$$

The capacity of the wire must now be at least 29.46 amps due to the higher temperature.

Derating for Conduit or Raceway Fill

Wires radiate heat as they conduct electricity. If many wires are placed within a single conduit or raceway, they can conduct enough heat to impact the ampacity rating of the cable.

In designs that incorporate 4-6 cables in a raceway, the ampacity of each cable must be derated by a factor of .80. If the raceway contains 7-9 cables, then each cable can only carry 70% of its originally rated ampacity, and so on.

If, in the above example, two source circuits were contained in the same raceway that had been derated for heat, there would then be four current carrying conductors (two positive and two negative) within the raceway. This circuit would then need to be further derated due to conduit fill.

NEC Table 310.15 (B)(3)(a) mandates a derate of .80 for conduit carrying four to six conductors, so conduit fill will result in:

$$29.46 \text{ amps} / .80 \text{ (derate factor)} = 36.825 \text{ amps}$$

The circuit will now require #10 AWG USE-2 wire (40 amp rating) at a minimum due to derating for conduit fill and wire in conduit or closed raceway exposed to sunlight.

Systems with Multiple Combiner Boxes

Electricity flows in all directions, and typically follows a path from higher voltage to lower voltage.

If multiple stings are connected in a combiner box, and then multiple combiner boxes are connected together, the current might **backflow** to a damaged section of the array, as shown in Figure 9-9.

BACKFLOW

For this reason, the PV source circuit must be designed to handle the maximum amps it may be subjected to, which includes the ampacity of ALL the combiner boxes to which it is connected.

The formula for calculating the ampacity rating of a PV source circuit that is part of a system that combines multiple combiner boxes is as follows:

$$(Np - 1) \times Isc \times Strings \times 1.25 \times 1.25 = \text{Total Short-Circuit Current}$$

In which,

Np = number of combiner boxes combined in parallel
Isc = the amp short circuit rating of the panel

The reason one is subtracted from the number of combiner boxes connected in parallel is that it is assumed at least one subarray is malfunctioning to cause the backflow of electricity (so no amps would flow from it).

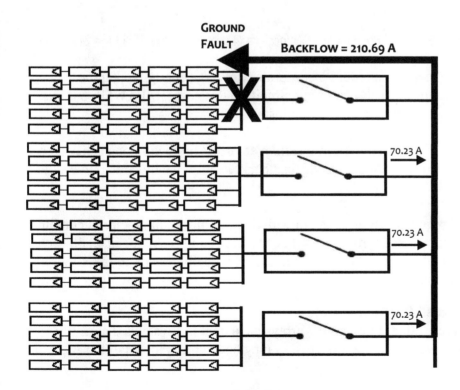

GROUND FAULT

BACKFLOW = 210.69 A

70.23 A

70.23 A

70.23 A

FIGURE 9-9: CURRENT BACKFLOW DUE TO GROUND FAULT

FIGURE 9-10: CURRENT
BACKFLOW PREVENTED
BY INCORPORATING
OVERCURRENT DEVICES

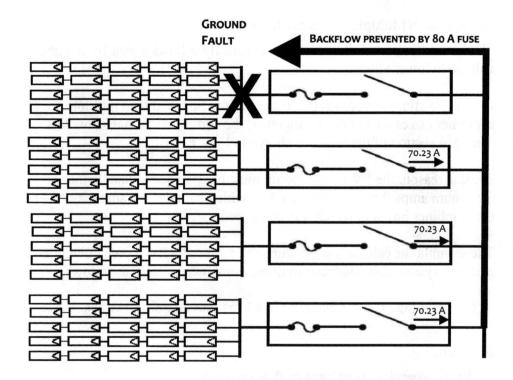

In this example, if the panel selected has an Isc of 8.99 amps, and there are four subarrays with five strings combined in parallel, then the amp rating for each subarray would be 8.99 A x 5 strings per combiner box = 44.95 A leaving each combiner box used in each subarray. Wires within the subarray would normally be sized 44.95 A x 1.25 x 1.25 = 70.23 A (#6 AWG PV wire). But accounting for backflow in the event of a ground fault, the amps may rise to:

(Np- 1) x Single PV Source Circuit Ampacity = (4 subarrays - 1) x 70.23 A = 210.69 A

In theory, the designer could incorporate wire large enough to handle the backflow amps on each PV output circuit (in this case #1/0 AWG), but this would prove expensive and hard to install.

Alternatively, the designer can install overcurrent protection on each source circuit that protects the strings against backfed amps, as illustrated in Figure 9-10.

The NEC requires that any system with three or more source-circuit combiner boxes must be fused (protected with either a circuit breaker or fuse) on each **feeder circuit** running from the source-circuit combiner box to the recombiner box.

FEEDER CIRCUIT

Separating AC & DC Conductors
Many large ground-mounted PV arrays have tracking systems that use AC power to drive the tracker systems. It may be tempting to install the AC

conductors in the same support system (conduit or raceway) as the DC source circuit conductors.

Even though both conductors (the AC and DC) are part of the same PV source circuit, they must be separated by a partition, an example illustrated in Figure 9-11.

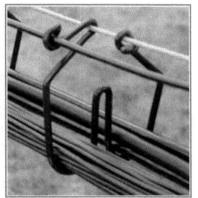

FIGURE 9-11: CABLE RING WITH THREE CABLE SECTIONS

(FROM CAB PRODUCTS)

Wiring the PV Output Circuit

The PV output circuit in a grid-tied system runs from the combiner box to the DC disconnect. In a stand alone system, it runs from the combiner box to the charge controller.

Within the combiner box, the wires leading from the multiple strings are connected together in parallel (negative to negative, positive to positive).

The voltage carried upon the wire leaving the combiner box will remain the same as that generated by each individual string, but the current will increase to the sum of the current from all the strings entering the combiner box.

If the ampacity rating of each circuit running from each string has been determined correctly (the Isc x 1.25 x 1.25), then the ampacity rating of the wire used in the PV output circuit is the sum of all the cables within the PV source circuit.

For example, if there are five strings entering a combiner box, each with an Isc 9.43, each string would be corrected to 9.43 A x 1.25 x 1.25 =14.73 amps.

The five strings combined in parallel results in:

5 x 14.73 A = 73.65 amps

This is the maximum amps that may run over the PV output circuit. Just as with the PV source circuit, this amp rating must be adjusted for temperature and/or conduit fill. If the PV output circuit is designed to run in conduit along a rooftop, and then down the side of the building to a disconnect, the temperature adjustment may be quite similar to the example used in sizing the PV source circuit.

However, if the PV output circuit will run in buried conduit from the combiner box to the DC disconnect (as might often happen with a ground mounted system), then no temperature correction would be required.

IF no temperature adjustment is required, then using the ampacity table (assuming 60°C terminations) then #3 AWG cable would be required for this circuit (with an ampacity rating of 85 amps).

Alternative Ampacity Calculation

What has been described to this point is the traditional method of determining the ampacity of the PV circuits. It is based on the the maximum current output of the PV modules as corrected for irradiance and temperature.

However the 2020 NEC allows for an alternative method. The new language (690.8(A)(2)) allows the circuit current to be determined by the rated input current of the conversion equipment (usually an inverter).

If the circuit in the above example (rated at 73.65 A using the traditional method) was to be connected to a 24 kW inverter with a maximum input current rating of 33 amps, then the wire size could be determined as follows:

33 A (maximum inverter input current) x 1.25 (safety factor) = 41.25 A

The designer/installer could then select #6 AWG cable (rated at 55 A at 60°C) rather than the #3 AWG cable as required under the traditional method.

When this method is used, the code also requires that the conductors must be protected by an overcurrent device rated not more than the circuit conductor ampacity. In this example, the overcurrent protection must be rated at 55 A or less.

Using MC Cable in DC Circuits

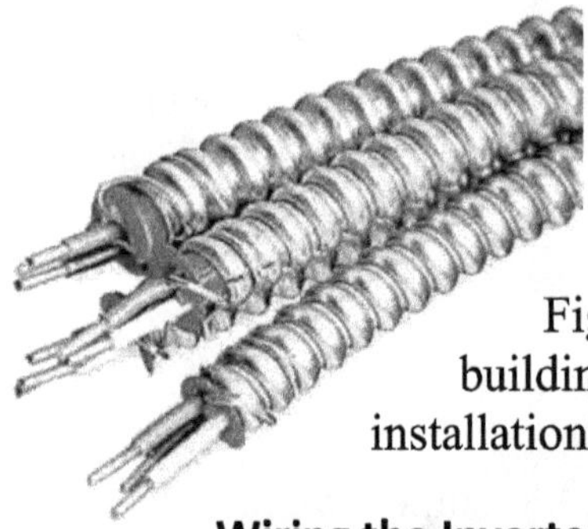

FIGURE 9-12: METAL-CLAD (MC) TYPE CABLE

MC CABLE

PV output circuits (in fact all DC circuits) that run within buildings must be contained within metal conduit (usually EMT). The 2017 NEC also now allows the use of **metal-clad (MC) cable** as well. MC cables, as depicted in Figure 9-12, may make DC cable runs within buildings easier to install where tight bends make the installation of EMT conduit difficult.

Wiring the Inverter Input Circuit

The inverter input circuit on a grid-tied system runs from the DC disconnect to the inverter. The only change from the PV output circuit is that a disconnecting device has been introduced into the system.

No ampacity adjustments are required in the transition from the PV output circuit to the inverter input circuit (other than perhaps temperature adjustments, if the system transitions from a high heat environment to a lower temperature environment at this point).

Often the wiring system transitions from outdoor to indoor at this point. If this is the case, indoor wire must be used in the inverter input circuit.

Also, the termination ratings for equipment connected to this circuit may change, so check the ratings of all terminations before selecting the conductors.

Systems that Incorporate Batteries

On systems that incorporate a battery bank, the circuit that runs between the inverter and the battery bank is considered the inverter input circuit. As load demand is pulled from the batteries to the inverter, the inverter specifications will dictate the size of the wire needed for this circuit.

Sizing of conductors and overcurrent protection for this circuit is accomplished through the following equation:

Maximum inverter rating (VA) / inverter efficiency /
lowest battery bank voltage/ AC ripple x 1.25 (NEC safety margin)

Remember, however, that a battery bank configured at a nominal 48-volts rating will actually operate within a range of voltage (42 to 56 V) depending on its state of charge. The lower the volts, the greater the amps required to draw the same amount of power. So select the lowest voltage the inverter will accept from the battery bank (probably around 44 volts).

For a 6,500 W, 95% efficient inverter, connected to a 48-volt battery bank, then...

6,500 VA / .95 / 44 Vdc = 155.5 amps

The effect of current ripple must also be taken into account when sizing this circuit. While no standard exists, it is assumed that the voltage ripple of the system must not exceed 3%.

Factoring in a voltage ripple of 3%, then...

6,500 VA /.95 / 44 Vdc = 155.5 amps / .97 (3% Vac ripple) = 160.3 amps

Then adjust the amps with the NEC safety margin used in all wire sizing, and...

160.3 amps x 1.25 (NEC safety margin) = 200.38 amps

Note that no solar variability adjustment to ampacity is required at this point, as the power over the line is now "pulled" from the battery rather than "pushed" from the solar array. The variability of sunlight no longer is a factor.

The Effect of Ripple on Inverters and Batteries:

Because power flows in a circuit (from the source to the load, then back to the source), the waveform of power coming from a DC source (such as a solar

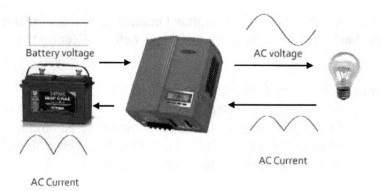

Battery voltage

AC voltage

AC Current

AC Current

panel or battery) is affected by the waveform of the AC load to which it is connected, as illustrated in Figure 9-13.

While a pure DC waveform is flat, the DC waveform influenced by the system to which it is connected will fluctuate slightly, or **ripple**.

RIPPLE

Ripple is wasted power, and has many undesirable effects in a DC circuit. It can heat components, cause noise and distortion, and may cause some digital circuits to malfunction.

Capacitors within the inverter will try to flatten out the ripple. However, the more resistance there is in the DC portion of the circuit, the greater the ripple.

Test for AC ripple on the DC portion of the system by using a multimeter set to test for AC voltage, but testing on the DC circuit. The meter will then only measure the variation in the waveform.

Excessive ripple may be the result of:
- a battery bank without adequate capacity (either too small or at too low a state of charge),
- battery cables that are too long or undersized,
- too many or low-quality switches, fuses or shunts.

Systems that experience high levels of ripple may find that:
- the lifetime of inverters decreases due to large currents in the capacitors,
- the battery lifetime is limited due to the discharge/charge effect
- the charge power is reduced due to ripple during charging,
- other connected loads will suffer from the same ripple.

For any fixed load (measured in watts), any variation in voltage will result in a corresponding increase (or decrease) in amps (as watts = amps x volts). So a drop in voltage due to ripple will result in a corresponding increase in the amps flowing through the circuit. As a result, the conductor used in the circuit must be sized to handle the increase in amps that is the result of ripple.

Wiring the Battery Input Circuit

In stand alone systems, an additional circuit must be sized. This runs between the charge controller and the battery bank.

For a system where the voltage from the array matches the voltage from the battery bank, no adjustment to the ampacity rating of the wire calculated for the PV output circuit is needed (assuming no temperature adjustment is required). Again, if the wire is to be used indoors, it must be rated for indoor use.

However, if the system is incorporating an MPPT charge controller, where the input voltage is stepped down from that of the array to that of the battery bank within the charge controller, then adjustments must be made.

First, obtain the maximum amp output rating for the model selected. For example, the Midnight Solar Classic 150 has a maximum output current of 76 amps. Take this rating and multiply by the NEC safety factor of 1.25 to size the wire (76 A x 1.25 = 95 A). In this example, #4 AWG high temperature wire could be used (rated for 95 amps). The solar variability derate factor does not apply in this circuit as the charge controller mitigates any variation in irradiance.

For any overcurrent protection on this circuit, simply select the maximum output current rating, without the safety factor adjustment (in this case, 76 A rounded up to an 80 amp overcurrent protection device).

If multiple charge controllers are combined in parallel to feed the battery bank, then their ampacities are added together to size the wires connecting them to the battery bank.

If a diverted load is incorporated into this circuit, the conductor to the diverted load must be 150% of the maximum current rating of the charge controller.

Wiring the Inverter Output Circuit

Everything changes within the inverter. Not only is the waveform changed from DC to AC, but the voltages and corresponding ampacities change as well.

While voltages anywhere up to 600 Vdc (for residential) and even higher for commercial systems may enter the inverter in a grid-tied system, and voltages typically at 48 Vdc in a stand alone system, the voltage leaving will typically be at 240 Vac (for a single-phase system). As power remains constant, amps clearly must be different on both sides of the inverter.

Grid-Tied Systems

The wire leaving the inverter must be sized to 1.25 the ampacity rating of the continuous current output of the inverter. For example, if the output power of the inverter is rated at 6,600 W, producing 240 Vac, then the continuous current leaving the inverter would be 27.5 amps. The wire must then be rated at 1.25 x 27.5 = 34.375 amps.

Termination Ratings

If, in this example, the conductor specified for this circuit is THWN, a quick look at NEC Table 310.15 (B)16 reveals that #10 AWG (rated to 35 amps) can be used if the inverter terminations and the breaker in the service panel both are temperature rated to 75°C.

If either termination is only rated to 60°C, then #8 AWG THWN (rated at 40 amps at 60°C) wire must be used.

Since equipment within the system may be changed during its lifetime, it is good practice to always assume the worse case rating for terminations (60°C) and size wire within the circuits accordingly.

Stand Alone Systems

Unlike a grid-tied system where the power flowing through the inverter is limited to the capacity of the array, a stand alone system's inverter must handle all loads within the building.

An inverter with a 4,000 W continuous load rating may actually deliver 8,000 W for several seconds under surge conditions. The wire in the inverter output circuit must be rated to handle the maximum current that can flow through the circuit, plus the 1.25 safety adjustment.

So the ampacity for a stand alone inverter with an 8,000 surge rating must be sized at:

$$8,000 \text{ W} / 240 \text{ Vac} = 33.33 \text{ A} \times 1.25 = 41.67 \text{ A}$$

So in this example, the minimum wire used in the inverter output circuit must be rated at least 45 amps, unless the circuit is limited by a breaker or fuse. For example, the breaker connecting the circuit to the service panel might be limited to 40 amps. This limitation would then allow smaller wire, but will also limit the ability of the inverter to handle severe surges.

Three-Phase Inverter Output Currents

Calculating the current limits on inverter output circuits in systems using three-phase inverters is a bit more complex than calculations required for single-phase systems.

Wye three-phase systems can make connections between two phases, and also between a single phase and a common neutral point, as illustrated in Figure 9-14.

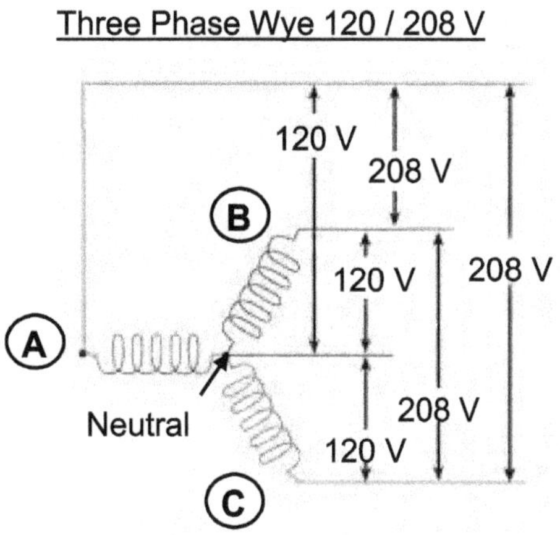

In a three-phase power source, there are three AC currents, each separated by a 120° phase angle. The currents are not added together as they would be in a single-phase system, but are calculated using the square root of three (√3).

Three Phase Wye 120 / 208 V

FIGURE 9-14: THREE-PHASE WYE 120/208 V DIAGRAM

As a result, when a three phase inverter is connected (phase-to-phase), the ampacity is calculated using the formula:

Phase Current =Inverter Output / V (phase-to-phase) / square root of 3

So if a 30 kW three-phase inverter was interconnected at 208 Vac (phase-to-phase) system as indicated in Figure 7-17, the ampacity would would be:

30,000 W (inverter) / 208 V / 1.732 (square root of 3) = 83.27 A

The minimum ampacity of the wire connected to the unit would then be multiplied by the 1.25 safety factor, or 83.27 A x 1.25 = 104 amps.

Wiring Multiple inverters

With grid-tied inverters, it is possible to combine the output together to increase the amount of energy available to the home or business. For example, a customer may decide to incorporate three 10 kW inverters into the system rather than selecting one larger 30 kW inverter.

While it is possible to configure a stand alone system in a similar manner, it is critical that the inverters used be **stackable** (designed to be compatible with each other). There will also likely be a **master-slave** relationship between the inverters, where one (the master) will set the voltage and frequency, with all other inverters keying off this setting (in slave mode).

STACKABLE

MASTER-SLAVE

Grid-tied inverters are designed to independently sync to the grid. If there are three grid-tied inverters, all three of them are looking for the frequency of the grid power independently. They are in no way aware that any other inverter exists within the system. The master-slave relationship ensures that all three inverters are producing at the fame voltage and frequency.

Multiple inverters are typically connected together in an **inverter subpanel**. Each inverter is connected to an individual breaker. A combined breaker then feeds to the load-side connection in the main electrical panel, or to a supply-side connection.

For example, assume a situation where three 5 kW inverters are connected in parallel. The maximum current output of each unit is 24 amps.

Each inverter would be fed to a breaker rated at 30 amps (24 A x 1.25). A 90 A breaker connects the subpanel to the main electrical panel.

The subpanel rating would have to be rated to handle the combined amperage of all the breakers feeding power to the subpanel. In this case it would be 3 (inverters) x 30 A (breaker size for each inverter) + 90 A (breaker size coming from the main service panel and ultimately from the grid).

Wiring for Generators

The wiring, breakers and disconnects in the circuit that runs from the generator to the inverter should be sized in a manner similar to any conventional AC load circuit.

The maximum current rating of the generator should be multiplied by the NEC safety factor of 1.25 when sizing the wires.

For example, assume a Generac 22 kW backup generator is connected to the system. According to the generator's specification sheet, the maximum current generated by the unit is 92 A.

$$92 \text{ A (maximum from generator)} \times 1.25 \text{ (safety factor)} = 115 \text{ A}$$

Checking the NEC ampacity table, #1/0 AWG wire (at 60°C) is rated for 125 A (#1 AWG is only rated for 110 A). So this is the minimum size wire that should be connected to the unit. Any fuses, breakers and disconnects should be rated for 125 A as well.

Connecting to the Utility

The inverter output circuit terminates at the point where the PV system connects to the electrical service from the utility. These can either be load side connections, or **supply side connections** (often referred to as line side connections).

Load Side Connections

For most residential and smaller commercial systems, the connection to the utility service will be made on the customer side of the main disconnect. This is referred to as a load side connection.

In most cases, this takes place by simply adding a breaker to the main service panel and connecting the conductors from the inverter to this breaker. Since more power is now entering the service panel box than when it was only being supplied from the utility, care must be taken to ensure that the current rating of the box (the busbar rating) is sufficient enough to handle the increased load.

If the sum of the breakers from the utility and the PV system do not exceed the busbar rating of the service panel, then the connection may be made anywhere on the panel where there is a free space for a double pole breaker.

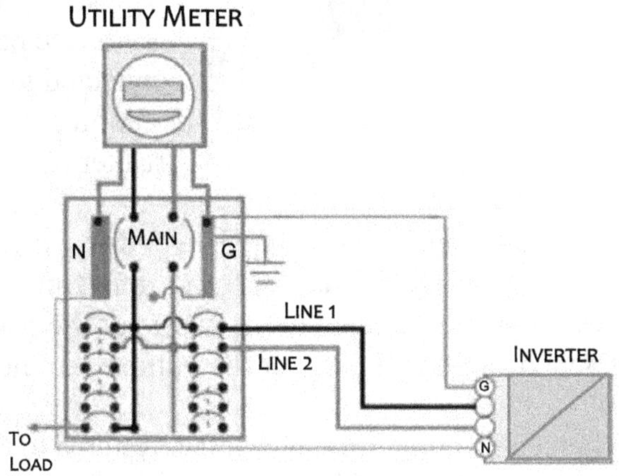

Scenario 1: A customer's existing service panel is rated at 200 amps. The service from the utility (the rating at the main disconnecting breaker) is 100 amps. The breaker from the PV system has been sized and determined to be 20 amps.

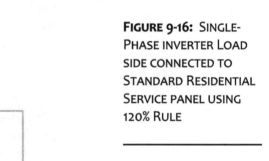

FIGURE 9-15: SINGLE-PHASE INVERTER LOAD SIDE CONNECTED TO STANDARD RESIDENTIAL SERVICE PANEL

Solution: Not a problem. The combination of the two systems feeding the service panel are 120 amps (100 A from the utility, 20 A from the PV system), which is less than the rating of the service panel box. The PV system can be connected to any space on the busbar where there is space for the double pole breaker feeding power from the inverter, as illustrated in Figure 9-15.

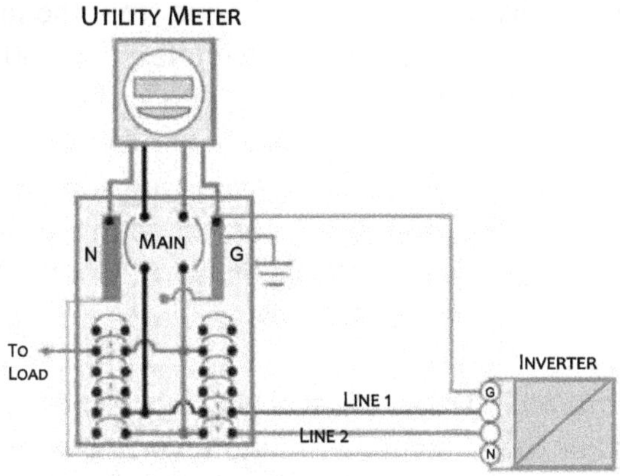

The NEC allows load side connections up to 120% of the busbar rating of the service panel (Article 705.12(2)(d)). If this **120% Rule** is used in the connection, however, the point of connection of the PV system must be located at the opposite end of the busbar from the main disconnect, as indicated in Figure 9-16.

FIGURE 9-16: SINGLE-PHASE INVERTER LOAD SIDE CONNECTED TO STANDARD RESIDENTIAL SERVICE PANEL USING 120% RULE

120% RULE

Scenario 2: A customer's existing service panel is rated at only 100 amps. The service from the utility (the rating at the main disconnecting breaker) is

MAIN   100 amps. The two-pole breaker from the PV system has been
sized and determined to be 20 amps.

PV CONNECTION

FIGURE 9-17: PV SYSTEM
LOAD SIDE CONNECTED
TO A MAIN LUG LOAD
CENTER AT OPPOSITE END
OF BUSBAR FROM MAIN
DISCONNECT

Solution: The 120% Rule will allow this
connection. The combination of the two
systems feeding the service panel are 120
amps (100 A from the utility, 20 A from the
PV system), which is 120% of the rating of
the service panel box. The PV system can be
connected to the busbar, but only at a
location at the opposite end of the main
breaker (as illustrated in Figure 9-17).

Locating the breakers at opposite ends ensures that no point on the busbar will
be subject to the full sum of the current from the supplying breakers. If the
main breaker is located in the center of the panel, then the PV system can be
attached at either the top or the bottom (but not both from multiple inverters).

When connecting three-phase PV systems to three-phase service panels, the
120% rule is applied in exactly the same manner as with a single-phase
system. The sum of the breakers feeding the panel (from the inverter and the
main) cannot exceed 120% of the busbar rating of the service panel. The
NEC also allows for a load-side connection within the service panel if the sum
of the breakers feeding the loads, plus the input breaker from the inverter, do
not exceed the rating of the main breaker.

For example, if a 100-amp service panel were fed by 100-amp service from
the utility and a 40-amp service from the inverter, as long as the sum of the
breakers serving the load were less than 60 amps, a load-side connection
could be made within this panel

Scenario 3: A customer's existing service panel is rated at only 100 amps.
The service from the utility (the rating at the main disconnecting breaker) is
100 amps. The two-pole breaker from the PV system has been sized and
determined to be 30 amps.

Solution: The 120% Rule has been exceeded and this connection cannot be
made in the main distribution panel as described. The combination of the two
systems feeding the service panel are 130 amps (100 A from the utility, 30 A
from the PV system), which is 130% of the rating of the service panel box.

One option would be to replace the main breaker with a 90 amp breaker,
reducing the total load to the service panel to within the 120% limit.

MAIN LUG LOAD
CENTER

FEED-THRU LUGS

Another solution would be to install a **main lug load center**, connecting it to
the main service panel through the **feed-thru lugs** at the bottom of the unit. A

main lug load center, often called a **secondary load center**, is similar to the main panel, but does not have a main disconnect. Connect the PV system within an appropriately rated secondary load center, rather than the main service panel, as illustrated in Figure 9-18.

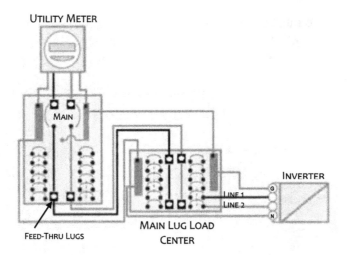

FIGURE 9-18: PV SYSTEM LOAD SIDE CONNECTED TO A MAIN LUG LOAD CENTER CONNECTED TO THE MAIN SERVICE PANEL THROUGH FEED-THRU LUGS

Grounding in Secondary Load Center

In the main distribution panel, the neutral conductors are bonded to the equipment grounding system (this is why the neutral is referred to as the grounded conductor). It is common to see ground wires placed on the neutral busbar and vice versa.

However in secondary load centers (subpanels) it is important to physically isolate the neutrals from the grounds. So ensure that terminations are made on the appropriate busbars and that the two are not bonded together.

Scenario 4: A customer's existing service panel is rated at 400 amps. The service from the utility (the rating at the main disconnecting breaker) is 400 amps, 120/208 V three-phase. The three-pole breaker from the PV system has been sized and determined to be 55 amps.

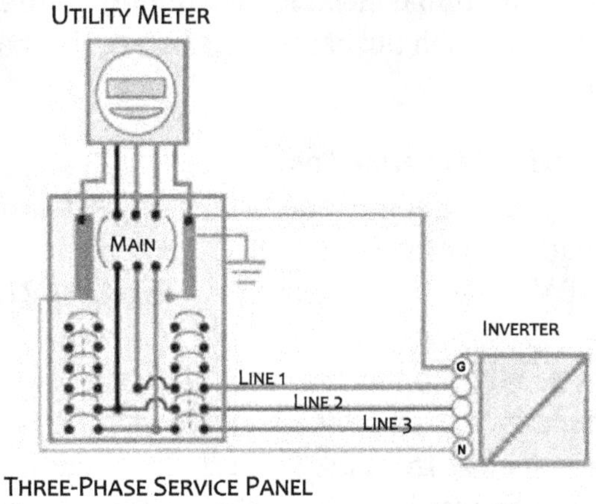

FIGURE 9-19: THREE-PHASE INVERTER LOAD SIDE CONNECTED TO A THREE-PHASE SERVICE PANEL

Solution: The 120% Rule will allow this connection. The combination of the two systems feeding the service panel are 455 amps (400 A from the utility, 55 A from the PV system), which is below 120% of the rating of the service panel box. The PV system can be connected to the busbar, but still should be at a location at the opposite end of the main breaker, as illustrated in Figure 9-19.

If multiple single phase inverters are to be connected to a three-phase service panel, this situation presents another challenge. The two hot wires of a single phase inverter are connected to two of the three phase lines from the utility.

Care must be taken to balance these incoming lines across all three phases. Most utilities require that no one phase in the system be supplied with 6,000 watts more or less than any other phase.

FIGURE 9-20: THREE SINGLE-PHASE INVERTERS LOAD SIDE CONNECTED TO A THREE-PHASE SERVICE PANEL

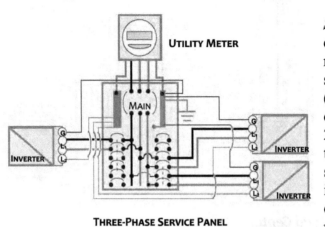

THREE-PHASE SERVICE PANEL

Scenario 5: A customer's existing service panel is rated at 400 amps. The service from the utility (the rating at the main disconnecting breaker) is 200 amps, 120/208 V three-phase. Three single-phase (208 V) inverters will be connected to the service panel. The three-pole breaker from each inverter has been sized and determined to be 35 amps.

Solution: The combination of the four systems feeding the service panel are 305 amps (200 A from the utility, 35 A from each of the three inverters), which is below the rating of the service panel box. The PV system can be connected to the busbar, in the fashion illustrated in Figure 9-20.

Care must be made to balance the connections between the three phases of the system. Imbalanced loads are limited to 3%. Note that two connections are made to each busbar within the service panel in this example, balancing the load.

Load Side Feeder Connection

LOAD SIDE FEEDER CONNECTION

A feeder circuit is one that connects the main service panel to a secondary load center (a subpanel). It may be desirable to tap into this circuit to connect a PV system, as illustrated in Figure 9-21.

FEEDER CIRCUIT

When this connection is made, the existing **feeder circuit**'s current has now been increased by the amps feeding into it from the inverter. So the feeder conductors from the point of connection to the subpanel, and the subpanel must be rated to:

Feeder Breaker + (Inverter Output x 1.25 Safety Margin)

For example, if the feeder breaker was rated at 100 A, and the Inverter output current is 35 A, then the conductors and the subpanel must be rated at:

100 A (feeder breaker) + [35 A (inverter output) x 1.25] = 143.75 A

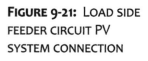

FIGURE 9-21: LOAD SIDE
FEEDER CIRCUIT PV
SYSTEM CONNECTION

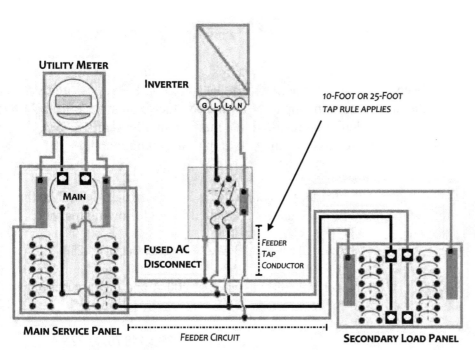

If it is not practical to increase the conductor size of the feeder circuit, or to change out an existing subpanel, then the designer may opt to reduce the size of the feeder breaker to accommodate the inverter (if the loads served from the subpanel allow for this reduction) or incorporate an overcurrent protection device between the point of connection and the subpanel, reducing the current to original levels to the subpanel.

When sizing the conductors between the inverter and the AC disconnect, simply multiply the inverter's output current by the safety margin of 1.25. The overcurrent protection device located in the AC disconnect will protect this portion of the system from any current effects of service from the utility.

However, the portion of the circuit from the AC disconnect to the tap may be subject to higher currents present on the feeder circuit should a fault occur.

For this reason, the conductor must be sized according to the **10-foot tap rule** or the **25-foot tap rule**, whichever applies.

10-FOOT TAP RULE

25-FOOT TAP RULE

FEEDER TAP
CONDUCTOR

10-Foot Tap Rule
If the length of the **feeder tap conductor**, the wire that connects the tap to the AC disconnect, is less than 10 feet, then the minimum current rating must be calculated in the following manner:

10% x [Feeder Breaker + (Inverter Output x 1.25)]

For example, if the feeder breaker was rated at 200 A and the inverter output current was 15 A, then:

$$10\% \times [200\ A + (15\ A \times 1.25)] = 10\% \times 218.75\ A = 21.875\ A$$

Had the 10% rule not applied, the ampacity calculation for this circuit would have been 15 A (inverter output current) x 1.25 = 18.75 A. With the 10% rule, the new minimum ampacity for the conductor must be at least 21.875 A. Had the 10% calculation resulted in a number smaller than 18.75 A (in this example), then the larger of the two amp ratings would apply.

25-Foot Tap Rule

If the length of the feeder tap conductor is between 10-25 feet, then the minimum current rating must be calculated in the following manner:

$$33.33\%\ (1/3) \times [\text{Feeder Breaker} + (\text{Inverter Output} \times 1.25)]$$

So again, if the feeder breaker was rated at 200 A and the inverter output current was 15 A, then:

$$33.33\% \times [200\ A + (15\ A \times 1.25)] = 33.33\% \times 218.75\ A = 72.9\ A$$

The longer the conductor, the more resistance. This increased resistance will impact the ability of the feeder breaker to trip in the event of a fault, so the conductor must be larger to avoid potential damage.

Except in the most rare of situations, no tap conductor located inside a building and incorporated within a PV system should be longer than 25 feet.

Supply Side Connections

Connecting the PV system somewhere between the main disconnect and the utility meter (or the utility's demarcation point) is referred to as a supply side, or line side connection.

Local utility requirements will govern where supply side PV connections can be made. The utility must be notified to turn off power to the facility before the connection is made.

Some reasons to opt for supply side connection may include:
- undersized service panel (does not qualify for the 120% Rule),
- service panel may incorporate a main breaker with ground fault protection (GFPE) that does not allow back-fed circuits. Connecting load side will damage the main breaker,
- the utility may require it,
- larger systems can be accommodated,
- penetrating the wall to make a connection in the service panel may be difficult and/or costly.

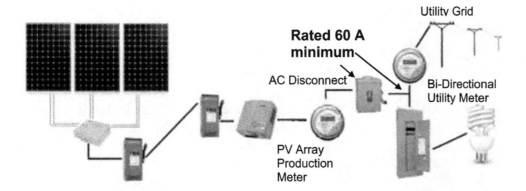

FIGURE 9-22: SUPPLY SIDE GRID CONNECTION

When connected supply side, the PV system is considered an additional service at the facility, and is therefore subject to the NEC provision that all service connections be rated at a minimum of 60 amps.

The conductors, as well as the PV system disconnect, must be rated for at least 60 amps, even if the anticipated load is below that threshold, as shown in Figure 9-22.

Insulated piercing connectors, or **taps**, as shown in Figure 9-23, allow the connection from the PV array to be "spliced" to an existing conductor coming from the utility without having to cut or disconnect the existing conductor. However, making these connections to live wires is not a recommended (or safe) practice.

FIGURE 9-23: INSULATED PIERCING CONNECTOR

(FROM RITELITE SYSTEMS LTD)

TAP

Such connections are routine in residential systems when the system will exceed the busbar rating. These are typically made within the service panel enclosure but on the supply side of the main disconnect, . An example is pictured in Figure 9-24.

It is more common, however, in supply side connected PV systems to cut into the conduit between the main disconnect and the meter and install a junction box where the PV system can be connected to the conductors from the utility, as shown in Figure 9-25.

FIGURE 9-24: LINE TAP SUPPLY SIDE CONNECTION ABOVE THE MAIN BREAKER IN A RESIDENTIAL SERVICE PANEL

(FROM CIVIC SOLAR)

When installed in this manner, the AC disconnect for the PV system is located between this connection point and the inverter(s).

The wiring and disconnect should be sized to handle at least 125% of the maximum potential current leaving the inverter(s). Note that this current is based on the capacity of the inverter, not the array to which it is attached.

At minimum, in this example, this new connection must use 60 A rated conductors and a 60 A fused disconnect. The conductors and disconnect can, however, be sized up to the amp rating of the existing service from the utility.

The conductors between the AC disconnect and the tap are unprotected service-entrance conductors. They are subject to all the same fault currents that might affect the existing service-entrance conductors. So it is recommended that the conductors between the point of connection and the first overcurrent protection device (usually in the system AC disconnect) be sized to match the service-conductors coming from the utility.

The first overcurrent protection device (usually within the AC disconnect) must be located within 10 feet of the point of connection to the utility service.

Labeling Wires

Before pulling wires, ensure that they are properly labeled. This practice will save time and money during installation and has the potential to avoid serious and dangerous errors during the connection process.

The NEC requires the identification of wiring during electrical installation, but it doesn't specify methods or materials to use. So the designer/installer is on their own in developing a process that works well for the site.

NEC 690.31(B)(1) states that all PV system circuit conductors must be identified at all accessible points of termination, connection and splices.

The steps involved in a good wire identification system may include:

- naming/numbering scheme from the owner or designer (if available),

- create a system that makes logical sense given the complexity of the system installed. For a very basic residential system, the labeling might simply identify the string and polarity for a conductor entering the combiner box (ie. STR2 -POS). For more complex systems the identification will of course become much more complicated.

- create a master index for the identification system on the project drawings,

- temporarily label the conductors before pulling. Stagger the labels when pulling multiple wires so they do not "bunch up" and cause a problem during the pull.

- use the right label for the job. There are a number of systems on the market that print labels for this purpose. Most are adhesive in nature that can be printed on a standard computer printer, but some print on heat shrink (as illustrated in Figure 9-26) that provide a permanent and professional identification system.

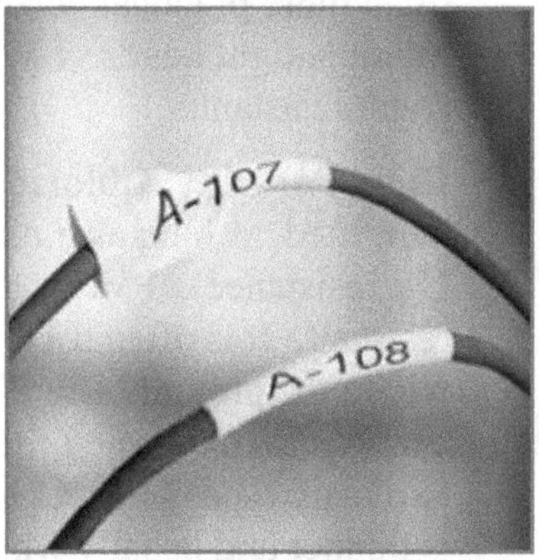

FIGURE 9-26: HEAT SHRINK WIRE LABELS

- apply the permanent label as each wire is cut and terminated..

Raceways and Conduit

Except for the PV source circuit, where pre-connectored pigtails link the panels together, the wire used in a PV system should be contained within raceways to protect it from exposure to the elements, contact from other conductors or grounds, or contact with humans and/or animals. A raceway may include conduits, tubing and square wireways.

There are essentially five types of conduit permitted by the NEC for PV systems. These include:

- **Electrical Metallic Tubing (EMT):** This is a thin-walled metal tubing that is easy to bend, inexpensive and widely available. For this reason it is used in the vast majority of PV installations, particularly for the PV output circuit. EMT fittings are typically either compression or set screw attached.

> ELECTRICAL METALLIC TUBING (EMT)

- **Rigid Metal Conduit (RMC)**. RMC is a thick-walled, rigid galvanized steel raceway, almost always made of galvanized steel. The end of each section is threaded, and require threaded couplings during assembly. It is much heavier than EMT and more difficult to bend. RMC also requires field threading when sections are cut, as illustrated in Figure 9-27. RMC does, however, provide a

> RIGID METAL CONDUIT (RMC)

FIGURE 9-27: FIELD THREADING RMC CONDUIT

higher level of physical protection to the wires than EMT. The cost of RMC is about twice that of EMT.

FLEXIBLE METALLIC TUBING (FMT)

- **Flexible Metallic Tubing (FMT):** FMT is a ribbed tubing which, as the name indicates, is quite flexible. This is more expensive than EMT but is often more practical when working in confined spaces or dealing with multiple tight bends. FMT is permitted only within buildings, as it is not water resistant.

RIGID POLYVINYL CHLORIDE (PVC)

- **Rigid Polyvinyl Chloride (PVC):** PVC non-metallic conduit is permitted, as long as it meets all the proper rating requirements (such as UV resistance). PVC is also inexpensive, widely available and moisture resistant. It is often used for PV output circuits where the cable is buried within the ground. But PVC expands and contracts when the temperature changes, so expansion fittings are required for long cable runs. There are two main types of PVC, **schedule 40** PVC and **schedule 80**. Schedule 40 is thinner and usually white in color. Schedule 80 is made with thicker walls (although the outside dimensions are the same) and is usually a dark gray color. PVC fittings attach with glue-like solvents.

SCHEDULE 40

SCHEDULE 80

LIQUID-TIGHT FLEXIBLE NONMETALLIC

- **Liquid-Tight Flexible Nonmetallic (LFNC):** LFNC is the flexible partner for PVC, this watertight conduit is appropriate for outdoor applications within confined spaces where flexibility is required.

The type of conduit selected is largely a factor of the environment into which it will be placed. High humidity, underground, or other areas subject to corrosion often use PVC conduit. For systems in areas where the conduit is exposed and there are wide swings in temperature and/or UV exposure may find that EMT or RMC conduit is the best choice.

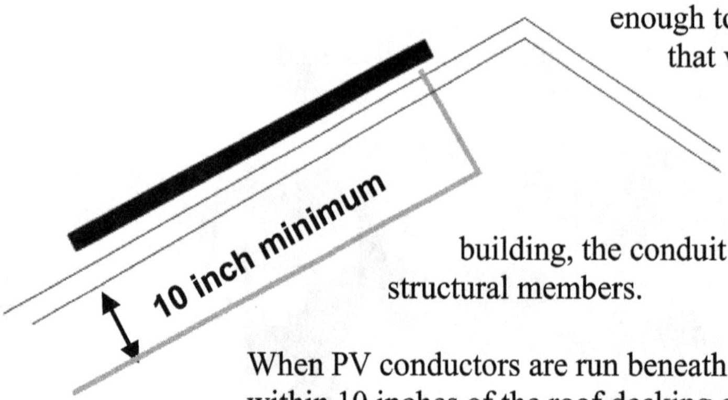

FIGURE 9-28: MAINTAIN 10 INCH MINIMUM CLEARANCE DISTANCE BETWEEN ROOF DECK AND CONDUIT

The NEC requires that all DC circuits located inside a building must be placed within metal conduit (not PVC). Metal Clad (MC) cable is also permitted for indoor DC circuits. Metal or PVC is allowed for outdoor DC circuits as well as all AC circuits.

Installing Conduit

When selecting the size of the conduit, it is important to make sure it is large enough to handle the anticipated number of wires that will be housed inside the conduit.

Metallic conduit should be used within enclosed spaces such as inside buildings and structures. Inside a building, the conduit should be routed along building structural members.

10 inch minimum

When PV conductors are run beneath roofs, they should not be installed within 10 inches of the roof decking or sheathing, as illustrated by Figure 9-

TABLE 9-9: NUMBER OF CONDUCTORS PERMITTED IN CONDUIT

EMT Conduit Trade Size	Wire Size (THHN & THWN)								
	10 AWG	8 AWG	6 AWG	4 AWG	3 AWG	2 AWG	1 AWG	1/0	0/4
1/2"	5	3	2	1	1	1	1	1	
3/4"	10	6	4	2	1	1	1	1	1
1"	16	9	7	4	3	3	1	1	1
1 1/2"	38	22	16	10	8	7	5	4	2
2"	63	36	26	16	13	11	8	7	4

28. This is to avoid a situation where a firefighter may cut through the roof of a building and hit energized wires. They should be installed on the underside of support members where possible.

On flat roofs, conduit runs between sub arrays and to DC combiner boxes should be designed and installed to follow the shortest path between the two connection points. With this goal in mind, DC junction/combiner boxes should be located as close as possible to the array.

Conduit Fill
The space within conduits are never completely filled with cables for a number of reasons.

These include:
- to allow for heat from the conductors to dissipate,
- for ease of pulling (both during the initial pull and later, should more conductors need to be added).

The NEC allows that a conduit be filled to a maximum of 26% of its capacity during its initial installation, and up to 40% fill when adding conductors to existing conduit. Calculating conduit fill can be a bit tricky. Table 9-9 can give a bit of guidance as to how many conductors can be placed in various trade sizes of EMT conduit.

Conduit Support
When supporting conduit (on a structure or rack), EMT conduit must be supported within 3 feet of each outlet box, junction box, cabinet, or fitting, and every 10 feet thereafter. Non-metallic conduit (such as PVC) requires more frequent support, as outlined in Table 7-10.

Conduit Size	Distance Between Supports
½ inch - 1 inch	3 feet
1 ¼ inch - 2 inch	5 feet
2 ½ inch - 3 inch	6 feet
3 ½ inch - 5 inch	7 feet
6 inch	6 feet

TABLE 9-10: SUPPORT DISTANCES FOR NON-METALLIC CONDUIT

FIGURE 9-29: CONDUIT EXPANSION FITTINGS, PVC (LEFT) AND EMT (RIGHT)

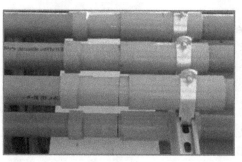 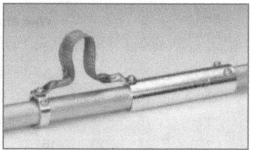

Flexible metal conduit and liquidtight flex must be supported at intervals not to exceed 4 1/ 2 feet and within 12 inches on each side of every outlet box or fitting.

When supporting loose conductors, such as within the PV source circuit under an array, they must be supported at minimum every 4 1/2 feet and within 12 inches of every box or connection. These are normally secured to support structures (such as the panel mounting rails) with the use of cable ties, velcro straps or specially designed clips.

Conduit Expansion

Non-metallic (and to a lesser extent metallic) conduits are prone to expand and contract when exposed to sunlight and/or extreme swings in temperature. Expansion fittings such as those shown in Figure 9-29 should be integrated within conduit runs to avoid damage in such instances.

For temperature swings of 100°F, which is common on rooftops, ¼ inch of expansion occurs over six feet of PVC, 16 feet of aluminum and 32 feet of steel.

Rooftop installations using PVC conduit systems will require expansion fittings for all constrained straight runs over 20 feet and require one 4-inch expansion fitting every 75 feet. EMT conduit requires expansion fittings for all runs over 100 feet, one 4-inch expansion fitting every 375 feet.

Underground Installation

The temperature changes underground are generally assumed to be relatively small. So conduit expansion and contraction is assumed not to take place in buried runs. However, if a PVC conduit is assembled in the sun, then placed in a trench, it may contract as it cools. Allow the conduit to cool to ground temperature before filling and compacting soil into the trench.

Backfill around all conduit must be smooth, granular soil with no rocks. The complete depth requirements for wire buried under ground are outlined in the NEC Table 300.5.

For photovoltaic installers, typical depth requirement for buried cable include:

- 24 inches deep for **direct buried cable** (although if at all possible, all buried cable should be in conduit),
- 18 inches deep when enclosed in PVC (in trench or under a driveway),
- 6 inches deep when enclosed in metallic conduit, 18 inches deep if running under a driveway.

Many AHJs require schedule 80 PVC where the conduit emerges from underground, whether or not there is exposure to vehicles. They may also require that RMC, rather than EMT conduit be used in locations when there are vehicles present.

The NEC requires that the location of all service conductors that are not encased in concrete must be marked with a warning tape. These tapes, as shown in Figure 9-30, should be placed in the trench at least 12 inches above the buried conduit.

FIGURE 9-30: WARNING TAPE MUST BE BURIED IN THE TRENCH 12 INCHES ABOVE BURIED CONDUIT.

As PV systems are considered a separate service, assume this provision applies to all buried conductors from the PV system.

Conduit Durability
As most PV systems are designed to last 25 years or longer, care should be used in selecting and installing conduit to ensure it lasts at least as long.

Issues include:

- UV resistance. Metal raceways do not degrade in sunlight, however PVC and liquid tight will be affected. For this reason it is recommended that metal conduit be used on rooftops or other areas that may be exposed to sunlight.

- Moisture resistance. Metal conduit may rust or corrode when exposed to moisture. Most EMT is made of galvanized metal that should resist corrosion in all but the harshest of environments (such as salt water spray at the beach).

- Fire resistance. Metal conduits will survive exposure to fire better than PVC.

Raceways

Conduits are essentially enclosed tubes. When wires are fed through them, they are physically protected from moisture, dirt, and dust. But once installed, the wiring is very difficult or impossible to access.

Cable raceways are a form of electrical conduit but are designed to allow easier access to the wiring inside after installation. Raceways, or wireways, are commonly used where access to the conductors within the raceway is

FIGURE 9-31: COVERED
CABLE RACEWAY

required to make terminations, splices, or taps to several devices at a single location.

Raceways typically cost much more than conduit, so they are typically only used for very short wire runs or in some commercial or industrial sites where the wiring is frequently revised and must be accessed relatively frequently. Both metal wireways and nonmetallic wireways are often called "troughs" or "gutters". Open cable ladder supports are often used where physical protection from the elements is not required, but the cables need substantial support.

These cable management systems come in a variety of styles and ratings.

Cable troughs are enclosures that are rated for conditions similar to other NEMA enclosure ratings (for example, NEMA 3R for outdoor wet conditions).

The may be covered or open, with covers that screw down, that lift off, or are hinged. (Figure 9-31) Some require the wire be fed through (with no accessible cover).

Raceways are manufactured in steel, aluminum, or fiber reinforced plastic (FRP), although aluminum accounts for about 70% of the cable trays used in industry.

The number and size of conductors intended and the allowable fill area for cable trays is detailed in Article 392 of the NEC.

Overfilling and improperly securing wires in cable trays can lead to a number of issues and hazards. All cable trays and their supports are rated for a specific maximum weight, based on the allowable fill area and the spacing of the supports.

Overloading the cable trays can cause the tray to fail, or weaken the supports and/or connection points. Overfilling enclosed trays can result in an excessive buildup of heat within the tray, resulting in damage or even fire.

The Cable Tray Institute indicates that cable trays should not be filled in excess of 40-50% of the inside area of the tray or of the maximum weight based on the cable tray specifications.

Additionally, cables in trays can be damaged by improperly securing and installing other cables and wires in the same cable tray.

As is the case with conduit systems, wires from different circuits cannot be placed within the same raceway, unless separated by a partition (NEC

690.31(B). The raceway must also be properly supported and metallic raceways must be bonded and grounded.

If AC and DC conductors are contained within the same raceway, they must be grouped and separated, at intervals not less then 6 feet (1.8 meters).

Grounding and Bonding the System

Bonding the conductive parts of the system together and connecting them to ground is an extremely important part of a PV system design and installation.

IT IS A MATTER OF LIFE AND SAFETY.

This is an area that really requires the expertise of someone who is knowledgeable in all things electrical. While the novice installer/designer (after studying the requirements of the NEC) may be able to design and install the grounding system – it is advisable at a minimum to have it inspected by an expert. Any flaw in the system could result in fire, serious injury, or even death.

While a properly installed bonding and grounding system will provide some limited lightning protection to the system, its main purpose is to provide some protection from shocks to any person who may come in contact with an exposed metal component that may have inadvertently become energized.

Bonding

All metal parts of the system, such as the aluminum frame of PV panels, the racks, metal conduit, metal disconnect boxes, etc, must be bonded together. Once electrical continuity has been established between all the metal in the system, it is then connected to the grounding system.

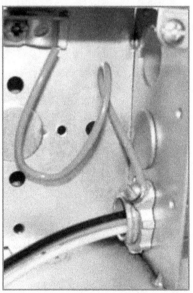

FIGURE 9-32: BONDING JUMPER ON CONDUIT LOCKNUT

Metal raceways operating at less than 250 volts to ground shall be bonded to the box or cabinet. For a proper bond, do one or more of the following:

- use listed fittings,
- for steel RMC or IMC, use two locknuts: one inside and one outside of boxes and cabinets. Some locknuts, such as the one pictured in Figure 9-32, incorporate a ground connector to ensure a more robust bond between the conduit and the box,
- use fittings, such as EMT connectors, with shoulders that seat firmly against the box or cabinet, with one locknut on the inside of boxes and cabinets.

BONDING JUMPER

EQUIPMENT GROUND CONDUCTOR (EGC)

FIGURE 9-34: BONDING RAILS WITH A BARE COPPER #6 AWG WIRE USING STAINLESS STEEL LUG

FIGURE 9-35: EQUIPMENT BONDING WITHIN DISCONNECT

EQUIPMENT GROUNDING

- Be sure to remove all paint where the locknut connects to the box, to ensure a continuous ground path. Repaint or cover any exposed area after installation is completed.

If multiple rails are required, then they must be bonded together with a **bonding jumper** such as the example illustrated in Figure 9-33.

Equipment grounding conductors (EGC) are then used to connect the various metal components to the grounding system. It is common to use #6 AWG bare copper wires for equipment grounding conductors, as shown in Figure 9-34.

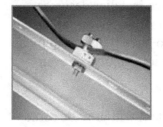

The NEC requires that equipment grounding conductors smaller than #6 AWG must be protected from physical harm by routing them inside raceways or conduits (NEC 250.120).

The equipment grounding conductor continues from the array, to the combiner box, and then along with the current carrying conductors within the conduit.

At each junction box or disconnect, the EGC bonds to the metal box (as shown in Figure 9-35), then continues on until it is terminated at the inverter. This portion of the bonding and grounding system is referred to as **equipment grounding.**

The equipment grounding system continues from the AC side of the inverter, bonding to any metal boxes or disconnects it may pass through, and terminates at the grounding busbar in the electrical service panel.

The sizing for equipment ground conductors can be found in NEC Table 250.122, a portion of which is recreated in Table 9-11.

Challenges in Equipment Grounding

Most panels and rails have an anodized surface that is non-conductive. Care must be taken to break through this layer to the metal surface below. It may require that the metal surface be prepared, removing any paint or other material that will prevent a solid electrical bond.

A bond between two different metals (such as aluminum and copper) will suffer **galvanic corrosion**, weakening the bond over time. Stainless steel can be used to connect these dissimilar materials.

Rating or Overcurrent in circuit ahead of Equipment (not exceeding)	Size (AWG)	
	Copper	Aluminum
15 Amps	14 AWG	12 AWG
20 Amps	12 AWG	10 AWG
60 Amps	10 AWG	8 AWG
100 Amps	8 AWG	6 AWG
200 Amps	6 AWG	4 AWG
300 Amps	4 AWG	2 AWG
400 Amps	3 AWG	1 AWG

TABLE 9-11: MINIMUM SIZE OF EQUIPMENT GROUNDING CONDUCTORS

(FROM NEC TABLE 250.122)

GALVANIC CORROSION

Take care that the copper grounding conductors do not come in contact with the aluminum frames of the panels (except at the rated connection point), or both the frame and the grounding conductor will corrode over time.

Equipment grounding is difficult to do correctly, making an improperly grounded system the most common of installation mistakes. It is also time consuming (adding to the installed cost of the system).

Installers must use connectors that are listed for grounding connections.

System Grounding

The grounding busbar in the existing service panel box should already be connected with a **ground electrode conductor (GEC)** to an existing AC **grounding electrode** (commonly referred to as a **ground rod**).

GROUND ELECTRODE CONDUCTOR (GEC)

GROUNDING ELECTRODE

GROUND ROD

The GEC must be a minimum #8 AWG copper or #6 AWG aluminum, regardless of the size wire used in the remainder of the PV system. But if the GEC is not contained within conduit (which is most common), then the unprotected conductor must be at minimum #6 AWG (copper or aluminum).

The GEC is connected to a grounding electrode. This grounding electrode is typically an 8-foot-long copper rod that is driven into the earth, leaving only an inch or two exposed at the surface. Connections are made with clamps designed for this purpose.

The NEC requires that a single ground rod have a maximum resistance to ground of 25 ohms (NEC 250.53(A)(2)).

When installing a second or supplementary grounding electrode, it must be located at least 6 feet (1.8 m) away from the existing grounding electrode. This increases the efficiency of the grounding electrode system.

The two grounding electrodes must then be bonded together with a bonding jumper. The bonding jumper that connects the two electrodes together must be sized at least as large as the largest grounding electrode conductor (GEC).

FIGURE 9-36: MULTIPLE
DC GROUNDING
ELECTRODE CONDUCTOR
TAPS

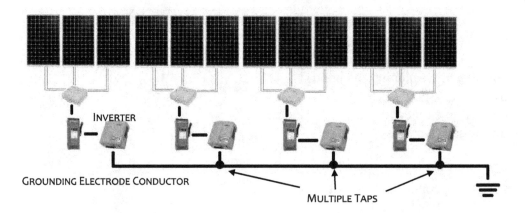

Once bonded, the two electrodes are considered a single unit (as far as the code is concerned).

Many jurisdictions require multiple ground rods (based on area soil testing). Many installers opt to install multiple ground rods as a matter of practice simply because it is cheaper than conducting a soil resistivity test.

GROUND LOOP

There should be only one connection to ground in a system. By connecting to a common grounding electrode, a **ground loop** is avoided. A ground loop or earth loop occurs when two points of a circuit intended to be at the same ground reference potential are at different potentials. Ground loops are a major cause of noise, hum, and interference in audio, video, and computer systems. By connecting the two electrodes together, the potential is balanced.

Also note that ground mounted systems require a supplemental grounding electrode be installed at the array. This electrode does NOT have to be bonded to the existing AC grounding electrode if it is located an adequate distance away from the existing electrode. Just what is considered "adequate" is unclear and will be determined by the inspector.

DC Grounding Electrode Conductor Taps
In larger systems with multiple inverters, it is permitted for several inverters to use the same grounding electrode conductor (GEC). Normally these inverters are connected to the GEC with approved taps, as illustrated in Figure 9-36.

The size of the tap conductors as well as the GEC must be as large as the largest conductor feeding the DC system.

Grounding Electrodes
In residential installations, by far the most common form of grounding electrode installed is the ground rod. Ground rods must be at least 8 feet long; is not less than 5/8 inch in diameter. They can be stainless steel, steel coated with either copper or zinc.

If a ground rod cannot be driven perpendicular to the ground or at an greater than 45°, it can be buried. Buried ground rods must be located at a depth of at least 30 inches.

While ground rods are the most common of grounding electrodes, other forms are permitted. NEC Section 250.52(A), allows the following options in addition to ground rods:

- Metal underground water pipes that come in contact with the ground for 10 feet or more. If a grounding electrode connection is made to a water pipe inside a building, it must occur within the first 5 feet from the pipe's point of entrance into the building.

- The structural steel of a building is permitted provided at least one structural member is in contact with the ground for at least 10 feet, or it is bolted to a concrete-encased electrode.

- Concrete-encased electrodes are permitted provided that each electrode is at least 20 feet long and is made of either at least ½-inch–diameter steel or 4 AWG bare copper. This system is commonly referred to as a **Ufer ground**. Commercial structures will often tie the foundation reinforcing rebar system to a grounding connection point to create this system. As it is assumed that the Ufer system will not contain wire larger than 4 AWG, the maximum size required for the ground electrode conductor for this system must also be 4 AWG (copper).

> UFER GROUND

- Ground rings are permitted provided that each ring is at least 20 feet long and made of 2 AWG copper. The ring needs to encircle the structure at a depth of 30 inches below the surface. Ground rings are often installed around large inverter pads and serve as grounding electrodes for multiple inverters.

- Metal plates not less than two square feet and at least 0.06 inches thick (0.25 inches for nonferrous metals) are also permitted. These plates must be made of iron or steel and must be buried at least 30 inches deep.

- In some cases, buried metal structures such as tanks, pipes and well casings are also permitted.

Grounding Clamps

Grounding clamps are used to connect the grounding electrode conductor to the ground rod. They come in two common styles, the acorn clamp and the bonding clamp (Figure 9-37).

An **acorn clamp** is an oval-shaped clamp with a bolt used to tighten it to the ground rod. An acorn clamp is the most commonly used clamp for ground rod connections and is

FIGURE 9-37: ACORN (LEFT) AND BRASS-TOOTHED BONDING CLAMP (RIGHT)

> ACORN CLAMP

approved for direct burial applications.

BONDING CLAMP

The brass-toothed **bonding clamp** is a two-piece clamp that has two setscrews used to secure it to the ground rod. It also has a center point with a hole to mount the wire and a set screw to tighten the wire.

Floating Ground

EARTH GROUND

FLOATING GROUND

If the electrical grounding system is physically connected to earth, then it is considered an **earth ground**. But there is another type of grounding system that is sometimes incorporated into a PV system - this is known as a **floating ground**.

A floating ground is a type of ground in which the ground doesn't have a physical connection to the earth, but simply serves as a type of 0 V reference line that serves as a return path for current.

Circuits powered by batteries generally do not have an earth ground. Therefore the batteries do not have have a physical connection to the earth. In this case it will be necessary to incorporate a floating ground.

GALVANIC ISOLATION

Galvanic isolation is used where two or more electric circuits with different ground potentials are connected together. This can happen when an earth grounded PV system is connected to a floating grounded battery bank.

This is not generally an issue with AC coupled systems, as the isolation happens automatically within the inverter.

In DC coupled systems where the battery bank is added to an existing array, it is necessary to install a DC-DC converter is to adjust for the voltage differences between the PV array and the battery. By incorporating a galvanically isolated DC-DC converter, the device can also isolate the different grounding potentials that may be present.

Ground Faults

When current is flowing through the grounding and bonding system, there is a problem. Somehow an electric current is energizing parts of the system not intended to be energized. This is known as a **ground fault**.

GROUND FAULT

GROUND FAULT CURRENT PATH

The purpose of a bonding and grounding system is to provide an effective **ground fault current path**, creating a low-impedance path for the ground fault current to follow from its source to the earth.

A ground fault protection device (GFPD) is required (as per NEC 690.5) for PV systems that are mounted on the roof of a dwelling unit. The purpose of a GFPD is to avoid fires and damage should large amounts of stray current find its way onto the system (through a lightning strike, for example).

In such cases, if the inverter (all grid-tied inverters should contain a GFPD) selected does not incorporate a GFPD, then an externally mounted GFPD must be installed. This GFPD device is designed to open the circuit (shut everything off) if excessive current flows through the grounded conductor.

According to the NEC, a GFPD must:
- detect ground faults in PV arrays,
- interrupt the fault current,
- indicate that a ground fault has occurred,
- disconnect the faulted part of the array.

In addition to ground fault protection, the NEC also requires that PV systems operating at 80 Vdc or more must also incorporate **arc fault protection.**

> ARC FAULT PROTECTION

When connections become corroded or are poorly installed, an arc fault may occur, resulting in a high power discharge of electricity (an arc) between the conductors. This can result in fire or damage to the system.

Most string inverters and microinverters now contain arc fault protection devices. There are also combiner box integrated solutions that contain arc fault protection available to system designers. These devices must, however, be rated for PV systems.

EMP Hardened Systems

Many solar customers install PV systems to ensure that power is available during an emergency. Some may wish to be protected even during extremely unlikely or rare power events, such as may occur during an **electromagnetic pulse (EMP).**

> ELECTROMAGNETIC PULSE (EMP)

When an EMP occurs, it disrupts the earth's magnetic field to such a great degree that it causes electrons to scatter randomly within the atmosphere. Those electrons interact with power lines and other conductive materials - resulting in power spikes. A large EMP could damage the grid as well as sensitive electronic devices.

An EMP can be caused by a number of phenomenon, but the two most likely EMP threats to the power grid are a nuclear explosion or a large solar flare.

In the event of a nuclear explosion, there will likely be many more pressing matters to worry about than whether the solar array is damaged, but **solar flares** are another matter.

> SOLAR FLARE

> CORONAL MASS EJECTION (CME)

Large solar flares, referred to as a **coronal mass ejection (CME)** sends waves of charged particles through space. They happen quite often; from between once per week to a few times a day depending on solar activity. The Aurora Borealis (Northern Lights) is a visible indication of these charged particles entering the upper atmosphere a a result of relatively minor solar flares.

If the earth happens to be in the path of a significant CME, the impact on the electrical grid could be dramatic.

The first modern recorded CME occurred in 1859. The resulting EMP caused extensive damage to large portions of the telegraph system.

In 1989 a large portion of the power grid collapse in Quebec, Canada as the result of a CME. In 2012 a very large CME just missed the earth. Officials estimated that had it struck, it would have resulted in about $2 trillion in damage to the electrical grid and taken years to repair.

Extensive studies were carried out during the height of the Cold War to determine infrastructure vulnerability in the event of an EMP. The results showed that electronics would suffer extensive damage, especially if hooked up the the grid, which would act as a massive antenna gathering in the stray current. Modern electronic devices are estimated to be about 1 million times more sensitive to EMP than the electronics of the 1960s.

According to experts, solar panels themselves are not very vulnerable to EMP damage, as they contain little in the way of electronics. However MLPEs, charge controllers and inverters would likely be damaged as a result of a CME, particularly if connected to the grid at the time of the event.

Since the electrical charge travels through the air (the electric wires simply concentrate the effect), the only way to protect electronics is to enclose the device within a **Faraday cage**.

FARADAY CAGE

A Faraday cage is essentially a container made of a conductive material that blocks out electromagnetic radiation. It works on the principle that when an electromagnetic field hits something that can conduct electricity, the charges remain on the exterior of the conductor rather than traveling inside.

A Faraday cage can be made of any material that can conduct electricity. This could be a wire mesh, metallic sheets or even aluminum foil.

In order to be effective, the isolation of the electronic device must be complete. Wires leading in and out of the cage could conduct the stray current. Also the cage should be grounded, or else the current would remain on the outside of the structure and pose a risk to people who may come in contact with it.

While an effective Faraday cage may block out harmful EMP signals, it will also block the device's ability to communicate with any WiFi device as well. Many modern solar electronics rely on this connection for troubleshooting and production reports.

While there may be no practical way of protecting a grid-tied system from EMP damage, some manufacturers do offer EMP hardened military-grade solar electronics that can be selected should the risk of an EMP be deemed a practical concern.

Chapter 9 Review Questions

1) When working with DC current, only use:
   a) stranded conductors
   b) solid conductors
   c) use solid conductors for grid tied systems and stranded for stand alone systems
   d) use either solid or stranded conductors

2) Conductors with a "-2" designation (such as USE-2) generally means that:
   a) the wire can handle 90°C continuous operating temperatures
   b) there are two conductors within the insulation sleeve
   c) the wire complies with the provisions found in NEC Article 305-2
   d) the wire is outdoor rated

3) The **NEGATIVE** conductor of a functionally grounded PV system should be color coded:
   a) red, black or any other color (other than white, gray or green)
   b) white or gray
   c) green or green with a yellow stripe
   d) no color coding is imposed on functionally grounded systems by the NEC

4) The NEC allows installers to indicate the intended color code of a wire by wrapping tape (rather than using the proper colored insulation) near each termination point when:
   a) working with DC circuits
   b) working with AC circuits
   c) for conductors smaller than #10 AWG
   d) for conductors larger than #6 AWG

5) A PV system designer is working on a ground-mounted residential system. The following factors come into play:
   - the array is 200 feet from the house
   - the PV output circuit is exactly 226 feet in length from the combiner box (where all strings are combined into a single conductor pair) to the DC disconnect
   - #10 AWG PV wire (stranded) with a rated resistance of 1.24 Ω per 1000 feet will be used in this circuit
   - the circuit will be buried
   - the array is comprised of two strings of 12 panels each, using Trina Solar 280 W monocrystalline panels with the following specifications:

Nominal Max Power (Pmax)	280 watts
Optimum Operating Voltage (Vmp)	31.7 V
Optimum Operating Current (Imp)	8.84 A
Open Circuit Voltage (Voc)	38.4 V
Short Circuit Current (Isc)	9.42 A
Module Efficiency	17.1%

What is the anticipated voltage drop of the PV output circuit?

a) 9.9 Vdc
b) 10.56 Vdc
c) 17.77 Vdc
d) 21.92 Vdc

6) Resistance from the grid in combination with resistance in the wiring of the circuits of the PV system may cause the inverter to attempt to operate at a voltage above its operating limits. This is normally the result of:

a) voltage drop
b) voltage rise
c) transient voltage
d) harmonic distortion

7) Which of the following does **NOT** have an impact on the ability of a conductor to safely carry current?

a) size of the conductor
b) conduit fill
c) exposure to sunlight
d) voltage of the circuit

8) The rating on overcurrent protection is known as:

a) ampere interrupt rating (AIR)
b) ampacity limitation rating (ALR)
c) ampacity disconnect rating (ADR)
d) ampacity trip setting (ATS)

9) A designer is working on a roof-mounted system for a distribution warehouse.

- the array will consist of 104 panels, configured into 8 strings of 13 panels each
- the strings are to be combined into a single PV output circuit, which is never exposed to sunlight
- the combiner box and the DC disconnect both have terminations rated for 90°C
- the panels to be used are Panasonic 330 W with the following ratings:

Nominal Max Power (Pmax)	330 watts
Max Power Voltage (Vmp)	58.0 V
Max Power Current (Imp)	5.70 A
Open Circuit Voltage (Voc)	69.7 V
Short Circuit Current (Isc)	6.07 A
Module Efficiency	19.7%

What is the **MINIMUM** conductor size required to handle the anticipated ampacity of the PV output circuit?

a) #10 PV wire (ampacity rating of 40 A)
b) #8 PV wire (ampacity rating of 55 A)
c) #6 PV wire (ampacity rating of 75 A)
d) #4 PV wire (ampacity rating of 95 A)

10) Any circuit breaker that will trip regardless of the direction of the current (line or load) is considered a:
   a) backfed breaker
   b) ground-fault circuit interrupter
   c) bi-directional overcurrent protection device
   d) bi-facial circuit breaker

11) The Inverter Input circuit has been sized and determined to require 42 A (with all heat and safety factors accounted for). The designer decides to use PV wire with a heat rating of 90°C. The DC disconnect and the inverter have not yet been selected. What wire size should the designer specify for this circuit?
   a) #10 AWG
   b) #8 AWG
   c) #6 AWG
   d) #4 AWG

12) A designer of a large commercial system has determined to incorporate 5 subarrays on the rooftop. Each subarray consists of 60 panels, configured into 6 strings of 10 panels each. She has opted to use Panasonic 330 W high efficiency panels with the following ratings:

Nominal Max Power (Pmax)	330 watts
Max Power Voltage (Vmp)	58.0 V
Max Power Current (Imp)	5.70 A
Open Circuit Voltage (Voc)	69.7 V
Short Circuit Current (Isc)	6.07 A

What is the potential backfed ampacity each PV source circuit should be designed to withstand in this system if no fuse or breaker is incorporated into the combiner boxes?
   a) 56.9 A
   b) 182.1 A
   c) 227.625 A
   d) 284.53 A

13) The **MINIMUM** ampacity rating of a conductor in an Inverter Output Circuit connected to a 10 kW (maximum AC output, including surge) three-phase (208 V) inverter should be:
   a) 34.7 A
   b) 48.08 A
   c) 60.09 A
   d) 75.12 A

14) A PV designer has been asked to size the battery bank input circuit conductors. It is a 48-volt system with a 650 Ah battery bank operating to a 70% DOD. The system anticipates a maximum power draw of 2400 W. It incorporates an Outback 3000 W 48-V inverter with the following specifications:

Instantaneous Power (100 ms)	6000 VA
Surge Power (5 sec)	5400 VA
Peak Power (30 min)	3200 VA
Continuous Power Rating (@ 25°C)	3000 VA
Nominal DC Input Voltage	48 Vdc
AC Output Voltage	120 Vac (100-130 Vac)
AC Output Frequency	60 Hz
Maximum Ripple	3%
Continuous AC Output Current (@ 25°C)	25 A
Typical Inverter Efficiency	93%
DC Input Voltage Range	42 to 68 Vdc

What is the **MINIMUM** ampacity rating of the conductor to be used in the Inverter Input Circuit?

a) 62.5 A
b) 84 A
c) 168 A
d) 198 A

15) Which of the following is **NOT** an advantage when using the trunk method versus the direct method when designing the wire layout of larger arrays?

a) uses less wire
b) requires less onsite labor
c) requires less advanced planning
d) simplifies the layout process

16) In a load side connection within a service panel with a busbar rating of 100 amps, service from the utility of 100 amps, and current from the inverter of 14 amps:

a) a larger service panel (200 amp-rated) must be installed
b) the 120% allows this connection anywhere within the service panel
c) the connection can be made, but only at the opposite end of the service panel away from the main breaker
d) the connection from the inverter should be made directly at the main breaker to avoid exceeding the busbar rating

17) A designer wishes to load side connect a large single-phase inverter to an existing three-phase service panel.
   a) These systems are incompatible. The designer should specify a three-phase inverter for the system.
   b) This type of connection can be made, but only through a single-phase secondary load center.
   c) The connection must be made on the supply side of the system to avoid harmonic shifts.
   d) The connection can be made as long as it complies with the 120% rule and care is taken to balance the incoming lines.

18) In sizing the battery input circuit, use the following formula:
   a) (maximum inverter rating (W)/ inverter efficiency/ lowest battery bank voltage/ AC ripple) x 1.25 (NEC safety margin)
   b) (maximum array output (W)/ battery bank nominal voltage/ AC ripple) x 1.25 (NEC safety margin) x 1.25 (solar variability margin)
   c) (maximum inverter output current output (A) / battery bank nominal voltage) x 1.25 (NEC safety margin) x 1.25 (solar variability margin)
   d) maximum inverter output current(A) x 1.25 (NEC safety margin) x 1.25 (solar variability margin)

19) Which of the following is **NOT** a cause of excess ripple within a system?
   a) nominal voltage of battery bank is not compatible with the nominal output voltage of the inverter
   b) battery cables are too long or undersized
   c) battery bank is too small
   d) battery bank is at a very low state of charge

20) The maximum ampacity output from a 208 V three-phase 15 kW (maximum AC output) inverter will be:
   a) 41.64 A
   b) 52.05 A
   c) 72.12 A
   d) 120 A

21) When working on larger systems, a designer will occasionally find that the optimal point of connection for a PV system is by connecting into the customer's electrical system at a point between the main service panel and a secondary load center (a subpanel). The link between the inverter and this connection point is called the:
   a) branch circuit connection
   b) feeder tap conductor
   c) feed-thru lug
   d) AC aggregation point

22) A designer of a large commercial system has decided to make a load side feeder connection. The design specifies that a string inverter will be connected to an AC disconnect, which is then connected to the feed circuit between the main distribution panel and the secondary load center.
- the maximum output current of the inverter is 50 A
- the breaker which connects to the secondary load center is 200 A
- the AC disconnect is rated for 100 A and is located six (6) feet from the point where it connects to the feeder circuit.

What is the minimum ampacity rating of the feeder tap conductor?
a) 26.25 A
b) 50 A
c) 87.5 A
d) 100 A

23) The designer conducts a site inspection for the system described in the previous question and finds that the only possible point of connection will actually be located 12 feet from the AC disconnect, rather than 6 feet. What is the minimum ampacity of the feeder tap given this new information?
a) 26.25 A
b) 50 A
c) 87.5 A
d) 100 A

24) When making a supply side connection between the customer's meter and the main disconnect, the conductor that connects the AC disconnect to this circuit must (at minimum) be rated:
a) at the same ampacity as the service from the utility
b) at the same ampacity as the main disconnect
c) at 60 amps
d) at the ampacity rating of the AC disconnect

25) The NEC requires that all DC circuits located within buildings:
a) be placed in metal conduit or use metal clad cable
b) be located within 10 inches of the roof decking
c) be supported every 4 ½ feet and within 12 inches of every outlet box or fitting
d) incorporate expansion fittings in high heat environments

26) Rooftop installations using PVC conduit systems with constrained straight runs over _____ require expansion fittings every 75 feet.
a) 10 feet
b) 20 feet
c) 50 feet
d) 100 feet

27) Underground cable runs should be located:
    a) 24 inches deep for direct buried cable
    b) 18 inches deep when enclosed in PVC
    c) 6 inches deep when enclosed in metallic conduit, 18 inches deep if running under a driveway
    d) all of the above

28) All equipment ground conductors smaller than _____ must be protected from physical harm by placing them in conduit or raceways.
    a) #10 AWG
    b) #8 AWG
    c) #6 AWG
    d) #4 AWG

29) When the grounding reference of two points in a circuit are at different levels of potential, this is called:
    a) a ground loop
    b) an Ufer ground
    c) a grounding jumper
    d) a ground fault

30) Which of the following will likely **NOT** be permitted as a grounding electrode for a PV system?
    a) metal underground water pipes that come in contact with the ground for 10 feet or more
    b) concrete encased ¾ inch rebar at least 20 feet in length
    c) a buried metallic abandoned gasoline tank located at least 30 inches below the surface
    d) the structural steel of a building that is in contact with the earth for at least 10 feet

31) Protecting an electrical system from possible damage from large solar flares or a nuclear explosion is known as:
    a) a coronal mass ejection
    b) being a prepper
    c) galvanic isolation
    d) EMP hardening

Chapter 10

Energy Storage Systems

Energy storage systems (ESS) integrated into a solar PV system have rapidly become the norm. From 2010 to 2020 the US PV industry saw the growth of **PV + storage** grow by an annual rate of 50% and prices decline by 88% (as shown in Figure 10-1).

While wholesale prices for lithium ion systems have declined dramatically, the retail installed cost remains stubbornly high. A 2021 study by EnergySage indicated that quoted prices for ESS systems range from $1,100 - $1,300 per kWh for residential customers.

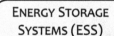

ENERGY STORAGE
SYSTEMS (ESS)

PV + STORAGE

Reasons for Integrating Storage

In the past, the cost of integrating batteries into a PV system was high enough that it rarely made sense unless the grid simply was not available. As a result, most battery banks were designed for stand-alone PV systems.

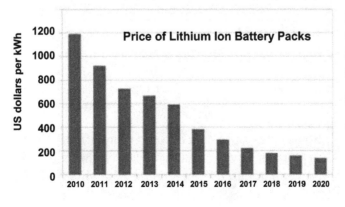

FIGURE 10-1: DECLINE IN WHOLESALE COST OF LITHIUM ION BATTERIES (2010-2020)

(DATA FROM BLOOMBERGNEF)

Declining prices and shifting billing practices by utilities have created new reasons and opportunities for integrating storage into grid-tied PV systems.

A recent (2021) industry survey by EnergySage indicated the top three reasons customers state when requesting storage be integrated into their PV system include:
- backup power: grid unreliable (64%),
- utility bill savings: time-of-use billing (47%),
- self-consumption: net metering policies (32%).

Only 11% of those responding indicated they were off grid. An additional 29% wished their system to be battery ready, but would not be installing a battery at the present time.

An Unreliable Grid

By all accounts, the US grid is becoming increasingly unreliable. In 2000, there were fewer than two dozen major power disruptions across the US. In 2020, the number surpassed 180.

High profile extreme weather events have contributed to a general unease about the future reliability of the grid. Severe hurricanes (Puerto Rico, New Orleans, Florida), freezing weather in Texas, wildfires in California; each event has resulted in PV customers rushing to purchase energy backup systems.

In 2020, utility customers on average experienced just over eight hours of power interruptions during the year, more than double the amount experienced just seven years earlier.

One big factor in the increasing unreliability is age. Much of the US transmission system was constructed just after World War II. Systems expected to last 50 years are now 70 years old and older. A 2021 report by the American Society of Civil Engineers found that 70% of transmission and distribution lines are well over their expected 50-year lifespan.

The local distribution network, which accounts for the majority of outages, is also aging.

Time-of-use Billing

TIME-OF-USE (TOU)

Increasingly utility companies are adopting **time-of-use (TOU)** billing practices. TOU rates are electricity rates that vary depending on the time of day. With TOU rates, electricity is most expensive during peak demand hours, such as the evening when most people are home.

So as battery systems become more affordable, it makes sense for customers to store energy when it is relatively cheap, and use that stored energy when power purchased from the grid is relatively expensive.

When installed for this purpose, the storage capacity can be relatively small, as the load shifting only needs to take place for a couple of hours.

Configurations that made use of short-duration batteries, in particular 2-hour batteries, provide the highest financial returns, according to a 2021 study by the Lawrence Berkeley National Laboratory. When configured in this manner, the study found that 46% the 100,000 customers surveyed would save money by installing short-duration battery systems.

Self-Consumption

When a utility's net metering policies pay retail for excess energy, then the **intermittency** of the solar energy is not a problem (assuming the grid is reliable). When the sun is shining, any excess energy is "stored" on the grid. In effect, the grid becomes a battery of unlimited capacity.

INTERMITTENCY

However, more and more utilities are changing their net metering policies, paying only a fraction of the retail price for excess energy fed back to the grid. When this is the situation, it may be economically prudent to store excess energy on site, and use it when power from the sun is not available. This process is known as **self-consumption** (consuming the stored energy on site, rather than exporting it to the grid). It is also sometimes referred to as **energy arbitrage** (especially when done in high volume).

SELF-CONSUMPTION

ENERGY ARBITRAGE

Benefits to the Grid

While the advantages of installing storage may be obvious and apparent to system owners, the widespread integration of storage capacity has a beneficial impact on the grid as a whole as well.

Ramp Rate Control

As clouds pass over solar arrays, the production from these systems fluctuate. Integration of batteries allow systems to compensate for these transient variations, reducing issues such as **voltage flicker** within the system.

VOLTAGE FLICKER

When supply drops fractionally within the system (as when a cloud passes over an array) but demand remains constant, there will be a slight drop in voltage. When supply increases, the voltage will rise. Battery systems can compensate in real time to these variations, improving power quality within the system as a whole.

Reducing/Deferring Grid Upgrade Requirements

As more power is consumed on site where it is produced, then upgrades to the wiring system of the grid can be deferred, as the transport of energy through the grid is reduced.

Increasing Grid Resiliency

Energy storage installed both in front of the meter and behind the meter increases the grid's capacity to respond to severe weather events and equipment outages.

Frequency Regulation

A stable frequency on the grid is essential to ensure the effective operation of the power systems connected to it. The frequency of the power systems is maintained by keeping a balance between demand and supply at all times.

However, frequency variations are inevitable due to the ever shifting power mismatch, especially during peak demand hours.

Grid operators can control the charging/discharging of energy storage systems through signals sent every two to four seconds - designed to balance generation and load within the system.

ESS Policy

Battery storage systems integrated into eligible wind or solar installations may qualify for the federal investment tax credit (ITC). The ITC credit for projects beginning construction in 2021 or 2022 is 26%, while the percentage for projects beginning construction in 2023 is scheduled to step down to 22%. Any project that begins construction after 2023 or is not placed in service for tax purposes prior to 2026 will only qualify for a 10% tax credit.

> 75% CLIFF RULE

One provision as to whether the ESS qualifies is known as the **75% cliff rule**. This IRS rule states that the battery system must be charged at least 75% of the time by the solar array rather than from the grid in order to be eligible for the ITC. If charged substantially from the grid (>25%), the IRS does not consider the battery storage to be part of the renewable energy generation system.

State Policies

Beginning January 1, 2023, California has become the first state to require solar power plus energy storage to be integrated into all future commercial structures. In addition, new rules require that all new residential construction must be ready for the addition of energy storage.

The 2022 Build Energy Efficiency Standards require that all commercial structures incorporate PV + storage. The PV must be sized to meet at least 60% of the building's loads. The storage must be sized to reduce exports to the grid to a maximum of 10% of the PV systems generation. Buildings and units less than 5,000 square feet are exempt from the storage requirement.

	Maximum Power Rating (MW)	Discharge Time	Max Cycles or Lifetime	Energy Density (Wh per liter)	Efficiency
Lead-Acid Battery	100	1 min - 8 hrs	6-40 years	50-80	80-90%
Li-ion Battery	100	1 min - 8 hrs	1,000-10,000	200-400	85-95%
Flow Battery	100	hours	12,000-14,000	20-70	60-85%
Hydrogen	100	minutes to weeks	5-30 years	600	25-45%
Flywheel	20	seconds to minutes	20,000-100,000	20-80	70-95%
Pumped Hydro	3,000	4-16 hours	30-60 years	0.2-2	70-85%
Compressed Air	1,000	2-30 hours	20-40 years	2-6	40-70%
Molten Salt	150	hours	30 years	70-210	80-90%

FIGURE 10-2:

COMPARISON OF VARIOUS ENERGY STORAGE SYSTEMS

(FROM WORLD ENERGY COUNCIL)

Other states, such as Colorado, New York, Massachusetts, Rhode Island and Maryland have recently adopted incentive programs to encourage the integration of storage into PV systems.

Major Types of Storage Systems

There are many forms of energy storage that can be deployed in systems both large and small; ranging from massive pumped hydro systems (which still account for 95% + of all energy storage on the grid) to compressed air to hydrogen-based to mechanical flywheels (as outlined in Figure 10-2).

At the individual customer level, battery storage systems remain the sole practical option. Batteries come in many shapes and sizes for a variety of applications (from watch batteries to car batteries and more). Traditionally, PV systems that incorporated storage relied on **lead-acid deep cycle** batteries. But in recent years, **lithium-ion** batteries have come to dominate, capturing more than 90% of the global grid battery storage market.

LEAD-ACID

DEEP CYCLE

LITHIUM-ION

Lead Acid Deep Cycle

Unlike a traditional car battery, deep-cycle lead-acid batteries are designed to provide a relatively constant stream of power for a long period of time. Car batteries, on the other hand, are designed to provide a short burst of power to start the vehicle's engine. After that, the alternator takes over and recharges the battery.

COLD CRANKING AMPS (CCA)

RESERVE CAPACITY

A car's battery can go its entire life without being drained more than 20% of its overall power. Traditional vehicle batteries are rated by their **cold cranking amps (CCA)** and their **reserve capacity (RC).**

The CCA refers to how many amps a battery can produce for 30 seconds at 0°C. And RC refers to the number of minutes a battery is able to produce 25 amps while maintaining a voltage rating of 10.5 volts or greater.

Deep cycle batteries are designed to discharge deeply (as much as 80% or more) often, without dramatically affecting the life of the battery or its performance. The reserve capacity of a deep cycle battery is typically two to three times that of a typical automotive battery. Conversely, a deep-cycle battery will only have about half as many cold cranking amps available.

FLOODED

GELLED

ABSORBED GLASS MAT (AGM)

The most common forms of lead-acid batteries include:
- **flooded (wet),** liquid electrolyte, either will removable caps or sealed,
- **gelled,** the electrolyte is suspended in a gelatin-like medium. Protects from spilling,
- **absorbed glass mat (AGM),** sometimes called "starved electrolyte" or dry batteries, because the fiberglass mat is saturated but there is no excess liquid present in the cell.

SAFETY NOTE: It should be assumed that all batteries (sealed or not) will vent off toxic fumes at some point during their life cycle. For this reason they should be stored in a well-ventilated location.

Battery Cycles

CYCLE

When discussing batteries, a **cycle** refers to a single instance when the battery goes from fully charged, to maximum discharge (which will vary from cycle to cycle) and then is fully recharged again. Car batteries, for instance, are designed simply to start the engine. They only discharge about 2-5% of their energy during each cycle. If they discharge more than this, the life of the battery will be shortened (dramatically).

DEPTH OF DISCHARGE (DOD)

Deep cycle batteries are designed to allow more of the energy they contain to be used by the system. The amount of energy that is drained during the cycle is referred to as its **depth of discharge (DOD)**. If a battery bank is drained of 80% of its power before being recharged, that is considered an 80% DOD. If only half the power is used before recharging, then the system is operating at a 50% DOD (and so on).

The lower the average depth of discharge a lead acid battery bank experiences, the longer it will last. As indicated in Table 10-1, a specific battery that cycles at 20% DOD may last 3200 cycles, but the same battery cycling at 70% DOD may only be expected to last for 1450 cycles.

Most lead-acid batteries are designed to operate at a 50% DOD. However battery banks incorporated into grid interactive systems (DC-coupled and AC-coupled) are typically

DOD (depth of discharge)	Number of cycles	Life Span
80%	1250	4.2 years
70%	1450	4.8 years
60%	1700	5.7 years
50%	2050	6.8 years
35%	2600	8.7 years
20%	3200	10.7 years

TABLE 10-1: AN EXAMPLE OF A DEEP-CYCLE BATTERY'S LIFE EXPECTANCY AT VARIOUS DOD SETTINGS

set to an 80% DOD, as they do not cycle as often as a stand alone system.

Most inverters designed to work with batteries allow the operator to determine the preferred depth of discharge. External low-voltage disconnects can also be incorporated into the system to control the depth of discharge of the battery bank.

Lead acid batteries should not be left discharged for more than 2 days as **sulfation** (a buildup of sulfur deposits within the battery's cells) will take place in a discharged battery.

SULFATION

The **state of charge (SoC)** of a battery is another method used in indicating how much energy remains in a battery. It is the inverse of a battery's depth of discharge. For example, a battery drained to a 40% DOD is said to be at a 60% state of charge (0% SoC = empty; 100% SoC = full).

STATE OF CHARGE (SoC)

Effect of Temperature on Batteries

Batteries are affected by temperature. Batteries will last longer when kept cool. For every 5.5°C (10°F) over 25°C (77°F) under which a lead-acid battery operates, the life of the battery can be cut in half. The life reduction of lead-acid versus lithium-ion batteries operated at high temperatures is outlined in Table 10-2. For this reason, lead-acid batteries should be stored in a cool or climate-controlled location. Ideal battery storage temperature conditions should be below 25°C (77°F) and above 0°C (32°F).

As temperatures fall, the energy capacity of the battery also falls. This is why a car may have trouble starting on a cold winter's morning. The rated charge capacity of a battery is measured at 25°C (77°F). The ability of a battery to fully charge falls by about 1% per degree below about 20°C

Operating Temperature	Lead Acid (Life Remaining)	Lithium-Ion (Life Remaining)
25° C (77° F)	100 %	100 %
30.5° C (87° F)	50 %	100 %
36° C (97° F)	25 %	100 %
41.5° C (107° F)	12.5 %	100 %
47° C (117° F)	6 %	100 %
52.5° C (127° F)	3 %	100 %
58° C (137° F)	0 %	100 %

TABLE 10-2: EFFECT OF HIGHER OPERATING TEMPERATURES ON THE LIFE EXPECTANCY OF BATTERIES

Capacity	Cap/AH	Current (I)
Capacity at the 100 hour rate	2490	24.9
Capacity at the 72 hour rate	2349	32.62
Capacity at the 50 hour rate	2172	43.44
Capacity at the 24 hour rate	1837	76.5
Capacity at the 20 hour rate	**1766**	**88.3**
Capacity at the 15 hour rate	1642	109.5
Capacity at the 12 hour rate	1536	128
Capacity at the 10 hour rate	1466	146.6
Capacity at the 8 hour rate	1377	172.2
Capacity at the 6 hour rate	1254	209
Capacity at the 5 hour rate	1183	237
Capacity at the 4 hour rate	1095	274
Capacity at the 3 hour rate	989	330
Capacity at the 2 hour rate	848	424
Capacity at the 1 hour rate	600	500

(68ºF). The capacity of the battery will fall by 50% when the temperature reaches -27ºC (-22ºF).

Deep cycle lead-acid batteries tend to undercharge at cold temperatures and overcharge at high temperatures at a rate of about +/- 1% per degree measured from 20ºC (68ºF). Overcharging or undercharging will decrease the life of the battery.

How Deep Cycle Batteries are Rated

The capacity of deep cycle batteries is rated by nominal voltage (6 Vdc, or 12 Vdc, or 24 Vdc, etc) and in **amp-hours (Ah)**. An amp-hour suggests that the battery can deliver one amp of power (at its nominal voltage) for one hour (or 10 amps for six minutes, or ½ amp for two hours, and so on).

AMP-HOUR (AH)

However, because of the internal resistance of batteries, the faster the energy is discharged, the less capacity is available within the battery.

For example, a battery, such as the one referenced in Table 10-3, that has a 2,490 Ah capacity when fully discharged over a 100 hour period of time, may only have 1,766 Ah available if the energy is used in only 20 hours – and only about 989 Ah of storage capacity if the energy is drained in just three hours.

RATED CAPACITY

A battery's **rated capacity** is generally set at the 20-hour level, so one system can easily be compared to another with regards to capacity.

RATE OF DISCHARGE

The **rate of discharge** of a battery is referred to as its **C-rate**.

C-RATE

A 1C discharge rate of current indicates that all the amp-hours within the battery are discharged in one hour. A 2C discharge rate would indicate the battery will be drained in 30 minutes, a 0.5C rate (also designated as C/2) would drain the battery in two hours.

In lead-acid batteries, the faster the discharge rate, the less capacity is contained within the battery.

For example, a lead acid battery that has a capacity of 100 Ah when drained at a 0.05C rate (over a 20-hour period or C/20) would only have a 60 Ah capacity when drained at a 0.8C rate (C/1.25).

Rate of Discharge	% Listed Capacity
20 hours (0.05C or C/20)	100 percent
8 hours (0.125C or C/8)	88 percent
6 hours (0.167C or C/6)	84 percent
3 hours (0.33C or C/3)	74 percent
1 hours (C1)	59 percent

TABLE 10-4: LEAD ACID BATTERY CAPACITY AT VARIOUS RATES OF DISCHARGE

Lithium-ion batteries hold the same energy capacity regardless of the rate at which current flows from them.

A battery fully discharged in one hour (C1) will have only 59% of the capacity of a battery discharged over 20 hours (0.05C or C/20), as indicated in Table 10-4. Generally manufacturers recommend that batteries not be discharged at a rate greater than C1.

Manufacturers recommend a **charge rate** of 0.33C for lead acid batteries (from empty to full in about 3 hours), but they can be charged at a higher rate for a portion of the charging cycle without creating oxygen and water depletion. Tests indicate that a healthy lead-acid battery can be charged at a rate up to 1.5C as long as the current is reduced as it reaches about a 80% state-of-charge (SoC).

CHARGING RATE

The accepted charging rate for lithium-ion batteries is between 0.5C (C/2) and C1, meaning a 1100 Ah rated lithium-ion battery can absorb 1100 Ah of power in as little as one hour.

The nominal voltage present within a battery is actually a range, rather than a fixed setting. For example, a fully charged 12 Vdc (nominal) battery will measure at about 12.7 Vdc when tested. This same battery with only about 20% of its capacity remaining (80% DOD) will measure at about 12 Vdc.

Charging settings will be higher to achieve these states of charge. For example, as indicated in Table 10-5, the charging setting during the bulk charging phase of a 12-volt battery bank may be around 14.8 volts.

During equalization, battery voltages rise even higher to assist in dissolving the sulfation within the cells. Battery voltages during equalization in a 48-volt system will rise to around 62 volts.

In very cold environments, charging voltages may rise even higher, as much as 10 Vdc. For example, a battery system in a weather monitoring station on a mountaintop

Nominal Voltage	Bulk Setting	Float Setting	Equalization
12 volts	14.8 volts	13.2 volts	15.5 volts
24 volts	29.6 volts	26.4 volts	31 volts
36 volts	44.4 volts	39.6 volts	46.5 volts
48 volts	59.2 volts	52.8 volts	62 volts

TABLE 10-5: TYPICAL CHARGE CONTROLLER SETTINGS AT VARIOUS STAGES OF THE CHARGING PROCESS

might experience voltages as high as 72 Vdc during equalization. Ensure that all connected equipment is rated to accept these higher voltages.

How Lead-Acid Batteries are Constructed

Flooded lead acid batteries consist of cells that contain two flat lead plates immersed in a pool of **electrolyte** solution. The positively charged plate is referred to as the **anode**. The negatively charged plate is referred to as the **cathode,** as illustrated in Figure 10-3.

The electrolyte is made up of water and sulfuric acid. As the battery discharges, the electrolyte becomes less acidic (more water). As a result, a battery at a low state of charge is more likely to suffer damage due to freezing, since water freezes at 0°C (32°F), while the freezing point of sulfuric acid is around -85°C (-121°F). As a result, a fully charged lead-acid battery will generally not freeze until temperatures drop below -60°C (-76°F), while a fully discharged battery may freeze at 0°C (32°F).

> ELECTROLYTE
>
> ANODE
>
> CATHODE

FIGURE 10-3: 2.1 VOLT SINGLE CELL

Deep cycle batteries contain a number of cells connected in series and/or parallel. Each cell produces approximately 2.1 volts.

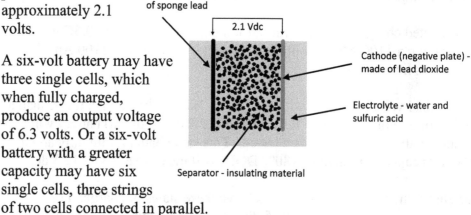

A six-volt battery may have three single cells, which when fully charged, produce an output voltage of 6.3 volts. Or a six-volt battery with a greater capacity may have six single cells, three strings of two cells connected in parallel.

A twelve-volt battery may be configured with the same six single cells by connecting them all in series, producing a fully charged output voltage of 12.6 volts, as diagrammed in Figure 10-4.

FIGURE 10-4: A NOMINAL 12-VOLT LEAD ACID BATTERY

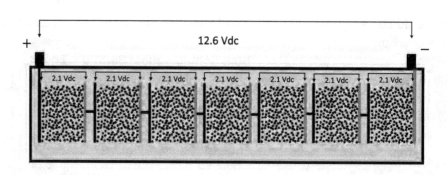

Lithium-Ion Batteries

Lithium-ion (Li-ion) batteries have always been considered a very expensive alternative to lead-acid batteries. But as costs decline, systems such as the Tesla Powerwall have become increasingly popular for residential use as emergency grid backup (with or without a PV system installed).

Lithium-ion battery technology is not new, first developed in 1912 but not commercially available until the 1970s. Lithium is the lightest of all metals, having the greatest electrochemical potential and the largest energy density by weight.

Advantages and Disadvantages of Lithium-ion
Advantages of lithium-ion batteries include:

- higher energy density by weight (about 140-150 Wh/kg versus about 35-40 Wh/kg for lead acid batteries), so lighter units can provide more power,

- significantly higher energy density by volume (about 400 Wh/liter versus about 70 Wh/liter for lead acid batteries), so smaller units can provide more power,

- more power available, as it is practical to drain lithium-ion batteries to 85% depth of discharge or more without a significant impact on the life of the battery,

- extended life cycle: tests show that after 2000 cycles, a lithium-ion battery will deliver 75% of its original capacity, as compared to 500-1000 cycles for lead-acid batteries,

- operate better in hot temperatures: Lithium-ion operating at 55°C has twice the life cycle as a lead-acid battery operating at 25°C,

- better discharge characteristics in cold temperatures, operating well in temperatures as low as -20°C, At temperatures below freezing (0°C) a lithium-ion battery will still discharge to 70% of its rated capacity, while a lead-acid will be limited to 45%.

- essentially maintenance-free, also spill proof, as they contain no liquid,

- low self-discharge: shelf life (when unused) can be as long as 5-10 years. They discharge at a rate of 2-3% per month, compared to 4-6% per month for lead-acid batteries. Lead-acid batteries must be recharged weekly, while lithium-ion batteries require recharge only every six months or so.

- faster charging. Lithium-ion batteries can charge at a rate about four-times that of lead-acid. This allows for quicker recovery when the battery bank is used as an emergency backup.

- better **roundtrip efficiency**. Roundtrip efficiency is the percentage of power that can be retrieved from a battery versus the amount of power that went into the battery during the charging cycle. With lead-acid

ROUNDTRIP EFFICIENCY

batteries, the roundtrip efficiency is typically around 80% (meaning that for every 100 Wh that go into the battery, only about 80 Wh can be retrieved). A typical lithium-ion battery has a roundtrip efficiency of around 95%.

- another advantage of lithium-ion batteries is that the capacity is independent of discharge rate.

Disadvantages of lithium-ion batteries include:

- a higher initial cost,

- that almost 70% of the global lithium deposits are concentrated in South America's ABC (Argentina, Bolivia and Chile) region. Most of the world's cobalt, another critical component in lithium-ion batteries, is mined in the Congo. This may cause supply chain disruption as this technology becomes more popular.

- that a lithium-ion battery can be permanently damaged if it is charged at low temperatures (below freezing). A lead-acid battery, however, can still accept a low current charge in cold weather.

- recycling lithium costs five-times as much as producing it initially. As a result, only a small number are currently recycled (as compared to 98% of all lead from lead-acid batteries that is currently recycled).

- when damaged, lithium-ion batteries can spontaneously combust.

- that lithium-ion cells and batteries are typically not as robust as lead-acid batteries. They require protection to ensure the current is maintained within safe limits. As a result, they require protection circuitry incorporated to ensure they are kept within their safe operating limits.

Battery Management Systems

SAFE OPERATING AREA (SOA)

Lithium-ion battery packs must operate within a relatively narrow range of current, voltage and temperature, known as its **safe operating area (SOA)**. The SOA will change constantly due to battery aging and environmental conditions, and as the battery function degrades as a result variations in resistance and capacity.

BATTERY MANAGEMENT SYSTEM (BMS)

As a consequence, lithium-ion battery packs used within solar installations almost always incorporate a **battery management system (BMS)**. The BMS is designed to:

- monitor the battery at the cell level as well as within cell groups (known as modules),
- provide battery protection by preventing the voltage, current, and temperature of any cell or module from exceeding defined SOA limits,
- balance all cells and modules within the battery pack to optimize the overall battery capacity and performance,
- report operational status to external devices.

Not all lithium-ion batteries have a full battery management system. Some employ **battery balancers** that only optimize cell voltage and protect them from over and under current while charging.

BATTERY BALANCER

Lithium-ion cells have different current limits for charging than for discharging. Battery cell manufacturers usually specify maximum continuous charging and discharging current limits, along with peak charging and discharging current limits. The incorporated BMS is designed to keep the battery operating within those limits.

In short, the BMS incorporated in lithium-ion battery packs is designed to manage the battery so that it functions in a safe (prevents thermal runaway), reliable (maintains it within safe operating area to extend the system's life) and optimized (by balancing all cells) manner. It also provides data to assist in monitoring its state of charge and to diagnose any issues that may develop.

Types of Lithium-Ion Batteries

While they are generally referred to as lithium-ion batteries, there are actually six major types as defined by their internal chemistry - primarily the composition of the cathode.

Each have advantages and disadvantages that feature in specific use markets. Within the PV and the electric vehicle industries, three options have historically been dominant, as indicated in Figure 10-5.

A great deal of lithium-ion battery research in recent years is aimed at reducing the amount of cobalt required for manufacturing. Cobalt is by far the most toxic and expensive ingredient in most lithium-ion batteries, and mining practices have raised environmental and human rights concerns.

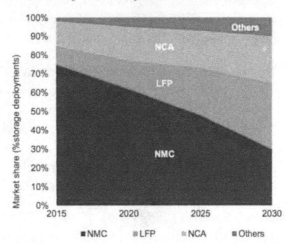

ESS battery chemistry market share forecast

FIGURE 10-5: MARKET SHARE OF ESS BATTERY CHEMISTRY

(FROM WOOD MACKENZIE)

The cathode material makes up the greatest share of the battery's cost, with the raw chemicals accounting for about 40% of the unit's cost basis.

Lithium Nickel Manganese Cobalt Oxide (NMC)

NMC batteries are widely used for power tools, energy storage systems (EES) and electric vehicles (EVs) which need frequent cycling.

LITHIUM NMC

TABLE 10-6:
COMPARISON OF
CHARACTERISTICS OF
VARIOUS LITHIUM-ION
BATTERY CHEMISTRIES

(DATA FROM BATTERY
UNIVERSITY)

Cell type	Cell Nominal Voltage	Cycles (Life)	Energy Density (Wh/Kg)	Applications
NMC	3.6 V	1,000+	150-220	EVs
LFP	3.2 V	2,000+	90-120	ESS, EVs
NCA	3.6 V	500-1,000	200-260	EVs
LTO	2.4 V	3,000–7,000	50-80	ESS, EVs
LCO	3.6 V	500-1,000	150-200	Laptops, Phones
LMO	3.7 V	300-700	100-150	Power Tools

The advantages of this technology include:
- long life cycle (shown in Table 10-6)
- relatively low cost
- high energy density (the most energy by weight and volume)

LFP

Lithium Iron Phosphate (LFP)

These batteries use phosphate as the cathode material and a graphitic carbon electrode as the anode. LFP batteries have a long life cycle with good thermal stability and electrochemical performance.

With a nominal voltage of 3.2 volts, connecting four of them in series results in a 12.8-volt battery. This makes LFP batteries a common type of lithium-ion battery when replacing lead-acid deep-cycle batteries.

LFP batteries are popular in applications requiring a large amount of power. Their primary benefits are durability, a long life cycle, and safety.

LITHIUM NCA

Lithium Nickel Cobalt Aluminum Oxide (NCA)

NCA batteries offer a high energy density with a long lifecycle. This means they can deliver a relatively high amount of current for extended periods while adding a relatively small amount of weight to the EV.

The downside is that these batteries are relatively expensive. While most EV makers use NMC batteries; Tesla uses NCA.

LTO

Lithium Titanate Oxide (LTO)

LTO chemistry offers an extremely safe battery with a long lifespan that charges faster than any other lithium battery type. They also exhibit excellent low temperature discharge characteristics.

However their relatively low energy density means that these units will be relatively heavy - not a problem with stationery ESS applications, but add a considerable amount of weight to EVs.

Lithium Cobalt Oxide (LCO)

LCO batteries have traditionally been used in products such as cell phones, laptops and electronic cameras. LCO batteries require frequent charging, have a relatively short lifespan, and are somewhat unstable.

They are losing popularity to other types of lithium-ion batteries due to the high cost of cobalt and concerns around safety.

LCO

Lithium Manganese Oxide (LMO)

LMO batteries are commonly found in portable power tools, medical instruments, and some hybrid and electric vehicles. The main downside to LMO batteries is their short lifespan.

LMO

Lithium-Ion Safety Standards

As more and more lithium-ion batteries are being integrated into homes and vehicles, there has developed a greater awareness of the risks these energy systems may present.

A number of industry standards have emerged in an attempt to mitigate these risks.

NFPA 855

The NFPA 855, *Standard for the Installation of Stationary Energy Storage Systems* was first released in 2020. This installation code addresses safety issues inherent in ESS systems. It includes specific criteria for facility ventilation, signage, fire protection systems, and emergency operations protocols.

NFPA 855

NFPA 1, Fire Code

The NFPA 1 is the US code that addresses fires and life safety issues for the public and for first responders. The 2021 revision of NFPA 1 includes requirements in Chapter 52 extracted from *NFPA 855, Standard for the Installation of Stationary Energy Storage Systems*.

NFPA 1, FIRE CODE

IEC 62619

IEC 62619, *Safety Requirements for Secondary Lithium Cells and Batteries, for Use in Industrial Applications* is an international standard that specifies requirements and tests designed to ensure the safe operation of rechargeable lithium cells and batteries used in ESS and in other industrial applications. Electrical safety is covered under Clause 8 of the standard.

IEC 62619

IEC 62933

IEC 62933, *Electrical Energy Storage (ESS) Systems* is an international standard that addresses various aspects of ESS, including testing methods, safety of grid-integrated ESS, as well as planning and performance assessment of ESS.

IEC 62933

UL 9540

UL 9540

UL 9540, *Standard for Energy Storage Systems and Equipment* is a product certification standard for all types of ESS. This standard evaluates the safety and compatibility of various elements and components when integrated into an ESS. This is a system standard, evaluating how individual components work together. Individual components must be tested to their own individual standards as well (for example, inverters tested to UL1741 SA).

UL 9540A

UL 9540

UL 9540A, *Standard for Test Method for Evaluating Thermal Runaway Fire Propagation in Battery Energy Storage Systems* is a product certification standard that details the testing methodology to assess the fire characteristics of an ESS that undergoes thermal runaway. ESS systems with greater capacity than the 50 kWh limit imposed in UL 9540 or separation distances less than those specified in UL 9540 must be tested to this standard as well.

UL 1642

UL 1642

UL 1642, *Standard for Lithium Batteries* is a product certification standard of lithium-ion batteries used as a power source. The standard's requirements are intended to reduce the risk of fire or explosion associated with the battery's use in any product, including in an ESS.

UL 1973

UL 1973

UL 1973, *Standard for Batteries for Use in Stationary, Vehicle Auxiliary Power and Light Electric Rail (LER) Applications* is a product certification standard for batteries and battery systems used for energy storage. The focus of the standard's requirements is on the battery's ability to withstand simulated abuse conditions.

High Voltage Battery Systems

Historically, the NEC has limited the voltage of battery systems within buildings to less than 50 Vac or 60 Vdc (basically 48 V nominal systems). In the 2017 NEC a new section, Article 706, was added that allows for and addresses permanently installed energy storage systems (ESS) with higher voltage battery systems.

HIGH VOLTAGE BATTERY SYSTEMS (HV)

Manufacturers such as Tesvolt, Samsung and LG quickly responded with **high voltage battery systems (HV)** that operate at voltages as high as 1,000 Vdc.

CONVERSION LOSSES

The advantage of the high-volt storage systems is that they do not impose the same level of **conversion losses** incurred by reducing higher voltages from the array to lower battery voltages, and then converting them to higher grid voltage levels. Additionally, these high voltage storage systems can be used with less complex (and therefore less expensive) inverters.

The NEC (706.30) restricts the voltage of an ESS within dwelling units to 100 volts. If the live parts of the system are inaccessible during routine maintenance (essentially only accessible by an authorized technician - not the homeowner), then the unit can operate at voltages exceeding 100 volt. In fact, the NEC does not specify an upper voltage limit for inaccessible units.

Self-contained energy storage systems (ESS) are often designed to allow for the higher voltage. These systems are assembled, installed, and packaged as a single unit. Typically, this type of ESS is manufactured and sold as a single product and listed to the UL 9540 standard.

SELF-CONTAINED ESS

Another acceptable option for exceeding the 100 Vdc limit for an ESS is to use pre-engineered matching and listed components that are connected in a "plug-and-play" fashion by the PV installer.

These components can be from a single manufacturer, or from multiple manufacturers but are designed to work as a complete system. The NEC refers to these systems as **ESS, pre-engineered of matched components**. The various components of these matched systems may be listed separately or as an assembled system.

ESS PRE-ENGINEERED OF MATCHED COMPONENTS

Regardless of what ESS system is selected, an **ESS disconnect** must be located within sight of the battery bank (NEC 706.7(A)).

ESS DISCONNECT

Sizing an AC Coupled or DC Coupled ESS

The size of the battery bank or ESS required in a grid-tied system is dependent upon a number of factors including:
- size of the PV array,
- daily load demand,
- primary purpose for incorporating storage.

Facilities install storage on site for a number of reasons, and these motivations will determine the amount of storage required.

The top reasons for incorporating storage include:
- an unreliable grid, so the ESS is to provide backup power for a period of time,
- load shifting , to self-consume power generated on site during times of available sunlight to times during the day when sunlight is not available but time-of-day pricing has made purchasing power from the grid relatively expensive,
- peak shaving, to run high consuming but short duration loads from storage rather than from the grid to lower demand charges that may be incurred from the utility.

Sizing for Grid Backup

Facilities often integrate battery storage as an insurance policy against power outages. In facilities where loads are extremely critical (like a hospital or cold

400V

Module	RESU7H	RESU10H	
		Type-R	Type-C
Total Energy [kWh] [1]	7.0	9.8	9.8
Usable Energy [kWh] [2]	6.6	9.3	9.3
Capacity [Ah]	63	63	63
Voltage Range [V]	350~450	350~450	430~550
Max Power [kW]	3.5	5.0	5.0
Peak Power [kW]	5.0 (for 5 sec.)	7.0 (for 10 sec.)	7.0 (for 10 sec.)
Dimension [W x H x D, in]	29.3 x 27.2 x 8.1	29.3 x 35.7 x 8.1	29.3 x 35.7 x 8.1
Weight [lb]	168	214	220
Enclosure Protection Rating	IP55		
Communication	RS485	RS485	CAN 2.0 B
Certificates	Cell	UL 1642		
	Product	TUV (IEC 62619) / CE / FCC / RCM	UL1973 / TUV (IEC 62619) / CE / FCC / RCM	

Compatible Inverter Brands : SMA (RESU10H) , SolarEdge (RESU7H, RESU10H) - More brands to be added
1) Total Energy is measured at the initial stage of battery life under the condition as follows: Temperature 77°F
2) Usable Energy is based on 95% of Depth of Discharge (Battery cell only)

food storage), even a few moments without available power could result in a significant impact to operations. As the national grid ages, power outages are becoming a more frequent concern.

When sizing a battery bank as a grid backup, a number of factors come into play. The facility owner will need to determine the number of **days of autonomy** (or hours) the system must operate critical loads without additional energy from the grid or from the array (assuming these outages may come at night or when of source other than the ESS is available.

Other factors will include the critical load demand the site will experience during that autonomous time period, as well as the maximum power draw the critical loads may require at any particular point in time.

For example, assume a small grocery store is located in an area that experiences frequent, but normally short duration power outages.

They have a backup generator that can handle long duration outages, but would like to install an ESS that can power their freezers, refrigeration units and lighting for short durations to avoid the noise as well as the wear and tear on their generator during momentary outages.

Several years ago they installed a 12 kW solar array with a SolarEdge inverter/optimizer system that is battery compatible. They have determined that they would now like to install an ESS that provides 2 hours of autonomy.

A critical load assessment has found that the critical loads will draw 4 kWh of energy per hour, with a maximum power draw (including surges) of 4.5 kW at any given moment.

With this information in hand, the designer has recommended a LG Chem RESU10H battery, the specifications are listed in Figure 10-6.

A review of the unit's specifications show that it will meet the energy demand (2 hours x 4 kWh/hr = 8 kWh) is below the **usable energy capacity** of the unit. The usable energy will be different than the rated energy, as it takes into account the depth of discharge (DOD) limitation of system. This particular ESS can only be discharged to 95% of its capacity, so:

USABLE ENERGY CAPACITY

9.8 kWh (ESS capacity) x 0.95 (95% DOD) = 9.3 kWh of energy available for use

Since the usable power is rated in available DC energy, but loads are typically AC, then the efficiency of the connected inverter must also be taken into account. If the inverter is 97% efficient, then the 9.3 kWh is adjusted by the inverter efficiency to determine how much energy is available to the loads:

9.3 kWh x 97% = 9 kWh AC energy available

The selected ESS must also be capable of supplying the maximum power draw of all critical loads. This unit can deliver 5 kW of continuous power and 7 kW of short term peak power. The maximum power draw required is 4.5 kW, so this unit meets this requirement.

It is also important to ensure the battery selected is compatible with the existing or installed inverter.

Sizing for Self Consumption

As utilities modify their net metering agreements (paying less than retail for exported power) and/or institute time-of-day pricing, increasingly consumers are incorporating ESS into their facilities to maximize the on-site consumption of power generated by the array, rather then exporting it to the grid.

When sizing a battery bank with this goal in mind, it may be helpful to calculate the facility's **self consumption ratio**. This ratio is essentially a representation of how much of the locally produced power is consumed on site. The higher the self consumption ratio, the less economic benefit from incorporating on-site storage.

SELF CONSUMPTION RATIO

For example, assume a restaurant located in southern California has installed a 20 kW array that generates on average 83 kWh of energy each day. This has been sized to meet their monthly load demand of 2,500 kWh/month (83 kWh/d x 30.5 days/month = 2,531 kWh per month).

Their utility pays retail (based on time of day) for power exported to the grid under their net metering contract. They have also instituted a time-of-day pricing policy where they charge $0.33 per kWh off peak and $0.53 per kWh during the peak hours of 5 pm to 9 pm.

So this restaurant will receive $0.33 per kWh exported to the grid, but will have to pay $0.53 during the evening, which happens to correspond to their highest consumption time of day. Assume that a load analysis has been conducted and it has been found that 58 kWh of their energy is consumed during peak hours.

Only 25 kWh of the energy generated by the array is either consumed on site while it is generated or compensated for at the same retail rate that would be charged for power from the utility.

So their self consumption ratio is 25 kWh/ 83 kWh = 0.30 (or 30%).

Effectively, 70% of the energy generated by the array is sold to the electric utility for $0.33 per kWh and then purchased back for $0.53 per kWh.

If a battery bank were installed where all the power generated on site could be consumed on site (by storing during the day and using that power in the evening), the business would save $11.60 per day or $4,234 per year.

$0.20 (difference between peak and off peak) x 58 kWh (peak power purchases per day) = $11.60 per day x 365 days per year = $4,234 per year

The installed estimate for the ESS is $12,000 and the unit is guaranteed for 10 years. So the payback in this situation is $12,000 / $4,234 = 2.8 years.

Sizing for Peak Shaving

Utilities often charge commercial or industrial customers demand charges that are based on the 15-minute increment during the month when their maximum load demand is at its highest. This is to compensate for the infrastructure required to deliver that amount of power, regardless of how long the power is used.

These demand charges can be significant, accounting for as much as 50% of a typical commercial bill.

Integrating an ESS can minimize these charges by powering high power, short duration loads from the battery and then recharging that battery over an extended period of time.

In an extreme example, assume a factory runs a large motor for 1 hour each day. That motor draws 50 kW of power when running or 50 kWh of energy per day. All other loads combined add an additional 50 kWh and are consumed at a constant rate.

Assume the utility charges $0.12 per kWh for consumed energy, but assesses demand charges of $14.91 per kWh based on the highest 15-minute time period during the month. The average monthly bill would be:

Electric Consumption: (100 kWh per day x 30.5 days) x $0.12 = $366
Demand Charge: 100 kW (maximum power draw) x $14.91 = $1,491
Total Invoice = $366 + $1,491 = $1,857

Now assume an ESS has been installed that powers only the motor. Each day the motor runs off the battery, and then the battery is recharged at a constant rate over a 24-hour period.

So now the daily load is still 100 kWh, but the maximum power draw has been reduced to:

2.08 kW (per hour to charge the battery or 50 kWh/24 hrs) + 50 kW from all other loads = 52.08 kW (maximum power draw)

So the new monthly bill would be:

Electric Consumption: (100 kWh per day x 30.5 days) x $0.12 = $366
Demand Charge: 52.08 kW (maximum power draw) x $14.91 = $776.51
Total Invoice = $366 + $776.51 = $1,142.51

So even though the same amount of energy is consumed each day, the facility will save about $714 per month by incorporating an ESS.

If sized for this purpose, the available power of the ESS must not only be sized large enough to meet the load demand offset, but also must be able to discharge at the rate required.

V2H Systems

While still in its infancy, the use of lithium-ion batteries contained in an electric vehicle is an attractive alternative to purchasing a separate (and expensive) emergency power source.

An ESS designed for residential use may have a storage capacity of 13.5 kWh, while the average EV hosts a 65 kWh capacity. It also has the additional benefit that when the battery is not being used to power the home, it can be driven.

A V2H system is much like any other AC-coupled system. It requires the addition of battery bank (in this case the vehicle), a battery-based inverter-charger, and a transfer switch to disconnect from the grid when in stand-alone mode.

These systems take grid-compatible AC electricity, convert it to high-voltage DC power (through the inverter-charger) and charge the vehicle's battery bank. When in discharge mode, the process is reversed, taking DC power from the vehicle, converting it the grid-compatible AC (again, through the inverter-charger) and servicing the home's loads.

A V2H system requires a bi-directional charging station (which usually doubles as the battery-based inverter-charger) to manage the process. The vehicle must also be designed to accommodate bi-directional charging. Since the charging station also serves as the inverter-charger, these units are relatively expensive.

As of 2022, only a few EVs have bidirectional DC charging capability; these include the later model Nissan Leaf (ZE1), the Mitsubishi Outlander, and the Eclipse plug-in hybrids.

Another approach to bi-directional charging is emerging. The Ford Lightning, for example, features a system where the inverter-charger is contained within the vehicle itself. The charging station is effectively an extension cord, taking AC power from the home and delivering it to the onboard inverter-charger. In discharge mode, the inverter-charger takes power from the battery bank and delivers AC power to the home.

A transfer switch will still be required, however, to disconnect the home from the grid when in stand-alone mode (to avoid islanding).

This onboard inverter system has a number of advantages. These include:

VEHICLE-TO-LOAD

- Compatibility. Since the inverter-charger is designed into the vehicle there is no danger the bi-directional charger will be incompatible with the vehicle.

- Allows for **vehicle-to-load (V2L)**. The vehicle can be equipped with outlets that can service AC loads when not connected to the charging station (for remote power use).

- Simplicity of installation. The charging system can be delivered in a plug-and-play type manner and requires little specialized electrical training to install.

- No need for an expensive charging station as the inverter-charger is incorporated into the cost of the vehicle.

Sizing a Lead Acid Battery Bank

When sizing a lead-acid battery bank, the following system parameters must be known:

- the size of the load to be serviced,
- the system voltage,
- how long will it operate independent of additional power from the solar array,
- the depth of discharge of the batteries,
- the lowest average ambient air temperature to which the batteries will be exposed,
- the efficiency of the inverter.

Unlike lithium-ion batteries, which are normally rated in kWh of capacity, lead-acid batteries are normally rated in amp-hours. So in order to determine the rated capacity of the battery (or battery bank), the nominal voltage will be multiplied by the Ah rating.

For example, a 48 V (nominal) battery bank with 125 Ah capacity = 6 kWh rated battery bank.

Ambient Temperature Adjustment

Lead-acid battery capacity is affected by the ambient air temperature. Cooler ambient temperatures will reduce the system's storage capacity, however the cooler temperatures will improve the cycle life of the battery. The cycle life of a battery bank will decrease by 50% for every 10°C over 25°C (77°F).

The rated Ah capacity of lead-acid batteries are determined at 25°C (77°F). As average operating temperatures drop, a multiplier (Table 10-7) must be used to calculate the increased capacity needed to achieve the desired capacity.

Capacity Multiplier	Temperature	
	Celsius	Fahrenheit
1	26.7°C	80°F
1.0	23.9°C	75°F
1.02	21.2°C	70°F
1.04	18.3°C	65°F
1.07	15.6°C	60°F
1.1	12.8°C	55°F
1.13	10°C	50°F
1.17	7.2°C	45°F
1.22	4.4°C	40°F
1.27	1.7°C	35°F
1.37	-1.1°C	30°F
1.42	- 3.9°C	25°F
1.51	- 6.7°C	20°F
1.63	- 9.4°C	15°F
1.77	- 12.2°C	10°F
1.95	- 15.0°C	5°F
2.17	- 17.8°C	0°F
2.21	- 20.6°C	-5°F
2.25	- 23.3°C	-10°F

TABLE 10-7: LEAD-ACID BATTERY AMBIENT AIR TEMPERATURE CAPACITY FACTORS

So, if for example it was determined that a 400 Ah battery bank was required, but it would be located in a garage that might experience temperatures of 10°F (-13°C), then:

400 AH battery bank capacity is required at 25°C (77°F)
Operating temp -13°C (10°F) = 1.77 temperature derate factor
1.77 X 400 = 708 Ah battery bank now required

Sizing Example

Assume a weather monitoring station will operate on a mountaintop with a daily load demand of 5 kWh. There is no grid available (a properly sized array is in place) and ambient air temperatures where the batteries will be stored will fall to 5°F (-15°C). The designer has determined to use lead-acid batteries.

This is a 48 Vdc stand-alone system, but because of periodic storms, it has been determined to install three days of autonomy within the system. This system will also be set to a 50% depth of discharge (DOD).

The battery bank would be sized as follows:

5 kWh (daily load) / 48 Vdc (nominal voltage) = 104 Ah per day
3 days of autonomy x 104 Ah per day = 312 Ah
312 Ah / .50 (50% DOD) = 624 Ah
624 Ah / .95 (95% inverter efficiency) = 657 Ah
657 Ah x 1.95 (temperature derate at 5°F /-15°C = 1,281 Ah battery bank required

Installing and Testing Lead Acid Battery Systems

The storage area has been designed and inspected. The battery bank has been sized and the battery selected. Now it is time to install.

Inspect and Test Each Battery

Do a physical inspection of each battery. Look for cracks or bulges in the casing. The top of the battery, posts, and connections should be clean, free of dirt, fluids, and corrosion.

If batteries are dirty:
- clean the battery top with a cloth or brush and a solution of baking soda and water. Do not allow any material to get inside the battery,
- rinse with water and dry with a clean cloth,
- clean battery terminals and the inside of cable clamps to a bright metallic shine using a post and clamp cleaner.

Check for moisture. Any fluids on or around the battery may indicate that the electrolyte solution is leaching or leaking out. Replace any damaged batteries.

Test the state of charge of each battery. This can be done in one of two ways. Through an **open-circuit voltage test**, or a **specific gravity test**.

OPEN-CIRCUIT
VOLTAGE TEST

SPECIFIC GRAVITY
TEST

Open-Circuit Voltage Test

Prior to testing, the battery should be disconnected from the system for at least 6 hours. In order to perform an open-circuit test:
- disconnect all loads from the batteries,
- measure the voltage using a DC voltmeter,

State of Charge	Specific Gravity	12 Volt	48 Volt
100 percent	1.277	12.73 volts	50.93 volts
90 percent	1.258	12.62 volts	50.47 volts
80 percent	1.238	12.50 volts	49.99 volts
70 percent	1.217	12.37 volts	49.49 volts
60 percent	1.195	12.27 volts	48.96 volts
50 percent	1.172	12.10 volts	48.41 volts
40 percent	1.148	11.89 volts	47.83 volts
30 percent	1.124	11.81 volts	47.26 volts
20 percent	1.098	11.66 volts	46.63 volts
10 percent	1.073	11.51 volts	46.03 volts

TABLE 10-8: SPECIFIC GRAVITY AND STATE OF CHARGE VOLTAGES FOR 12-VOLT AND 48-VOLT BATTERIES

- check the state of charge against the anticipated open-circuit voltages in Table 10-8,
- charge the battery if it registers less than a 70% state of charge.

If after recharging, the battery still does not register at 100% state of charge, then the battery may have been left discharged too long (severe sulfation) or it may have a bad cell. Replace the battery.

Specific Gravity Test
While testing batteries with a multimeter is a quick and convenient way to check their state of charge, a more accurate method for flooded lead acid batteries is to perform a specific gravity test.

This test is performed with a **hydrometer**, as illustrated in Figure 10-7.

Wiring the Battery Bank
Choosing the correct size (diameter) and length of cable is important for the overall efficiency of a battery bank. Cables that are too small or too long will result in power loss and increased resistance.

FIGURE 10-7: TESTING SPECIFIC GRAVITY OF A FLOODED LEAD ACID BATTERY WITH A HYDROMETER

HYDROMETER

Short wires connecting batteries together must be equal in length, as should the longer cables connecting the battery bank to the inverter (Figure 10-8). This allows for equal resistance applied to all batteries, ensuring they charge and discharge at the same rate.

FIGURE 10-8: TYPICAL
CABLES FOR BATTERY
BANK

(FROM ENERDRIVE)

Undersizing the wires in a battery bank is a common error. Generally #4/0 AWG cables should be used if possible, but wire size at a minimum should be:

- #6 AWG for loads of up to 90 amps,
- #2 AWG for loads of up to 150 amps,
- #1/0 AWG for loads of up to 250 amps,
- #4/0 AWG for loads of up to 400 amps.

Cables used in battery bank systems are typically fine stranded, as they are quite large and this type of cable is easy to bend. The NEC requires (690.31(H)) that all fine-stranded cables must be terminated with specifically designed terminals, lugs, devices or connectors. In other words, they cannot simply be stripped and wrapped around a terminal, then tightened into place.

When making the battery connection, lightly brush and coat the battery terminal and the cable lug with protective grease. Torque the connection hardware to its recommended setting.

After the series connection has been made (for example, four 12-volt batteries to create a 48-volt system), check the voltage to ensure all connections have been properly made. If the measured voltage is not as expected, track down the cause. It may be a loose connection or reversed polarity of one of the connections. If a battery is installed with reverse polarity, the measured voltage for the string of batteries will be reduced from the expected value by twice the open-circuit voltage of an individual battery.

If multiple series are connected in parallel, connect them together following the same process as before. When testing the system voltage, the expected voltage should be the average of all the string voltages.

It is generally recommended that no more than three (3) strings of batteries be connected in parallel. If the system requires more power than can be supplied by three (3) strings, select a larger battery.

Battery Safety

Battery systems create a number of unique safety concerns. Some good safety practices when working with batteries include:

- Ensure that the batteries are not damaged or leaking before working with the battery bank.

- Do not expose a battery to open flame, smoking or electrical sparks. A battery can produce flammable gasses, and a small spark can cause an explosion. According to UL, electrolyte gases are about 45% more combustible than propane. Proper venting of battery systems is a must to avoid concentrations of these gasses.

- Remove all metal jewelry and metallic clothing when working with batteries.

- Use only insulated tools.

- Wear safety goggles/face shield and gloves.

- Battery acid in the eye should be flushed with clean water, then get professional help immediately. Acid on the skin should be rinsed with cool, clean water for at least 20 minutes.

- Spilled liquid from damaged or dropped batteries should be treated with baking soda to neutralize the acid.

- Batteries can be quite heavy, so use proper lifting techniques (lift from the legs) and wear steel-toed boots (in case a battery is accidentally dropped).

Lithium-ion batteries also present a limited number of safety concerns. These include:

- Overcharging. Charging voltages over 65 volts can cause damage to a 48-volt lithium-ion system

- Temperature. Avoid charging batteries under extreme cold (below 0°C) or extreme heat.

- Mechanical damage. Lithium-ion batteries can experience **thermal runaway** (burst into flames) if physically damaged. Protect batteries in proper enclosures and/or rooms.

THERMAL RUNAWAY

Chapter 10 Review Questions

1) Which of the following is **NOT** a type of lead-acid deep cycle battery?
   a) flooded (wet)
   b) alkaline
   c) gelled
   d) absorbed glass mat

2. A lead-acid battery bank is undergoing bulk charging under the following conditions:
   - the charge controller has no temperature control
   - the temperature of the room where the batteries are stored is at 0°C (32°F)
   - the battery bank is at a depth of discharge of 50% when bulk charging begins

   Assuming charging continues with no load until the charge controller has completed the charging cycle:
   a) the battery bank will reach 100% state of charge (0% depth of discharge) and then the charge controller will disconnect from the array
   b) the battery bank will overcharge, while the state of charge cannot exceed 100%, there may be significant out-gassing and possible damage to the battery bank
   c) the battery bank will likely undercharge, probably obtaining only an 80% state of charge
   d) to avoid overcharging, the charge controller will divert excess production from the array to a load dump when the battery bank reaches 95% SoC

3) Which of the following is **NOT** a typical reason a home or business owner might choose to add an ESS to their facility?
   a) to condition the power
   b) the grid is unreliable
   c) time-of-use billing from the utility
   d) unfavorable net metering policies

4) Which of the following is **NOT** a typical reason a grid operator might choose to add an ESS to their system?
   a) to condition the power
   b) ramp rate control
   c) to increase system resiliency
   d) to make unfavorable net metering policies unnecessary

5) The 2017 NEC restricts the voltage of inaccessible self contained energy storage systems located within buildings to:
   a) 50 Vac or 60 Vdc
   b) 100 Vdc
   c) 1,000 Vdc
   d) there is no voltage limit on self contained ESS

6) A battery that is charged from empty (0% SoC) to full (100% SoC) in two hours experiences a charge rate of:
   a) C2
   b) 2C
   c) 2/C
   d) 0.5C

7) Which of the following is generally **NOT** a part of a lead-acid battery or battery system?
   a) battery balancer
   b) anode
   c) cathode
   d) electrolyte

8) Which of the following is **NOT** an advantage of lithium-ion battery technology over lead-acid deep cycle batteries?
   a) longer life
   b) better roundtrip efficiency
   c) lower depth of discharge
   d) less self-discharge

9) Lithium-ion battery systems must operate within a relatively narrow range or current, voltage and temperate - known as the:
   a) safe operating area (SOA)
   b) maximum power point (MPP)
   c) battery balance point (BBP)
   d) equalization charge

10) The Tesla Powerwall 2 is a popular example of a:
    a) DC coupled system solution
    b) AC coupled system solution
    c) stand alone system solution
    d) grid tied system solution

11) How long a battery bank system can operate independently of additional power from the array is known as:
    a) days of autonomy
    b) round-trip efficiency
    c) conversion losses
    d) C-rating

12) A novelist has decided to install a lead-acid battery bank on a remote island retreat with the following conditions:
- the daily load of the cabina has been estimated at 4.2 kWh per day
- the maximum power draw is 2.1 kW
- the average annual insolation is 6.3 hrs
- it is a 48 Vdc system
- the array is sized at 1.5 kW
- Average ambient air temperature is 25°C (77°F)
- he has also decided on 5 days of autonomy
- the selected inverter has a 3 kW capacity and operates at 95% efficiency
- the entire system derate has been estimated at 72%
- the inverter has been set to allow for a 60% depth of discharge
- a 98% efficient charge controller has been installed that will direct excess power from the array to a small hot water heater

What is the minimum size battery bank (in amp-hours) the system will require?
a) 153.5 Ah
b) 437.5 Ah
c) 768 Ah
d) 1,013 Ah

13) The usable energy capacity of a lithium-ion ESS is different than its rated energy capacity because it takes into account:
a) roundtrip efficiency
b) depth of discharge
c) self consumption
d) reserve capacity

14) Which of the following is a test that can be used to determine the voltage of a flooded lead-acid battery?
a) specific gravity test
b) ampacity rating test
c) Ufer bond test
d) load shifting

15) When wiring a battery bank:
a) use #4/0 AWG cables whenever possible
b) use solid conductors only
c) size conductors by multiplying the Ah rating of the battery bank by the 1.25 NEC safety margin
d) test the security of each connection terminal annually using a hydrometer

16) Lithium-Ion batteries have been known to burst into flames when damaged due to:
a) specific gravity
b) load shifting
c) conversion losses
d) thermal runaway

17) The novelist from Question #6 has decided to install a lithium-ion battery bank rather than a lead-acid battery bank. The depth of discharge can now be set to 95% and the round-trip efficiency of the battery bank has increased the system efficiency to 92%. All other factors remain the same:
   - 4.2 kWh per day
   - maximum power draw is 2.1 kW
   - average annual insolation is 6.3 hrs
   - 48 Vdc system
   - 1.5 kW array
   - 5 days of autonomy
   - inverter has a 3 kW capacity and operates at 95% efficiency
   - charge controller operates at 98% efficiency

   What size battery bank is required?
   a)   4.2 kWh
   b)   4.6 kWh
   c)   7.5 kWh
   d)   22 kWh

18) PV systems that incorporate batteries to balance load demand through load shifting and peak shaving are often referred to as:
   a)   self-consumption grid-tied systems
   b)   current transformer systems
   c)   Ufer systems
   d)   capacity enabled systems

19) Lithium ion battery system manufacturers generally recommend a charge rate:
   a)   between 0.1C and 0.5C
   b)   between 0.5C and C1
   c)   between C1 and C2
   d)   between C/2 and C/20

20) When designing an AC coupled system, which of the following is **NOT** true?
   a)   the battery bank should not charge at a rate faster than C5
   b)   the battery-based inverter should be sized with a load capacity of at least 125% of the existing grid-tied inverter
   c)   battery banks for AC coupled systems can be sized in a manner similar to sizing a battery bank for a stand alone system
   d)   load dumps should never be incorporated into the system as the grid functions in that capacity

21) A battery bank that will be exposed to freezing temperatures and used to power loads under those conditions:
   a)   must incorporate a battery balancer
   b)   will be subject to higher conversion losses
   c)   must be sized larger than if operating under rated conditions
   d)   must be temperature adjusted, as batteries will not discharge at temperatures below freezing

Chapter 11

PV Mounting Systems

At its most basic, a mounting system is a metal assembly that secures the solar panels together and to whatever structure it is to be attached to. There are dozens of commercial racking systems available on the market.

The brand and style selected will be determined by the site, budget, and preferences of the owner. Typically the system will come with very detailed installation instructions and each system will present its own unique challenges.

Racking System

A great advantage of using a complete packaged racking system (rather than designing one) is that the systems have already been completely engineered to account for live and dead load weight issues, structural integrity, aesthetics and maintenance issues. Using a "pre-engineered" system also may be critical in obtaining a permit in some jurisdictions.

Broadly speaking, racking systems will fit into one of four broad categories:
- roof mounted,
- ground mounted,
- pole mounted,
- or building integrated.

In most cases, the racking system selected will be made of metal (a conducting material). The aluminum frames on the solar panels, as well as the racking, can act as a lightning rod (especially when placed on a rooftop). Other stray and unwanted random power can also find its way onto these conducting materials (short circuits, down electric lines, etc). For this reason, all metallic parts of the system must be bonded together and connected to the grounding system to provide any stray current a safe pathway to ground.

UL 2703

UL 2703

UL 2703 Mounting Systems, Mounting Devices, Clamping/Retention Devices, and Ground Lugs for Use with Flat-Plate Photovoltaic Modules and Panels is the manufacturing standard that addresses PV mounting rack constructional requirements. This includes mounting systems and clamping devices designed for rooftop, ground mounted or building integrated systems with voltages up to 1,000 Vdc.

These requirements cover the assembly's mechanical strength, material suitability as well as grounding and bonding.

FIRE CLASSIFICATION

The standard also provides for the testing and classification of the racking system as to its ability to deal with exposure to fire. **Fire classification** (Class A, B, or C) reflects a properly mounted assembly's resistance to external fire exposure when the rack mounting system is installed in combination with specific PV modules.

Fire classes are outlined in Section 1505 of the International Building Code and the standard rates unit's resistance when exposed to external fire as light (Class C), moderate (Class B), and severe (Class A). Mounting systems not evaluated for a Fire Classification are marked as "Not Fire Rated".

Roof Mounted Systems

FLUSH-TO-ROOF

STANDOFF MOUNT

The most popular roof mounted system for residential units is the **flush-to-roof** racking system (also called **standoff mounting**). Most of these systems are designed to work with asphalt shingle roofs (the most widely used system in the U.S.), but specialized systems are available to mount on metal, slate and even tile roofs.

While there are advantages to roof mounted systems (at many installation sites it may be the only location on the site with the available space and sunlight for a PV system), there are concerns that must be addressed before deciding to place the array on the roof.

- Check the condition of the roof to ensure it is structurally able to support the added weight imposed by adding an array. If unsure, consult with a structural engineer. Most PV systems only add between 2.5 - 4 psf (pounds per square foot) weight to a roof, about the same weight as a second layer of shingles. A structurally sound roof should have no problem supporting this weight. Many jurisdictions also impose a 45 psf weight limit at each attachment point. Most commercially available systems are designed to fall well below this limit.

- Many systems cannot be installed in areas where wind loading may exceed a predetermined psf. Check with local officials to determine if this is the case.

- Regions with extremely heavy snow may not be suitable for these types of installations. Not only do they increase the load on the roof, but this location may be difficult to clear and adversely impact the operation of the system.

- In instances where the roof structure is suspect, local authorities may require a stamped **engineered drawing** to attest to the condition of the structure.

ENGINEERED DRAWING

Roof mounted systems incorporate **footings** that attach to the roof and hold the array parallel to the surface at a distance of between 2 to 10 inches. Great care must be taken when attaching these footings to ensure that the penetrations holding them in place are waterproofed properly to avoid future roof leaks.

Many systems incorporate flashing (such as the system illustrated in Figure 11-1) to help avoid leaks.

FIGURE 11-1: FLUSH-TO-ROOF MOUNTED FOOTING WITH FLASHING INCORPORATED INTO THE DESIGN

(FROM QUICK MOUNT PV)

FOOTING

The footing mounts must be attached to the support rafters (shown in Figure 11-2), not simply to the plywood decking of the roof. So it is critical to mark the location of the rafters. It may help to snap a chalk line on top of the shingles to indicate where the rafters are located during the installation process. If it is impossible to hit a rafter with each footing mount, it is common to attach a 2 x 4 or 2 x 6 brace between the two rafters, then attach the mount to the brace. Metal rails are then attached to the footing units.

The lag bolts that secure the footing mounts to the roof rafters must be able to hold up to the forces exerted by the dead load of the array (usually 3-5 lbs per sq ft) as well as the live loads (which might be much greater, as much as 25-50 lbs per sq ft).

Pull-Out and Shear Loads
The mounting hardware of a PV system on a roof will be subject to a number of stresses. These can be lateral, or **shear loads**. Or they can be vertical, or **pull-out loads**.

SHEAR LOADS

PULL-OUT LOADS

FIGURE 11-2: FLUSH-TO-ROOF MOUNTING LAYOUT ON ROOF

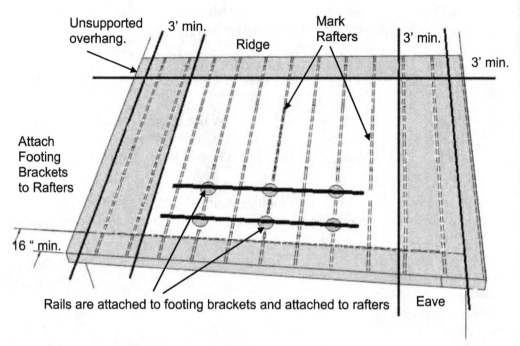

Unsupported overhang.

3' min.

Ridge

Mark Rafters

3' min.

3' min.

Attach Footing Brackets to Rafters

16 " min.

Rails are attached to footing brackets and attached to rafters

Eave

These live loads may be the result of seismic activity, but more commonly they are exerted by the force of wind moving against and over the array. Local building codes typically have sections that deal with wind loading, but the most comprehensive guide for estimating wind loads on structures is Standard No. 7 of the American Society of Civil Engineers (ASCE)

Wind loading on solar panels depends on three (3) basic factors: wind speed, the height of the panel above the roof, and the relative location of the panel on the roof.

When calculating pull-out loads, there are a number of free online calculators that will do the calculations, but they do require a bit of site-specific information, some of which may not be intuitive.

These include:
- wind exposure category,
- occupancy category,
- roof type (hip, gable, sloped or flat),
- three-second wind gust speed (many sources available online for specific locations),
- roof zone,
- tributary area to footing,
- dimensions of the roof,
- roof slope,
- height of array off the ground.

These variables for a specific installation will be required to calculate the **wind uplift force** (or **pull-up force**) for a given installation. Online tools are available to assist in these calculations.

WIND UPLIFT FORCE

PULL-UP FORCE

Wind Exposure Category

The amount of wind hitting a building is affected by the characteristics of the area immediately surrounding the structure, or its **surface roughness**. An open field or lake will be subject to much more wind than a building in the middle of a forest.

SURFACE ROUGHNESS

The **wind exposure categories** that impact the placement of solar arrays include:

- Exposure B. Urban and suburban areas, wooded areas or other terrain with many closely spaced obstructions.
- Exposure C. Open terrain with scattered obstructions with heights less than 30 feet located more than 1,500 feet from the building site.
- Exposure D. Flat unobstructed areas exposed to wind flowing over open water, and smooth grasslands for a distance of not less than 5,000 feet from the building site.

WIND EXPOSURE CATEGORIES

Occupancy Category

Building codes often factor in the use or activity which takes place within a building when determining just how stringent the code must be for that structure. For example, a carport is not as critical as an emergency shelter, so need not be built to the same specifications. **Occupancy categories** include:

- Risk Category 1 includes buildings that are a low hazard to human life in event of failure, such as agricultural facilities.
- Risk Category 2 includes residential structures, as well as all other buildings that don't fit into categories 1, 3, or 4.
- Risk Category 3 includes buildings that are a significant hazard to human life, such as public assembly buildings, power-generating stations and water treatment facilities.
- Risk Category 4 includes essential buildings, such as hospitals, and fire, rescue ambulance and police stations.

OCCUPANCY CATEGORIES

Roof Zone

Not all parts of the roof area are affected in the same way by wind flowing over it. The edges will experience greater pull-out loads than will the center of the roof, and the corners will experience even greater loads.

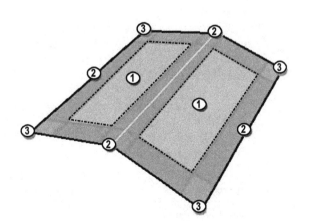

FIGURE 11-3: WIND LOAD ZONES ON A PITCHED ROOF

ROOF ZONE

FIGURE 11-4:

CALCULATING
TRIBUTARY AREA OF A
SINGLE FOOTER

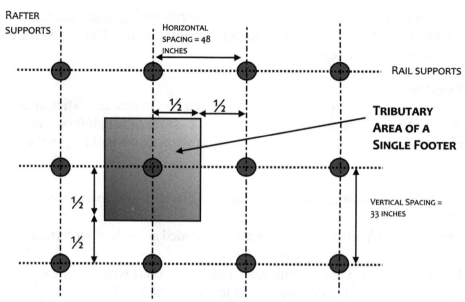

RAFTER
SUPPORTS

HORIZONTAL
SPACING = 48
INCHES

RAIL SUPPORTS

TRIBUTARY
AREA OF A
SINGLE FOOTER

VERTICAL SPACING =
33 INCHES

A typical roof is divided into zones, as indicated in Figure 11-3. If the PV system is designed with proper perimeter setbacks, then the array should fall within zone 1.

Tributary Area to Footing

TRIBUTARY AREA

The **tributary area** on a roof is the area supported by a particular rafter, or in this case, footer. It is calculated by finding the area halfway between the supports, then calculating the square footage within that area, as shown in Figure 11-4.

For example, if footers are placed every four feet (every other 24-inch-on-center rafter) horizontally, and the vertical rails are spaced every 33 inches (most solar panels are about 65 inches long, but this will vary), then:

Tributary Area = 4 feet (48 inches) x 2.75 feet (33 inches) = 11 sq ft

If the size of the array and the uplift force is known, then the pull-up force per footer can be calculated in the following manner:

Example:
- 9.6 kW system
- 2 x 4 pine truss roof on 24" centers with composite shingle roof
- 32 modules (Solar World 300W) @ 18 sq ft per module = 577.28 sq ft
- 26 mounting brackets (every other rafter)
- 25 psf uplift force

577.28 sq ft x 25 lbs/sq ft uplift force = 1,443.23 lbs of force / 26 mounting footers = 555 lbs per footer

The pull-out (withdrawal) capacity of the lag bolt is a factor of the size of the bolt, the length (how many inches it is secured into the wooden rafter) and the type of wood from which the rafter is made. Common examples of pullout capacity are shown in Table 11-1.

TABLE 11-1: PULL OUT
CAPACITY OF COMMON
LAG BOLTS

Lag Bolt/Screw Size	Allowable Withdrawal (pounds/inch thread)		
	Pine	Spruce	Douglas Fir
#10 screw	90 (lbs/inch)	146 (lbs/inch)	173 (lbs/inch)
#18 (5/16 inch)	205 (lbs/inch)	235 (lbs/inch)	266 (lbs/inch)
#20 (3/8 inch)	235 (lbs/inch)	269 (lbs/inch)	304 (lbs/inch)

So if 5/16 inch lag bolts were selected for this example, then the minimum length required would be 3 inches.

555 lbs pull-out load per footer / 205 lbs/inch (force rating pine roof truss with 5/16 lag bolts) = 2.7 inches (round up to 3 inches)

For a greater margin of safety, larger and/or longer lag bolts can be used. The lag bolt length, however, should be at least ½ inch less than the combined thickness of the sheeting and rafter, to avoid splitting the wood should the bolt exit the bottom of the rafter.

Pull-out loads could also be reduced by placing the supports closer together. In this example, the spacing of the footers could be every rafter (24 inches) rather than every other rafter (48 inches). Spacing requirements will vary depending on the code requirements. Often a steeper sloped roof will require a tighter spacing of support brackets (as illustrated in Table 11-2).

Manufacturers will provide spacing requirements for their specific system.

Lag screws require pilot holes. For shingle roofs, use a 5/32-inch diameter pilot hole for 1/4-inch lag screws, a 3/16-inch diameter pilot hole for 5/16-inch lag screws and a 1/4-inch diameter pilot hole for 3/8-inch diameter lag screws.

Be sure to treat all penetrations with an appropriate sealant, even when using flashed mounting assemblies.

Roof Slope	Maximum Horizontal Anchor Spacing (on center)		
	16 inch	24 inch	32 inch
Flat to 6:12 (0-26°)	5 feet 4 inches	6 feet 0 inches	5 feet 4 inches
7:12 to 12:12 (27°-45°)	16 inches	24 inches	32 inches
13:12 to 24:12 (46°-63°)	16 inches	24 inches	32 inches

Mounting Panels on Rails

Once the footing brackets are secure, and the rails attached, it is time to attach the panels.

FIGURE 11-5: TOP-DOWN CLAMP USED TO SECURE PV PANELS TO THE RACKING SYSTEM

TOP-DOWN
MOUNTING CLAMP

Because the panels are mounted so closely to the roof decking, it will be necessary to mount them using a **top-down mounting clamp** such as the one illustrated in Figure 11-5.

These clamps, as well as the other fasteners required to assemble the racking system will be included in the system provided by the manufacturer.

To best support the panel, the rails should always be oriented to cut across the short side of the panel, rather than the long side. So on a roof-mounted system, the run of the rafters will likely determine whether the array is mounted in a **landscape** or **portrait** orientation.

LANDSCAPE

PORTRAIT

When placing panels on rails, remember that the conductors from the panels are live when exposed to sunlight. Ensure that any breakers are in the open position during installation. If possible, wait to connect panels in series until after they are mounted. This may not be possible on a rooftop installation, but is typically not a problem when mounting panels on a ground mounted racking system.

Rail-less Systems

Every second that can be saved in the installation process reduces the cost of the PV system. With this in mind, a number of manufacturers have developed mounting systems that use the structure of the panel rather than a support rail.

RAIL-LESS SYSTEM

FIGURE 11-6: RAIL-LESS SOLAR PANEL MOUNTING SYSTEM

Rail-less systems such as the one illustrated in Figure 11-6 attach the mounting bracket directly to the side of the panel. Systems of this type

occasionally require a special panel that is designed to receive the mounting bracket.

While these systems save money on parts, shipping and even installation, rail-less systems do take a bit more planning up front to properly lay out and level the mounts. Wire

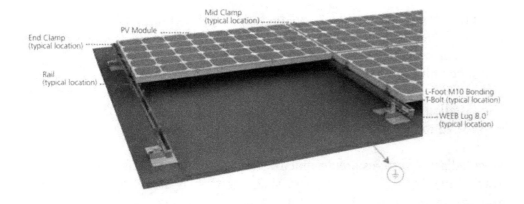

management can also be an issue, as the rails cannot be used to support the
cables.

Shared Rail Systems

Another recent innovation in mounting design is the **shared rail system**. In
these systems, the rails are mounted on the perimeter of the panels and interior
rails are shared between two panels, as illustrated in Figure 11-7.

As with rail-less systems, advocates point to the lower part count that result in
faster installations. Detractors argue these systems are difficult to mount on
uneven surfaces and often do not incorporate bonding, so bonding jumpers
must be installed.

Flat Roof Systems (Ballasted)

Flat roofs, typical on commercial structures, are notorious for leaking, even
under the best of circumstances. Adding hundreds of mounting penetrations
necessary for a standard railed PV system would almost certainly result in
leaks. As a result, most flat roof installations utilize a ballasted (weighted)
mounting system rather than lag bolts that penetrate the roof membrane, such
as the one illustrated in Figure 11-8.

Installation of **ballasted systems** can vary dramatically depending on the
system design. These system typically utilize concrete blocks placed in
integrated pans to hold the system in
place.

Common concrete landscaping
pavers can deteriorate over time due
to exposure to UV light, moisture
and freezing/thawing. It is
recommended that installers ensure
the concrete blocks used are rated
for local conditions.

(SHARED RAIL SYSTEM)

(BALLASTED SYSTEM)

FIGURE 11-8: BALLASTED
MOUNTING SYSTEM FOR
FLAT ROOF

(FROM SOLAR PANELS PLUS)

For larger commercial systems, a structural engineer should be involved in the design. Wind traveling over parapets (the small walls around many flat roofs) can have a dramatic effect on wind loading. There could be as much as ten times the uplift in corners as in the middle of the roof.

The installed dead weight of most ballasted systems is between 3-7 psf, and engineered to withstand wind speeds of up to 150 mph.

Most ballasted systems are designed with pre-determined offsets between the rows to avoid the issue of inter-row shading. If the system does not integrate row offsets, make sure shading is planned for in the layout design.

EAST/WEST MOUNTING SYSTEMS

East/west flat roof mounting systems (shown in Figure 11-9) are designed to address the inter-row shading problem, but are also gaining in popularity for a number of reasons, even when shading is not an issue.

In these systems, the panels are oriented in a pyramid fashion, with one row facing east and the alternating row facing west. The energy loss experienced

FIGURE 11-9: EAST/WEST FLAT ROOF MOUNTING SYSTEM

(FROM KINETIC SOLAR RACKING AND MOUNTING)

with an east-west orientation (rather than solar south) is typically more than made up for due to increased panel density (can fit more panels on a limited roof space). This is especially true the closer the site is to the equator, where the sun will track higher in the sky exposing the flatter panels to more energy throughout the day.

Advantages of these systems include:
- can fit more modules on a roof (avoids inter-row shading),
- more consistent energy production throughout the day,
- less wind resistance, as panels present a lower profile,
- time-of-day production may match well with the utility's peak load demand (increased late afternoon production).

Disadvantages include:
- lower profile may make wire management difficult and wires may be exposed to increased moisture and pooling water,
- can be difficult accessing panels for maintenance and repair.

Squirrel Guards

Many animals may find the space between the solar array and the roof a delightful location to set up house. Birds, raccoons and most particularly squirrels often nest in this warm, dry location and can cause significant damage to the installation and a potential safety hazard to the home.

Squirrels and other rodents are especially troublesome as they tend to chew on electrical wires. In short order they can chew through the insulation, causing arcs or short circuits.

Accumulated debris from nests can also pose a moisture issue or even a fire hazard.

To avoid these problems, it is often a good idea to install a **squirrel guard** (or critter guard) around the perimeter of a rooftop installation, as shown in Figure 11-10. There are a number of products on the market designed specifically for this purpose.

SQUIRREL GUARD

Avoid any product that might block the flow of air under the array, as this air flow is necessary to cool the solar panels.

Ground Mounted Systems

Ground mounted arrays are generally installed on galvanized steel and/or aluminum support structures. Once the support structure is in place, the remainder of the system (rails, clamps, grounding) is installed in a manner similar to a rooftop system. The addition of the support structure will add to the overall cost of the installation. As a result, ground mounted systems are typically a bit more expensive than roof mounted systems.

When siting a ground mounted system (especially very large systems) a number of factors must be considered. These include:

- local zoning issues (there may be rules in place the prohibit the siting of the system at a specific location),

- agricultural status. Many farm sites that may appear ideal for solar may be under contract with agricultural programs that will impact whether a solar array can be placed at the location.

- interconnection distance. Medium to large solar facilities (> 50 kW) must be near a three-phase electric distribution line (ideally less than 2000 feet away), which has spare capacity and appropriate voltage to accommodate the solar array.

- environmental impact. The site may contain sensitive animal or plant life that may be adversely impacted by the installation. There may be wetlands that require special permitting, or the site might contain some form of ground-source pollution that may be disturbed during installation (former landfill, mine site, etc).

- Is the site accessible from the road? Heavy equipment will be needed during construction. The construction of access roads will add a great deal to the cost of construction and delays in permitting.

- Slope of the site. Uneven ground requires a more robust support structure. There may be additional issues and costs associated with array design and installation as well (site grading, drainage issues, etc). Arrays are typically not installed on slopes greater than 20%, and some municipalities have restrictions on the maximum slope on which a solar facility can be installed.

Pier Supports

There are a number of options available to support the metal posts. The type of foundation used is based on the design of the racking system. The most common type of anchoring options include driven piles, helical piles, ground screws, concrete footings, concrete ballast or a mixture of these.

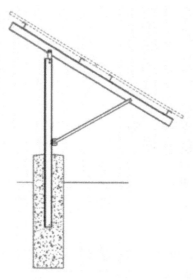

Ground mounted systems typically employ either single post or double post support structure.

Single post foundations support the racking with a single row of posts located in the center or rear center of the array, as seen in Figure 11-11. Most systems of this type employ cantilevered struts and braces.

Double pole foundations (Figure 11-12) utilize two rows of foundations that support piers, typically referred to (in the northern hemisphere at least) as the southern pier (front) and the northern pier (back).

FIGURE 11-11: SINGLE POST FOUNDATION SUPPORT

Concrete Footings

Many ground mounted arrays are supported on metal poles that are imbedded in concrete. Holes for these supports must be dug to below the **frost line** (the point where soil no longer freezes). This avoids the shifting and heaving that may occur as the soil freezes (and expands) and melts (and contracts).

The frost depth will vary from location to location (again, check with the local building department), from as much as 100 inches in northern Minnesota, to as little as five inches in central Georgia. In any case, most jurisdictions will require that footings be placed at least 12 inches below **unsettled soil** (soil not previously disturbed by construction).

FIGURE 11-12: DOUBLE POST FOUNDATION SUPPORT

FROST LINE

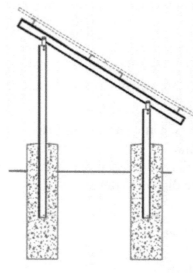

UNSETTLED SOIL

Tracking Systems

When evaluating solar tracking systems, they are usually classified into two broad categories: single axis and dual axis tracking. This classification is based on the range and number of directions the system rotates, generally referred to as the unit's **degree of freedom**.

DEGREE OF FREEDOM

Single-Axis versus Dual-Axis Tracking

A single-axis tracker is usually aligned north and south, allowing panels to track the daily arc of the sun from east to west.

A dual-axis tracker allows panels to move on two axis, aligned both north-south and east-west. This tracking system maximizes the amount of time the panels face directly towards the sun, both on a daily basis as well as adjusting for changes in altitude that occur seasonally.

Single-axis tracking systems typically cost less, have a longer projected lifespan, and are less prone to maintenance issues - however dual-axis systems are more efficient and may be the preferred option when space is limited.

Passive versus Active Tracking

Tracking systems may also be classified based on their driving system, which can be divided into active and passive tracking systems.

Passive tracking systems use the thermal differences created by sunlight and shade on the different sides of the array. The driving system contains liquids or gases with a low boiling point or springs made from material with formed memory to move the axes of the tracking system.

PASSIVE TRACKING SYSTEMS

The thermal differences move the unit until the pressures on each side of the system are in balance. Passive systems do not require any additional power supply to operate. However they are not generally very precise or robust, so are only suitable for small arrays.

Active tracking systems use electrical drives/motors and mechanical assemblies to operate. The main components within these systems are a microprocessor, an electric motor, gearboxes, and sensors.

ACTIVE TRACKING SYSTEMS

Open -Loop versus Closed-Loop Control Systems

Active tracking systems can be further classified into two categories: open-loop control systems and closed-loop control systems.

An **open-loop control system** uses a mathematical algorithm to determine the position of the array. The control system uses data that predicts the exact location of the sun relative to the specific GPS position of the array to precisely position the panels.

OPEN-LOOP CONTROL SYSTEM

A **closed-loop control system** uses feedback from sensors (light dependent resistors) to move the array in relation to the position of the sun. Closed-loop control tracking systems are generally more expensive than open-loop because of the required additional sensor devices.

Online Design Tools for Racking Systems

Since 2007, companies such as Mounting Systems have offered online tools engineered to streamline the process of designing racking systems for solar arrays.

FIGURE 11-13: EXAMPLE OF ONLINE RACKING DESIGN TOOL

(FROM IRONRIDGE)

Since that time, most racking system manufacturers offer online design tools (such as advertised in Figure 11-13) that factor in a location's wind loading, snow loading, rafter span and other factors - then generate a engineer-reviewed and code-compliant design, as well as a complete bill of materials.

Once site details have been entered (zip code, slope of roof, size of array, etc), the system will ask for specific product options, such are whether the system is ground mounted or roof mounted, flush-to-roof or ballasted. It will also ask for the specific panel that has been selected for the project, pulling the structural details of that panel from a database to size the system.

Based on size and loading, the online system will generate a system drawing indicating span lengths, support locations, as well as engineered diagrams that can be submitted the permitting authorities. Normally the systems will also generate a complete bill of materials required to complete the racking system.

Chapter 11 Review Questions

1) A rooftop racking system that is mounted four (4) to ten (10) inches from the surface of the roof on rails mounted directly to the roof's surface is called:
   a) a ballasted system
   b) a building integrated system
   c) an offset mounting system
   d) a flush-to-roof mounting system

2) Prior to installing a rooftop racking system, an installer/designer should do all the following **EXCEPT**:
   a) conduct a load compression test on the roof's substrate
   b) check the structural condition of the rafters to ensure they can bear the added weight of the system
   c) verify the wind load and snow load for the location
   d) determine if there are specific local codes or regulations that will affect the placement of the array on the building

3) The amount of lateral (side-to-side) stress placed on a mounting system is known as:
   a) shear loads
   b) pull-out loads
   c) live weight
   d) substrate tension

4) Wind loads on a solar array on a rooftop are affected by all the following **EXCEPT**:
   a) wind speed
   b) latitude
   c) height of the panel above the roof's surface
   d) relative location of the panel on the roof

5) When calculating the pull-out load of a rooftop system, a designer must take into account all of the following **EXCEPT**:
   a) hours of insolation
   b) wind exposure category
   c) occupancy category
   d) roof zone

6) The characteristics of the land that affects wind speed around a building or array is known as:
   a) surface roughness
   b) occupancy category
   c) tributary area
   d) zone of exposure

7) The portion of the array that is supported by a single footer is known as the:
   a) support region
   b) live load exposure area
   c) roof zone
   d) tributary area

8) A solar array is place on a rooftop constructed with vertical rafters (they run from the eave to the peak). The rafters are constructed on 16 inch centers. Footers are attached to every other rafter. The rails are spaced 34 inches apart running horizontally (parallel to the ridge of the roof). What is the tributary area of a single footer on this array?
   a) 1.89 square feet
   b) 3.78 square feet
   c) 7.55 square feet
   d) 15.11 square feet

9) A rooftop solar array has been designed for a home with pine rafters. The reference chart indicates that pine is rated for 235 pounds per inch when using 3/8 inch lag bolts (which will be used on this project).

   A measurement of the array finds it will occupy 730 square feet of roof space (40 panels measuring 39.4 inches wide by 65.95 inches tall with ½ inch gap between panels). The array will be oriented portrait in 4 rows of 10 panels. Footers will be located on every other rafter, which are spaced on 2-foot centers. Calculations show that 32 footers will be required for the array.

   If there is 25 pounds per square foot (psf) of uplift force at this location, what is the minimum length of lag bolt that will be required to mount the footers to the rafters?
   a) 1 ½ inch
   b) 2 ½ inch
   c) 3 ½ inch
   d) 4 ½ inch

10) When preparing footings for ground mounted systems, holes for these supports must be dug to below the frost line. In milder climates where the ground does not freeze, regulations usually require footings be located at least:
   a) three feet (36 inches) below the surface
   b) one foot (12 inches) deep for every 60 pounds of vertical pressure
   c) to a depth one half the distance of the span between the northern pier and and southern pier of a ground mounted system
   d) one foot (12 inches) below unsettled soil

11) Larger ground mounted systems require all the following **EXCEPT**:
   a) a fence around the entire array
   b) a 10-foot clear pathway around the perimeter of the array, between it and the fence
   c) fences must be at least 8-feet in height with posts located not more than 10 feet apart
   d) metal fences must be grounded

12) When placing a ground mounted system, consider all of the following **EXCEPT**:
   a) slope of the site
   b) land status (agricultural, residential, commercial, etc.)
   c) altitude
   d) accessibility

13) The range and number of directions a tracking system rotates is referred to as:
   a) sun tracking
   b) degrees of freedom
   c) azimuth and altitude adjustment
   d) loop control

14) Conductors located in a "readily accessible location" must be protected from unqualified persons. This can be accomplished through all of the following **EXCEPT**:
   a) place the conductors in a conduit or raceway
   b) use MC4 connectors
   c) locate the conductors at least six (6) feet above the ground surface
   d) construct a fence around the array (for ground mounted systems)

Chapter 12

Managing the Project

The tasks involved in managing a project are largely dependent upon the size of the project, the size and organization of the company managing the project, and local laws, restrictions and codes.

A two-person team installing a system on a home requires quite different management skills than a large design/consulting/installation firm installing a commercial system for a Google data center.

However, typically a project manager will be required to:
- prepare bid packages
- review project design
- coordinate installation schedules
- procure materials, equipment and services as needed
- develop project budget and track costs
- manage installation/design staff
- coordinate permitting process
- oversee safety and work processes on the job site
- manage logistical concerns at site
- serve as point-of-contact for customers/clients during the project
- provide progress reports and other status updates to client and management as required
- maintaining project records and databases
- troubleshoot issues relating to installations

Project Timeline

The actual installation of an array is likely to be the fastest, least time-consuming part of the process.

Even small residential systems can take a surprisingly long time to complete once the decision to go forward with the project has been made and the contracts signed.

Average time required for the various stages include:
- site assessment and system design: 30-45 days,
- permit applications: 30-40 days,
- installation of the system: 1-3 days,
- inspections and permission to operate: 15-30 days.

And that is when everything goes smoothly.

Larger commercial systems will likely take longer. Times required for the various tasks may include:
- site assessment and utility pre-screen: 10 days,
- system design and utility interconnection application: 40-50 days,
- procurement of product and equipment: 40-50 days,
- installation of the system: 7-10 days,
- inspections and permission to operate: 15-30 days.

Preparing Bid Packages

For small installations, the bidding process might be as simple as taking a walk around a homeowner's property, looking at the roof, service panel, and meter location - and then sitting down at the kitchen table over a cup of coffee and sketching out the proposed system with some rough cost estimates.

Larger systems (and well planned smaller installations for that matter) undergo a much more formal process. The bidding process often starts with a **Request for Proposal (RFP)**.

REQUEST FOR PROPOSAL (RFP)

The RFP is a formal bid document that outlines the project's product or service requirements, the contract terms, and the bidding process. The RFP will typically include:
- overview and background of the project,
- scope of work and deliverables (size of system, power generated, etc.),
- any specific requirements,
- submission process and key dates,
- selection criteria and process,
- required bidder submission documents .

Bidders will often be asked to provide:
- company profile information and resumes of key personnel that will be involved in the project,
- examples of previous installations,
- references,
- proof of insurance,
- the technical solution/scope of work (essentially the project design).

The scope of work may include:
- technical approach, design, equipment, installation plan,
- panel, inverter, racking specifications,
- equipment and workmanship warranties,
- exhibits showing proposed layouts and system single line diagrams,
- production estimates of the proposed system,
- proposed monitoring system/solution,
- any operations & maintenance (O&M) plan offered for the project.

Determining a bid price is more of an art than a science. Many factors will come into play. Smaller projects typically cost more per watt than larger projects. Market competition, system design, site conditions, the client's budget - all will be factors.

There are a number of online or project software packages that will assist in the bidding process. A very popular program, offered free from NREL, is the **System Advisor Model (SAM)**.

> SYSTEM ADVISOR
> MODEL (SAM)

The SAM program has weather and solar availability databases integrated so the project manager must simply select the location of the array, size, azimuth

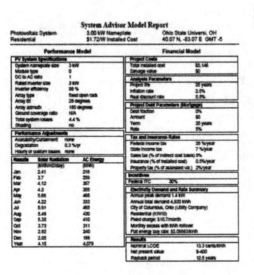
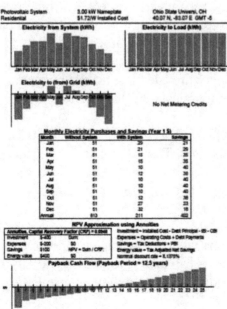

FIGURE 12-1: SAMPLE REPORT FROM SYSTEM ADVISOR MODEL (SAM)

and angle, derate factors, and inverter efficiency. The program will automatically generate an energy production estimate. It even allows for an estimate of the degradation over time of energy output.

DIRECT CAPITAL COST

INDIRECT CAPITAL COST

Financial data is then entered, such as **direct capital costs** (equipment, labor and overhead) and **indirect capital costs** (permitting, site engineering, interconnection fees, land acquisition costs, sales tax, interest costs of any loans) and operation and maintenance costs (if they are part of the estimate).

Any incentives available for the project, such as the 30% federal tax credit, are then entered.

SAM is integrated with a database of most utility rate schedules, which can be searched by zip code or selected from a database. Applicable utility rates are then applied, and a financial projection report such as illustrated in Figure 12-1 is generated.

Review Project Design

Prior to submitting a bid, make sure that the system as designed matches the specifications outlined in the request from the customer. A number of factors may require changes to the original design. These might include a poor site survey (distances for conduit runs, for example, were not accurately recorded), product availability, etc.

When changes to the original design are required, make sure to update all diagrams to reflect these changes and modify budgets to reflect any financial impacts of the changes.

Coordinate Project Schedule

Every project (not just solar) seems to take twice as long as expected and cost twice as much as expected. Sometimes delays are outside the control of a project manager, and sometimes schedules are disrupted because they are poorly planned or unrealistic.

Make sure adequate time is budgeted for each phase of the project, and communicate this to the client (don't over promise).

Typical phases and expected time frames for a typical residential project can be seen in Table 12-1. A project that may only take one day to install, may require months to complete from the initial deposit to the system providing power to the customer. For larger projects, much more time is typically required.

Many tasks are dependent upon a previous task, or sequential in nature. Others can take place during the same timeframe. For example, ordering product and scheduling an installation can happen simultaneously. However, a system cannot be inspected until it has been installed.

It may also be necessary to add **lag time** or a **lead time** to any of the project tasks. A lag time creates a delay between one task and another. For example, it may only take one day to pour a concrete pad for a ground mounted array, but may be necessary to wait 2-3 days for the concrete to set up before the support structure can be installed.

Description	Approx. Time
Secure Financing	Depends on Financial Institution
Local Incentive Approval	3-6 weeks
Utility Connection Approval	2-4 weeks
Engineering Approvals	1-2 weeks
Permits	2-4 weeks
Installation Scheduling	6-8 weeks
Procurement of Equipment & Product	6-8 weeks
Installation	1 day
Inspection	1-2 weeks

TABLE 12-1: TYPICAL RESIDENTIAL PROJECT TIME FRAMES FOR PV PROJECT

LAG TIME

LEAD TIME

With any project, but especially large installations, managing the schedule can become quite a complex task. A **Gantt chart** software management program is often used to manage this complexity.

GANTT CHART

These programs generate schedule reports, such as illustrated in Figure 12-2, that can assist in ensuring the project stays on track.

Procure Materials, Equipment and Services

Most products used in a solar installation are purchased through distributors or local retailers (for wire, conduit, etc). Seldom does an installer purchase directly from the manufacturer, except on rare occasions for speciality products or very large installations.

Find a distributor who is fair, delivers what and when promised, and carries a full line of quality products.

It may also be necessary in some instances to check with local utility and city officials to ensure all product selected is approved for that jurisdiction. Some new or uncommon devices may not be approved for use in all areas.

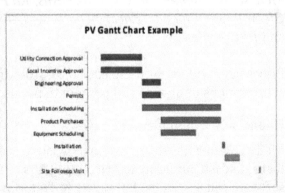

Task Name	Start	End	Duration (days)
Utility Connection Approval	1/16/2018	2/16/2018	31
Local Incentive Approval	1/16/2018	2/16/2018	31
Engineering Approval	2/16/2018	3/2/2018	14
Permits	2/16/2018	3/2/2018	14
Installation Scheduling	2/16/2018	4/16/2018	59
Product Purchases	3/2/2018	4/16/2018	45
Equipment Scheduling	3/2/2018	3/28/2018	26
Installation	4/17/2018	4/19/2018	2
Inspection	4/19/2018	4/30/2018	11
Site Followup Visit	5/15/2018	5/16/2018	1

FIGURE 12-2: GANTT CHART REPORT FOR PV PROJECT

Equipment used during the installation, such as lifts, scaffolding, augers, earth movers, will need to be scheduled well ahead of the installation and provisions will need to be made to receive them on site and secure them during installation.

Software Packages

Increasingly solar developers are relying on software packages to design and manage projects. These programs fall into a number of common groups.

Customer Identification

There are a number of solar-specific programs such as , *EnergySage, MODSolar, Faraday, PowerScout, Choose Energy* and *Google Project Sunroof* that serve as an online marketplace to match installers and potential customers. Often these packages allow facility owners/managers to enter their address and an image of the property (using Google Earth). Installers can then offer quotes and financing options.

Customer Relationship Management (CRM)

There are a number of software packages that have been designed to assist salespeople in maintaining data regarding new and existing customers. These are referred to as **customer relationship management** or CRM software. Programs such as *SalesForce* are used in any number of industries for this purpose.

> **CUSTOMER RELATIONSHIP MNGT**

There are a number of CRM packages tailored specifically to the solar industry, such as *MODsolar, ESolar CRM, enACT* and *solarnexus*.

System Design

There are quite a number of solar design software packages that incorporate satellite data, product databases, and even historical weather data to facilitate the creation of bid packages and complete system design. Some packages even incorporate features for pre-qualification, sales, permitting and financial analysis fo the project.

Popular software options include: *HelioScope , Aurora Solar, Open Solar, MODsolar, Sighten, enACT, solarnexus, Ra Power Management, solarnexus, Clean Power Finance, Energy Toolbase, UtilityAPI, Genability, HST Solar* and *PVComplete*.

Prices vary widely for these packages, from free (Open Solar for example) to subscriptions of about $150 per month per user.

Financial risk management

Many commercial solar customers wish to see their financing options, from loans, to cash purchase, to leases, to PPAs. Financial risk management software can access the latest data to factor in electric rate schedules, tariffs, rebates and other incentives - as well as current interest rates and fees. This allows for informed decisions on how best to finance or pay for the system.

Popular examples of this type of software include: *enACT, Mercatus, Sighten, T-REX, Ra Power Management, beEdison, Evervest* and *kWh Analytics.*

Operations/Energy Management

After the installation is complete, operations/energy management software can help owners monitor and manage solar sites. Some O&M software can also help reduce demand charges for systems with storage. Others can help improve efficiency and accuracy of asset management.

Popular examples of O&M software tailored to the solar industry include: *BPS Asset Management, Arbo, PowerHub, Power Factors, Diaspark Energy,* and *Voltaiq.*

Subcontractors

Hiring subcontractors during any project is always a process that presents many challenges. Subcontractors do not always show up when scheduled or perform their tasks in the manner or quality expected.

It is always a good idea to formalize any subcontractor arrangement with a **subcontractor agreement**. In the agreement, specify that the subcontractors aren't your employees, and that they're responsible for paying for their own benefits and taxes. It should allow both parties to terminate the agreement with proper notice.

> SUBCONTRACTOR AGREEMENT

The agreement should include the scope of the project, the subcontractor's responsibilities, the pay rate, and any deadlines that must be met. It should also detail how any disputes will be settled.

It is advisable to obtain proof of insurance from any subcontractors, plus any equipment operator certifications required, and have them sign an **indemnity agreement**. This agreement states that the subcontractor takes responsibility for their work should a lawsuit be filed that is directly related to their portion of the project.

> INDEMNITY AGREEMENT

There may arise some question as to whether or not a person assisting in the installation of a project is a contractor or should be treated as an employee. Clearly if an earthmoving firm is hired to prepare the site, they are a contractor. But arranging for an independent installer to help out on a large project might not be so clear cut.

The IRS has a number of criteria that is used in determining if a hire is a contractor or an employee. These include:

- Contractors are not required to follow, nor are they furnished with instructions to accomplish a job.
- Contractors typically do not receive training by the hiring firm. They use their own methods to accomplish the work.
- Contractors are hired to provide a result and usually have the right to hire others to do the actual work.
- Contractors set their own work hours.
- Usually contractors don't have a continuing relationship with a hiring company. The relationship can be frequent, but it must be at irregular intervals, on call or whenever work is available.
- Contractors offer their services to other firms or the general public.
- Contractors determine the order and sequence in performing their work.
- Contractors are paid by the job, not by time.
- Usually contractors furnish their own tools.
- Contractors should be able to make a profit or a loss. Employees can't suffer a loss.
- Contractors are responsible for the satisfactory completion of a job or they may be legally obligated to compensate the hiring firm for failure to complete.

1099 MISC

When a specific subcontractor has been paid more than $600 during a calendar year, the firm hiring them must file a **1099-MISC form** with the IRS. Many business-related payments do not have to be reported, although they may be taxable to the recipient. These include

- payments to corporations,
- payments for merchandise, telephone, freight, storage, and similar items.

Managing the Project Budget

Proper management of budgets ultimately define the success or failure of any company. A few strategies for maintaining control of costs include:

MOVES, ADDS AND CHANGES

CHANGE ORDERS

AS-BUILT DRAWINGS

- Communication with the client. Make sure both the client and the installing firm are clear as to the expectations, dates and deliverables of the project. Also make it clear that any **moves, adds and changes** that are requested by the customer are included in the final price. These charges for modifications should be well-defined before the project begins. These can be formalized in the form of **change orders**, and all modifications should be incorporated into the **as-built drawings**, diagrams that describe how the system was actually installed as opposed to how it was originally designed.

- Budget for surprises. Always build in some room in the budget for the unexpected (which nearly always occurs).

KEY PROJECT INDICATOR (KPI)

- Develop and track **key project indicators (KPIs)**. These indicators help determine if things are progressing as expected. Examples of common KPIs include:

- Actual cost of work performed (ACWP), shows how much money has been spent on a project to date.

- Cost variance (CV) indicates whether the estimated project cost is above or below expectations.

- Earned value (EV), shows the approved budget revenues for performed activities up to a particular time.

- Planned value (PV), is the estimated cost for activities planned/scheduled as of reporting date.

- Return on investment (ROI) shows a project's profitability.

Review the budget frequently. Waiting until the end of a project gives little or no opportunity to take corrective actions.

Keep all key players informed and hold them accountable for delivering what was promised when it was promised.

Project Team

Most solar installation companies operating in the US are small, with 64% comprised of fewer than 10 employees (according to NREL surveys).

For small installations a number of roles may be conducted by a single person, for larger projects each function may require a team of people. The project team may include:

- salesperson - makes the initial sale,

- designer - evaluates the site, determines optimal system configuration based on cost and performance, selects the appropriate equipment, and provides detailed electrical and mechanical drawings,

- project manager - coordinates all aspects of the PV installation from start to finish, ensuring PV performance, longevity, and financial feasibility,

- construction supervisor - procures equipment and materials, applies for appropriate permits, constructs the PV system, makes final electrical connections or tie-ins, commissions the system to verify proper performance, and warrantees craftsmanship,

- logistical coordinator - ensures equipment and product are available and on site when and where they are needed,

- installers - work with the construction supervisor to actually install the system,

- equipment operators/ subcontractors - operate specialized equipment (lifts, site grading, etc) as needed,

- manufacturers/distributors - supplies product, gives technical advice on best applications for equipment, and warrantees the equipment,

- O&M contractor - provides ongoing monitoring, inspection, and maintenance services and guarantees a defined level of performance.

Larger installations may also involve:

- civil/structural engineer - perform site evaluations to determine if the site is suitable for and can physically support the solar array,

- facility manger - corporate representative to work with the PV team to provide access to the site and minimize disruptions to the facility during construction,

- financial managers/auditors - provides financing and may require a performance guarantee

Permits and Contracts

Before any project can get underway, there will be a small amount of paperwork which must be addressed. A number of legal contracts must be completed with the utility, and in many cases there are permits required prior to installation.

There may also be in place a number of restrictions that can affect the solar installation. Many cities and/or homeowners associations (HOA) prohibit the installation of solar arrays within the neighborhood. In many states there are laws that prevent home owner's associations from prohibiting solar power system installations, including (as of 2018):

California, Colorado, Florida, Hawaii, Illinois, Indiana, Iowa, Louisiana, Maine, Maryland, Massachusetts, Nevada, New Hampshire, New Jersey, New Mexico, North Carolina, Oregon, Texas, Vermont, Virginia, Washington, West Virginia, and Wisconsin.

In these states HOAs cannot prevent you from installing a PV system on your home, but they may be able to place reasonable restrictions on the size and location of the panels.

The Utility

In a grid-tied system, the local utility must approve the interconnection. The interconnection application should be submitted early in the project development phase to ensure that the system is approved and to prevent it from sitting idle while waiting for approval.

Rules vary significantly by state, locality, and utility. Contacting the local utility is the best means of gathering information about the interconnection procedures and requirements.

Some utilities have a fast-track process for systems that meet certain requirements. If possible, design the PV system to meet the fast-track

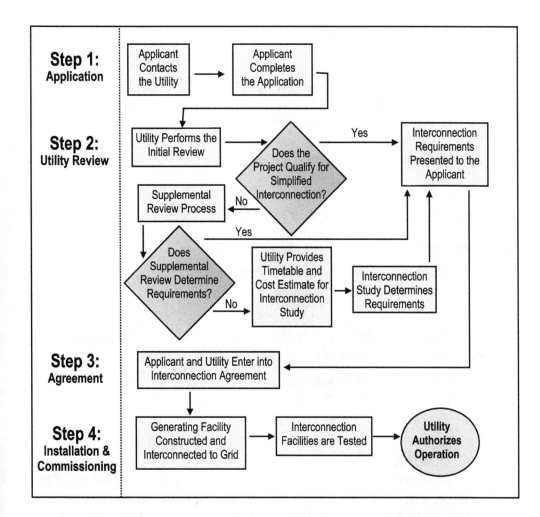

FIGURE 12-3: FLOW DIAGRAM OF CALIFORNIA INTERCONNECTION PROCESS

Step 1:
Application

Applicant Contacts the Utility → Applicant Completes the Application

Step 2:
Utility Review

Utility Performs the Initial Review

Does the Project Qualify for Simplified Interconnection?

Yes → Interconnection Requirements Presented to the Applicant

Supplemental Review Process

No

Does Supplemental Review Determine Requirements?

Yes

No → Utility Provides Timetable and Cost Estimate for Interconnection Study → Interconnection Study Determines Requirements

Step 3:
Agreement

Applicant and Utility Enter into Interconnection Agreement

Step 4:
Installation & Commissioning

Generating Facility Constructed and Interconnected to Grid → Interconnection Facilities are Tested → Utility Authorizes Operation

requirements in order to reduce the time, effort, and costs devoted to the interconnection process.

The approval process can, in some situations, be time consuming and relatively complicated, as the flow diagram for California's interconnection process illustrates (Figure 12-3).

Most utilities have created standard forms required from homeowners who intend to install a PV system. Bear in mind that there will likely be fees associated with each of these requirements. These include:

- **Interconnection Agreement.** This document sets forth all the terms and conditions under which the system can be connected to the utility grid. It includes information about the homeowner's obligation to obtain permits and insurance, plus it outlines how the system must be operated and maintained.

INTERCONNECTION AGREEMENT

- **Net Metering Agreement.** This document, often called the "sale/purchase agreement", spells out the conditions under which the excess power from the system will be purchased by the utility, and the

NET METERING AGREEMENT

rates that will be charged to the homeowner for the power purchased from the utility.

- Insurance Requirement. Most utilities require the homeowner provide insurance to protect the utility's system and personnel from any problems that might be the result of connecting the photovoltaic array to the grid. Basic homeowner's insurance may already be adequate, or a rider may need to be purchased to meet this requirement.

The representative from the utility company may also be able to outline other permits that are required within their jurisdiction.

County or City Building Department

Requirements vary widely from place to place, as will the fees charged. But applying for a permit requires preparation. Typically a jurisdiction will require:

ELECTRICAL PERMIT

MECHANICAL PERMIT

- an **electrical permit** (assessing the system from an electrical perspective, such as wiring size, bonding and grounding, equipment ratings, etc.),

- a **mechanical permit** (assessing the structural elements such as the racking system design, effects of the PV load on the structure of the home, etc.),

- licenses and/or certifications may also be required by the local jurisdiction.. It may be necessary to check with the state's licensing board to determine what licenses are required to install PV systems. For example, a licensed electrician may be required to install the wiring portion of the system. Or the municipality may require that the system be designed by a certified professional (certified in PV design through an organization such as ETA or NABCEP).

The Application Package

Much of the success of the permitting process depends upon how prepared the applicant is when first approaching the permitting agency. A complete application packet will be invaluable years down the line in monitoring and maintaining the system. Don't neglect this important step of the overall process. There is no such thing as providing too much information at this stage.

While specific requirements vary from jurisdiction to jurisdiction, the application typically includes:
- the site address and contact information,
- the make and model of all specified equipment (as well as copies of the manufacturer's specifications),
- system component warrantees,
- AC output rating of the system,

ONE-LINE DRAWING

- a **one-line drawing** of the PV design,

- the racking manufacturer's installation instructions (displaying the array support structure),
- any structural assessment of the building's ability to support the load (from an engineer or the rack manufacturer). For a roof mounted system, information may include: age of roof, roof type, rafter size and spacing, rafter span, weight of array,
- a **plan view** that provides a "bird's eye" view of the site, showing all the locations of the various components,
- photos of the site,
- a copy of the necessary license (if required),
- a copy of the necessary certification (if required),
- a copy of a utility bill (for grid-tied systems),
- battery bank location and venting (for stand-alone systems),
- a schedule of warning labels that will be installed onto the system.

PLAN VIEW

The One-Line Drawing

A one-line drawing is a simple electrical drawing that uses boxes to represent the various components of the system and lines to represent the conductors and conduits connecting these components together.

A very detailed one-line drawing will not only assist in the permitting process, but will be of great help during the installation of the system as well. The drawing can be made by hand or as is more common, created with the assistance of a CAD program.

The one-line drawing (as illustrated in Figure 12-4) should include:
- the site address and the installer's contact information,
- the make and model of all the equipment,
- the PV array system information (rating, modules, strings, STC panel specifications),
- hot and cold temperatures used for sizing strings,
- wire sizes, types and run lengths,
- conduit sizes and wire counts within each raceway,
- general location of equipment (inside, outside, on roof, etc),
- specifications for the point of interconnection with the grid,
- conductor size calculations,
- voltage drop calculations.

The Plan View

The plan view provides a "bird's eye" view of where the system and its various components will be located on the property. Images from Google Earth can be used in creating this document.

The plan view is quite helpful in determining if all the components will fit on the site, or if any obstacles will prevent the design from being implemented in

One Line Drawing - Sample

SITE ADDRESS: _____

CONTACT PERSON: _____

CONTACT TELEPHONE: _____

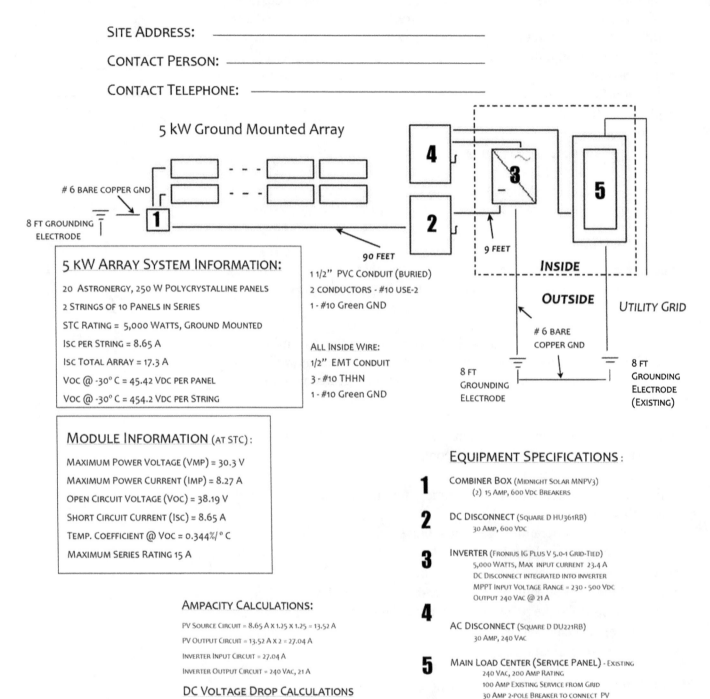

5 kW Ground Mounted Array

6 BARE COPPER GND

8 FT GROUNDING ELECTRODE

90 FEET

9 FEET

INSIDE

OUTSIDE

UTILITY GRID

6 BARE COPPER GND

8 FT GROUNDING ELECTRODE

8 FT GROUNDING ELECTRODE (EXISTING)

5 KW ARRAY SYSTEM INFORMATION:

20 ASTRONERGY, 250 W POLYCRYSTALLINE PANELS

2 STRINGS OF 10 PANELS IN SERIES

STC RATING = 5,000 WATTS, GROUND MOUNTED

ISC PER STRING = 8.65 A

ISC TOTAL ARRAY = 17.3 A

VOC @ -30° C = 45.42 VDC PER PANEL

VOC @ -30° C = 454.2 VDC PER STRING

1 1/2" PVC CONDUIT (BURIED)

2 CONDUCTORS - #10 USE-2

1 - #10 Green GND

ALL INSIDE WIRE:

1/2" EMT CONDUIT

3 - #10 THHN

1 - #10 Green GND

MODULE INFORMATION (AT STC):

MAXIMUM POWER VOLTAGE (VMP) = 30.3 V

MAXIMUM POWER CURRENT (IMP) = 8.27 A

OPEN CIRCUIT VOLTAGE (VOC) = 38.19 V

SHORT CIRCUIT CURRENT (ISC) = 8.65 A

TEMP. COEFFICIENT @ VOC = 0.344%/° C

MAXIMUM SERIES RATING 15 A

EQUIPMENT SPECIFICATIONS:

1 COMBINER BOX (MIDNIGHT SOLAR MNPV3)
(2) 15 AMP, 600 VDC BREAKERS

2 DC DISCONNECT (SQUARE D HU361RB)
30 AMP, 600 VDC

3 INVERTER (FRONIUS IG PLUS V 5.0-1 GRID-TIED)
5,000 WATTS, MAX INPUT CURRENT 23.4 A
DC DISCONNECT INTEGRATED INTO INVERTER
MPPT INPUT VOLTAGE RANGE = 230 - 500 VDC
OUTPUT 240 VAC @ 21 A

4 AC DISCONNECT (SQUARE D DU221RB)
30 AMP, 240 VAC

5 MAIN LOAD CENTER (SERVICE PANEL) - EXISTING
240 VAC, 200 AMP RATING
100 AMP EXISTING SERVICE FROM GRID
30 AMP 2-POLE BREAKER TO CONNECT PV

AMPACITY CALCULATIONS:

PV SOURCE CIRCUIT = 8.65 A X 1.25 X 1.25 = 13.52 A

PV OUTPUT CIRCUIT = 13.52 A X 2 = 27.04 A

INVERTER INPUT CIRCUIT = 27.04 A

INVERTER OUTPUT CIRCUIT = 240 VAC, 21 A

DC VOLTAGE DROP CALCULATIONS

DC CONDUCTOR LENGTH = 99 FT

V DROP = 17.3 A X 1.24 / 1000 FT X 2(99 FT) = 4.25 VDC

4.25 V / 303 V = 1.4% VOLTAGE DROP

TOTAL SYSTEM DERATE = .87

FIGURE 12-4: ONE-LINE DRAWING OF 5 KW GROUND MOUNTED PV SYSTEM USING A STRING INVERTER

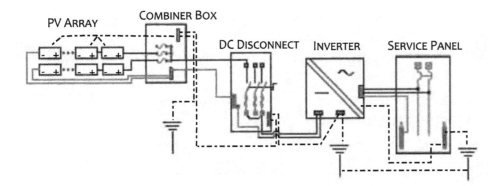

the "real world." Or if the system intrudes into easements or over property lines.

Three-Line Drawing

Electricians are usually more comfortable working from three-line wiring diagrams that illustrate all the conductors in a circuit and utilize standard electrical symbols.

The single-line drawing is typically used to work out the overall design of the project, and is typically required as part of the application process. The three-line diagram gets into a bit more detail.

The **three-line drawing** is typically part of the detailed design document. It is used in designing circuit diagrams, control circuits, phase sequencing, transformer connections, etc.

THREE-LINE DRAWING

In a three-line diagram, all conductors are shown individually, as are the internal connection points of switches and inverters, as shown in Figure 12-5.

Daily Briefings and Toolbox Talks

It is normal on the job site that the project manager or lead technician conducts daily informal briefings, outlining the day's goals, scheduling issues, deliveries, and safety concerns. These meetings are typically brief and informal, taking place on the job site just before beginning a task or shift.

A **toolbox talk**, sometimes referred to as a **tailgate meeting**, is an informal safety meeting that outlines safety concerns or topics for a specific job. These might be unusual weather conditions, a specific planned hazardous activity, or simply a generalized reminder of safe work practices.

TOOLBOX TALK

TAILGATE MEETING

Toolbox talks are intended to facilitate health and safety on the job site and promote the organization's safety culture. The firm's safety plan should be distributed to all employees and contractors, and reinforced daily through these short briefings.

It is the project manager's responsibility to ensure that the work site is complying with safe working practices. To ensure a safe work site:

- Ensure that all site personnel are equipped with complete personal protective equipment for the task.

- Make sure all areas are clear of hazards and have clear signage identifying any hazard that may exist.

- Ensure that all appropriate barriers and enclosures are in place.

- Control access to site and inform visitors and workers on safety risks and procedures.

- Designate a health and safety coordinator on site.

- Periodically stop work and verify that all safety measures are in place and followed.

- Verify that a first aid kit is available and assessable.

For larger installations, the site manager may also wish to meet with local "first responders" such as fire marshal, local fire department, and police to familiarize them with access and shutoffs.

Project Documentation

There is a substantial amount of paperwork and record keeping incorporated into a well-managed solar PV installation. Aside from the original project bid and application, project managers should maintain and assemble:

- as-built documentation incorporating any moves, adds or changes,
- copies of any required permits,
- copies of interconnection and net metering agreements,
- subcontractor agreements,
- insurance documentation,
- photographs of the site before, during and after installation,
- equipment specification documentation (**data sheets),**
- documentation of all equipment serial numbers,
- equipment and/or installation warranty information,
- change orders,
- inspection forms and certificates of inspection,
- commissioning forms,
- documentation of all system test results,
- operation and maintenance manual.

DATA SHEETS

Operation and Maintenance Documentation

Once the system is up and running, it is good practice to maintain documentation that will ensure the system functions for many years to come.

This **operation and maintenance (O&M) documentation** should include all the documentation listed above, as well as:

OPERATION AND
MAINTENANCE
DOCUMENTATION

- procedures for verifying the proper system operation,
- emergency shutdown procedures,
- contact information for: system owner, utility, local authorities having jurisdiction, building owner, emergency numbers,
- a maintenance schedule,
- future site improvements that might affect the array,
- warranty documents for all components of the PV system as well as maintenance requirements to keep warranties valid,
- an inventory of spare parts kept onsite,
- a troubleshooting checklist.

Customer Orientation Meeting

Once the system is up and running, it is always a good idea to sit down with the customer and orient them to the system. In addition to providing them with a copy of the operation and maintenance documentation, the project manager should:

- Conduct a complete walk through of the system, explaining each part and its function.

- Explain and demonstrate the startup and shutdown procedures for the system.

- Detail any safety issues or concerns regarding system access and operation.

- Explain code requirements such as clearance around equipment.

- Discuss realistic energy production expectations.

- Outline the operation and maintenance requirements and processes.

- Train the customer to perform operation and maintenance (O&M) activities.

- Demonstrate system monitoring software.

- Address any remaining customer concerns.

Photograph the system and the production output readings, so there is a record that the system was performing as expected when it was "handed off" to the client. It may also be a good idea to have the customer sign a completion of work document to that effect as well.

Chapter 12 Review Questions

1) A formal bid document created by the potential customer that typically includes the scope of work, specific requirements, selection criteria, required documents, etc. is referred to as:
   a) a request for proposal (RFP)
   b) an operation and maintenance document (O&M)
   c) a system bid package (SBP)
   d) a rapid response document (RRD)

2) Which of the following would **NOT** be considered as one of a project's direct capital costs?
   a) permitting fees
   b) purchase price of solar panels
   c) labor costs of installers
   d) all the above should be considered direct capital costs

3) A tool typically used in managing the scheduling of a project is:
   a) a Gantt chart
   b) an RFP
   c) a key project indicator (KPI) matrix
   d) a MACRS schedule

4) A software program designed to assist with maintaining new and existing customer data is called:
   a) customer identification system (CIS)
   b) customer retention package (CRP)
   c) lead management system (LMS)
   d) customer relationship management (CRM)

5) Which of the following indicates an individual is an employee rather than an independent contractor?
   a) the installer is paid by the job rather than by the hour
   b) the installer uses tools supplied by the installation firm
   c) the installer works for a number of installation companies
   d) the installer sets his or her own hours to complete the task

6) The actual cost of work performed to date, earned value as of a specific date, cost variances and return on investment are examples of:
   a) key project indicators (KPI)
   b) change orders
   c) Gantt projections
   d) indirect capital costs

7) Which of the following would likely **NOT** be included in a project application package?
   a) a one-line drawing
   b) a three-line drawing
   c) an electrical permit
   d) a plan view

8) An informal daily safety meeting that generally takes place at the job site is often referred to as:
   a) a plan view
   b) a "come to Jesus" meeting
   c) a tailgate party
   d) a toolbox talk

9) Operation and Maintenance (O&M) documentation should include all of the following **EXCEPT**:
   a) emergency shutdown procedures
   b) change orders
   c) a troubleshooting checklist
   d) warranty documentation

Chapter 13

Project Safety

Chapter Objectives:

- Understand the critical importance of safety on all projects.
- Develop comprehensive safety policies and procedures.
- Assess safety issues prior to beginning work on a site.
- Identify the specifications for and situations that require personal protective equipment.
- Review the requirements and specifications of guardrails.
- Understand ladder safety and specifications.
- Identify the risks involved in using power tools.
- Ensure proper lifting and carrying procedures are followed on the site.
- Assess risks involved in working with electricity.
- Develop a lock-out tag-out process.
- Design and utilize proper scaffolding systems as appropriate.
- Identify safety issues that arise when working in trenches.

When it comes to actually installing a PV system, reading and following the manufacturer's instructions will likely be the primary guide. Each product fits together just a bit differently - and it is impossible to anticipate all the variations.

However, there are a number of commonalities that can and should be identified.

But before beginning the actual install, it is every installer's obligation and responsibility to ensure that the site is a safe working environment.

Safety First

People who work with or come in contact with photovoltaic systems are exposed to a certain amount of risk. Developing a culture of safety for yourself and the company you work for will help minimize these risks.

PV installers often work at height (on ladders and rooftops) that expose them to fall hazards. Working with electrical circuits can result in injury and/or death from electrocution and arc-flash.

There are dangers from working long hours on hot rooftops in direct sunlight. The use of power tools and heavy equipment operation poses the constant risk of injury. Many a back is injured by lifting heavy loads improperly. And then there are the respiratory hazards and other risks associated with working within confined spaces.

Developing a safe workplace culture is not only good practice, it is good business and it is the law. From the perspective of the business owner, aside from the obvious pain, suffering and trauma associated with a workplace injury, there is also:

- lost productivity due to down-time,
- time lost by an injured employee,
- time lost by others helping the accident victim,
- cleanup and start-up of operations interrupted by an accident,
- time to hire and/or train a new worker to replace the injured worker until they return to work,
- time and cost to repair or replace materials damaged in the accident,
- cost of paying the employees wages while they are recovering,
- cost of completing paperwork generated by the accident,
- any costs resulting from lawsuits.
- increased insurance and worker's compensation costs,
- OSHA penalties,
- negative reputation or publicity,
- and perhaps the inability to bid on future jobs due to a poor safety record.

BUREAU OF WORKER'S COMPENSATION

According to the **Bureau of Worker's Compensation**, the average cost (in 2010) for workplace accidents caused by slip and fall injuries was $41,393. For accidents involving electrical burns, it was $40,995. If a worker is killed on the job, the average cost was $1,390,000.

OSHA (the Occupational Safety and Health Administration) is responsible for creating the laws that govern worker safety for private-sector employees in all 50 states. It was established by the US Congress in 1971 within the Department of Labor. It requires all private businesses to provide a safe working environment for their employees.

Since coming into existence, government statistics show a 42% decline in workplace injuries and a 62% decline in work-related deaths. Even so, every day 15 people (on average) die in the US from work-related incidents.

OSHA establishes workplace safety requirements, enforces them (through site visits and penalties for non-compliance) and offers consulting services to companies to help improve workplace safety.

OSHA 300

Any employer with more than 10 employees must maintain and submit a log, called the **OSHA 300,** that details all work-related injuries and illnesses resulting in lost workdays, restricted work or transfer to another job, and any incident that requires more than first aid treatment.

Many businesses also require certificates in safety training, such as OSHA-10 (10-hour training program) or OSHA-30 (30-hour training program).

Rules and regulations for workplace safety can be found in the **Code of Federal Regulations (CFR) Title 29**. Those addressing **occupational hazards** associated with the construction industry can be found in **Part 1926**.

CFR TITLE 29

OCCUPATIONAL HAZARDS

PART 1926

Companies risk fines from OSHA if they fail to put workplace safety policies in place, do not supervise the implementation of workplace safety practices, do not enforce workplace safety practices, or do not adequately train employees in workplace policies and procedures.

Typical safety related hazards include:
- heat-producing operations, hot objects, or flames,
- unstable or slippery walking/working surfaces,
- unguarded openings,
- electrical hazards,
- chemical hazards,
- abrasive surfaces and edges,
- moving equipment or materials,
- extreme weather conditions.

OSHA regulations require that the employer place a **competent person** on the job site to oversee and manage potentially dangerous situations. They define a competent person as "one who is capable of identifying existing and predictable hazards in the surroundings or working conditions which are unsanitary, hazardous, or dangerous to employees, and who has authorization to take prompt corrective measures to eliminate them."

COMPETENT PERSON

In other words, there must be someone on site who is both trained and knowledgeable in workplace safety and also has been given the authority to enforce safe practices.

Before Arriving at the Site

Before a single worker sets foot on the job site, the job supervisor should have asked and answered questions such as the following:

- Are safety policies and procedures in place?

- Have all employees been trained in the company's safety practices?

- Is there a process in place to enforce safety practices?

- Are employees trained to safely perform the job with which they are tasked?

- What prep-work is required at the site prior to the job?

- What safety equipment is required at the site and is it in place and in good working order?

- Are employees working from ladders or roof tops? Is fall protection required?

- Are there any severe or unusual conditions at the site that may impact the safety of workers?
- Is someone on the job site at all times who is trained in first aid and emergency procedures?
- What medical facilities are nearby and what is the plan of action should an accident occur?
- What job tasks are required after the installation has been finished and has enough time been allocated to complete them safely?

Safety Policies and Procedures

Every installation should have safety policies and procedures in place prior to beginning the job. These practices should also be well communicated to every individual who will be on the job site.

These safety practices should include (but are not limited to):
- a personal protective equipment policy,
- procedures for using power tools and extension cords,
- maintaining an uncluttered work environment,
- proper lifting and carrying procedures,
- proper ladder use policies,
- processes to reduce the risk of heat exhaustion and de-hydration,
- policies and procedures for working with solar electric PV panels,
- ensuring proper safety equipment is in place on the job site,
- avoiding electric shock and arc-hazard risks,
- establishing lock-out tag-out procedures.

Work Site Hazard Assessment

Prior to beginning an installation at a job site, and then again before each shift, the assigned competent person in charge of workplace safety should assess the project location and determine if there are any identifiable safety concerns.

Look for hazards in these categories:
- impact,
- penetration,
- falling objects or potential for dropping objects,
- compression (roll-over),
- chemical,
- heat,
- inhalation,
- light (optical) radiation.

For example:

- Will the job take place on a roof where there is a potential of dropping tools or materials on pedestrians below?

- Is scaffolding to be used that must be assembled and inspected?

- Is a boom truck to be used on site, with the potential to damage people and property as it moves about the site?

Specifically look for:
- unstable or slippery walking or working surfaces,
- unguarded openings or ledges,
- electrical hazards,
- chemical hazards,
- abrasive surfaces and edges,
- moving equipment or materials,
- extreme weather conditions,
- heat producing operations, hot objects, or flames.

Identify these work site hazards and ensure that adequate protective measures are taken to reduce the risk, such as warning signs, barricades, clear pathways, etc.

Next, identify any workers that may be exposed to these hazards and make sure they are aware of them. Verify that each worker has the appropriate **personal protective equipment (PPE)** required for the tasks they are to perform.

PERSONAL PROTECTIVE
EQUIPMENT

Personal Protective Equipment

Nothing can assure that an individual will not sustain an injury on the job, but the use of properly maintained personal protective equipment can help reduce the risk of injury should something unexpected occur. In most cases, the employer must pay for and provide protective equipment if it is required for and used exclusively for the job-related tasks.

On every site and for every worker, it should be determined:
- when personal protective equipment is necessary,
- what type of PPE is necessary,
- how to properly put on, remove, adjust, and wear PPE,
- the limitations of the PPE,
- the proper care, maintenance, useful life and disposal of the PPE.

Some examples of personal protective equipment include:

FIGURE 13-1: MUST WEAR ANSI Z87.1 RATED SAFETY GLASSES WHEN WORKING WITH ELECTRICITY

- Foot and leg protection (safety shoes, for example)
- Eye and face protection (ANSI Z87.1-1989) - as shown in Figure 13-1. Employers must ensure that their employees wear eye protection if if there is flying debris (dust, metal, wood) or exposure to chemicals.
- Head protection: Employers must ensure that their employees wear head protection if: objects might fall from above and strike them on the head; they might bump their heads against fixed objects, such as exposed pipes or beams; or there is a possibility of accidental head contact with electrical hazards.

Hard Hats

Hard hats are divided into three industrial classes:

CLASS A HARD HAT

CLASS B HARD HAT

CLASS C HARD HAT

FIGURE 13-2: STAMP IN HARD HAT INDICATES IT WAS MANUFACTURED IN SEPTEMBER, 2004.

- **Class A hard hats** (may be referred to as Class G or general use) provide impact and penetration resistance along with limited voltage protection (up to 2,200 volts).

- **Class B hard hats** (may be referred to as Class E or electrical use) provide the highest level of protection against electrical hazards, with high-voltage shock and burn protection (up to 20,000 volts). They also provide protection from impact and penetration hazards by flying/falling objects.

- **Class C hard hats** (may be referred to as conductive) provide  lightweight comfort and impact protection but offer no protection from electrical hazards (often made of aluminum).

Because ultra violet light degrades the plastic (makes it brittle), hard hats are dated (see Figure 13-2). Typically a hard hat will have to be replaced after every three years of use.

Other personal protective equipment includes:
- protective gloves,
- hearing protection,
- **personal fall arrest systems (PFAS).**

PERSONAL FALL ARREST SYSTEM

Fall Protection

Falls are a leading cause of death in the workplace, accounting for 13% of all workplace fatalities and 20% of all workplace injuries as detailed in Figure 13-3.

Fall protection is required whenever there is the possibility that a worker may fall from one level to another level that is more than six feet. below This protection may take the form of **guardrails**, cages, safety nets or personal fall

GUARDRAILS

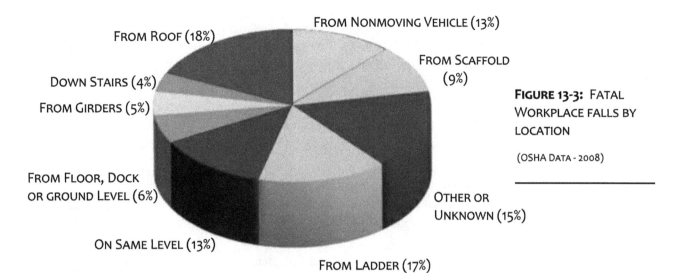

FROM NONMOVING VEHICLE (13%)

FROM ROOF (18%)

FROM SCAFFOLD (9%)

DOWN STAIRS (4%)

FROM GIRDERS (5%)

FIGURE 13-3: FATAL WORKPLACE FALLS BY LOCATION

(OSHA DATA - 2008)

FROM FLOOR, DOCK OR GROUND LEVEL (6%)

OTHER OR UNKNOWN (15%)

ON SAME LEVEL (13%)

FROM LADDER (17%)

arrest systems (PFAS) such as a **safety harness** and **lanyard**, as illustrated in Figure 13-4.

SAFETY HARNESS AND LANYARD

Personal fall arrest systems consist of:
- an anchorage,
- connectors,
- a body harness.

The safety harness has a metal ring attached at the back to which a safety line is attached. The other end of the safety line is then secured to the roof.

The anchorage for a fall-arrest system must support at least 5,000 pounds.

FIGURE 13-4: HARNESS AND LANYARD

(FROM MUTUAL INDUSTRIES)

PFAS are required if workers have the potential to fall 10 feet or more. They should be rigged so that the worker cannot free fall more than 6 feet, or hit a surface below when the system is fully extended.

Self-retracting lifelines, as shown in Figure 13-5, and lanyards that automatically limit free fall distance to 2 feet (0.6 meters) or less should be capable of sustaining a minimum tensile load of 3,000 pounds applied to the device with the lifeline or lanyard in the fully extended position.

SELF-RETRACTING LIFELINE

When using a fall arrest system, there must be another person present who can assist the worker should they fall, to avoid prolonged suspension which in itself can cause serious injury or death.

Fall protection must be provided when employees are exposed to the following hazards of falling 6 feet or more:
- holes (such as openings or skylights workers could fall into),
- wall openings,
- established roofs, floors, mezzanines, balconies and walkways with unprotected sides or edges,
- excavations.

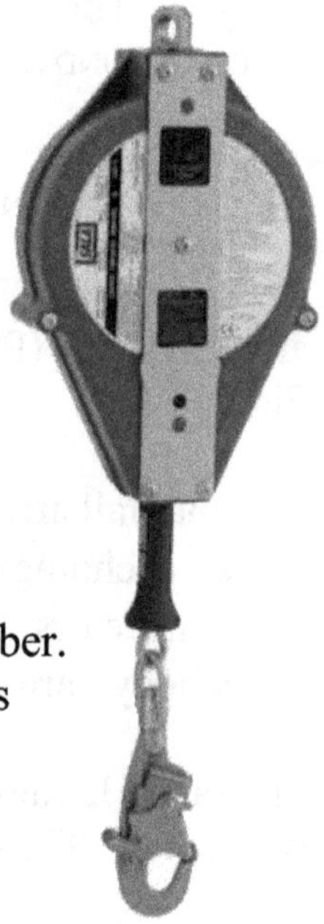

All PPE should be well cared for, clean, inspected regularly, and stored properly. Body harnesses, belts, and lanyards should not be stored in areas where they can become damp or exposed to direct sunlight.

FIGURE 13-5: SELF-RETRACTING LIFELINE

TOPRAIL

MIDRAIL

TOEBOARD

Guardrails

A guardrail system is a common type of fall protection. It consists of a **toprail**, **midrail**, and intermediate vertical member. They also often incorporate a **toeboard** that prevent materials from rolling off the working surface.

Guardrails are often used and/or required:
- on unprotected edges of a ramp or runway
- on the unprotected sides or a building or edges of holes

FIGURE 13-6: PROPERLY DESIGNED GUARDRAIL SYSTEM

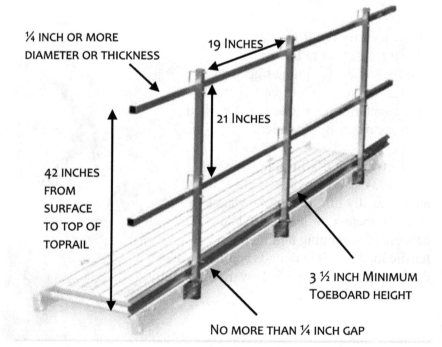

¼ INCH OR MORE DIAMETER OR THICKNESS

19 INCHES

21 INCHES

42 INCHES FROM SURFACE TO TOP OF TOPRAIL

3 ½ INCH MINIMUM TOEBOARD HEIGHT

NO MORE THAN ¼ INCH GAP

- around hoisting areas with a chain or gate placed across the hoist opening when not in use.

Guardrail systems must be free of any imperfection that might cut a worker or snag a worker's clothing. If guardrail systems are used around holes that are used as access points (such as for a ladder), gates must be installed.

Guidelines for constructing guardrail systems are very specific, as shown in Figure 13-6, and include:
- system must be capable of withstanding 200 pounds of pressure,
- toprail must be 42 inches above the surface (plus or minus 3 inches),
- toprail must be at least ¼ inch in diameter or thickness,
- bottom rail (toeboard) not more than ¼ inch above surface, but must be a minimum of 3 ½ inches up from the surface, solid or constructed so that no hole is bigger than 1 inch,
- midrail must be installed halfway (21 inches) from ground to the toprail,
- vertical supports should be located not more than 19 inches apart,
- the ends of toprails and midrails must not overhang the end posts, except where it does not constitute a projection hazard.

Ladder Use

One obvious disadvantage of a roof-mounted system is that it is located up on a roof. The installation process makes it necessary to get the materials, equipment and people up there and do it safely.

Any time there is a break in elevation of 19 inches or more, OSHA requires that the worker be provided with a ladder or stairs. Ladders are prone to damage, so inspect all ladders prior to each use.

If workers are exposed to fall hazards on the job, their employer must provide a training program that teaches how to recognize the hazards of falling and the procedures to follow to minimize those hazards.

To move from one level to another (say from the ground to a rooftop) often requires the use of a ladder.

Description	Type	Load Rating	Color
Light Duty	Type III	200 pounds	Red
Medium Duty	Type II	225 pounds	Green
Heavy Duty	Type I	250 pounds	Blue
Extra Heavy Duty	Type IA	300 pounds	Orange
Special Duty	Type IAA	375 pounds	Yellow

TABLE 13-1: RATING SYSTEM FOR LADDERS

When working with electricity (always a concern in a PV system), only **fiberglass** ladders should be used. These are non-conductive and will help keep those working with electricity safe from the ladder accidentally coming in contact with a "live" wire. OSHA requires their use in any workplace situation where the ladder may in contact with electrical conductors.

Ladders are rated and color-coded based on how much weight they are designed to carry safely, as indicated in Table 13-1. Bear in mind that this weight rating does not just apply to the weight of the person climbing the ladder, but also includes the tools and materials that person might be carrying while on the ladder.

All portable ladders must be capable of supporting at least 4 times their rated weight.

The length of portable ladders is also restricted. If the distance is greater than limits listed below, a permanent fixed ladder must be installed, or lifts used.
- stepladders must be no longer than 20 feet,
- single ladders must not be longer than 30 feet,
- extension ladders must not be longer than 60 feet.

Carrying Ladders

Ladders should be carried horizontally when moving them from place to place. Look up when moving ladders to avoid coming in contact with overhead power lines. Use two people to carry extension ladders whenever possible.

Placing a Ladder

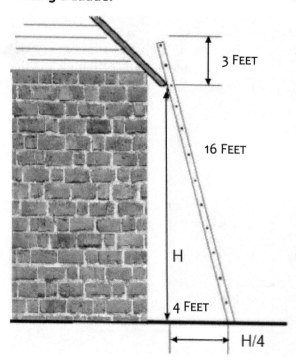

FIGURE 13-7: PROPER PLACEMENT OF A LADDER

3 FEET

16 FEET

H

4 FEET

H/4

When placing a portable ladder against a building, the base of the ladder should be about one-fourth the distance from the building as the height where the top of the ladder touches the building.

In other words, if the ladder touches the eave of the building at 16 feet above ground level (as illustrated in Figure 13-7), then the base should be placed four feet from the vertical line where the ladder touches the structure.

Additionally, for ladders up to 36 feet in length, the top rung of the ladder should extend at least three feet (three ladder rungs) above the roof line. Ladders should extend a minimum of 4 feet above the roof line for ladders 36-48 feet, and 5 feet for ladders longer than 48 feet.

Any fixed ladder (one which is permanently mounted to the building) that is over 24 feet tall must incorporate fall protection, such as a safety line or a cage.

A second ladder is required if 25 or more employees are in an area.

Securing Ladders
It is safer, and often required, that a ladder placed against the building be secured at the top and at the bottom.

While there is no standard way of accomplishing this, on dry level ground the base can be secured by tying it with a rope to a stake driven into the ground or bolted to the wall (as demonstrated in Figure 13-8).

The top of the ladder should also be secured on the first trip up the ladder. There are a number of products available on the market to accomplish this task (as illustrated in Figure 13-9) or it can be secured temporarily as demonstrated in Figure 13-10.

Climbing a Ladder
The five steps to safe ladder climbing include:
- Step 1: Check shoes
- Step 2: Look up
- Step 3: Mount the ladder
- Step 4: Climb
- Step 5: Center your body

When climbing a ladder, utilize the **three points-of-contact** technique. This requires that at all times the climber must face the ladder and have two hands and one foot, or two feet and one hand in contact with the **cleats** and/or **rails**. This will minimize the chance of slipping and falling from the ladder.

FIGURE 13-8: BASE OF LADDER PROPERLY SECURED

(FROM DIY ADVICE)

FIGURE 13-9: INSTALLED POINT WHERE THE LADDER CAN BE SECURED TO THE ROOF.

FIGURE 13-10: A STRAP IS CLAMPED TO THE FASCIA BOARD TO PROVIDE LADDER STABILITY

(FROM QUALCRAFT)

THREE POINTS-OF-CONTACT

CLEATS

RAILS

It is important to note that the climber must not carry any objects in either hand that can interfere with a firm grip on the ladder.

Other ladder climbing safety tips include:
- always face the ladder when climbing,
- no more than one person on the ladder at one time,
- use the 3-point climbing technique,
- keep the area around the bottom and top of the ladder clear of debris or obstacles,
- do not use in windy conditions,
- raised ladders should never be left unattended,
- wear slip-resistant shoes when climbing ladders,
- keep your body centered, your belt buckle should never stray outside the rungs of the ladder.

Using Power Tools

Power tools, such as drills, are common on the job site. They must be maintained in safe working condition, and be inspected by a competent person prior to use to ensure they are in safe operational condition.

Where possible, use battery-operated power tools to avoid the hazards associated with electrical cords on the site. Ground fault circuit interrupters should be installed on construction sites using 120-volt single-phase temporary receptacles.

To prevent hazards associated with the use of power tools, installers should take the following precautions:
- Never carry a tool by the cord.
- Never pull the cord to disconnect it from the receptacle.
- Keep cords and hoses away from heat, oil, and sharp edges.
- Disconnect tools when they are not in use.
- Secure work with clamps or a vise, freeing both hands to operate the tool.
- Maintain tools. Keep them sharp and clean for best performance.
- Follow instructions in the user's manual.
- Be sure to keep good footing and maintain good balance when operating power tools.
- Wear proper apparel for the task. Loose clothing, ties, or jewelry can become caught in moving parts.
- Use the proper PPE for the task.
- Keep people not involved in the task away from the work area.
- All persons using the tool must be trained in their safe use.
- Make sure all tool guards are in place and in good working order.
- Remove all damaged portable electric tools from use and tag them: "Do Not Use."

Some pneumatic or powder-actuated tools are extremely powerful. Projectiles from these tools can travel through walls or plywood, injuring people on the other side.

Reduce the Risk of Heat Exhaustion and De-hydration

As the heat index rises above 103° F (40° C), there is a high risk of heat-related illnesses and injuries to workers. The heat index is a combination of heat and humidity - basically how hot it "feels" to humans. It is much hotter on a roof than the ambient air temperature.

To reduce the risk of heat exhaustion and de-hydration, workers should:
- Keep drinking water. Workers need about four cups of cool water each hour in high temperatures.
- Work in the cool of the morning and in the evening if at all possible (avoiding the hottest part of the day).
- Be aware of the signs of heat-related problems. If a worker suddenly becomes confused, or uncoordinated, it may be a sign of heat stroke. Heat stroke can be fatal if not treated immediately.
- Take frequent breaks and rotate workers to handle strenuous tasks.
- Provide workers with personal cooling devices (for example., water-dampened clothing, cooling vests with pockets that hold cold packs, reflective clothing, or cool mist stations).
- Provide shade and fans if possible.
- Encourage workers to wear sunscreen, hats and sun glasses.
- Set up a buddy system to watch for signs of fatigue and/or heat related distress.

Maintain an Uncluttered Work Environment

A clean and orderly job site is a safe job site. Construction debris scattered about the site can present a trip and fall hazard. Extension cords, ropes and safety lines can also become unsafe obstacles.

Tools, equipment and debris left on the roof can not only present a tripping hazard, but might also fall and injure a worker standing below.

Also make sure the roof and ground areas are free of water, oils, ice or other materials that can make footing slippery or hazardous.

During roofing work, materials and equipment should not be stored within 6 feet (1.8 meters) of a roof edge unless guardrails are in place., Any materials piled, grouped, or stacked near a roof edge must be stable and self-supporting.

Proper Lifting and Carrying Procedures

Much of the equipment used on site is heavy and/or awkward. Batteries are especially heavy and solar panels are large and can weigh upwards of 50 pounds. Without using proper lifting and carrying procedures, it is quite easy and common for an installer to be injured.

When lifting an object off the ground:
- lift with the legs (not with the back),
- do not twist while lifting,
- load heavy items last into the bed of a truck to avoid pushing them far,
- always use two people to lift and load large and heavy items,
- if the item is difficult to manage safely by hand when lifting it to the roof, then find another method (crane or lift or scaffold),
- use carts and/or dollies if possible.

Electric Shock and Arc Flash Risks

When an individual comes in contact with an exposed conductor that is carrying a current, an electric shock may occur. It doesn't take much current for the body to feel the effects of electricity.
- at 0.001 amps, skin will feel the tingle of an electric current,
- at 0.02 amps, muscles can freeze, often making it impossible to let go of the electrical source,
- at 0.1 amps, ventricular fibrillation can occur. This is an uncontrollable contraction of the heart that may result in death if medical help is not immediately available,
- at 0.5 amps, the heart can cease to function,
- at 1.5 amps, skin can start to burn and death is often the immediate result.

The damage to the body from even small amounts of electrical current are severe and rapid.

How badly a worker is injured when coming in contact with electricity is dependent upon:
- the amount of the electric current flowing through the body,
- the path taken by the electric current through the body,
- the duration that the body is part of the electrical path.

FIGURE 13-11: A WORKER CAUGHT IN AN ARC FLASH BLAST.

Electric shocks are not the only risks inherent when working with electricity. An arc flash such as illustrated in Figure 13-11 can occur when electricity jumps (short circuits) between two connectors.

Common injuries from arc flashes include:
- Burns. An arc flash contains plasma that can reach temperatures of 35,000°F, or four times the surface temperature of the Sun. Some studies indicate that up to 80%

of the injuries received by electrical workers are the result of burns from arc flashes.

- Eye damage. Unprotected eyes can result in severe damage and even blindness when subjected to the intense heat and light of an arc flash.

- Blast pressure. Blast pressure waves have thrown workers across rooms and knocked them off ladders. Pressure from an arc flash can be higher then 2000 lbs/sq. ft. Workers can be injured by the blast, thrown into a more dangerous place, or suffer hearing loss. A blast can occur when a pressure wave develops around an arc from the heating of air and the expansion of surrounding metal as it is vaporized. This is known as an **arc-blast.**

> ARC-BLAST

Preventing Electrical Injuries

As always, the elimination of potential electrical hazards is the best way to prevent injury. Methods to do so include:

- Inspect and maintain equipment and tools.

- Use safety features when available, like grounded plugs (three-prong), tools that are double-insulated, and safety switches.

- Make sure electrical equipment is properly grounded.

- Follow lockout and tagging procedures.

- Use proper personal protective equipment such as insulated gloves, shoes and clothing designed to help protect against electrical shocks.

- Always assume conductors and metal near conductors are "live." Test them for voltage using a multimeter prior to working with or near them.

- Mark and avoid buried cables.

- Knowledge. The better an installer's understanding of how electricity works, the safer the work environment.

- Situational Awareness. Stay alert to the hazards involved in working with and near electricity

Responding to Electrical Emergencies

When someone suffers a serious electrical shock, they may be knocked unconscious and unable to communicate.

If the victim is still in contact with the electrical current, DO NOT touch the person. First turn off the electrical current at the source. If it is not possible to disconnect the power source, separate the victim from the power source with a nonconductive object, such as a dry wooden 2 x 4.

Have someone call for emergency medical assistance immediately. Administer first aid, as appropriate once it is safe to do so.

In the case of an electrical fire, use "C" rated extinguishers. Never use water.

LOCK-OUT/ TAG-OUT
(LOTO)

Lock-Out Tag-Out

A **lock-out/tag-out (LOTO)** procedure is designed to ensure that electrical devices are properly shut off and not started up again prior to the completion of maintenance or servicing work.

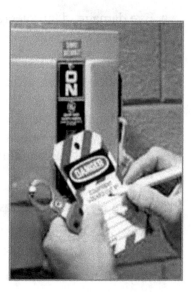

Procedures may vary, but typically they include:

- Turn off the device or disconnect to ensure it has been "isolated and rendered inoperative."

- Lock the device in some manner so it cannot easily be turned back on by mistake.

- Tag the device with a note (as shown in Figure 13-12) to let others know the device should remain inoperative until the service or maintenance work has been completed.

FIGURE 13-12: DEVELOP AND FOLLOW A COMPREHENSIVE LOCK-OUT, TAG-OUT PROCEDURE WHEN WORKING WITH ELECTRICITY

(FROM ELECTRICAL SAFETY FORUM)

Scaffolding

It is common when installing PV systems to use a scaffolding system in order to install rooftop (and even some ground mounted) systems. These systems provide a safe working platform from which installers can work.

There are three major categories of scaffolding. These include:

- **Supported scaffolds**, which consist of one or more platforms supported by rigid, load- bearing members, such as poles, legs, frames, outriggers, etc.

- **Suspended scaffolds**, which are platforms suspended by ropes, chains or other non-rigid,supports secured from above. These scaffolds are common on high-rise buildings, for window cleaning and exterior maintenance.

SUPPORTED SCAFFOLDS

SUSPENDED SCAFFOLDS

AERIAL SCAFFOLDS

FIGURE 13-13: PORTABLE AERIAL SCAFFOLD EQUIPMENT

- **Aerial scaffolds**, commonly called booms, scissor lifts, or cherry pickers, an example of which is illustrated in Figure 13-13.

Fall protection (such as

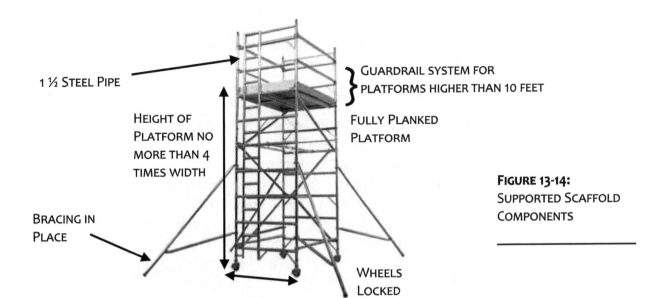

1 ½ STEEL PIPE

GUARDRAIL SYSTEM FOR
PLATFORMS HIGHER THAN 10 FEET

HEIGHT OF
PLATFORM NO
MORE THAN 4
TIMES WIDTH

FULLY PLANKED
PLATFORM

FIGURE 13-14:
SUPPORTED SCAFFOLD
COMPONENTS

BRACING IN
PLACE

WHEELS
LOCKED

harness/lanyard, guardrails, etc) is not required unless the scaffold can reach a height of 10 feet or more above the surface below. This is known as the **trigger height**, above which normal fall protection is required.

> TRIGGER HEIGHT

When constructing supported scaffolds, the scaffolding height is restricted to no more than four times the width of the base.

Other issues regarding scaffold construction, as illustrated in Figure 13-14, include:

- erect scaffolds on stable and level ground,
- the front edge of the scaffold must not be more than 14 inches from the front of the building,
- wheels (if present) must be locked in place,
- braces must be locked,
- use toeboards to prevent tools from falling below,
- for wooden units, posts must be made from construction grade lumber at least 2 X 4 inches, no more than 8 feet apart,
- for pipe railings, the posts must be at least 1 ½ inch diameter pipe, not more than 8 feet apart,
- for scaffolds where the working surface is more than 10 feet above the surface below, guardrails must be installed,
- the working surface should be fully planked (no gaps or holes).

Falling Objects

When working at height, not only is there the risk of falling, but there is a risk to those below of being hit by objects that may fall from the work site. When work is performed at height on the site:

- create a **limited access zone (LAZ)** restricting access to areas beneath the work site through the use of barriers or access monitors,
- use toeboards, screens or guardrails to prevent items from falling,

> LIMITED ACCESS
> ZONE (LAZ)

- use debris nets, catch platforms or canopies, or debris chutes,
- ensure all those below the work site wear hard hats

Heavy Equipment

When working around heavy equipment, make sure:
- anyone in the area is visible to the operator at all times,
- the vehicle's rated load is never exceeded,
- the cab shield is in place to protect the driver,
- the vehicle is driven only on designated areas,
- it is locked and in neutral when not in operation,
- the parking brake is engaged when parked on an incline,
- barricades are in place to keep unauthorized people away,
- the vehicle is inspected before each operation,
- there is proper communication between the operator and any workers in the area.

Trenches

TRENCHES

Photovoltaic installers may find themselves working in an environment where **trenches** are present. A trench is defined as "a narrow excavation made below the surface of the ground."

The depth of a trench is greater than its width, but the width of a trench (measured at the bottom) is not greater than 15 feet (4.6 m).

While any size trench may present a trip and fall danger, those large enough for a person to enter present the greater workplace hazard.

When working with trenches, one of the biggest hazards is being caught in a cave-in should the walls collapse. Workers can be crushed by the soil, or they can asphyxiate (be unable to breathe) while buried under the dirt. A cubic yard of earth weighs about 2,200 pounds, or about the same as a small car.

Trenches should be inspected for hazards before each shift (daily at a minimum), after rainstorms, or if heavy vibrations nearby may have caused the earth to shift or crack.

SPOILS

Spoils, the materials (earth) removed when creating the trench, must be placed at least two feet from the edge.

Several ways to prevent trench collapse include:

- Keep spoils, materials or equipment at least two (2) feet from the edge of the trench.

- Use a retaining device such as a trench box or bracing within the trench to prevent wall collapse.

- Slope the sides rather than create vertical walls.

Trench Access and Exits

When working in a trench, it is important that it is possible to get out of it quickly if something bad happens. Trenches that are four (4) feet or more deep, require stairways, ladders, ramps, or some other safe entry and exit point.

Workers should never have to travel more than 25 feet laterally to get to a safe exit.

A competent person must design ramps that are used solely for accessing or exiting a trench. The competent person also has to evaluate earthen ramps that are used for accessing or exiting a trench.

Chapter 13 Review Questions

1) Companies with more than 10 employees must maintain a log that details all work-related injuries known as the:
   a) CFR Title 29
   b) OSHA 300
   c) RFP ledger
   d) BWC 5000

2) OSHA regulations require that an employer place a _____ on the job site to oversee and manage potentially dangerous situations.
   a) security camera
   b) guardrail or fall protection
   c) competent person
   d) all the above

3) A safety policy and procedures document should contain all of the following **EXCEPT**:
   a) proper lifting and carrying procedures
   b) established LOTO procedures
   c) a key project indicator (KPI) matrix
   d) a PPE policy

4) When conducting a work site hazard assessment, which of the following are appropriate questions to ask?
   a) Will the job take place on a roof where there is a potential to drop tools on pedestrians below?
   b) Is scaffolding to be used that must be assembled and inspected?
   c) Is a boom truck to be used on site, and is there the potential to damage people and property as it moves about the site?
   d) All of the above.

5) Personal protective equipment include all of the following **EXCEPT**:
   a) hard hat
   b) protective boots and gloves
   c) personal fall arrest system
   d) guardrail system

6) What is the required height (above the standing surface) of the toprail of a guardrail system?
   a) 44 inches exactly
   b) 36 inches, plus or minus 12 inches
   c) no more than 48 inches
   d) 42 inches, plus or minus 3 inches

7) OSHA requires that a ladder be present any time there is a break in elevation greater than:
   a) 19 inches
   b) 36 inches (3 feet)
   c) 42 inches
   d) 48 inches (4 feet)

8) A portable Type 1A (Orange) ladder is load rated for 300 pounds. It must therefore be capable of supporting at least:
   a) 300 lbs
   b) 600 lbs
   c) 900 lbs
   d) 1200 lbs

9) Any ladder that is permanently mounted to a building and is more than 24 feet in length must:
   a) be load test to at least 300 lbs
   b) incorporate fall protection
   c) extend at least 5 feet above the roof line
   d) all of the above

10) If more than 25 workers are in the area where a ladder is used, the site must also include:
   a) a self-retracting lifeline
   b) a posted OSHA 300 checklist
   c) a competent person
   d) a second ladder

11) When the heat index rises above _____, it should be assumed there is a high risk of heat-related illnesses or injuries.
   a) the ambient air temperature
   b) 103°F (40° C)
   c) the OSHA air temperature limit
   d) body temperature

12) How badly a worker is injured from an electric shock is dependent upon:
   a) the amount of current flowing through the body
   b) the path taken by the current through the body
   c) the amount of time the current is present in the body
   d) all of the above

13) In the case of electrical fires, extinguish them using:
   a) baking soda then flush site with water
   b) a fire suppression blanket
   c) a "C" rated fire extinguisher
   d) all of the above will work

14) Lock-Out, Tag-Out (LOTO) procedures normally involve which of following?
    a) disconnect the device
    b) lock the disconnect so that it cannot easily be turned back on by mistake
    c) inform others that the device should remain off while work is performed
    d) all of the above

15) A "cherry picker" would be an example of:
    a) a guardrail system
    b) a supported scaffold
    c) a suspended scaffold
    d) an aerial scaffold

16) When working on a scaffold, fall protection is typically not required unless the scaffold reaches 10 feet or more above the surface below. This is known as the:
    a) OSHA limit
    b) trigger height
    c) PFSA limit
    d) limited access zone (LAZ)

17) To avoid or prevent the walls of a trench from collapsing:
    a) place spoils at least 2 feet from the edge of the trench
    b) brace the walls with supports
    c) slope the sides rather than create vertical walls
    d) all of the above

18) Trenches that are more than _____ require stairways, ladders or ramps.
    a) 2 feet deep
    b) twice the depth as their width
    c) 4 feet deep
    d) 25 feet in length

Chapter 14

Testing and Troubleshooting

Chapter Objectives:

- Identify the steps involved in inspecting a completed system.
- Inspect and torque all mechanical connections.
- Conduct continuity tests on all circuits.
- Test for proper polarity.
- Conduct current, voltage and insulation tests.
- Learn how to test for and correct PID.
- Initiate a proper inverter startup.
- Conduct system function tests.
- Verify energy production of the system.
- Test phase rotation in three-phase systems.
- Understand what is involved in testing the grounding system.
- Identify situations that may result in an arc fault.
- Troubleshoot ground faults.
- Identify common issues that may result in poor system output or complete system failure.

Once the installation has been completed, but before it has been turned on for the first time, it is time to test and inspect the system.

Prior to inspecting, make sure that all disconnects are open, fuses are removed, and proper lockout/tagout (LOTO) procedures are in place.

In addition to requirements found in the NEC, the international standard *IEC 62446 Grid Connected PV Systems – Minimum Requirements for System Documentation, Commissioning Tests, and Inspection* is a helpful standard once the system has been installed. It defines minimum documentation, commissioning tests and inspection criteria for grid-connected PV systems.

Testing and troubleshooting a PV system can be dangerous. Typically the task is undertaken because some problem has occurred, and this problem might present a hazard to those working on or near the system.

Safety, Safety, Safety

Always follow best practices for avoiding and preventing electrical and other common safety hazards associated with PV installations.

- Carry out a risk assessment before conducting any work at the site.
- Work on electrical equipment and circuits in a de-energized state whenever possible, using documented lockout/tagout procedures.

- Wear the appropriate PPE, including protective clothing, nonconductive Class E hard hat, electrical hazard (EH) rated foot protection, and safety glasses at all times.

- Use electrically insulated hand tools and properly grounded or double-insulated power tools maintained in good working condition.

- Avoid contact with overhead power lines and buried electrical conductors.

- Use ladders with fiberglass rails when working on or near energized conductors.

- Lower the risk of fall hazards by using personal fall arrest systems (PFAS) whenever working at unprotected heights of six (6) feet or more.

- Do not work alone.

- Plan and review all testing, safety and emergency procedures in advance.

- Maintaining an orderly work site and cautious approach.

When testing and troubleshooting systems and equipment, specialized testing equipment is typically used. When working with these testing tools:
- follow manufacturer's instructions for their safe operation,
- only use test instruments for their intended purpose, within their established limits and ratings,
- carefully inspect test equipment and leads prior to each use,
- properly maintain test instruments and recommended calibrations.

Inspection of the System

It may be helpful to create a checklist of items to inspect during this phase of the commissioning process. These may include (but are certainly not limited to):

PV Modules:
- Are the correct modules installed (match the plans and specifications)?
- Are the correct number of modules installed in the array?
- Are the strings configured according to the plans?
- Is each string generating the expected open circuit voltage?
- Are any of the panels damaged?
- Are the connectors tightly attached?
- Are the proper connections are made within the junction box (negative to negative connector, etc) even if the unit came pre-wired from the manufacturer?

Racking Systems:
- Were footings installed at the proper locations and spaced properly?
- Was the proper hardware used and tightened to the appropriate torque?
- Is the racking system properly connected to the footings?

- Are the modules properly connected to the racking system with the appropriate hardware?
- Are all jumpers, WEEBs or other bonding hardware in place and providing an adequate bond?

Conductors:
- Is the conductor insulation type installed suitable for the environment?
- Do wire gauge sizes match the design drawing?
- Are all conductors in place?
- Is there any visual sign of damage to any of the conductors?
- Is the color coding correct (green for ground, red for positive, etc)?
- Are all connections tight?
- Is the appropriate polarity maintained in the connection?
- Are all conductors secured "out of reach" of untrained persons that may come in contact with them?

Conduits and Raceways:
- Have the correct conduit types been used in each environment?
- Is the conduit supported correctly?
- Have expansion fittings been installed where needed?
- Are proper labels attached to the conduits and raceways?

Disconnects:
- Are the disconnects rated for the current of the circuit to which they are attached?
- Are they located in the proper places (as per the utility's requirements) and mounted properly?
- Is the correct conductor (ungrounded) being disconnected within the device?
- Is the disconnect rated for its environment (indoor, outdoor)?
- Are the disconnects properly labeled?

Grounding System:
- Have all the panels been grounded to the racking system?
- Have all the metal enclosures been properly grounded?
- Have any metal conduit and/or raceways been properly grounded?
- Have the grounding electrodes been placed in their proper location and bonded to the grounding conductor?
- Confirm that the ground fault protection fuse in the inverter is present.

Overcurrent Protection Devices (OCPD):
- Is the current rating of the OCPD properly sized for the circuit?
- Is the voltage rating of the OCPD appropriate for the circuit?
- Do the OCPDs appear to be in good condition?
- Does the circuit open when the OCPD is removed or turned "off"?

Inverters:

- Is there adequate clearance around the inverter for maintenance and cooling?
- Has the inverter been properly installed and configured as per the manufacturer's specifications?
- Is the inverter secure from environmental damage?
- Does the inverter's operating voltage window comply with the array's DC voltage output after it has been adjusted for temperature extremes?
- Does the inverter's output match the local utility?
- Is the inverter ANSI/UL listed?
- Has the inverter been properly labeled?

Charge Controllers:

- Has the charge controller been properly installed and configured as per the manufacturer's specifications?
- Is the charge controller secure from environmental damage?
- Does the charge controller's operating voltage window comply with the array's DC voltage output after it has been adjusted for temperature extremes?
- Does the charge controller's output voltage match the nominal voltage of the battery bank?
- Is the charge controller's current rating adequate for the array's output?

Battery Bank:

- Are the batteries installed in proper enclosures?
- Are the batteries properly vented to the outside?
- Are the correct batteries installed (match the plans and specifications)?
- Are the correct number of batteries installed in the bank?
- Are the strings configured to the proper nominal voltage?
- Are any of the batteries damaged or leaking?

Checking Mechanical Connections

TORQUE

Ensure that all connections of hardware and conductors are secure and within the limits specified by the equipment. Most components that require assembly will provide recommended connection methods and **torque** specifications. Ensure that these connections have been made correctly.

Using a Torque Wrench

PRELOAD

Threaded fasteners (nuts and bolts) are used to hold many mechanical components together. As a bolt is tightened, the fastener actually flexes and stretches. This stretching is not permanent, but it gives the joint force that holds it together, called **preload**, or tension.

Each fastener is designed for a certain range of tension. Too much tightening will deform the threads or the parts of the system to which it is connected. Too little preload will mean the fastener will loosen over time.

To apply the correct tension to each fastener, a torque wrench such as the one pictured in Figure 14-1 can be used to calibrate the connection to the correct tension.

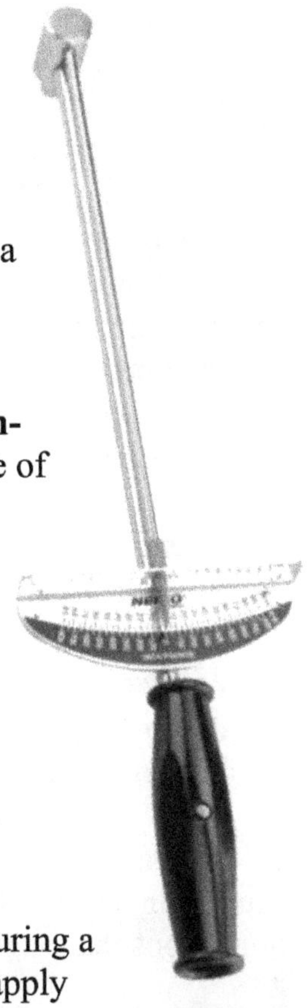

Torque is measured as a unit of force acting on a rotating lever of some set length. In the USA, the common unit used to measure torque is the **inch-pound** (in-lb). This is a measure of the force of one pound acting at the end of a lever (wrench) only one inch long.

INCH-POUND

Globally, the accepted torque measurement is the **Newton-meter (Nm)**. One Newton-meter is a measure of the force of one Newton on a meter long lever.

NEWTON-METER

To tighten a bolt using a torque wrench, apply pressure in a steady and smooth motion, avoid sudden, "jerking" movements.

FIGURE 14-1: COMMON TORQUE WRENCH

When the wrench reaches the set torque the handle will automatically click or the needle will indicate the desired tension setting.

The tension or torque on a bolt will change over time. During a torque audit, in the tightening direction, begin to slowly apply force to the torque wrench until the first movement in the fastener is noted. This is a good way to determine the **residual torque** of the connection. It is also helpful in catching any bolts that may not have been fastened correctly during installation.

RESIDUAL TORQUE

Once it has been determined the bolt has been correctly tightened, it is common to mark it as shown in Figure 14-2.

FIGURE 14-2: BOLT MARKED WITH SEALANT THAT HAS LOOSENED OVER TIME

There are special sealants and markers made for this purpose. The reason for marking the bolt is to see at a glance if the bolt or nut has moved over time.

This mark serves as a reference point, so that during inspections it is clear if there has been any movement.

Checking Electrical Connections

Once the physical installation has been inspected and verified, it is time to test the electrical characteristics of the system. Common types of testing conducted on PV systems include:

- Continuity and resistance test. This test verifies the integrity of grounding and bonding systems, conductors, connections and terminations.
- Polarity test. This verifies the correct polarity for DC circuits, and proper terminations for DC equipment.
- Voltage and current test. This verifies that the array is producing as expected and that this power is finding its way to the inverter.
- Insulation resistance test. This test verifies the integrity of wiring and equipment, and used to detect any faults in the wire's insulation.
- Performance test. Verifies the system power and energy output are consistent with expectations given the current environmental conditions.

For systems that incorporate batteries, additional tests may include:
- Measure the battery voltage, capacity and specific gravity.
- Verify charge controller set points and temperature compensation.
- Verify charging current and load control functions.
- Verify the performance and wiring integrity for other sources, such as generators.

As tests are conducted, visually inspect all electrical connections. Jiggle the wire (again, ensure the terminals are not energized) and tighten any connections that may be loose.

Continuity Tests

CONTINUITY TEST

RESISTANCE TEST

It is helpful to verify connections by performing a simple **continuity** or **resistance test**.

Set a multimeter to test for resistance, then place one lead at one end of the connections being tested; the other lead at the other end. If there is continuity (a solid connection through which power can flow), the reading should be zero. If there is no continuity, the reading will be one or infinite.

Use this test to verify the integrity of the bonding and grounding systems, conductors, connections and terminations. This can also be used to test the operation of disconnects as well as overcurrent protection devices.

ANODIZING

Use continuity tests to check the bonding and grounding system:
- Verify the finish or **anodizing** (an electrochemical durable, corrosion-resistant, anodic oxide finish often found on aluminum or other metallic components) that are bonded together (such as the panel and the rail) has been removed or penetrated to establish a secure and permanent bond.

- Verify that metal parts of all PV module frames, support structures and other equipment are bonded to the equipment grounding system.

- If there are multiple grounding electrodes in the system, verify that they are bonded together to form a single grounding system.

- Verify the grounding electrode conductor is securely attached to the grounding electrode.

- Verify that any metal raceways, enclosures, frames, fittings, and other components serving as equipment grounding conductors are properly bonded together.

- Verify that all metallic raceways and enclosures are bonded together to form a continuous electrical conductive path.

- If a panel or piece of equipment is removed from the circuit for any reason, ensure the continuity of equipment grounding connections with the use of temporary bonding jumpers.

Polarity Tests

Polarity tests simply verify that the positive conductor and the negative conductor have not in some way been switched, or reversed.

POLARITY TEST

Reversed polarity can result in damage to the modules, equipment, wiring and battery systems. A reversed polarity array can also act as a load, and discharge current from a battery.

Reversing the polarity of an individual PV source circuit within a combiner box will simply cancel the current output from other parallel-connected strings wired with proper polarity.

For larger PV installations with dozens of source circuits terminating at several combiner boxes, keeping track of each source circuit and its polarity can be a challenge. Proper labeling and testing during installation should avoid this problem.

Before connecting the MC4 connectors on each panel, insert the positive lead from a multimeter set to read the appropriate level of DC voltage into the positive (male) connector, and the negative lead into the negative (female) connector. If the resulting reading is positive, then the polarity is correct If the result is a negative number, then the polarity has been reversed.

In addition to testing the polarity at each module, polarity should also be tested:
- on all PV source circuits,
- on all PV output circuits,
- at all disconnects,
- on any battery and charge controller circuits,

- at the inverter input terminations,
- on any DC electrical loads.

Voltage and Current Tests

VOLTAGE TEST

CURRENT TEST

Basic **voltage and current tests** are conducted on both the DC and AC circuits to verify they are functioning within acceptable limits prior to closing all disconnects and starting up the system. These test are designed to check proper operation, but not the performance of the system (that test comes later).

Most PV systems with string inverters are configured with identical strings consisting of the same number of series connected modules. If this is the case, similar open-circuit voltage readings should be expected under the same testing conditions, typically within 5% of each other.

FIGURE 14-3: TESTING CURRENT USING CLAMP-ON AMMETER

Open-circuit voltage tests require a voltmeter capable of reading AC and DC voltages of 600 V to 1000 V.

Prior to turning on the system for the first time, open circuit voltages (with no load) should be tested for the following circuits and sources:

- Verify AC voltage and correct phasing at the utility supply, inverter AC terminals and disconnects, and electrical generators if present.

- Verify DC voltage for each panel, PV source circuit, and PV output circuit.

When testing short circuit current, suitable test equipment, capable of safely short-circuiting high-voltage DC circuits is required.

AMMETER

Most digital multi-meters can measure DC current up to 10 amps, but require a shorting device to safely measure the current. Clamp-on **ammeters**, such as the one illustrated in Figure 14-3, are available for DC current measurements.

Insulation Tests

INSULATION TEST

Insulation tests are necessary to check the integrity of the insulation around the conductors. Like a leak in a water pipe, any imperfection in the insulation can allow electricity to escape. No insulation is perfect, and there will always be a trace amount of current leaking from the conductors. But excessive leaking can result in nuisance tripping of breakers or even create a dangerous ground fault condition.

Damage to conductors may take place during installation (pulling through conduit, for example) or may happen gradually over time. Insulation is subject to many stresses that can cause it to fail – mechanical damage, vibration, excessive heat or cold, dirt, oil, corrosive vapors, moisture and humidity.

As pin holes or cracks develop, moisture and foreign matter can penetrate the surfaces of the insulation, providing a low resistance path for leakage current.

For this reason, routine insulation testing is necessary. Insulation testing is done with the use of a **megohmmeter** (as illustrated in Figure 14-4), or **Megger,** as it is commonly called.

FIGURE 14-4: A MEGOHMMETER, OR INSULATION TESTER

The process by which insulation is tested is performed by applying a high and constant (DC) voltage to two conductors. If the resistance measured is high, then there is no extraordinary current loss.

The theory is similar to testing a plumbing system for leaks. If the system is closed (no open faucets), and high pressure is applied, any leaks will show up by comparing the pressure within the system with the pressure applied. If, for example, 500 psi were applied and the meter read only 400 psi, water is leaking out somewhere.

The same holds true for electrical conductors. If 1,000 Vdc is applied to two conductors, a reading of around 1 mega-ohms (1,000,000 Ω) should be detected.

Prior to Testing

A Megger will introduce a very high voltage into the wire and any equipment to which it is connected. Although the current is very small, this high voltage can cause severe damage to people as well as sensitive equipment. Use caution when performing an insulation test, and disconnect all loads from the circuit tested.

Prior to testing a circuit:
- Disconnect all loads and power to the circuit. Never connect a Megger to energized lines or equipment. When testing conductors, it is best to disconnect terminals at both ends, so only the conductor itself is being tested. Test the conductors with a multimeter to ensure no voltage or current is present.
- Inspect the installation very carefully to determine what equipment is connected and will be included in the test.
- Test the Megger to ensure it is working properly. The manufacturer of the testing unit will provide instructions on how best to test the particular model.

- Discharge any capacitance that may be on the line or equipment to be tested.
- Use appropriate safety equipment such as eye protection, rubber gloves, insulated tools, etc.

Testing Conductors

The insulation test is to determine if any power is leaking from any conductor. If DC voltage is placed on two conductors that are not connected together, there should be infinite resistance between the two (as found in a continuity test).

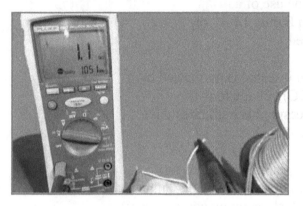

FIGURE 14-5: TESTING CONDUCTORS USING A MEGGER

However, no insulation is perfect, so there will likely be a trace amount of leakage (which shows up in the form of resistance) when tested. Too much, however, indicates a problem.

In a typical DC circuit, there are three conductors: the positive, the negative, and the ground. Test to see if there is any leakage between any two, as shown in Figure 14-5. In other words, perform three tests - positive and ground, negative and ground, positive and negative. The results should be the same for all three if the terminals on both ends of the conductor are open and disconnected and the conductors are undamaged.

Effect of Temperature on Insulation Resistance

The resistance of insulating materials decreases as temperature increases. The rule of thumb is that for every 10°C increase in temperature, the resistance will be cut in half. Conversely, for every 10°C decrease, the resistance characteristics of the wire will double.

When comparing test results, make sure they have been conducted under similar temperature conditions.

Testing for and Correcting PID

POTENTIAL INDUCED DEGRADATION (PID)

Potential induced degradation or PID occurs when the potential of the module, with respect to ground, is reduced over time. This reduces the power output of the module. Power may be reduced by as much as 80%.

Often accelerated by high temperatures and high humidity, this relatively common problem is caused by the high voltages present between the encapsulated solar cells and the front glass surface of the module. This glass is grounded through the frame of the panel.

The presence of PID is not visibly detectable, generally showing up weeks or months after installation and apparent only due to a loss of power production.

There are a number of ways to test for PID. By far the most common method is to use an IV Curve Tracer (such as the unit shown in Figure 14-6).

PID Test using an IV Curve Tracer

On a sunny day during a period when production would normally be high, use an **IV curve tracer** to measure the current-voltage characteristics of the panel.

FIGURE 14-6: HT I-V500W I-V CURVE TRACER

(PHOTO FROM HT)

While different units may operate slightly differently, the process is generally pretty straightforward.

- Attach the unit's temperature sensor to the back of the panel.

- Mount the unit exposed to the sun at the same angle as the panel (there is normally a bracket provided for this purpose).

- Connect the positive and negative leads from the solar panel to the testing unit (making sure the proper polarity is maintained).

- Enter in the module's expected production values (Vmp, Imp, etc). Normally these units incorporate a database of panels, so it is likely that this process will be accomplished by simply selecting the panel model from the list of modules provided.

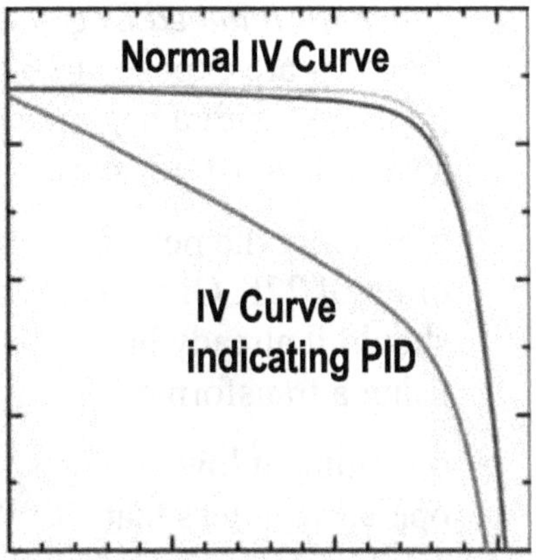

FIGURE 14-7: NORMAL IV CURVE COMPARED TO IV CURVE OF PANEL SUFFERING FROM PID

Normal IV Curve

IV Curve indicating PID

- The IV curve tracer will then generate an IV curve of the module's production at that moment.

Figure 14-7 illustrates the difference between an IV curve from a normal panel (the top line) versus an IV curve from a panel experiencing severe PID (the bottom line).

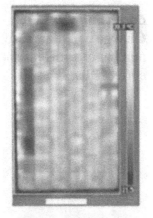

FIGURE 14-8: INFRARED IMAGE OF PANEL AFFECTED BY PID

(PHOTO FROM PV-TECH.ORG)

PID Test using an Infrared Camera

Solar cells affected by PID operate at a higher temperature than those free of PID. The use of an **infrared camera** will highlight those cells affected, as seen in Figure 14-8. The darker cells indicate those affected by PID.

Images should be taken when the panel is operating in full sunlight.

FIGURE 14-9: EL IMAGE
OF PANEL AFFECTED BY
PID

(PHOTO FROM PV-TECH.ORG)

PID Test using Electroluminescence (EL) Imaging

Electroluminescence (EL) imaging takes advantage of an optical and electrical phenomenon in which a material (in this case a solar cell) emits light in response to an electric current. In the image shown in Figure 14-9, the PID affected cells appear darker.

These images must be taken in darkness (at night). This is also a method used to identify micro cracks and breaks within the panel.

Avoiding PID

As with every problem, the best way to correct it is to avoid it in the first place. PID can be prevented by:

- using certified PID resistant modules. Panel manufacturers can test for and have their panels certified as "PID-Free" based on the *IEC TS 62804-1: 2015 "Photovoltaic (PV) Modules – Test Methods for Detecting Potential Induced Degradation (PID)*standard. Under this standard, modules are exposed to 60 °C (140 °F) ambient air temperature and 85% humidity, with a negative potential of 1000 V for a period of 96 hours. The cells must not show a power decrease of more than 5%.

- grounding the negative terminal of strings through a high resistance of the order of 22K Ohm. This option will prevent PID, but will not reverse it should it already have occurred. It is also typically not an option when using a transformerless inverter.

- operating at low voltages. Typically PID does not occur in systems operating at less than 500 Vdc. So this is not typically an issue in residential systems designed to a maximum of 600 Vdc.

- installing anti-PID equipment. Anti-PID equipment installed early in the life of the system can prevent PID. If PID does occur, it can then be installed to correct the situation.

Correcting PID

Charge equalizers, commonly referred to as **PID boxes**, are available from a number of firms (as shown in Figure 14-10) and are designed to prevent or correct PID.

PID boxes take advantage of the polarization nature of the PID effect. A voltage bias is responsible for the polarization. Applying a reverse bias will remove the effect of PID on the panel.

An installed PID box senses the PV output from the array. If the voltage is higher than a set point (in other words generating power) the output of the array is allowed to pass to the inverter.

At night, when the voltage falls below the set limit, the PID box disconnects the inverter. DC voltage is then applied to the array so that a controlled depolarization current flows through the panel, reversing the PID effect that has accumulated during the day. Charge equalizers can be used with new installations or in older installations that have been diagnosed to be suffering from PID.

String Inverter Startup Sequence

Once the visual inspection is complete, the panels have been checked for polarity and performance, the voltage of the strings measured, and the insulation of the conductors tested - it is time to turn on the inverter.

Typically, the steps will include the following:
- verify all connections,
- verify the correct AC voltage is present at the AC disconnect (there is proper power coming from the utility),
- verify the correct DC voltage and polarity are present at the DC disconnect(s),
- close the AC disconnect,
- verify the AC voltage at the inverter's AC terminals,
- close the DC disconnect(s),
- verify the DC voltage and polarity at the inverter's DC terminals,
- turn on the inverter,
- wait for the inverter to step through its internal startup sequence.

System Function Tests

Once the system is operational, the next step is to determine that all components are functioning as expected.

SYSTEM FUNCTION

How this is accomplished will vary depending upon the components selected, and manufacturers will provide detailed steps to conduct this verification process.

During the verification process it is important that the installer verify:
- that all disconnects stop the flow of electricity when in the open position,
- that the inverter is receiving the anticipated voltage from the array or the battery bank,
- that grid-interactive inverters shut down when disconnected to the grid, and re-energize when the connection to the grid is re-established,
- that charge controllers are properly charging the battery bank,
- that the system is producing the anticipated amount of energy based on current environmental conditions.

Verify Energy Production

The output of solar modules are rated based on standard test conditions. It would, however, be a rare day indeed if those conditions (25° C, 1000 watts per square meter of irradiance) happened to occur as the panel was being tested.

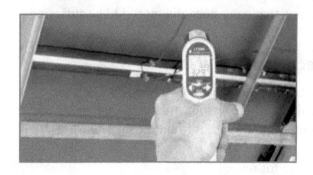

FIGURE 14-11:
MEASURING BACK OF PANEL WITH INFRARED THERMOMETER

(FROM HOME POWER MAGAZINE)

So adjustments must be made to determine if the panels (and thus the array) are performing as expected under current environmental conditions.

Calculating the power output based on current conditions is accomplished in the following manner:

INFRARED THERMOMETER

- Adjust the array's maximum power voltage (Vmp) based on the current temperature.
- Measure with an **infrared thermometer** the backside of the module (to measure actual cell temperature, as demonstrated in Figure 14-11). Find the difference (or delta **Δ**) between this reading and 25° C.
- Multiply the temperature deviation from standard test conditions by the temperature coefficient of the module (for Vmp).

Temperature coefficients are expressed as a percentage +/- of voltage produced for every degree measured from standard test conditions.

If the measured cell temperature is higher than 25° C, subtract the result from 100% and multiply the result by the Vmp (at STC) to find the temperature adjusted Vmp.

If the cell temperature measured was lower than 25° C, add the result to 100% and multiply the result by the Vmp (at STC) to find the temperature adjusted Vmp.

For example, if the Vmp (at STC) of selected panel is 30.3 Vdc, with a temperature coefficient of 0.344%/°C and the measured cell temperature was 37° C, then...

$$37° \text{ C} - 25° \text{ C} = \Delta \text{ } 12° \text{ C} \times 0.344\%/°\text{C} = 4.13 \text{ \% (less voltage than STC)}$$

$$100\% - 4.13 \text{ \%} = 95.87 \text{ \% } /100 = .9587 \times 30.3 \text{ Vdc} = 29.05 \text{ Vdc}$$

So the temperature adjusted Vmp for this panel when the cell temperature is 37° C will equal 29.05 Vdc (slightly less than its rating under standard test conditions).

Conversely, if the measured cell temperature were COLDER than standard test conditions, say 7° C, then...

$$25° \text{ C} - 7° \text{ C} = Δ \text{ } 18° \text{ C} \times 0.344\%/°\text{C} = 6.19 \% \text{ (more voltage)}$$

$$100\% + 6.19 \% = 106.19 \% /100 = 1.0619 \times 30.3 \text{ Vdc} = 32.18 \text{ Vdc}$$

So the temperature adjusted Vmp for this panel when the cell temperature is 7° C will equal 32.18 Vdc (slightly higher than STC).

- Adjust the array's maximum power current (Imp) based on the measured irradiance.

Again, it will be highly unlikely that the irradiance at the time of commissioning the system will be exactly 1,000 watts per square meter. The maximum power current will need to be adjusted based on the available sunlight.

Using an **irradiance meter** (such as shown in Figure 14-12) held at the base of a panel and at the angle of the array facing the sun, measure the irradiance at the front of the panel. Take several readings and average them - since the readings will tend to vary from moment to moment.

IRRADIANCE METER

Divide the reading(s) by 1000 W/m^2. Then multiply the result by the maximum power current (Imp) as rated at STC.

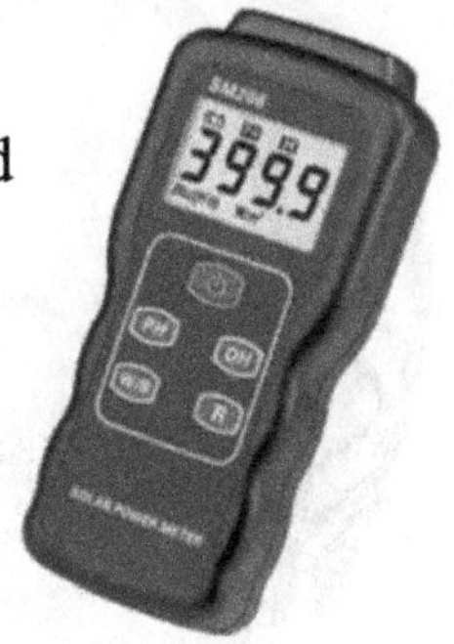

For example, if the averaged reading was 778 W/m^2, and the Imp for a specific panel was 8.27 A, then...

$$(778 \text{ W/m}^2) / (1000 \text{ W/m}^2) = .778 \times 8.27 \text{ A} = 6.434 \text{ A}$$

FIGURE 14-12: A PYRANOMETER, OR A SOLAR IRRADIANCE POWER METER

- Multiply the temperature-adjusted voltage determined in step 1 by the irradiance-adjusted current determined in step 2 to obtain the expected power output of the array under the current measured conditions.

In this example,

$$29.05 \text{ Vdc (Vmp adjusted)} \times 6.434 \text{ A (Imp adjusted)} = 186.9 \text{ W}$$

So even though the panel was rated at 250 watts under STC, given the current conditions, each panel will only produce about 187 watts when functioning properly. Now multiply this number by the total number of panels to calculate the DC output from the array.

- Multiply the DC output from the array by the total system efficiency after accounting for losses within the system (derate the system).

  Grid-tied systems should be about 90% efficient (a derate factor of .90) in converting the DC power generated by the array into usable AC power output from the inverter. Systems that incorporate batteries will be somewhat less efficient.

  The PV Watts derate calculator (available online at www.NREL.gov) is a handy tool to assist in calculating a more exact system derate factor. A derate factor of 1.00 indicates there is no effect on the system from this item (the system is operating at 100% efficiency).

  So if it is determined that the system has a derate factor of .91, then the array DC output should be multiplied by this factor. If the array tested consists of 16 panels with the adjusted output anticipated to be 187 watts for each panel (as determined in step 3) then...

  187 W x 16 panels = 2,992 W x .91 derate = 2,723 W

  In this example, the inverter should be generating 2,723 W of AC power.

- Check the value calculated in step 4 with the display on the inverter. If they match, the system is operating as anticipated.

- Document the results

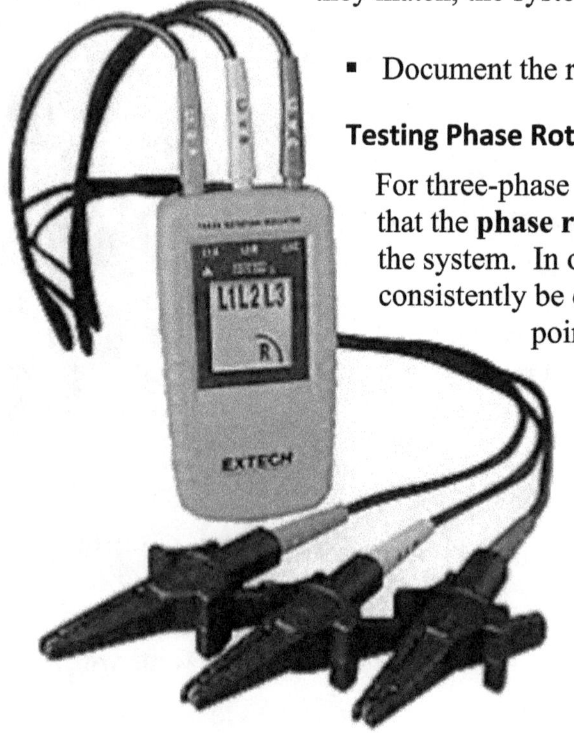

Testing Phase Rotation

For three-phase systems, it is important to test that the **phase rotation** is consistent throughout the system. In other words, Line 1 should consistently be connected to Line 1 connection points throughout the system, Line 2 to Line 2 connections, and Line 3 to Line 3 connections.

If the phase rotation is out of sync, equipment may not work properly and/or any connected motors may run backwards.

FIGURE 14-13: PHASE SEQUENCER TESTER

(FROM EXTECH)

PHASE ROTATION

PAGE 492 DESIGNING & INSTALLING SOLAR PV SYSTEMS

Testing phase rotation is fairly simple with the use of a phase sequence tester, such as the one shown in Figure 14-13.

Connect the color-coded leads to the color-coded conductors (brown to brown, red to red, etc) and the display will indicate the sequence. The correct sequence should always read L1, L2, L3.

Unbalanced Loads

Single Phase Systems

In a single phase system, an imbalance of the loads may be caused within the service panel. In a single phase-split phase service panel, the branch circuits should be designed in such a way that the current draw on each side of the busbar remains roughly equal.

If a disproportionate amount of energy is used on one side versus the other, the system can be out of balance. This can lead to overheating of electrical components and possibly overloading the panel.

Three Phase Systems

In a three-phase system, the phases of power supply should be 120 degrees apart and equal in terms of phase angle and magnitude of their peaks.

All of the current entering a system must return to its source. In a balanced system, one phase should match the other phases and result in no current flows through the neutral conductor. When they are out of balance, the neutral will carry current to equalize the system.

Unbalanced voltages can be the result of a number of factors. These include:

- the switching on and off of heavy loads that can result in surges, causing the phases to become unbalanced,
- a large single-phase load connected to only one phase of the system, causing more current to flow through that particular phase, resulting in voltage drop on line,
- a worn motor with degraded rotor and stator windings, affecting both the magnitude and phase angel of the current waveform differently within the various phases,
- a current leakage within a connected load from a single phase through bearings or motor body, causing fluctuating current,
- an unbalanced incoming waveform from the utility supply,
- faults or grounds in the power transformer,
- a blown fuse on a three-phase bank of power factor improvement capacitors.

UNBALANCED
VOLTAGE

Calculating Voltage Unbalance

To calculate the amount of voltage unbalance is present in a three-phase system, measure the voltages present on each phase of the system. Then:

% voltage unbalance= 100 x (maximum deviation from average voltage) / (average voltage)

For example, assume the phase-to-phase voltages are measured and found to be 218 V, 227 V and 208 V.

The average voltage is:

Voltage = (218 + 227 + 208) / 3 = 217.67 V

The maximum deviation from the average is:

227 V - 217.67 V = 9.33 V

% voltage unbalance = 100 x (9.33 V / 217.67 V) = 100 x 0.043 = 4.3%

Effects of an Unbalanced System

It is generally considered acceptable to up to a 2% unbalance within the system. Unbalanced voltage causes power loss within the system. This lost power takes the form of heat.

As the unbalance increases, so does the heat. At high levels, this may require additional derating of conductors and will also result in increased wear and tear on loads - as well as higher than necessary electric bills.

If a ground fault occurs in an unbalanced system, the balancing effect of the neutral may be lost. In those instances, higher voltages may flow through one leg of the circuit, with corresponding lower voltages flowing through the other. This may result in damaged loads, due to the higher or lower voltages they experience during the fault.

Testing the Grounding System

Many problems experienced in a PV system are the result of an inadequate or faulty grounding system. It can also be particularly difficult to track down the specific cause and then correct the problem. For the safety of people and equipment working on and around the installation, it is important to verify that the grounding system is properly functioning.

The entire point of a grounding system is to take any unwanted current away from potentially dangerous locations and direct it into the ground. But if the earth resists or does not readily accept the current, the system will not work as designed.

Soil Type	Resistivity (Ohm-cm)		
	Average	Minimum	Maximum
Fills: ashes, cinders, brine wastes	2,370	590	7,000
Clay: shale, gumbo, loam	4,060	340	16,300
Same: varying proportions of sand/grave	15,800	1,020	135,000
Gravel, sand, stones with little clay/loam	94,000	59,000	458,000

TABLE 14-1: EARTH RESISTIVITY FOR VARIOUS SOIL TYPES

The term **earth resistivity** measured in **ohm-centimeters (ohm-cm)** is one basic variable affecting resistance to earth of a grounding electrode system. A number of factors can affect the amount of resistance in the soil.

EARTH RESISTIVITY

OHM-CENTIMETER

These include the:
- type of soil,
- moisture content in the soil,
- dissolved salt content in the soil,
- temperature of the soil.

Type of Soil

The type of soil present will effect how readily it accepts electrical current. As is demonstrated in Table 14-1, clay or loam has a much lower resistance than does sand or gravel.

However the type of earth can be difficult to describe accurately, for instance "clay" can describe quite a number of different soil types. And there are generally a combination of many different types at any given location.

Whether a soil is largely clay or very sandy, for example, can change the earth resistivity a great deal. It isn't easy to define exactly a given soil; "clay" can cover a wide variety of soils.

Water Content in Soil

The amount of moisture in soil radically affects its resistivity. Dry soil is fairly resistant to electrical current, while moist or wet soil is a better conductor.

As demonstrated in Table 14-2, the same soil that may be a good

Moisture Content, Percent by Weight	Resistivity (Ohm-cm)	
	Top Soil	Sandy Loam
0.0 %	$1,000 \times 10^6$	$1,000 \times 10^6$
0.5 %	250,000	150,000
5.0 %	165,000	43,000
10.0 %	53,000	22,000
15.0 %	21,000	13,000
20.0 %	12,000	10,000
30.0 %	10,000	8,000

TABLE 14-2: AFFECT OF MOISTURE CONTENT ON EARTH RESISTIVITY

TABLE 14-3: AFFECT OF DISSOLVED SALT ON EARTH RESISTIVITY

Added Salt, % by Weight of Moisture	Resistivity (Ohm-cm)
0.0 %	10,700
0.1 %	1,800
1.0 %	460
5.0 %	190
10.0 %	130
20.0 %	100

path for current at 30% moisture content, is highly resistant when dry.

Obviously the amount of water in the soil varies with the weather, time of year, nature of sub-soil, and depth of the permanent water table.

Dissolved Salt in Soil

Pure water is infinitely resistant to electrical current. Naturally occurring salts in the earth, dissolved in water, lower the resistivity.

Only a small amount of salt in the soil can reduce earth resistivity dramatically, as seen in Table 14-3.

TABLE 14-4: AFFECT OF TEMPERATURE ON EARTH RESISTIVITY

Temperature of Soil

Since water plays such a large role in the resistivity of earth, and an increase in the temperature of water decreases its resistivity, then logically increasing the temperature of the soil (which contains the water) will lower its resistivity.

As evidenced in Table 14-4, the lower the temperature, the more resistive the soil. When water freezes, resistivity increases dramatically as ice is highly resistive to the flow of electricity.

Temperature	Resistivity (Ohm-cm)
20 °C (68 °F)	7,200
10 °C (50 °F)	9,900
0 °C (32 °F) water	13,800
0 °C (32 °F) ice	30,000
-5 °C (23 °F)	79,000
-15 °C (14 °F)	330,000

FIGURE 14-14: FALL-OF-POTENTIAL EARTH RESISTIVITY TEST

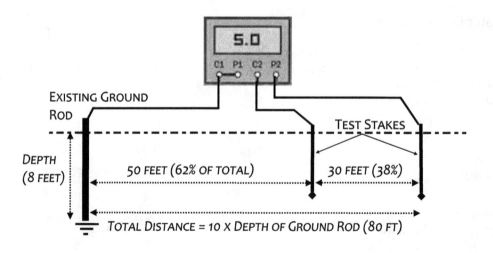

Ground Resistance Testing

Ground resistance should be tested after the grounding electrode is installed, and periodically thereafter. This ensures that over time, the resistance-to-ground does not increase.

There are two standard methods of testing this system:

- **3-point** or **fall-of-potential test**
- **induced frequency** or **clamp-on test**

3-Point or Fall-of-Potential Test

To conduct a fall-of-potential test of the grounding system, first disconnect the grounding electrode from the system (just the rod in the earth with no conductors attached).

The length of the grounding electrode must be known. In the US, an eight-foot ground rod is most common.

In a straight line from the grounding electrode, drive two metal rods or stakes into the ground as illustrated in Figure 14-14. The outside stake (furthest from the existing ground rod) should be placed about 10 times the depth of the grounding electrode away. In other words, if the grounding electrode is an 8-foot ground rod, place the outside stake 80 feet from it. The depth of the test stake is not important as long as good contact with the soil has been achieved.

Attach the three leads from an **earth ground test meter** as shown in Figure 14-15 to the ground rod, the center stake and the outside stake (the testing unit will indicate which leads connect to which stake).

The meter will generate a result in ohms. Single rod systems must have a ground resistance of 25 ohms or less (NEC 250.53). If resistance measures higher than this, supplemental ground rods are required. A second rod will lower resistance to about 60% of that of a single rod system. Adding a third rod will lower it to about 40% of the original resistance value, and a fourth rod will lower it to about 33% of the resistance of a single grounding electrode system.

While 25 Ω is the minimum, it is better and safer to achieve a resistance of less than 5 Ω.

3-POINT TEST

FALL-OF-POTENTIAL TEST

INDUCED FREQUENCY TEST

CLAMP-ON TEST

EARTH GROUND TEST METER

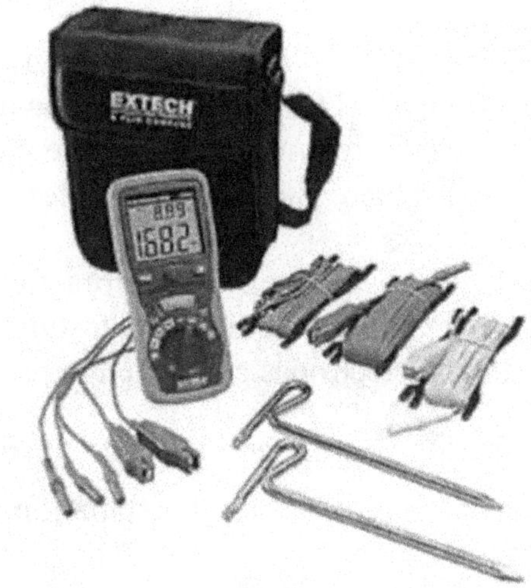

FIGURE 14-15: EARTH GROUND TEST KIT

(FROM EXTECH)

FIGURE 14-16: CLAMP-
ON TEST OF GROUNDING
ELECTRODE CONDUCTOR

Clamp-On Test

While the fall-of-potential test is the most
accurate for testing ground conductivity, it
does present a number of challenges. This
test is:

- labor intensive and time consuming,
- the ground must be disconnected from the system,
  presenting possible safety issues while the test is
  conducted,
- in some cases disconnecting the grounding
  electrode simply is not possible.

An alternative method of testing is to use an earth
ground test meter equipped with a voltage clamp and a
current clamp, as shown in Figure 14-16.

With this test method, two clamps are placed around the ground rod or the
grounding electrode conductor and each are connected to the tester. Ground
test stakes are not used at all.

A known voltage is induced by one clamp, and the current is measured using
the second clamp. The tester automatically determines the ground loop
resistance at this ground rod.

If there is only one path to ground, as is the case in many residential
situations, this method will not provide an acceptable measurement and the
fall-of-potential test method must be used. The clamp-on method of
measurement requires that multiple grounds are connected in parallel
(otherwise there is no return path for the current).

While this method may not be practical for smaller residential systems, it can
save a great deal of time when testing larger commercial systems with many
grounding electrodes connected in parallel.

Measuring Ground and Leakage Current

GROUND CURRENT

Even in the best electrical installation, some current will flow through the
ground conductor to ground. This is referred to as a **ground current**. Ideally
the amount of current flowing from the electrical system to the ground would
be zero, but this is rarely the case.

LEAKAGE CURRENT

Leakage current commonly flows in the insulation surrounding conductors
and in the filters protecting electronic equipment. There is a certain amount of
normal leakage current going from the neutral and the phase conductors to
ground in all electrical systems.

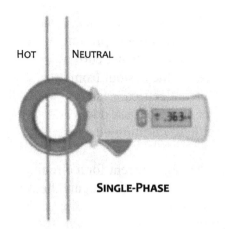

HOT   NEUTRAL

SINGLE-PHASE

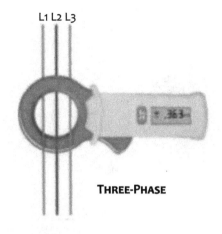

L1 L2 L3

THREE-PHASE

On circuits protected by GFCIs (Ground Fault Current Interrupters), such as string inverters, leakage current can cause unnecessary and intermittent tripping. These often trip when they detect leakage currents in excess of 5 mA.

In extreme cases, very high leakage current can cause the voltage in non-current carrying conductive parts to rise to dangerous levels.

Current leakage can be caused by worn or damaged insulation, excessively long conductors, and/or poor connections.

Electronic equipment contains filters designed to protect against voltage surges and other disruptions. These filters normally incorporate capacitors on the input, which adds to the overall capacitance of the wiring system and can result in an increased level of leakage current.

To measure current leakage within the system, use a clamp meter such as illustrated in Figure 14-17.

So, how can you eliminate or minimize the effects of leakage current? Quantify the leakage current and then identify the source. One way of going about this is to use a leakage current clamp meter. These are very much like the clamp meters used for measuring load currents, but deliver significantly better performance when measuring currents below 5 mA. Most clamp meters simply won't register such low currents.

To test for ground current, use a clamp type ammeter. Test the grounding electrode conductor. While this measurement will indicate whether current is flowing from the system to the ground, it will not be much help in determining the source of the problem.

In most electrical systems, the sum of all the conductors (line, neutral and ground) should be equal to zero amps. If the entire circuit is measured and the resulting measurement is not zero, this is known as the **net current**.

NET CURRENT

FIGURE 14-18: NET CURRENT TEST

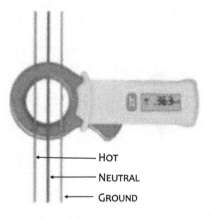

HOT
NEUTRAL
GROUND

There may be a number of causes that result in net current being present on the system. In many cases net current is introduced onto the system from other interconnected electrical systems, so it may be necessary to track down and disconnect these co-mingled system.

To test for leakage current for a circuit, place the meter around the hot and neutral conducts in a single-phase system, and around all three conductors in a three-phase system, as indicated in Figure 14-18. If any equipment is attached to the circuit, this will test leakage from the equipment as well. It may be helpful to isolate the conductors only (disconnect the equipment) when testing to determine if the problem comes from the wiring or from the equipment connected to the wire.

Troubleshooting Ground and Leakage Current

The source of excessive ground current may be difficult to isolate. When troubleshooting a situation where current is flowing to the ground:

- test the grounding electrode conductor to determine ground current is present,
- disconnect and/or turn off all equipment attached to the feeder and branch circuits, and test individually to determine where the problem is occurring,
- if the problem is not identified in the wiring, connect equipment and test. The problem may exist within the equipment itself.

Arc Faults

An arc fault is an unplanned high powered discharge of electricity between two or more conductors, as illustrated in Figure 14-19. This discharge results in heat, which can damage or break conductors and possibly cause an electrical fire. Common sources of an arc fault include corroded or damaged conductors, loose connections, shorts within equipment, etc.

There are three types of arc faults that are of particular concern within PV systems. These include:

SERIES ARC FAULT

- **Series arc faults,** which occurs when a connection is pulled apart while under current. Any intermittent or loose connection in the DC circuit has the potential for producing a DC arc fault. Places where series arc faults commonly occur within PV systems include soldered joints within the module, compression type wire connections, or within MC4 connectors.

PARALLEL ARC FAULT

- **Parallel arc faults,** which occur when there is damage or wear in conductor insulation. Two conductors of opposite polarity in the same

DC circuit often are located next to each other within raceways or conduit. The insulation between the two wires can become damaged for a number of reasons,.

- Ground faults, that require the failure of only one insulation system.

Since 2011 nearly all inverters are required to have arc fault detectors which can detect and interrupt an arc fault, usually by disconnecting the inverter. Once disconnected, the inverter must be manually re-energized.

When an inverter registers an arc fault and disconnects, the source of the fault must be determined prior to re-energizing the system. Trace all connections from the inverter, in the manner similar to tracing a ground fault.

FIGURE 14-19: AN ARC FAULT

The use of an infrared camera can help detect arc faults, as they typically generate a significant amount of heat. However faults in the PV source circuit may be difficult to access and locate using this method, especially on rooftop installations.

Often, due to the nature of an arc fault, the location may be readily apparent due to burned, scorched or damaged conductors and/or equipment. Once the source has been located, be sure the DC power from the array has been disconnected at the source before conducting repairs.

If the panels themselves are damaged, remember that even severely damaged panels can produce dangerous voltage levels when exposed to sunlight.

If the fault has occurred within the array, connect the positive output lead from the array to the positive lead of a multimeter. Connect the negative lead to the frame or rack of the array, to determine if any voltage is leaking from the system.

The presence of water (such as rain) can dramatically increase the risk of metal in contact with damaged modules becoming energized. Aside from racking, metal roofs, conduit, gutters, and ladders touching the roof can also become energized when in contact with damaged modules.

If possible, cover the array with an approved material (fire resistant blankets, for example) to reduce the output voltage. Remember, not all coverings eliminate all the voltage the system may produce (blue tarps, for example, allow a significant amount of light through).

Ground Faults

Common causes of a ground fault within a PV system include: damaged or pinched wire, improper connections, or a damaged module. Ground faults can also be caused by wiring errors.

If the grounded DC conductor comes in contact with the grounding system outside the inverter, it will activate the GFDI protection system, and the inverter will shut down. Remember, the system should be connected to ground at only one location (almost always within the inverter).

SAFETY ISSUE: The presence of a ground fault can be extremely dangerous. It is likely that metal surfaces not intended to carry current may now be energized, and very likely that the current is not properly flowing to ground. Wear proper personal protective equipment.

It is also possible that the ground fault will result in electrical arcs, which pose a risk of fire. Do not try to extinguish an electrical fire without proper training. Call emergency services should an arc fire occur.
Whenever a ground fault detector indicates a ground fault, technicians should assume that a conductor or piece of equipment is damaged and in need of repair. A common cause of a ground fault is the result of failure of the insulation that isolates current-carrying conductors from contact with grounded, conductive surfaces.

Residual Current Device (RCD)

RESIDUAL CURRENT
DEVICE (RCD)

All certified inverters contain ground fault detection in the form of a **residual current device (RCD)**. The RCD detects current leakage into the grounding system on the DC side. These often will detect rapid changes as well as slowly rising leakage currents.

An external RCD is required in some countries. The installer must check which type of RCD is required by the specific local electric codes.

The IEC 60755 standard specifies three different types of RCDs, defined by their ability to sense, properly trip, and withstand different types of current.

These include:
- Type AC – sensitive to residual sinusoidal alternating current (AC).
- Type A – sensitive to residual sinusoidal alternating current (AC) or pulsed direct current (DC).
- Type B – sensitive to residual AC, pulsed DC, or smooth DC currents.

Testing for a Ground Fault

If the indicator on the string inverter indicates that a ground fault has occurred, typical troubleshooting techniques include:

- Turn off (open) the DC disconnect and wait several minutes to ensure all capacitors have discharged.

- Check any ground fault fuses or breakers to determine they are in good working order.

- Disconnect the DC inverter connections, isolating the inverter from the array.

- Turn on (close) the DC disconnect, energizing the conductors which have been disconnected from the inverter.

- Using a multimeter, test the positive and negative conductors for voltage. This should measure the open circuit voltage of the array.

- Take a voltage reading from the positive conductor to ground. Then measure voltage from negative conductor to ground. If there is excessive voltage present on either of these tests, a ground fault likely exists in the DC portion of the system. It is normal for PV systems to have small leakage currents flowing between the PV cells and ground. How much current depends on a variety of factors, including the size of the system, the amount of conductive surface in contact with circuits, the presence of moisture in the system, and damage to the integrity of the conductors. For PV arrays constructed with crystalline silicon modules, typical ground currents for properly operating residential systems are a few microamps; typical current flows for a 500-kW PV array are a few milliamps.

- If a fault is present, beginning at the inverter, check and test each connection point back to the array.

- At each connection point, disconnect (conductors in free air) and perform a voltage test of the positive and negative (should read open circuit voltage), positive and ground (should read zero), negative and ground (should read zero). If any voltage is present on the ground test, the ground fault exists prior to the connection tested.

Isolation Resistant Faults (RISO)

Isolation resistance faults (RISO) (sometimes referred to as insulation resistance faults) are the most common type of DC ground fault occurring within solar PV systems. It is estimated that 50% of all PV RISO faults go undetected.

> ISOLATION
> RESISTANCE FAULTS

Such faults are usually the result of either small nicks or cuts made during installation to the cable's insulation, or the premature degradation of the outer insulation of the cable over time.

Normally RISO faults do not occur spontaneously, but rather manifest over time as the electrical insulation of the PV array degrades.

Ground fault detection devices (set to a sensitive level of detection) may indicate the presence of a RISO fault. Test for the fault using standard ground fault detection methods or with the use of a megohmmeter to locate the flaw in the cable's insulation.

Power Factor Correction

Any facility with a high proportion of inductive loads (motors, for example) may find that it experiences a low power factor. The power factor at its most basic is the proportion between the amount of power delivered by the utility (apparent power) and the amount of power used by the loads to do work (real power).

A low power factor results in the need for utilities to supply more power than is actually being used (or metered) at the facility. Most utilities penalize (with additional fees) companies with a power factor below 0.95 or 0.90. They may also offer financial incentives to raise power factors above a certain level.

FIGURE 14-20:
CAPACITOR SIZING MULTIPLYING FACTOR CHART (INDICATING FOR POWER FACTOR CORRECTION FROM 0.77 TO 0.96)

	80	81	82	83	84	85	86	87	88	89	90	91	92	93	94	95	96	97	98	99	100
50	0.982	1.008	1.034	1.060	1.086	1.112	1.139	1.165	1.192	1.220	1.248	1.276	1.306	1.337	1.369	1.403	1.442	1.481	1.529	1.590	1.732
51	.937	.962	.989	1.015	1.041	1.067	1.094	1.120	1.147	1.175	1.203	1.231	1.261	1.292	1.324	1.358	1.395	1.436	1.484	1.544	1.687
52	.893	.919	.945	.971	.997	1.023	1.050	1.076	1.103	1.131	1.159	1.187	1.217	1.248	1.280	1.314	1.351	1.392	1.440	1.500	1.643
53	.850	.876	.902	.928	.954	.980	1.007	1.033	1.060	1.088	1.116	1.144	1.174	1.205	1.237	1.271	1.308	1.349	1.397	1.457	1.600
54	.809	.835	.861	.887	.913	.939	.966	.992	1.019	1.047	1.075	1.103	1.133	1.164	1.196	1.230	1.267	1.308	1.356	1.416	1.559
55	.769	.795	.821	.847	.873	.899	.926	.952	.979	1.007	1.035	1.063	1.090	1.124	1.156	1.190	1.228	1.268	1.316	1.377	1.519
56	.730	.756	.782	.808	.834	.860	.887	.913	.940	.968	.996	1.024	1.051	1.085	1.117	1.151	1.189	1.229	1.277	1.338	1.480
57	.692	.718	.744	.770	.796	.822	.849	.875	.902	.930	.958	.986	1.013	1.047	1.079	1.113	1.151	1.191	1.239	1.300	1.442
58	.655	.681	.707	.733	.759	.785	.812	.838	.865	.893	.921	.949	.976	1.010	1.042	1.076	1.114	1.154	1.202	1.263	1.405
59	.618	.644	.670	.696	.722	.748	.775	.801	.828	.856	.884	.912	.939	.973	1.005	1.039	1.077	1.117	1.165	1.226	1.368
60	.584	.610	.636	.662	.688	.714	.741	.767	.794	.822	.850	.878	.905	.939	.971	1.005	1.043	1.083	1.131	1.192	1.334
61	.549	.575	.601	.627	.653	.679	.706	.732	.759	.787	.815	.843	.870	.904	.936	.970	1.008	1.048	1.096	1.157	1.299
62	.515	.541	.567	.593	.619	.645	.672	.698	.725	.753	.781	.809	.836	.870	.902	.936	.974	1.014	1.062	1.123	1.265
63	.483	.509	.535	.561	.587	.613	.640	.666	.693	.721	.749	.777	.804	.838	.870	.904	.942	.982	1.030	1.091	1.233
64	.450	.476	.502	.528	.554	.580	.607	.633	.660	.688	.716	.744	.771	.805	.837	.871	.909	.949	.997	1.058	1.200
65	.419	.445	.471	.497	.523	.549	.576	.602	.629	.657	.685	.713	.740	.774	.806	.840	.878	.918	.966	1.027	1.169
66	.388	.414	.440	.466	.492	.518	.545	.571	.598	.626	.654	.682	.709	.743	.775	.809	.847	.887	.935	.996	1.138
67	.358	.384	.410	.436	.462	.488	.515	.541	.568	.596	.624	.652	.679	.713	.745	.779	.817	.857	.905	.966	1.108
68	.329	.355	.381	.407	.433	.459	.486	.512	.539	.567	.595	.623	.650	.684	.716	.750	.788	.828	.876	.937	1.079
69	.299	.325	.351	.377	.403	.429	.456	.482	.509	.537	.565	.593	.620	.654	.686	.720	.758	.798	.846	.907	1.049
70	.270	.296	.322	.348	.374	.400	.427	.453	.480	.508	.536	.564	.591	.625	.657	.691	.729	.769	.811	.878	1.020
71	.242	.268	.294	.320	.346	.372	.399	.425	.452	.480	.508	.536	.563	.597	.629	.663	.701	.741	.783	.850	.992
72	.213	.239	.265	.291	.317	.343	.370	.396	.423	.451	.479	.507	.534	.568	.600	.634	.672	.712	.754	.821	.963
73	.186	.212	.238	.264	.290	.316	.343	.369	.396	.424	.452	.480	.507	.541	.573	.607	.645	.685	.727	.794	.936
74	.159	.185	.211	.237	.263	.289	.316	.342	.369	.397	.425	.453	.480	.514	.546	.580	.618	.658	.700	.767	.909
75	.132	.158	.184	.210	.236	.262	.289	.315	.342	.370	.398	.426	.453	.487	.519	.553	.591	.631	.673	.740	.882
76	.105	.131	.157	.183	.209	.235	.262	.288	.315	.343	.371	.399	.426	.460	.492	.526	.564	.604	.652	.713	.855
77	.079	.105	.131	.157	.183	.209	.236	.262	.289	.317	.345	.373	.400	.434	.466	.500	.538	.578	.620	.687	.829
78	.053	.079	.105	.131	.157	.183	.210	.236	.263	.291	.319	.347	.374	.408	.440	.474	.512	.552	.594	.661	.803
79	.026	.052	.078	.104	.130	.156	.183	.209	.236	.264	.292	.320	.347	.381	.413	.447	.485	.525	.567	.634	.776
80	.000	.026	.052	.078	.104	.130	.157	.183	.210	.238	.266	.294	.321	.355	.387	.421	.459	.499	.541	.608	.750
81	—	.000	.026	.052	.078	.104	.131	.157	.184	.212	.240	.268	.295	.329	.361	.395	.433	.473	.515	.582	.724
82	—	—	.000	.026	.052	.078	.105	.131	.158	.186	.214	.242	.269	.303	.335	.369	.407	.447	.489	.556	.698
83	—	—	—	.000	.026	.052	.079	.105	.132	.160	.188	.216	.243	.277	.309	.343	.381	.421	.463	.530	.672

Power factor correction is generally achieved by adding capacitors in parallel into the circuit feeding the inductive load, either at the load itself or at the service panel.

Sizing the Capacitor

While there are several methods of determining the required size of a capacitor bank in order to correct the power factor, the simplest is to use a power factor correction table similar to the example in Figure 14-20.

To size the capacitor bank, locate the current power factor (left-hand column). In that row, scan right until reaching the column with the desired power factor. Then multiply the power used by the unit by the selected correction factor to determine the size of capacity needed (in kVAR).

For example, assume an office building has an air conditioning unit that draws on average 75 kW when operating. It currently has an 0.77 (77%) power factor but the facility owner would like to increase this to 0.96 (96%). In looking at the chart, the correction factor is found to be 0.538. So the capacitor required is:

75 kW (power) x 0.538 (correction factor) = 40.35 kVAR capacitor

Troubleshooting the System

Many problems experienced over the life of a PV system likely have their roots in a poor initial design and/or installation.

Common mistakes that will impact performance may include:

- *Not accounting for future shading:* Remember, trees grow, neighbors build things. While the array may have been free of shading issues during the early days of its life, shading may become a factor down the road.

- *Poor site survey:* The orientation of the array may not have been optimized. The roof structure may not have been up to the task. Supports for ground mounted systems may not have been placed in a way that avoids shifting and sinking. Wiring and systems may be affected by heat issues that were not anticipated.

- *The balance of systems (BOS) may be undersized or oversized.* Most electronic equipment such as charge controllers, or inverters, operate best within a limited range. If the power is too great or not enough, performance will suffer.

- *Undersized wire and/or conduit:* Loss due to voltage drop or capacity affected by heat is a common problem when the conductors and conduit have not been sized properly.

- *Poor installation:* A badly designed and installed grounding system, poor mounting, lack of space for cooling (panels on rooftop, or equipment near buildings), poorly connected conductors - all can combine to cause a host of problems as the system ages.

Typical System Problems

Some common problems that may occur within a PV system include:
- lower than expected power output from the array,
- sudden system failure,
- battery failure.

It should be noted that all troubleshooting (and maintenance for that matter) should begin with a thorough visual inspection of the system. Nine times out of ten this process will identify the problem (a panel is damaged, a squirrel chewed through a wire, a circuit breaker was tripped, etc).

Poor System Output

A few common problems that can affect the output of the array include:

- *Dirt and/or debris on the modules.* The fix is pretty easy. Simply clean the panels and clear away any debris.

- *Shading issues.* Visually inspect to see if a tree or shrub has grown enough to shade a portion of the array. Remove the shading element if possible.

- *Problems with a module.* Physically inspect the module for cracks, burn marks, loose connections, etc. If possible, test each module with a multimeter. If not possible, shade a significant portion of each module (with a hat or piece of cardboard) and note if the array output declines. If shading a module does not affect output, there may be a problem with that module.

> HEAT FADE

- *Heat fade.* Solar modules perform less well as the heat increases. The amount of heat each module would be exposed to should have been anticipated and accounted for in the design process. However a weak module may react even more adversely to heat than anticipated. Test this by cooling the deck of the roof below the panels by spraying water from a hose. Do not spray the water directly on the panels, as it might cause the glass to crack if the shock between the excessive heat and the cold water is too abrupt.

- *The array may be incorrectly wired.* Make sure all strings have the same number of modules. Check all string voltages in the combiner box, making sure the system is turned off and all breakers in the open position.

- *Burnt terminals and/or diodes.* A visual inspection should show if there has been a catastrophic failure. If the array has been struck by lightning, for example, these connections may fail.

- *Loose connections.* Check the wiring system to ensure all connections are secure. Again, make sure the system is turned off before checking these connections.

- *Overcurrent protection.* Check all fuses and breakers to make sure they have not been blown or tripped. There may have been a power surge and the overcurrent protection has done its job and shut down part of the system.

- *Check conduit fittings.* Wind, disruption or simply age may have caused fittings to loosen, allowing water to enter conduits.

- *Inspect the inverter.* Make sure the inverter is functioning properly and the cooling system (fan) is operating. Check for clogged filters if present.

Sudden System Failure

There are also times when the system shuts down completely. Reasons for this may include:

- *The grid is down.* On grid-tied systems the system is designed to shut down when the power from the grid is interrupted. There may be no problem and the system is simply working as it should.

- *A ground fault.* If the inverter detects a ground fault on the DC side of the system, the ground fault interruption device should shut down the system and indicate that there is a ground fault that must be addressed.

- *A bad inverter.* While the PV array has no moving parts, most string inverters do - and they will eventually fail. Follow the troubleshooting instructions provided by the inverter manufacturer to determine if the problem is with the inverter.

- *Something is turned off.* Check to see that the inverter, all disconnects, breakers and other system equipment remains in the on (closed) position.

- *A fuse has blown.* A sudden surge (a lightning strike, for example) has caused a fuse to blow or a breaker to open.

Battery Failure

In stand-alone systems, the inclusion of a battery bank and a charge controller complicates matters a bit. Problems with the battery bank may simply be an indication of problems elsewhere in the system.

Remember, when working with batteries, always wear approved eye, face and hand protection to avoid injury.

- *Poor connections.* Using a multimeter, test the voltage of all batteries connected in series. The readings should be within a few tenths of a volt of each other. Amp readings for all batteries connected in parallel should be the same and within 5% under charging and discharging conditions.

- *Bad battery.* Batteries do fail. Disconnect and test each battery. All voltage readings should be within a tenth of a volt or so.

- *Excessive loads.* If the array has been undersized, or the loads have increased, the battery bank may not be able to fully recover from load demand. Many charge controllers and/or inverters maintain data regarding the performance of battery banks. Daily records of amp-hours delivered to and extracted from the battery bank will indicate if the battery bank is able to routinely fully recover from daily load demands.

- *Too many parallel strings.* The battery bank design should not call for more than three parallel battery strings. The resulting bank will tend to lose its equalization, resulting in accelerated failure of any weak cells.

- *Poor temperature control.* When the temperature falls below 0° C (32° F), batteries will lose about 25% of their available charge. Avoid heaters that will keep some batteries warmer than others.

Chapter 14 Review Questions

1) The tension applied to a nut and bolt with a wrench, that holds the connection together is referred to as:
   a) preload
   b) applied force
   c) continuity
   d) applied pressure

2) In the US, torque is normally measured in inch-pounds (in-lb). In most countries around the world, torque is measured in:
   a) millimeter-kilograms (mm-kg)
   b) Newton-meters (Nm)
   c) kilograms per m/s² (ma)
   d) ohm-centimeters (ohm-cm)

3) Common tests used to ensure proper electrical connections include:
   a) continuity and resistance tests
   b) polarity tests
   c) insulation resistance tests
   d) all of the above

4) An installer using a multimeter checks the DC voltage output of a string. The reading indicates negative 275 Vdc (-275 Vdc). This test indicates:
   a) the polarity of the string is reversed
   b) the system is likely functioning normally
   c) the meter is faulty
   d) none of the above

5) An installer suspects that the insulation of a cable pulled through a conduit has been damaged. What tool would be used to test this?
   a) an ohmmeter
   b) an anemometer
   c) a fall-of-potential meter
   d) a megohmmeter

6) As temperature increases, the resistance of the insulation on conductors:
   a) will decrease by 50% for every 10°C increase
   b) will decrease by 10% for every 10°C increase
   c) will increase by 50% for every 10°C increase
   d) will increase by 10% for every 10°C increase

7) An issue that occurs in some high voltage systems where the power output of the array may be reduced by as much as 80% in the weeks or months after installation is known as:
   a) potential induced degradation
   b) light induced deterioration
   c) power intensity degradation
   d) current transfer deterioration

8) Which of the following is **NOT** a common test to check a system for PID?
   a) IV curve tracer
   b) megohmmeter
   c) infrared camera
   d) electroluminescence imaging

9) When verifying the energy output of a system, the temperature used should be:
   a) the ambient air temperature, plus 25°C for ground mounted, 30°C for ballasted systems, or 35°C for flush-to-roof mounted systems
   b) the ambient air temperature without correction factors
   c) the cell temperature measured at the front of the panel
   d) the cell temperature measured at the back of the panel

10) To properly test the earth resistivity, an installer must first know:
   a) the temperature of the soil
   b) the dissolved salt content of the soil
   c) the moisture content of the soil
   d) all the above

11) In a properly functioning circuit, the net current when measured with a clamp-on ammeter should be:
   a) the expected voltage, for example 120 Vac or 300 Vdc
   b) the ampacity rating of the conductor
   c) zero
   d) the ampacity rating of the overcurrent protection device to which the conductor is attached

12) Which of the following situations will likely **NOT** result in unbalanced voltages in a three phase system?
   a) a large single-phase motor has turned on
   b) a large three-phase motor has turned off
   c) a ground fault in a connected power transformer
   d) reversed polarity in the DC circuit

13) An installer has just completed installing a PV system with a string inverter. The system is comprised of two strings of 11 panels with the following specifications:

Nominal Max Power (Pmax)	330 watts
Max Power Voltage (Vmp)	58.0 V
Max Power Current (Imp)	5.70 A
Open Circuit Voltage (Voc)	69.7 V
Short Circuit Current (Isc)	6.07 A
Temperature Coefficient (Pmax)	-0.258%/°C
Temperature Coefficient (Voc)	-0.17 V/°C
Temperature Coefficient (Isc)	3.31 mA/°C

An infrared thermometer is used to test the back of the panel, and the reading is 39°C. An irradiance meter is used and the reading indicates 892 W/m². The derate of the system (including inverter conversion) is 90%.

What would be the expected output from the inverter?
a) 2,492 W
b) 4,983 W
c) 5,537 W
d) 8,029 W

14) Conductors leading to a load are quite hot. Which of the following is likely **NOT** a situation that might result in excess heat in the conductors?
a) too much resistance in the circuit
b) unbalanced voltage
c) wires are undersized for the load
d) high earth resistivity in the ground

15) An installer is doing a final system check. She measures voltage and amps at the grounding electrode and finds that 2 mA of AC current are leaking into the ground.
a) this is likely caused by damaged conductor insulation and a megohmmeter should be used to locate the fault
b) this is perfectly normal
c) a GFCI should be installed in the circuit to correct this problem
d) the earth resistivity is likely too high, causing current buildup on the conductor. A second grounding electrode should be installed.

16) An installed system is suddenly producing about 40% less energy than was previously reported. Which of the following might be a cause of this lower-than-expected production?
a) a ground fault
b) an arc fault
c) the grid is down
d) a loose connection

17) A loose connection in the DC output circuit may result in a:
   a) a series ground fault
   b) a series arc fault
   c) a parallel ground fault
   d) a parallel arc fault

18) A _____ is normally built into the inverter and will detect current leakage into the grounding system on the DC side of the system.
   a) residual current device (RCD)
   b) ground fault detection device (GFDD)
   c) arc fault detection device (AFDD)
   d) RISO indicator

19) When correcting for a low power factor in a facility, a _____ should be installed within the system.
   a) residual current device (RCD)
   b) isolation resistance device (RISO)
   c) energy storage system (ESS)
   d) capacitor bank

Chapter 15

Inspections and Commissioning

Throughout the installation process, a **quality assurance** process should be in place to avoid problems from occurring.

This is accomplished by beginning with a good design, ensuring the system complies with all applicable codes and standards, communicating effectively with all who are involved in the installation (vendors, installers, sub-contractors, customers, etc.), and constant monitoring to ensure the installation is completed in a workmanlike manner.

But after quality assurance comes **quality control.** Quality control is aimed at identifying any defects in the finished product and correcting them. After the PV system has been installed and the components tested, but before the system has been turned on, there are a number of steps that should be completed to ensure everything is as it should be. This process is known as **commissioning** the system.

Commissioning involves a final inspection and documentation of the system to verify that it has been properly installed and will operate in a safe and efficient manner.

The *IEC 62446 Grid Connected PV Systems – Minimum Requirements for System Documentation, Commissioning Tests, and Inspection* standard defines minimum documentation, commissioning tests and inspection criteria for grid-connected PV systems.

QUALITY ASSURANCE

QUALITY CONTROL

COMMISSIONING

Chapter Objectives:

- Conduct a final installation checkout.
- Verify the system complies with all applicable codes.
- Ensure the system is properly labeled.
- Thoroughly inspect the array, grounding system, wire management, conductors, overcurrent protection, electrical connections, charge controllers, disconnects, inverters, and batteries.
- Ensure the system complies with all fire safety requirements.
- Verify the system functions as designed and document the results.

Commissioning the System

A complete and thorough commissioning process serves a number of purposes. It will:
- verify that the installation matches the plans,
- ensure compliance with all applicable code requirements,
- confirm that the system will operate safely when energized,
- verify that all the components are operating as specified,
- document the state of operation when the system was first employed,
- verify that the operation and maintenance documentation has been completed.

Many of the same tests conducted during the commissioning process will later be repeated as part of periodic maintenance. Later results can be compared to those obtained during commissioning to determine if there is any unexplained deterioration of performance.

A well-planned commissioning process includes:
- final installation checkout,
- visual inspection of the system,
- verification of code compliance,
- electrical verification tests,
- system functioning tests,
- verification of array power and energy production,
- verifying AC power output,
- documenting all results,
- training the system owner,
- cleanup and restore the site to pre-construction condition.

Final Installation Checkout

PUNCH LIST

The final installation checkout is conducted by the installer before initiating any tests. A **punch list** can be developed during the design and installation phases of the project and then verified during the checkout process. These lists typically verify that:
- all structural components such as racking systems, conduit supports, battery cabinets, etc have been installed,
- all electrical circuits are in place and conduit/raceways installed as required,
- all wiring connections have been made,
- all equipment has been calibrated and set according to manufacturer's instructions. This equipment will not only include critical items such as inverters and charge controllers, but also temperature sensors, communications systems for monitoring devices, meters, etc.

Verification of Code Compliance

There are a number of code and standard setting bodies that a PV designer/installer will come into contact with during the course of a project. While the authority having jurisdiction (the code inspector) has the final say, they will rely upon these guidelines during the inspection process.

National Electrical Code (NEC)

Ensure that the system is in compliance with all applicable codes.

NEC articles that apply to PV systems include (but are not limited to):

- Article 100: Definitions
- Article 110: Requirements for Electrical Installations
- Article 200: Grounded Conductors
- Article 240: Overcurrent Protection
- Article 250: Grounding and Bonding
- Article 300: Wiring Methods
- Article 310: Conductors for General Wiring
- Article 314: Outlet, Device, Pull, and Junction Boxes
- Article 338: Service-Entrance Cable: Types SE and USE
- Article 344: Rigid Metal Conduit: Type RMC
- Article 352: Rigid Polyvinyl Chloride Conduit: Type PVC
- Article 356: Liquidtight Flexible Nonmetallic Conduit: Type LFNC
- Article 358: Electrical Metallic Tubing: Type EMT
- Article 400: Flexible Cords and Cables
- Article 408: Switchboards, Switchgear and Panelboards
- Article 445: Generators
- Article 450: Transformers
- Article 480: Storage Batteries
- Article 690: Photovoltaic Systems
- Article 691: Large Scale PV Systems
- Article 705: Interconnected Electric Power Production Sources
- Article 706: Energy Storage Systems

International Code Council

The **International Code Council (ICC)** is an organization that seeks to develop comprehensive international model construction codes focused on building safety and fire prevention.

INTERNATIONAL CODE COUNCIL (ICC)

Many ICC Codes apply to PV installations, including:

- International Building Code (IBC) - The IBC covers all buildings except detached one and two-family dwellings and townhouses not more than three (3) stories in height. It has been adopted for use as a base code standard by most jurisdictions in the United States.

- International Fire Code (IFC) - The IFC focuses on the safeguarding of life and property from all types of fire and explosions hazards. It is in use or has been adopted in 41 states, as well as the District of Columbia, New York City, Guam, and Puerto Rico.

- International Residential Code (IRC) - The IRC establishes minimum regulations for one- and two-family dwellings and townhouses up to three stories.

- **International Green Construction Code (IGCC)** - IGCC is a code focused on new and existing commercial buildings addressing green building design and performance.

INTERNATIONAL GREEN CONSTRUCTION CODE

IEEE

The Institute of Electrical and Electronics Engineers (IEEE)
The **Institute of Electrical and Electronics Engineers (IEEE)** is the world's largest association of technical professionals with more than 420,000 members in over 160 countries around the world. Its objectives are the educational and technical advancement of electrical and electronic engineering, telecommunications, computer engineering and allied disciplines.

To this end, the organization creates and publishes a number of standards related to photovoltaics. These include:
- 929 - Recommended Practice for Utility Interface of Residential and Intermediate Photovoltaic (PV) Systems
- 937 - Recommended Practice for Installation and Maintenance of Lead-Acid Batteries for Photovoltaic Systems
- 1013 - Recommended Practice for Sizing Lead-Acid Batteries for Stand-Alone Photovoltaic Systems
- 1361 - Guide for Selection, Charging, Test and Evaluation of Lead-Acid Batteries Used in Stand-Alone Photovoltaic Systems
- 1526 - Recommended Practice for Testing the Performance of Stand Alone Photovoltaic Systems
- 1547 - Standard for Interconnecting Distributed Resources with Electric Power Systems
- 1547.1 - Standard for Conformance Tests Procedures for Equipment Interconnecting Distributed Resources with Electric Power Systems
- 1547.2 - Application Guide for IEEE 1547 Standard for Interconnecting Distributed Resources with Electric Power Systems
- 1547.3 - Guide For Monitoring, Information Exchange, and Control of Distributed Resources Interconnected with Electric Power Systems
- 1547.4 - Guide for Design, Operation, and Integration of Distributed Resource Island Systems with Electric Power Systems
- 1547.6 - Recommended Practice For Interconnecting Distributed Resources With Electric Power Systems Distribution Secondary Networks
- 1561 - Guide for Optimizing the Performance and Life of Lead-Acid Batteries in Remote Hybrid Power Systems

- 1562 - Guide for Array and Battery Sizing in Stand-Alone Photovoltaic Systems
- 1661 - Guide for Test and Evaluation of Lead-Acid Batteries Used in Photovoltaic (PV) Hybrid Power Systems
- 2030 - Guide for Smart Grid Interoperability of Energy Technology and Information Technology Operation with the Electric Power System (EPS), and End-Use Applications and Loads

Underwriters Laboratories

Underwriters Laboratories Inc. (UL) has created more than 1,000 safety standards for a wide variety of products.

UL standards that specifically apply to the PV industry include:
- UL 1699, for Arc-Fault Circuit-Interrupters
- UL 1699B, AC AFCIs
- UL 1703, for Flat-Plate Photovoltaic Modules and Panels
- UL 1741 – Inverters, Converters, Controllers and Interconnection System Equipment for Use With Distributed Energy Resources
- UL 2703 – Rack Mounting Systems and Clamping Devices for Flat-Plate Photovoltaic Modules and Panels
- UL 3703 – Trackers.

PV designers/installers should verify that all the products used in their installation comply with these product standards.

Programing the Inverter

Commissioning an inverter can often be a complex and time-consuming process. Each unit operates in its own unique fashion, and will come with instructions (and often videos) to assist in this process. That said, there are a number of steps common to all systems that must be followed.

Steps involved to commission the inverter include:
- establish a connection to the user interface. This may be as simple and turning on the unit and entering options into a menu that appears on an LCD screen, or increasingly the user interface is web-based. Connect the inverter to the web, either through a wireless or direct connection to a modem will be required.
- log into the user interface. An account may need to be established with the manufacturer to accomplish this step.
- select the system configuration and update any software as directed.
- select the proper country, state or region code and language for the installation location.
- pair any MLPE devices with the inverter.

SOLAR COMMISSIONING FORM

A: GENERAL SITE INFORMATION

SITE CONTACT NAME: ———————————————————————————————

SITE ADDRESS: ————————————————————————————————————

LEAD TECHNICIAN'S NAME: ——————————————————————————————

DATE: ————————————— TIME: ——————— WEATHER: ———————————

CURRENTLY PRODUCING WATTS (TOTAL FROM ALL INVERTER DISPLAYS): ——————————

TOTAL SYSTEM WATTS (AT STC): —————————

MAXIMUM SYSTEM VOLTAGE: ———— SITE HIGH TEMP: —————— LOW TEMP: ————————

UTILITY METER NUMBER: ——————

ACTUAL GRID VOLTAGE (AT POINT OF INTERCONNECTION): L1-L2: ———— L1-N: ———— L2-N: ————

BACK OF MODULE TEMP: ————————— SOLAR IRRADIANCE: ——————————

B: ARRAY INFORMATION

	Array A	Array B	Totals:
Array true azimuth (degrees)			n/a
Array tilt (degrees)			n/a
Shading (Pathfinder at 4 corners of array)	%	%	% avg
Inverter (Manufacturer / Model)			n/a
Number of Inverters			
Module (Manufacturer/ Model)			n/a
Number of Modules			

C: INVERTER INFORMATION

Label	Array (A,B) / String (1,2,3,4)	Serial Number	Output (W)
Inverter 1			
Inverter 2			
Inverter 3			
Inverter 4			

D: STRING INFORMATION

String	# of Modules	Voc	Imp
String 1			
String 2			
String 3			
String 4			

Notes:

- program system settings as required (power factor, grid import/export options, etc).
- synchronize the inverter with the grid (this is normally done automatically).
- check the production of the system with the current temperature and irradiance conditions.

Many systems that incorporate MLPE will provide individual module monitoring. It will be necessary to map the array using the online software so that the system knows which MLPE is associated with each specific module.

System Documentation

Good documentation is critical to the commissioning process. The installer should:
- record the results of the visual inspections.
- document all wiring and electrical test results, completing a commissioning form such as the example depicted in Figure 15-1.
- record all the test results.
- interpret and/or summarize the test results.
- note any performance anomalies.
- note any special maintenance needs or corrective actions.
- detail any changes to the system design that have been incorporated into the installed system.
- date the results and obtain any signatures from the responsible persons.
- photograph the system and all its components to provide a visual record of the system at the end of the commissioning process. If possible, photograph the display results from the inverter and other equipment that demonstrate it is working as designed.
- verify that all required system and equipment labels, markings and placards are correct and in the proper locations.

System documentation requirements for grid-tied PV systems are laid out in IEC 62446. They are organized into six categories:
- system data,
- wiring diagrams,
- datasheets,
- mechanical design information,
- O&M information,
- test results and commissioning data.

System Data

Minimum system data requirements include basic information about the project, such as the rated system power as well as the equipment manufacturers, model numbers and quantities of PV modules and inverters.

The system data should also include contact information for the customer, system designer and system installer, plus relevant project dates.

Wiring Diagram

The documentation should, at minimum, include a one-line wiring diagram of the system. This should include general information about the quantity and type of modules, as well as specific details about the various circuit voltages and currents (Voc, Isc, Vmp, Imp). IEC 62446 also requires information about the location and types of balance of system components. Details need to be provided regarding conductor sizes and overcurrent protection device ratings.

Details regarding the bonding and grounding system, any connection to an existing lightning protection system, and the locations, types and ratings of AC or DC surge protection devices should be documented. IEC 62446 also notes what information is required as to the existing AC electrical system.

Datasheets

The datasheets (or spec sheets) of the various products used within the system should be organized and included in the project documentation.

Mechanical Design

A design of the array mounting system should be provided, at a minimum. Where applicable, structural engineering documents, soil testing results, etc can also be provided.

O&M Information

Proper documentation of system O&M information depends upon the audience and may involve a significant investment in time and resources. While basic O&M templates can be developed for residential and small commercial clients, templates for larger commercial projects will likely be much more project specific.

O&M documentation should include:
- site specific safety issues,
- roof access process (if applicable),
- inspection checklist,
- procedures for verifying correct system operation,
- checklist of what to do should a system failure occur,
- emergency shutdown procedures,
- cleaning procedure and recommendations,
- any unusual maintenance requirements (dealing with emissions from nearby factory, dealing with seagulls for coastal installation, etc),
- any security issues (maintaining access restrictions, access to enclosures, etc),
- snow removal process and recommendations.

Ground mounted systems may also include items such as:

- soil erosion issues,
- animal abatement issues,
- vegetation control,
- storm water management.

Test Results and Commissioning Data

Copies of test results and commissioning data should be included in the documentation package.

Common tests conducted during commissioning include:

- Continuity and resistance tests designed to verify the integrity of grounding and bonding systems, conductors, connections and other terminations.
- Polarity tests that verify the correct polarity for PV DC circuits, and proper terminations for DC equipment.
- Voltage and current tests that verify the array and system are operating as designed. IV curves may be produced for strings and/or individual panels.
- Insulation resistance testing to verify the integrity of the insulation and to test for degradation and faults.
- Performance tests to verify the system power and energy output are consistent with expectations given the current temperature and irradiance.

Labeling the System

Section 690.56 of the National Electrical Code (NEC) sets out a number of requirements for labeling of PV systems.

Labels must be permanently affixed to equipment or wiring and may not be hand written. They must also be durable enough to withstand the environmental conditions to which they are exposed.

Additionally, labels must be reflective, all letters must be capitalized, and a minimum height of 3/8 inch (9.5 cm). Many labels are required to be white letters on a black background. A number of commercial labeling products are available designed to meet the code requirements.

Labeling requirements change over time. There are system label packages available from a number of vendors, each indicate which version of the NEC the labels comply with. There are also additional labels required for stand-alone systems.

Labels must appear throughout the system, as indicated in Figure 15-2. Following a typical system from the array to the loads, the following labels (based on the 2020 NEC) should be in place on grid-tied systems prior to activating the system:

FIGURE 15-2: LABELS
FOR TYPICAL GRID-TIED
PV SYSTEM

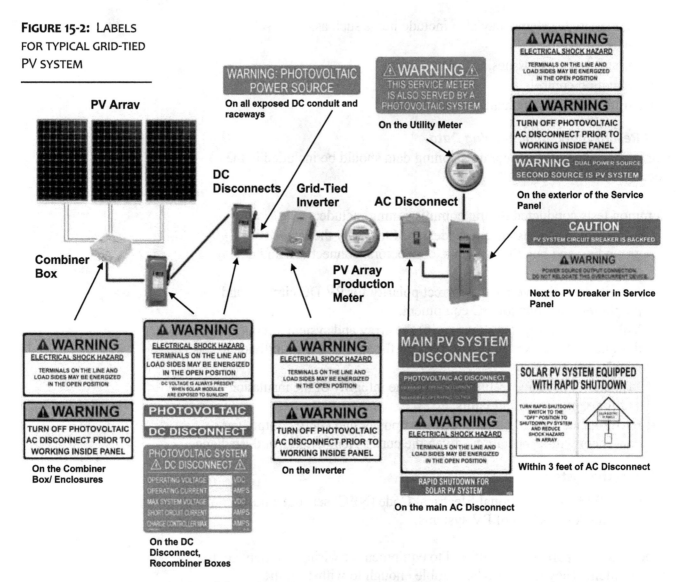

Conduit, Raceways and Junction Boxes

FIGURE 15-3: LABEL FOR
CONDUIT

NEC 690.31(D)(2)

A photovoltaic power source warning label (Figure 15-3) should be placed on all conduit, raceways, pull boxes and junction boxes throughout the system. They must be located every 10 feet (3 meters) and within one foot of each bend or building penetration.

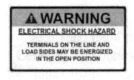

FIGURE 15-4: ENERGIZED
ON LINE AND LOAD SIDE
LABEL

NEC 690.13(B)

Since power is fed through the system from two directions (the array and the grid) at every junction box, pull box and enclosure, a label (Figure 15-4) is required warning that turning off one disconnect may not mean that power is no longer present in the system.

FIGURE 15-5: WARNING
LABEL TO TURN OFF
MAIN AC DISCONNECT

A second warning stating that the system should be disconnected from the grid prior to working inside the enclosure is also required (Figure 15-5).

DC Disconnects

All means of disconnection on the DC side of the system (including combiner boxes with a means of disconnection), must include labels that indicate they are a means of disconnection (Figure 15-6), and that even when disconnected, the conductors may still be energized when the sun is shining. (Figure 15-7)

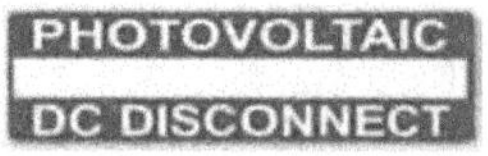

Additionally, a label should be in place on the DC disconnect to indicate, as shown in Figure 15-8, the rated voltage and current of the system. The installer must fill in the details on this label with a permanent marker.

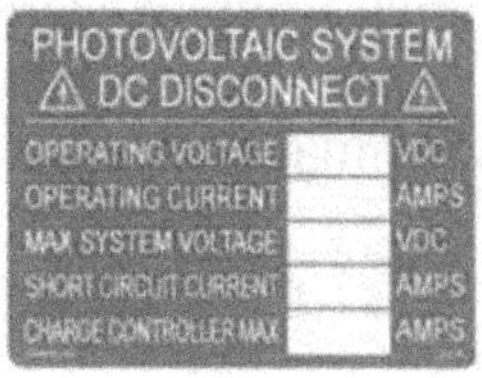

Inverter

If the inverter incorporates a DC disconnect, then the labels required for a DC disconnect must also be applied at this point. If an AC disconnect is also present, then the labels required for an AC disconnect are also required.

Additionally, an inverter is also an enclosure, so the labels required for enclosures should also be applied. If the system incorporates a solidly grounded bipolar design (which is uncommon), then a label such as Figure 15-9 should be applied.

Main AC Disconnect

The main AC disconnect must be labeled to indicate that it is indeed the main point of disconnection (Figure 15-10). Additionally, it should be labeled to indicate the rated operating AC voltage and current of the system, as shown in Figure 15-11.

The AC disconnect is also an enclosure, so all the appropriate labels for an enclosure should also be placed on the AC disconnect.

Rapid Shutdown

Systems installed that incorporate rapid shutdown, must indicate this with a label located within three (3) feet (one meter) of the main disconnect. Since rapid shutdown requirements have been changing in recent years, the NEC requires that labels indicate which version of the code the system complies with.

Figure 15-12 indicates that the system was installed in compliance with the rapid shutdown provisions outlined in the 2017 NEC. This

FIGURE 15-6: LABELS FOR DC DISCONNECTS

NEC 690.13(B)

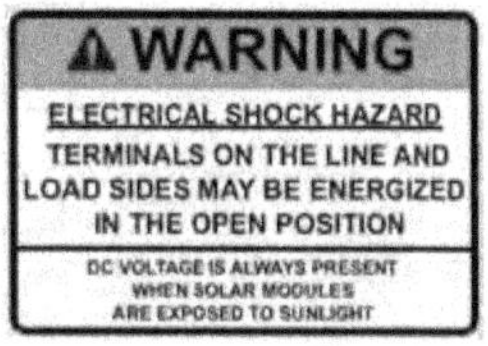

FIGURE 15-7: ENERGIZED WHEN OPEN WARNING

NEC 690.13(B)

FIGURE 15-8: LABEL INDICATING MAXIMUM DC VOLTAGE OF THE SYSTEM

NEC 690.53

FIGURE 15-9: GROUNDED BIPOLAR SYSTEM WARNING LABEL

NEC 690.31(E)

FIGURE 15.10: MAIN AC DISCONNECT LABEL

NEC 690.13(B)

FIGURE 15-11: RATED VOLTS & CURRENT ON AC DISCONNECTS

NEC 690.54

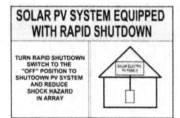

FIGURE 15-12: RAPID SHUTDOWN LABEL INDICATING SYSTEM COMPLIES WITH 2017 NEC

NEC 690.56(C)

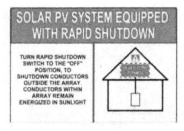

indicates that by opening the AC disconnect, the conductors within the array and those leaving the array will be shut down.

For systems that incorporate rapid shutdown only for conductors leaving the array (those within the array field are still energized). This was compliant with the 2014 NEC. When 2014 NEC compliant (but not 2017 rapid shutdown compliant) the label shown in Figure 15-13 should be used.

FIGURE 15-14: RAPID SHUTDOWN LABEL FOR MAIN DISCONNECT

NEC 690.56(C)(2)

The main disconnect for the system must have a label indicating that it is the

rapid shutdown point for the PV system, as indicated in Figure 15-14.

If the main PV disconnect can not, for some valid reason approved by the AHJ, be located within 10 feet of the utility entrance (usually the meter), then a plaque must be posted indicating where the disconnect is located.

Electrical Panel

Warnings must be given to those working on the electrical panel. Again, an electrical service panel is an enclosure, so all warning labels for enclosures should be present.

It is normal that when the main disconnect is opened (turned off), it is assumed that the rest of the panel is de-energized. But by adding a PV system, a second source of power is coming into the panel on the load side. So labels are placed on the cover of the service panel such as those indicated in Figure 15-15.

When looking inside the panel at the breakers, an additional warning label such as the one shown in Figure 15-16 should be posted next to the breaker that delivers power from the PV system. The 120% rule may dictate the specific location of the breaker within the box, so this label warns that moving the breaker later is not permitted.

Utility Meter

A warning label must also be affixed to the utility meter, warning utility personnel and first responders that the location is serviced by a photovoltaic power system. The label should appear similar to that in Figure 15-17.

FIGURE 15-17: WARNING LABEL FOR UTILITY METER

NEC 705.12

Battery Labels

If an energy storage system (ESS) is installed, then a lockable DC disconnect must be installed within sight of the battery bank or as near a practicable.

This disconnect should have a label indicating that it is indeed the ESS disconnect (Figure 15-18) as well as a label that documents the voltages and current associated with the system, plus the date those readings were documented (Figure 15-19).

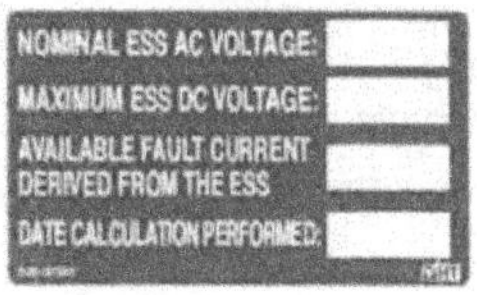

FIGURE 15-18: ESS DC DISCONNECT LABEL

NEC 706.15(C)

FIGURE 15-19: VOLTAGE AND CURRENT READINGS FOR ESS DISCONNECT

NEC 706.15(C)

Stand-Alone Systems

Any structure with a stand-alone PV system must have a permanent plaque or directory posted in a readily visible location. The sign must show where the system can be disconnected.

The disconnects should be labeled in a manner similar to the DC and AC disconnects within a grid-tied system.

Inspection

Before the system can become operational, it is normally the case that the authority having jurisdiction (AHJ) will require an inspection. In many locations only the electrical system will be inspected. In others, a structural inspection may also be required, especially if the system has been installed on a building.

A thorough inspection will include all parts of the system, ensuring they have been installed in a workmanlike manner, and comply with all the relevant codes and standards.

While processes vary, there are generally three different types of electrical inspections. These may occur independently (three different inspections) or in combination (all three at the same time).

The first is a **rough-in electrical inspection** where wires, conduits, and electrical panels and boxes will be inspected. An inspector will make sure that wires are intact, and check for any obvious fire hazards. This typically happens during the installation process prior to closing up any walls or filling any trenches.

> ROUGH-IN INSPECTION

The second type is a **service inspection**. During this inspection, the electrical equipment will be checked to make sure everything has been properly installed and fastened. Also the inspector will check the grounding and bonding system.

> SERVICE INSPECTION

Then there is the **final inspection**. Obviously the installation must be complete. An inspector may conduct a number of tests of the electrical system to test its safety and effectiveness.

Inspection Checklist

The Interstate Renewable Energy Council (IREC) has created a model PV inspection checklist that has been adopted widely by electrical inspectors across the nation. It is a very good idea for the project manager to ensure that the system complies with all its provisions prior to inspection.

Array
- Module manufacturer, make, model, and number of modules match the approved plans.
- PV modules are listed to UL 1703.
- DC modules are properly marked and labeled.
- AC modules are properly marked and labeled.
- Modules are attached to the mounting structure according to the manufacturer's instructions and the approved plans.
- Roof penetrations are flashed and counter-flashed.
- PV modules are in good condition (i.e., no broken glass or cells, no discoloration, frames not damaged, etc.).
- Residential one and two-family dwelling limited to maximum PV system voltage of 600 volts.
- Rooftop systems are designed in accordance with the IBC.
- Roof access points, paths and clearances need to comply with the IFC.

Grounding System
- A complete grounding electrode system is installed.
- Modules are grounded in accordance with manufacturer's installation instructions using the supplied hardware or listed equipment specified in the instructions and identified for the environment, using the grounding point identified on the module and in the manufacturer's instructions.
- Properly sized equipment grounding conductors are routed with the circuit conductors. AC and DC grounding electrode conductors are properly connected. Separate electrodes, if used, are bonded together.
- Bonding fittings are used on concentric/eccentric knockouts with metal conduits for circuits over 250 volts.
- Bonding fittings are used for ferrous metal conduits enclosing grounding electrode conductors. Wire Management
- Wires are secured by staples, cable ties, straps, hangers or similar fittings at intervals that do not exceed 4.5 feet.
- Wires are secured within 12 inches of each box, cabinet, conduit body or other termination.
- Cable closely follows the surface of the building finish or of the running boards.

- Exposed single conductors, where subject to physical damage, are protected.

Conductors

- Exposed single conductor wiring is a 90°C, wet rated and sunlight resistant type USE-2 or listed PV wire. If the wiring is in a conduit, it is 90°C, wet rated type RHW-2, THWN-2, or XHHW-2.
- Exposed single conductors used for ungrounded (transformerless) systems are listed and identified as "PV wire."
- Conductor insulation is rated at 90°C to allow for operation at 70°C+ near modules.
- Where conductors or cables are installed in conduits exposed to direct sunlight on or above rooftops, correction factors for ambient temperature adjustments are applied.
- Solidly grounded conductors are identified white or gray.
- Open conductors are secured and protected.
- Conductors are not in contact with the roof surface.
- DC conductors inside a building are in a metal raceway or MC metal-clad cable that complies with 250.118(10), or metal enclosures.
- If more than one nominal voltage system conductor is installed in the raceway, permanent identification and labeling is required.
- For underground conductor installations, the burial depth is appropriate and warning tape is in place.
- Aluminum is not placed in direct contact with concrete.
- DC source circuit conductors are rated at 1.25 x 1.25 = 156% short-circuit (ISC) current from modules.
- PV circuit and premises wiring is separated.
- PV system conductors shall be grouped and identified.

Overcurrent Protection

- Overcurrent devices in the DC circuits are listed for DC operation.
- DC source circuit overcurrent protection devices are rated at 1.25 x 1.25 = 156% short-circuit (ISC) current from modules.
- Inverter output circuit overcurrent protection device (point of connection to AC system breaker) is sized based on the maximum inverter output current x 125%.
- Overcurrent protection is required for the PV source circuit (modules and parallel connected modules), PV output circuit (conductors between source circuits and inverter), inverter output circuit, battery circuit conductors and equipment.
- Where three or more strings are combined, a listed combiner box (UL1741) is used and fuses are required. When DC source circuits (strings) are connected in parallel, the current through a failed circuit can be the sum of the current connected from the other strings, therefore special consideration must be taken to ensure the sum of the total number

of strings minus one does not exceed the module manufacturers series fuse rating, or conductor ampacity.

- When a back-fed breaker is used as a utility interconnection means, the breaker does not read "line and load."
- the PV interconnect breaker is located at the opposite end of the buss from the feeder connection, unless using 100% rated equipment.

Electrical Connections

- Crimp-on terminals are listed and installed using a listed tool specified for use in crimping those specific crimps.
- Pressure terminals are listed for the environment and tightened to manufacturer recommended torque specifications.
- Connectors are listed for the voltage of the system and have appropriate temperature and ampere ratings.
- Twist on wire connectors are listed for the environment (i.e. wet, damp, direct burial, etc.) and installed per manufacturer's instructions.
- Power distribution blocks are listed.
- Terminals containing more than one conductor are listed for multiple conductors.
- Connectors and terminals used for fine strand conductors are listed for use with such conductors.
- Connectors that are readily accessible and operating at over 30 volts require a tool for opening.
- Module connectors are tight and secure.
- Wiring and connections of inverters, PV source circuits, battery connections, etc., and all interconnections are performed by qualified personnel.

Charge Controllers

- Charge controller is listed to UL Standard 1741.
- Exposed energized terminals are not readily accessible.
- Diversion charge controllers that are used as the sole means of regulating charging of batteries have a second independent means of control to prevent overcharging.

Disconnects

- Disconnects used in DC circuits are listed for DC operation.
- Disconnects are installed for all current carrying conductors of the PV source.
- Disconnects are installed for the PV equipment. NOTE: For inverters and other equipment that are energized from more than one source, the disconnects must be grouped and identified.
- Disconnects and overcurrent protection are installed for all ungrounded conductors in ungrounded (transformerless) PV power systems.

Inverters

- Inverters are listed to UL 1741. NOTE: grid-tied system inverters need to be identified for use in interactive power systems.
- Point of connection is at a dedicated breaker or disconnect.
- Total rating of the overcurrent devices supplying equipment does not exceed 120% of the equipment rating.
- Listed AC and DC disconnects and overcurrent protection are grouped and identified.
- No multi-wire branch circuits are installed where single 120-volt inverters are connected to 120/240-volt load centers.
- The plastic barrier is re-installed between the AC, DC wiring and communication wires.

Batteries

- Live parts of battery systems for dwellings are guarded to prevent accidental contact by persons or objects.
- Flexible battery cables are listed RHW or THW, 2/0 minimum for battery cell connections. NOTE: welding cables, marine, locomotive (DLO), and automotive cables do not meet the current Electrical Code requirements.
- Flexible battery cables do not leave the battery enclosure.
- Flexible, fine strand cables are only to be used with terminals, lugs, devices, and connectors that are listed and marked for such use.
- Listed high-interrupt DC-rated fuses or circuit breakers are used in battery circuits. The AIC is at least 20,000 amps.
- Cables to inverters, DC load centers, and/or charge controllers are in a conduit.
- Conduits enter the battery enclosure below the tops of the batteries. NOTE: this is to avoid accidental ventilation of gases into electrical equipment where sparks may occur. Follow battery enclosure manufacturer's instructions for venting and conduit locations.
- A disconnect means is provided for all ungrounded conductors derived from a stationary battery system over 30 volts.
- Area is well ventilated and the batteries are not installed in living areas.

Signs and Labels

- All interior and exterior conduit, enclosures, raceways, cable assemblies, junction boxes, combiner boxes, and disconnects are marked appropriately as per the NEC.

Fire Safety

- Rooftop mounted PV panels and modules have the proper fire classification rating.
- Rooftop DC conduits are located as close as possible to the ridge or hip or valley and from the hip or valley as directly as possible to an outside wall to reduce trip hazards and maximize ventilation opportunities.

- Conduit runs between sub arrays and to DC combiner boxes are installed in a manner that minimizes total amount of conduit on the roof by taking the shortest path from the array to the DC combiner box.
- DC Combiner Boxes are located so that conduit runs are minimized in the pathways between arrays.
- DC wiring in enclosed spaces in buildings is installed in metallic conduit or raceways. Conduit runs along the bottom of load bearing members.
- DC wiring methods shall not be installed within 25 cm (10") of the roof decking or sheathing except where directly below the roof surface covered by the PV modules and associated equipment.
- All roofs have an access point that does not place ground ladders over openings such as windows or doors, are located at strong points of building construction, and in locations where the access point does not conflict with overhead obstructions such as tree limbs, wires, or signs.
- Roofs with slopes greater than 2:12 have solar panel layouts that meet the following criteria:
  - Hip Roofs: Panels/modules are located so that there is a 3-foot wide clear access pathway from the eave to the ridge on each roof slope where panels/modules are located.
  - Hips and Valleys: If panels/modules are placed on both sides of a hip or valley they are located no closer than 18 inches to a hip or valley. If the panels are located on only one side of a hip or valley that is of equal length, then the panels can be placed directly adjacent to the hip or valley.
  - Single Ridges: Panels/modules are located so that there are two 3-foot wide access pathways from the eave to the ridge on each roof slope where there are panels/modules installed.
  - Ridges: Panels/modules are located no higher than 3 feet from the top of the ridge in order to allow for fire department smoke ventilation operations.
  - Access pathways are located at a structurally sound location capable of supporting the load of fire fighters accessing the roof.

Permission to Operate (PTO)

After the AHJ has completed the inspection and approved the system, energizing must still wait until the utility has granted **permission to operate (PTO)**.

The utility may require additional system documentation as well as copies of the AHJ inspection report in the application for PTO. Once all paperwork is in hand, they will schedule their own site inspection.

Normally the utility is focused on ensuring a system disconnect is properly located, the components are properly labeled, and anti-islanding equipment

(UL 1741) components have been installed. However the inspection may be much more involved that that.

The utility may also replace the meter, or reprogram the existing meter to ensure that it functions in a net metering situation. Once completed, they will indicate the system can now be energized - giving permission to operate.

Chapter 15 Review Questions

1) A well-planned commissioning process involves:
    a) a visual inspection of the system
    b) electrical verification tests
    c) verifying system output
    d) all of the above

2) Grounding and bonding requirements are outlined in what section of the NEC?
    a) Article 200
    b) Article 250
    c) Article 690
    d) Article 705

3) Labels on PV components must:
    a) be permanently affixed to equipment and wiring
    b) not be hand written
    c) a minimum of 3/8 inch in height
    d) all of the above

4) Which of the following is **NOT** a typical inspection of a PV system?
    a) electrical inspection
    b) rough-in inspection
    c) service inspection
    d) final inspection

5) Every exposed (not in conduit) conductor must be:
    a) USE-2 or PV wire rated for 90ºC
    b) USE-2 or PV wire rated for 75ºC
    c) RHW-2 or THWN-W when exposed to wet conditions
    D) red, black or any other color, other than green or bare copper wire

6) Which of the following is **TRUE**?
    a) DC wiring shall not be installed within 10 inches of the roof decking except where located directly below the roof surface covered by the PV modules.
    b) DC wire must be enclosed in metallic conduit when inside a building.
    c) disconnects and overcurrent protection are installed for all ungrounded conductors
    d) all of the above

7) The final step of a commissioning process is generally to obtain _____ from the utility company.
    a) an interconnection agreement
    b) permission to operate
    c) net metering agreement
    d) a bidirectional meter

Chapter 16

Maintaining the System

Chapter Objectives:

- Understand how to properly monitor an operational system.
- Identify all the steps required to properly maintain a system.
- Understand the various component warranties.
- Comprehend the environmental factors that impact solar panels and the affect they have on performance and warranty issues.
- Identify the impact of environmental factors on the support structures of arrays and how to properly maintain them.
- Understand the steps involved in inspecting an inverter.
- Identify all required maintenance for a battery bank.

One of the beauties of a PV system is that it requires very little maintenance to function properly for 20-25 years, or even longer. With no moving parts, the bulk of the system simply sits there generating energy unless acted upon by an outside force.

But, as with any system devised by humans, things happen. Parts age, break, wear out, are hit by falling objects, chewed on by squirrels or submerged in flood waters. If you can imagine it - it has probably happened.

So periodic maintenance is required to keep the system functioning up to expectations. The maintenance schedule should be outlined and data recorded in the systems operation and maintenance (O&M) document.

Monitoring Performance

Most systems come with monitoring software or displays. Some are Internet based, some can be accessed by smart phone, and some require a periodic trip down into the basement to check the displays to make sure everything is behaving itself.

A routine monitoring schedule should be established. Most new owners are excited enough that they monitor their system almost constantly. But over time, it may require more effort.

With routine monitoring, any problems that do develop can be identified and dealt with quickly.

System Maintenance

Maintaining a PV system does not require a great deal of time (with the exception of stand-alone systems that incorporate a large battery bank). A good annual maintenance checklist includes:

- Periodic debris removal. Remove leaves, trash and other clutter from around the PV system. Snow removal in some areas is another concern. This not only avoids shading issues, but removes a fire hazard, habitat for insects and vermin, and possible drainage problems.

- Shading control. Trim trees, shrubs and other vegetation that may grow to shade the array.

- Cleaning the array. Generally the rain will take care of this, but in areas that experience infrequent rain, it might be necessary to wash the panels periodically.

- Weather sealing. The flashing and weather sealing of the footings for roof mounted systems should be inspected annually and resealed as required.

- Mechanical inspection. Inspect all mounting systems to ensure they are still tightly fitted and torqued to specification. Check for signs of corrosion on enclosures and racking systems.

- Wiring inspection. Inspect all conductors in all circuits. Make sure the insulation is intact, and all connections are tight. This is especially a concern for the PV source circuit where conductors are more generally exposed to the elements than in other circuits. ensure roof penetrations are watertight, if applicable. Make sure they are not hanging loose from the array.

- Confirm all the proper system signage and labels are still in place and legible.

- Confirm that all conduit expansion joints are working properly and there is no sign of stress along long conduit runs. Check the tightness of all conduit joints and fittings.

- Make sure electrical enclosures are still only accessible to authorized personnel, and are secured with locks.

- Make sure all working clearances are still maintained around equipment.

- Check for cleanliness throughout the site. There should be no debris in or around the equipment and the array.

- Look for any signs of animal damage or infestation around the equipment and/or the array.

Solar Panels

The solar panels are the "engine" of the system. Maintaining them in good working order is critical to generating the power output designed into the system.

Warranties

A solar panel manufacturer generally provides two warranties: one warranty that address the panel's performance and another that warranties the equipment..

While under-performing or defective panels will generally be replaced (or refunds issued), the manufacturer's product warranty does not normally cover the cost of labor to diagnose and/or replace the panel - or the shipping costs to get the replacement panel on site.

Performance Warranty

Most solar panel manufacturers back their product with a **performance warranty** for a period of time, normally from 25 to 30 years. This performance warranty guarantees that the module will generate above a specified degradation rate (the decline in output over time that all solar panels experience).

PERFORMANCE WARRANTY

Most solar panel manufacturers offer a **linear performance warranty**. For example, a manufacturer may guarantee the panel will not suffer more than 0.7% production loss every year at a constant rate year-over-year, for a 25 year period. With this warranty, the module will be performing as expected if at the end of the 25 years it is producing only 82.5% (25 yrs x 0.7% = 17.5%) of what it produced on the day it was installed.

LINEAR PERFORMANCE

Some manufacturers offer **step performance warranties** on their panels. Under this warranty structure, the performance guarantee remains at a flat rate for a period of them, then steps down at certain milestones.

STEP PERFORMANCE

For example, panels may be guaranteed to produce at greater than 90% efficiency from installation to year 10. Then it steps down to 80% until year 25.

The amount of electricity a solar panel produces will decline slightly every year. The industry generally estimates that a normal panel's output will fall off by about 0.5% each year, or roughly 12.5%

Cell Type	Loss/yr
Amorphous silicon (a-Si)	0.87 %
Cadmium telluride (CdTe)	0.4 %
Copper indium gallium selenide (CIGS)	0.96 %
Monocrystalline silicon (mono-Si)	0.36 %
Polycrystalline silicon (poly-Si)	0.64 %

TABLE 16-1: AVERAGE ANNUAL LOSSES FOR VARIOUS CELL TYPES

over the course of 25 years. Various types of panels will degrade at different rates, as determined by NREL and results listed in Table 16-1.

Workmanship Warranty
Panels are also generally warranted against defects that may occur during the manufacture of the product. Some examples of equipment defects include:
- imperfections in the frame or glass,
- loose junction boxes,
- faulty connectors,
- bad cells or damaged cell connections,
- defective backsheet.

WORKMANSHIP WARRANTY

These **workmanship warranties** generally do not cover damage in shipping (that is handled through the distributor and/or shipper), nor do they cover normal wear-and-tear that occur in the field.

It is generally assumed that product defects will be apparent early in the life of the panel, so time periods for these warranties are often shorter, ranging from 5 years to as long as 25 years.

The solar industry is still in its infancy, with many products and manufacturers emerging onto the scene and disappearing just as quickly. As a result, often manufacturers offer warranties that are backed by a third party, insured by financial groups such as Lloyds of London or the Carlisle Group.

Damage to Panels
Solar panels operate in a harsh environment. A number of internal and external forces can act upon them to limit their effectiveness in generating power. Typically these panels must simply be replaced. This damage may or may not be covered by the warranty, depending on the cause.

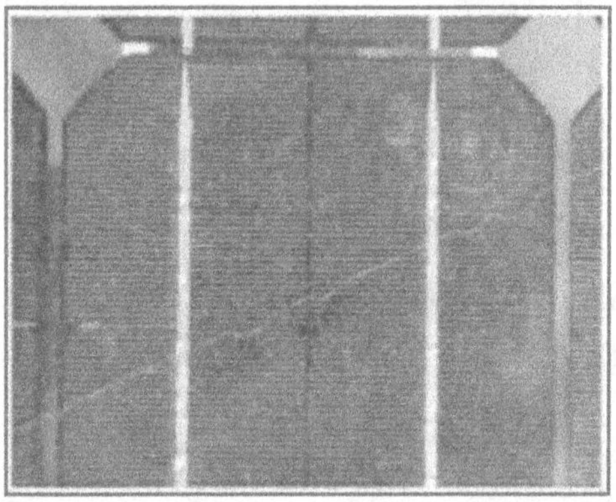

FIGURE 16-1: CRACKED SOLAR PANEL

Cracks may develop, as shown in Figure 16-1, that cause light to penetrate the surface of the panel differently. These may be the result of micro cracks created during the manufacturing or shipping process that grew into larger cracks over time. A careful inspection of all panels prior to installation may avoid these problems.

Panels may discolor over time,. As a result, solar cells are less exposed to solar irradiation, and therefore generate less energy. Some factors that cause discoloration are defects in manufacture, high temperatures, humidity, and salt in the air for systems located near oceans.

Rating	Description
1	Sample did not crack when hit twice in the same spot with a steel ball measuring 1.25 inches in diameter.
2	Sample did not crack when hit twice in the same spot with a steel ball measuring 1.50 inches in diameter.
3	Sample did not crack when hit twice in the same spot with a steel ball measuring 1.75 inches in diameter.
4	Sample did not crack when hit twice in the same spot with a steel ball measuring 2.00 inches in diameter.

TABLE 16-2: HAIL RESISTANCE RATINGS AS MEASURED BY UL 2218

Minor damage may include: corrosion, hot spots, snail trails (discoloration due to micro cracks), broken interconnects, cracks, burn marks, delamination, yellowing, inner-layer cracking, glass defects, loss of AR coating, and junction box defects.

Such damage may be quite common. A 2018 study by Dupont found that of the 4.2 million installed panels studied, 22.3% displayed at least one defect. Rooftop mounted systems were 2.5 times more likely to show defects than ground mounted systems.

Panels can also become damaged by objects, such as rocks thrown by a lawnmower, or hail.

Resistance to Hail Damage
In 1996, Underwriters Labs developed the first test standard to assess the impact resistance of roof coverings – *UL 2218 Impact Resistance of Prepared Roof Covering Materials*. This standard has subsequently been used to measure the effectiveness of solar panels and solar shingles in resisting damage from hail.

UL 2218

The test uses steel balls ranging in size from 1.25 inches to 2.0 inches in diameter to simulate damage that might occur in a hail storm. The steel balls are dropped from heights of 12 feet for the 1.25 inch ball to 20 feet for the 2 inch ball. The test assembly is struck with the steel ball twice in the same location.

To meet the acceptance criteria of UL 2218, the solar panel's exposed surface and back surface must show no evidence of tearing, fracturing, cracking, splitting, rupture, or other evidence of opening.

Qualifying products are given a class rating depending upon successful performance of the assembly under impacts as noted in Table 16-2.

Snow Removal

Annual losses due to snow can be as high as 15% in some locations where the snow load is heavy and the orientation of the panel is relatively flat. In such cases, it may be desirable to manually remove snow, carefully so as not to scratch or damage the panel.

But in many cases this is impractical. Panels are often located on rooftops that makes snow removal difficult and dangerous. Large commercial systems make snow removal costs prohibitive.

Solar panels generally operate at temperatures about 20° C warmer than ambient air temperatures. So a small amount of exposed surface rapidly causes the panel to heat up when exposed to sunlight.

Also, panels located in areas that experience frequent snow loads are generally mounted at a significant angle (due to latitude), allowing snow to slide off rather quickly.

As a result of the combination of these factors, most array owners simply wait for the snow to melt.

Soiling

Periodic rain will normally clean panels very effectively, making manual cleaning unnecessary.

However in dry dusty locations, or near a construction site, it may be necessary to periodically clean the array to increase production. Also panels mounted at low angles (less than 5°) may not be effectively cleaned by rainfall. Some panel manufacturers recommend that the array be cleaned every six months or so when these conditions exist.

When cleaning the array:

- Check the solar panel manufacturer's instructions. They might have specific recommendations for cleaning and varying from these could damage the panel and/or void the warranty.
- Do not attempt to clean rooftop panels without the proper safety equipment and training.
- Solar panels can become very hot in sunshine. Clean the panels in the early morning before they have had a chance to heat up.
- Do not use metal objects or abrasive detergents when cleaning. These can scratch the surface of the panel, causing permanent damage. If soap must be used (usually water alone is just fine), use a mild dishwashing detergent.
- Use a simple garden hose under low pressure. Do not use a high pressure hose. High pressure spray may damage the panels.
- For smaller systems, it is best to simply clean the panels with clean water and a soft cloth or sponge.

Larger arrays in dusty environments often install automatic cleaning systems such as illustrated in Figure 16-2. These systems are designed to periodically clean the panels (often at night so as not to interfere with energy production).

FIGURE 16-2:
AUTOMATED SOLAR
PANEL CLEANING SYSTEM

(FROM ECOPPIA)

Studies have shown that annual production losses due to soiling can be as much as 50% in some parts of the Middle East. Dust that mixes with nighttime dew can undergo a cementation process, making it extremely difficult to remove.

Corrosion

Most solar arrays are installed in relatively harsh environments, so some locations are worse than others. Arrays located near the coast may be subject to frequent salt-water mists. Arrays near factories may be subject to harsh pollutants and/or the effects of acid rain.

Salts and acids can accelerate the corrosion of panels, wiring, connections and equipment.

When faced with these environments, the panels and equipment should be cleaned regularly. Also, coastal installations should use panels that have been tested and rated to the **IEC 61701** standard for salt mist resistance.

IEC 61701

Panel Mounts and Racking Systems

Over time, connections on hardware can become loose. Such unintentional loosening is frequently called **vibrational loosening** and can be caused by wind, nearby construction, passing vehicles, or freeze/thaw cycles. Racking manufacturers typically advise that connection torque be checked at least once a year.

VIBRATIONAL
LOOSENING

If the connections have been marked during installation, a visual inspection may be all that is required. Re-torque any connections that the marks indicate have moved since installation. If the connections were not marked, then applying a torque wrench or torque screwdriver for each connection point may be required.

Ballasted Systems

Typically larger rooftop systems on flat roofs rely on weight (ballast) to hold the racking in place, rather than bolts. Over time, these systems can shift and move, again due to vibration or because of wind. This movement can damage the roof membrane below the racking, resulting in leaks.

The racking manufacturer will normally specify the requirements for **slip-sheets** located between the ballast feet and the roof membrane. Even with this

SLIP-SHEETS

sacrificial layer, however, maintenance will be required to maintain the integrity of the membrane.

Make sure these slip-sheets are still in place under racking contact points. The slip-sheets can sometimes work themselves loose over time. If the slip-sheets are worn or damaged, determine the cause of this unusual wear, correct it, and replace the slip-sheet.

Flat roofs are not truly flat. They are pitched slightly to allow rain to drain. A ballasted PV array may interfere with this drainage. Check to ensure that no debris (leaves, trash, etc) has accumulated or is caught in the support structure of the system. Particular attention should be paid to ice damming that can easily occur as heavy snows melt.

Ground-Mounted Systems

Additional maintenance issues arise with systems mounted on the ground.

Vegetation management (mowing, trimming, nearby crops, etc) is a concern for ground mounted systems, as weeds and bushes grow and eventually create shading issues.

FIGURE 16-3: SHEEP CONTROLLING VEGETATION AROUND ARRAY

(FROM ANTIOCH COLLEGE)

Mowing beneath arrays can be very labor-intensive and expensive. Cost estimates are around $1-$2 per square meter (10 square feet), or between $40,00-$80,000 annually for a 2-MW system. Spraying herbicide is less expensive but spraying has to be done repeatedly over time and there are environmental concerns.

Some owners have turned to herbaceous animals, such as sheep (Figure 16-3), goats and even emus to control weeds and grass. But where this type of control system is used, the arrays must be high enough to prevent the animals from damaging or climbing on the panels.

Selecting the appropriate ground cover during the design and installation phase of the project may be helpful in reducing the maintenance costs of a ground mounted system.

Applying gravel as a ground cover was identified by a recent NREL survey as prohibitively expensive and problematic as it creates uneven work surfaces, changes site runoff , and ultimately does not provide a long-term weed abatement solution.

Replanting the site with low-growth, native plants is a viable solution. Some larger systems are even opting for pollinator-friendly ground cover to promote a healthy and even more green ecology.

Site preparation and the array itself can create erosion problems. In addition to the normal problems caused by erosion, it can also undermine the stability of the rack foundation and support structure.

Ensure proper drainage is maintained and clear any weeds or debris that interfere with this system.

Tracking Systems

Tracking systems have moving parts and therefore require much more maintenance, not only on the load-bearing moving parts of the array, but also, for the associated **actuators** (the device that moves the array) and controls.

> ACTUATOR

Routine maintenance should include:
- Check the mechanical connections to ensure they have maintained their proper torque values.
- Check the electrical connections for wear and make sure they are secure.
- Lubricate all moving parts as recommended by the manufacturer.
- Remove all snow that might prevent the smooth operation and movement of the tracking device.
- Use a digital level to check the calibration and positioning of the **inclinometers** (tilt sensor).

> INCLINOMETER

String Inverter

Each inverter manufacturer will have specific requirements for inspection, testing, servicing, and the documentation they require to meet warranty obligations. Follow these instructions.

Typical steps involved in maintaining a string inverter include:
- record and check all voltages and energy production readings,
- make sure the inverter's mounting is still secure to the wall or ground,
- make sure all warning labels are in place and legible,
- clean the inside of the cabinet,
- clean and/or replace any filters,
- examine the gaskets and seals. Treat with the appropriate product if they appear brittle, dry or worn,
- check fans to ensure they are working properly,
- check all fuses and breakers,
- verify the torque on terminations,
- look for any discoloration that may indicate heat build up within the unit,
- check the continuity of the grounding system,
- make sure all disconnects are working properly,
- check for any corrosion on the case, wire or terminals,

- verify that any software updates have been installed,
- document any maintenance work performed.

Inverter Warranties

Solar inverters are usually warranted for a period ranging from 5 to 15 years, with an average standard warranty period of 10 years. Some companies offer an extended warranty for an additional fee.

For example, on many of their inverters, SolarEdge offers a 12-year warranty on defects in workmanship and materials. This covers the cost of parts and shipping or the replacement of the unit. It does not generally cover the cost of labor to repair the unit.

On the HD-Wave 11.4 kW unit, an extension of the warranty from 12-years to 25-years can be purchased within 24 months of the original purchase date for an additional $450 (prices as of 2022). The optimizers that work with the system are warranted for 25 years.

Battery Bank Maintenance

Maintenance for battery banks incorporated into stand-alone systems, where they are cycled (charged and discharged) regularly, should be repeated every month or so.

For grid-interactive systems with a battery bank that is cycled less often, six months or so can pass between maintenance tasks.

For systems incorporating lead-acid batteries, these tasks include:

- Inspect and clean the battery racks, cases trays and terminations. Clean any corrosion or sulfation from surfaces. Terminals may be coated with petroleum jelly or special battery terminal corrosion gels.
- Inspect battery disconnects, overcurrent devices and wiring systems.
- Check battery connections: Battery terminals are made of soft metal (generally lead). They can easily become loose over time. Check them and tighten as needed.
- Check each battery for signs of cracking, bulges, or any other damage. Look to see if any electrolyte is seeping from the battery into the tray.
- Check water levels: Unsealed lead acid batteries will vent hydrogen over time, depleting the water within them. Add distilled water to the fill line of all batteries as needed.
- Equalize flooded batteries. Most charge controllers allow for the periodic equalization of batteries. This can be done either manually or automatically (as determined by the settings on the charge controller). It should be done every three months or so. Follow the battery's manufacturer's recommendations. Ensure that the battery is well vented

prior to equalization. Also ensure that it has not been overfilled with water. Hydrogen gas will be emitted and water will boil off during the equalization process. Check water levels after equalization and fill if required.

- Measure voltages. Test each battery, either with a multimeter or a hydrometer to ensure voltages remain in specified ranges.

- Check and verify the set points on the charge controller to ensure they are still within design parameters.

- Ensure the battery room or cabinet's ventilation system is performing as designed.

- Make sure restricted access to the batteries is secure.

- Verify all appropriate signage is in place and legible.

Lithium-ion batteries generally require no maintenance. All ESS systems include a battery management system (BMS) that automatically monitors each battery cell for temperature, state of charge, cycle life and more to maximize performance.

As long as the storage system is installed within acceptable temperature ranges and altitudes, no routine maintenance should be required.

Battery Warranties

Lead acid batteries generally offer warranties against defects in workmanship and materials that are effective for 1-3 years. These warranties do not apply to battery systems that have been installed improperly or subjected to environmental conditions (heat and cold) outside the manufacturer's recommendations.

Once again, most warranties only apply to replacement of the product, not for the cost of diagnosing the problem or replacing the unit.

Lithium-Ion battery manufacturers for solar ESS products generally offer longer warranties than do those who manufacture lead-acid battery solutions. The average warranty period for materials and workmanship on these products is 10 years.

Like solar panels, the performance of lithium-ion batteries deteriorate over time. So again, like solar modules, ESS manufacturers offer both workmanship warranties and performance warranties.

For example, LG Chem offers a 10-year warranty on their lithium-ion products against defects in products and workmanship. They also incorporate a performance limitation, stating that the unit will retain at least 60% of its initial nominal energy for 10 years after the date of invoice. In other words, the system could lose 4% of its capacity annually and still be considered to be working properly as far as the warranty is concerned.

Since the effectiveness of the storage system is expected to decline over time, so too is the compensation should the unit need to be replaced. LG Chem states (in their warranty) that they will refund 100% of the purchase price if the unit must be replaced during the first two years. After that, the amount refunded declines. In year three they will refund only 72% of the purchase price, year four 58% of the purchase price, and so on. In year 10 of the warranty, should the unit need to be replaced, LG Chem will only refund 2% of the initial purchase price.

Operation and Maintenance Contracts

Many individuals and companies simply do not have the time, inclination or expertise necessary to effectively manage and maintain their solar resource. For this reason, they outsource the operation and management of the solar array.

O&M contracts for large solar arrays can range in price from $5.50 - $10 per kW per year. In other words, an annual contract for a 200 kW system may cost up to $2,000 per year. Generally, the smaller the system, the higher the cost per kW.

Costs (according to a study by Wood Mackenzie) break down to about:
- $1.60/kW/year for vegetation control,
- $1.10/kW/year for module cleaning,
- $1.40/kW/year for corrective maintenance (fixing problems as they occur),
- $2.00/kW/year for monitoring and administration, and
- $3.50/kW/year for preventative maintenance.

A comprehensive maintenance contract should define:
- the duration of the agreement,
- amount of technical support provided (are they on call to answer technical questions),
- response times,
- specifics about the scope of work provided (and what reports will be generated),
- production guarantees (at what point will corrective action be required if energy production does not meet expectations),
- safety plans,
- frequency of preventative maintenance.

Chapter 16 Review Questions

1) The maintenance requirements of an installed system are typically documented in a:
   a) system maintenance (S&M) manual
   b) request for proposal (RFP) document
   c) moves, adds and changes (MA&C) manual
   d) operation and maintenance (O&M) document

2) A guarantee by the manufacturer (of a solar panel, for instance) against any defects that may have occurred during the creation of the product is a:
   a) quality warranty
   b) workmanship warranty
   c) performance warranty
   d) linear performance warranty

3) Most solar panel warranties estimate that a solar panel's production will:
   a) decline by about 0.5% each year over the term of the warranty
   b) remain constant during the term of the warranty
   c) not exceed 90% of initial production by the end of the warranty
   d) decline by 5% over the term of the warranty

4) Most owners of solar arrays in areas subject to snow deal with snow accumulation on panels by:
   a) waiting for the snow to melt
   b) installing a tracking system to dump snow off during the day
   c) hiring a maintenance crew to deal with snow removal
   d) installing the array at a 20° pitch or less so snow will slide off naturally

5) To be awarded a hail damage rating of four (4), under UL 2218 a panel must show no evidence of tearing, fracturing, cracking, splitting, rupture or other evidence of an opening:
   a) after 15 year of operation
   b) in temperatures below - 55ºC
   c) when exposed to a force in excess of 25 Newton-meters (Nm) per square centimeter
   D) when hit with a two-inch diameter steel ball dropped from 20 feet twice in the same location

6) Rooftop ballasted systems often require _____ to protect the roof from damage.
   a) a hail rating of 4
   b) slip sheets
   c) squirrel guards
   d) all of the above

Formulas

Common formulas used in photovoltaics:

Power Equation:

Watts = Amps x Volts
(W = I x V, or P = I x E)

Ohm's Law:

Volts = Amps x Resistance
(V = I x R)

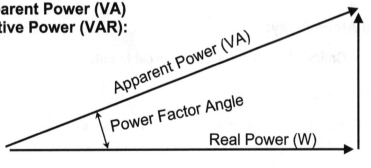

Voltage Drop of a Circuit:

Voltage Drop =   Amps at Maximum Power
Point x Resistance (per 1000 feet) x twice the distance of the circuit (in feet)

Vd = Imp x R x 2d/1000 ft

Relationship between Apparent Power (VA) Real Power (W), and Reactive Power (VAR):

Power Factor:

Power Factor = P (power in watts) / S (VA delivered by generator or utility)

Load Factor:

Load Factor = Total kWh for the billing period / Peak Demand x # of Days x 24 Hours

Peak Sun Hours:

Peak Sun Hours = Total Daily Energy from the Sun (watts) / 1000 (watts)/hr

Summer and Winter Bias:

summer bias = latitude - 15°   winter bias = latitude + 15°

Inter-Row Shading:

$d = h / \tan \alpha$

Where,
- d is the minimum distance between rows;
- h is the height differential between the top of one row and the bottom of the row to the north; and
- α is the altitude angle of the sun at that location at 9 am on the winter solstice (the moment when the sun will be at its lowest point relative to the horizon).

California Mandate Sizing:

KW PV required = (CFA x A) / 1,000 + (NDwell x B)

Where,
- CFA = conditioned floor area
- NDwell = number of dwelling units
- A = adjustment factor from table
- B = dwelling adjustment factor from table

Climate Zone	A - CFA	B - Dwelling Units
1	0.793	1.27
2	0.621	1.22
3	0.628	1.12
4	0.586	1.21
5	0.585	1.06
6	0.594	1.23
7	0.572	1.15
8	0.586	1.37
9	0.613	1.36
10	0.627	1.41
11	0.836	1.44
12	0.613	1.40
13	0.894	1.51
14	0.741	1.26
15	1.56	1.47
16	0.59	1.22

Sizing an Array:

Array Size (W) = kWh per day / hrs of insolation / derate of system

Sizing Stand Alone Array:

Array Size (W) = Critical Month Daily Load / Critical Month Insolation / derate of system

Ground Cover Ratio:

Ground Cover Ratio (GCR) = area of actual panels / area within the array boundary
In no gaps or rows, the GCR = 1.0 or 100%

Demand Factor:

Demand factor = actual maximum load / possible maximum load

Inverter Load Ratio:

Inverter Load Ratio (ILR) = incoming DC watts / outgoing AC watts

Area Required for an Array:

Total Area Required = Array Power Output / (1000 W/m^2 x Panel Efficiency)

Payback Period:

Payback Period = Initial Net Cost / (Annual Blended Savings - O&M Costs)

Calculating Backflow in System with Multiple Combiner Boxes:

Total Short-Circuit Current = (Np - 1) x Isc x Strings x 1.25 x 1.25

Where,
    Np = number of combiner boxes combined in parallel
    Isc = the amp short circuit rating of the panel

Sizing Battery Bank Output Circuit:

Ampacity of Wire =   Maximum inverter rating (watts) / inverter efficiency / lowest battery bank voltage/ AC ripple x 1.25 (NEC safety margin)

Calculating Ampacity in Three-Phase Wiring:

Phase Current (A) = Inverter Output (W) / V (phase-to-phase) / square root of 3

10-Foot Tap Rule:

Ampacity of Feeder Tap = 10% x [Feeder Breaker (A) + (Inverter Output (A) x 1.25)]

25-Foot Tap Rule:

Ampacity of Feeder Tap = 33.33% x [Feeder Breaker (A) + (Inverter Output (A) x 1.25)]

Calculating Battery Bank:

[(AC Daily Load	/ Inverter Efficiency)	+ DC Daily Load]	/ DC System Voltage	= Amp hrs per Day
[(15 kWh	/ .90)	+ 0 Wh]	/ 24 Vdc =	694.44 Ah
Amp hrs per Day	**x Days of Autonomy**	**/ Depth of Discharge**	**/ Battery Ah Capacity**	**= Battery Strings**
694.44 Ah	x 2	/ .40	/ 1,284 Ah =	2.7 (3)
DC System Voltage	**/ Battery Voltage =**	**# of Batteries in Series**	**X Battery Strings**	**= Total Batteries**
24 Vdc	/ 2 Vdc =	12	x 3 =	36

Calculating Tributary Area of a Mount Footer:

Tributary Area = distance between vertical supports x distance between horizontal supports

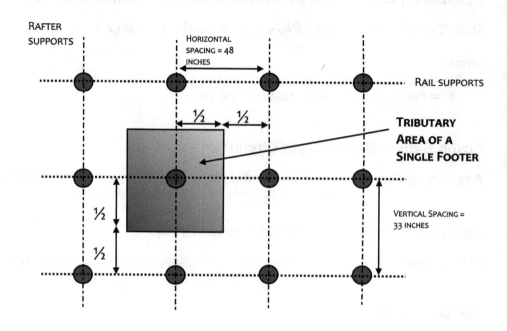

FIGURES

Tables

Acronyms

a-Si	amorphous silicon
AC	alternating current
ACELA	American Clean Energy Leadership Act
ACES	American Clean Energy and Security Act
ACWP	actual cost of work performed
ADMS	advanced distribution management system
AESO	Alberta Electric System Operator
AFCI	arc-fault circuit interrupter
AGC	automatic generation controls
AGM	absorbent glass mats
AGS	automatic generator start
Ah	amp-hour
AHJ	authorities having jurisdiction
AIC	ampere interrupting capacity
AIR	ampere interrupt rating
ARRA	American Recovery and Reinvestment Act
ASCE	American Society of Civil Engineers
ASES	American Solar Energy Society
ASHRAE	American Society of Heating, Refrigerating and Air-Conditioning Engineers
ATS	automatic transfer switch
AWG	American wire gauge
BIPV	building integrated photovoltaic
BMS	battery management system
BOS	balance of systems
BUR	built-up roofing
CAD	computer-aided design
CAES	compressed air energy storage
CAISO	California Independent Systems Operator
CCA	community choice aggregation
CCA	cold cranking amps
CCOHS	Canadian Centre for Occupational Health and Safety
CCS	combined charging system
CdTe	cadmium telluride
CE	conformité européenne
CEC	California Energy Commission
CEC	Canadian Electrical Code
CENELEC	Central European Normalization Electrotechnique
CFA	conditioned floor area
CFR	Code of Federal Regulations
CHP	combined heat and power
CIS/CIGS	copper indium gallium selenide
C-Si	crystalline silicon
CME	coronal mass ejection
COD	commercial operation date
CPV	concentrator photovoltaic modules
CRES	competitive retail electric service
CRM	customer relationship management
CSA	Canadian Standards Association
CTs	current transformers

CV	cost variance
DC	direct current
DCD	DC disconnect
DER	distributed energy resources
DERMS	distributed energy resource management system
DG	distributed generation
DISCO	distribution company or distribution utility
DOD	depth of discharge
DOE	Department of Energy
DSIRE	Database of State Incentives for Renewables & Efficiency
DSM	demand side management
EDU	electric distribution utilities
EERS	energy efficiency resource standard
Eg	band gap energy
EGC	equipment grounding conductor
EIA	Energy Information Administration
EIS	environmental impact statement
EL	electroluminescence
EMCB	energy management circuit breaker
EMP	electromagnetic pulse
EMT	electrical metallic tubing
EPC	engineering, procurement and construction
ERCOT	Electric Reliability Council of Texas
ESS	energy storage systems
ETA-I	Electronic Technicians Association International
ETL	Electrical Testing Labs/Intertek
EU-OSHA	European Agency for Safety and Health at Work
EV	earned value
EV	electric vehicle
eV	electron volt
EVSE	electric vehicle supply equipment
EWG	exempt wholesale generator
FAA	Federal Aviation Administration
FERC	Federal Energy Regulatory Commission
FIT	feed-in tariff
FLA	flooded lead acid (battery)
FMT	flexible metallic tubing
FRP	fiber reinforced plastic
GATS	Generation Attribute Tracking System
GCR	ground cover ratio
GEC	grounding electrode conductor
GFCI	ground-fault circuit interrupter
GFP	ground fault protection
GFPD	ground fault protection device
GFPE	ground-fault protection of equipment
GW	gigawatt
HJT	heterojunction solar cell
HMT	harmonic mitigating transformer
HOA	homeowners associations
HV	high-voltage
HVAC	heating, ventilation and air conditioning
HVDC	high-voltage direct current
Hz	Hertz

I	ampere (amp)
IBC	International Building Code
IBC	interdigitated back contact
ICC	International Code Council
IEC	International Electrotechnical Commission
IECC	International Energy Conservation Code
IEEE	Institute of Electrical and Electronics Engineers
IESO	Ontario Independent Electricity System Operator
IFC	International Fire Code
IGCC	International Green Construction Code
ILR	inverter load ratio
Imp	maximum power current
in-lb	inch-pound
IoT	Internet of things
IOU	investor-owned utility
IR	infrared
IRC	International Residential Code
IREC	Interstate Renewable Energy Council
Isc	short circuit current
ISO	Independent Systems Operator
ITC	investment tax credit
IV	amps-volts
KPI	key project indicator
kV	kilo volt
kVA	kilo volt-amp
kW	kilowatt
kWh	kilowatt-hour
LAZ	limited access zone
LCO	lithium cobalt oxide
LCOE	levelized cost of energy
LED	light emitting diode
LFNC	liquid-tight flexible nonmetallic
LFP	lithium iron phosphate
LID	light induced degradation
Li-ion	lithium-ion
LLC	limited liability company
LMO	lithium manganese oxide
LOTO	lock-out/tag-out
LSE	load-serving entities
LTO	lithium titanate oxide
MACRS	modified accelerated cost-recovery system
MC	metal-clad cable
MC3	multi contact unit with a 3mm² contact assembly pin
MC4	multi contact unit with a 4mm² contact assembly pin
MISO	Midcontinent Independent System Operator, Inc.
MLPE	module-level power electronics
Mono-SI	monocrystalline
MPP	maximum power point
MPPT	maximum power point tracking (or transfer)
MWh	megawatt hour
NABCEP	North American Board of Certified Electrical Practitioners
NBPSO	New Brunswick Power System Operator
NCA	(lithium) nickel cobalt aluminum oxide

NEC	National Electrical Code
NEM	net energy metering
NEMA	National Electrical Manufacturers Association
NERC	North American Electric Reliability Corporation
NFPA	National Fire Prevention Association
NiFe	nickel iron battery
Nm	newton-meter
NMC	(lithium) nickel manganese cobalt oxide
NOCT	nominal operating cell temperature
NPS	National Park Service
NREL	National Renewable Energy Laboratory
NYISO	New York Independent System Operator
O&M	operation and maintenance
OCPD	overcurrent protection device
ohm-cm	ohm-centimeters
OJT	on-the-job
OSHA	Occupational Safety and Health Administration
PACE	property assessed clean energy
PACE-C	property assessed clean energy - commercial
PACE-R	property assessed clean energy - residential
PBI	performance (or production) based incentives
PCC	point of common coupling
PERC	passivated emitter and rear cell
PF	power factor
PFAS	personal fall arrest system
PHEV	plug-in hybrid electric vehicle
PID	potential induced degradation
PII	permitting, inspection and interconnection
PJM	Pennsylvania-Jersey-Maryland Interconnection
PMAX	maximum power point
POA	plane of array
POC	point of connection
POI	point of interconnection
Poly-SI	polycrystalline
PPA	power purchase agreement
PPC	point of common coupling
PPE	personal protective equipment
PPL	plug and process loads
PSC	Public Service Commission
PTO	permission to operate
PUC	Public Utility Commission
PURPA	Public Utilities Regulatory Act of 1978
PV	photovoltaics
PV	planned value
PVC	rigid polyvinyl chloride
PVRSE	rapid shutdown equipment
PVRSS	rapid shutdown system
PWM	pulse width modulation
R	resistance
RC	reserve capacity
RCD	residual current device
REAP	Rural Energy for America Program
REC	renewable energy certificate

REP	retail electric provider
RFP	request for proposal
RISO	isolation resistance faults
RMC	rigid metal conduit
ROI	return on investment
RPS	renewable portfolio standards
RSI	rapid shutdown initiator
RTO	regional transmission organization
RTP	real-time pricing
SAM	System Advisor Model
SCADA	supervisory control and data acquisition
SEP	state energy program
SEIA	Solar Energy Industry Association
SEPA	Solar Electric Power Association
SF	shading factor
SOA	safe operating area
SoC	state of charge
SPI	Solar Power International
SPP	Southwest Power Pool
SREC	solar renewable energy certificate
STC	standard test conditions
TC	temperature coefficient
TDSP	transmission & distribution service provider
TDU	transmission and distribution utility
THD	total harmonic distortion
TOF	tilt and orientation factor
TOU	time of use rates
TPO	third party ownership
TSRF	total solar resource factor
UL	Underwriter's Laboratory
UPS	uninterruptible power source
USDA	United States Department of Agriculture
USP	utility scale power
UV	ultra violet
V	volt
V1G	smart charging
V2B	vehicle to building (or business)
V2G	vehicle to grid
V2H	vehicle to home
V2L	vehicle to load
V2V	vehicle to vehicle
V2X	vehicle to everything
VA	volt-amperes
VAR	volt amps reactive
Vmp	maximum power voltage
VNM	virtual net metering
Voc	open circuit voltage
VPP	virtual power plant
VRLA	vented and recombinant or valve regulated lead-acid
W	watt
WEEB	washer electrical equipment bond
Ω	ohm

Index